THE RESTAURANT GUIDE 2022

Published by AA Publishing, a trading name of AA Media Limited, whose registered office is Grove House, Lutyens Close, Lychpit, Basingstoke RG24 8AG. Registered number 06112600.

28th edition published 2021

Image credits: AA Media Limited wishes to thank the following photographers and organisations:

3 (top) courtesy of Road Hole Restaurant; 3 (centre, top) courtesy of The Hoop; 3 (centre, bottom) courtesy of The Hanoi Bike Shop; 3 (bottom) courtesy of Northcote Restaurant; 5 courtesy of Timberyard

Every effort has been made to trace the copyright holders, and we apologise in advance for any unintentional omissions or errors. We would be pleased to apply any corrections in a following edition of this publication. Photographs in the preliminary pages and gazetteer are provided by the establishments.

Restaurant descriptions were contributed by Jim Barker, Jackie Bates, Phil Bryant, Mike Pedley, David Popey, Allen Stidwill and Mark Taylor.

AA Media would like to thank Tracey Freestone, Nicky Hillenbrand, Lin Hutton, Ian Little, David Popey and Victoria Samways in the preparation of this guide.

Cover design by Austin Taylor.

Maps prepared by the Mapping Services Department of AA Publishing.

Maps © AA Media Limited 2021.

Contains Ordnance Survey data © Crown copyright and database right 2021.

Ireland map contains data available from openstreetmap.org © under the Open Database License found at opendatacommons.org

Printed in the UK by Bell & Bain.

ISBN: 978-0-7495-8279-1

A05776

Discover restaurants with Rosettes as well as AA-rated hotels, B&Bs and more at www.ratedtrips.com

CONTENTS

The restaurants

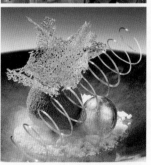

Welcome to the AA Restaurant Guide 2022

At the time of writing in 2021, it's not been an easy year for the restaurant industry to say the least. Sadly, many venues have closed as a direct result of the pandemic, and there are many notable absences in this year's guide.

Our inspectors' challenge

The closure of much of the hospitality industry during the pandemic has meant our inspectors have had a very limited window in which to visit and assess. It also meant that the absence of the 2021 guide was the first time for over 50 years that we didn't publish a guide containing the latest restaurants with Rosettes.

New to the guide

Skipping a year does have its advantages – there are over 100 restaurants that are new to the guide since the 2020 edition – most have received either 1 or 2 Rosettes, but a couple have gone straight in at three Rosettes, including Davies and Brook in Claridge's hotel, London and Where the Light Gets In in Stockport, Manchester.

We've spotlighted many of the new entrants, including restaurants who are joining the ranks of venues with 3, 4 or 5 Rosettes on pages 14-17

You might also spot a few fresh faces, alongside some established names, in our feature on pages 18–21. We interviewed chefs to ask them about their work and how they arrived at their current position. It's a fascinating read.

Toasting the best

The Notable Wine List accolade (see page 22) singles out restaurants that our inspectors feel have shown a real passion for and knowledge of wine. There are 270 notable wine lists throughout the guide – so look out for ⌕ NOTABLE WINE LIST .

Things can change

The transient nature of the hospitality industry means that chefs move around all the time, and restaurants may change ownership. Unfortunately, some close. As any change at the multi-Rosette (3, 4 or 5) level requires a new inspection to verify their award, some of these restaurants appear in the guide with their Rosette level suspended at the time of going to press.

Raise a glass

What does the future have in store for our nation's well-loved restaurants? When writing the previous edition of the guide in 2019, we couldn't have dreamed of the tumult our industry was to face in the following two years. So, for 2022, let's not predict anything and instead raise a glass to an industry that has adapted and emerged from one of its greatest ever challenges.

Using the guide

A few handy tips to help you get the most out of using the guide. We regularly ask restaurants to refresh their information and this is then used alongside updates from our inspection team.

1 ORDER: Restaurants are listed in country and county order, then by town and then alphabetically within the town. There is an index by restaurant name at the back of the guide.

2 AA ROSETTE AWARD: Restaurants can be awarded from 1 to 5 Rosettes (see pages 8–9). 'Rosettes suspended' indicates that an award of 3 Rosettes or above was suspended shortly before going to press.

3 FOOD STYLE: A summary of the main cuisine type(s).

V indicates a vegetarian menu. Restaurants with some vegetarian dishes available are indicated under Notes. The description may provide further information about the food style.

4 NOTABLE WINE LIST: The ▲NOTABLE WINE LIST symbol indicates a wine list chosen as notable by our inspectors (see page 22).

5 MAP REFERENCE: Each town or village is given a map reference – the map page number and a two-figure reference based on the National Grid. For example:

Map 18, SD49

18 refers to the page number of the map section at the back of the guide
SD is the National Grid lettered square (representing 100,000 sq metres) in which the location will be found
4 is the figure reading across the top and bottom of the map page
9 is the figure reading down at each side of the map page. For Central London and Greater London, there is a map section starting on page 176.

6 CHEF: The name of the chef(s) is as up-to-date as possible at the time of going to press, but changes in personnel often occur, and may affect both the style and quality of the restaurant.

7 SEATS: Number of seats in the restaurant and private dining room.

8 OPEN/CLOSED: We note if a restaurant is open all year. Otherwise, we list a period or periods when a venue is closed. Check in advance via the venue's website for daily opening times.

9 PRICES: We list minimum prices for Starter (S), Main (M) and Dessert (D) based on details provided by the restaurant. Service charges are not included here and may vary depending on the size of the party. Most restaurants will have some form of service charge.

10 PARKING: Number of spaces for on-site parking or nearby parking.

11 NOTES: Additional information regarding the availability of vegetarian dishes and their policy towards children. We recommend that you phone in advance to ensure that the establishment you have chosen has appropriate facilities.

Please note, 6–11 are omitted from all restaurants listed with 1 and 2 Rosettes for this guide due to the sheer scale of change during the period of the pandemic. We hope that normal service will resume next year.

Photographs
Many restaurants have chosen to enhance their entry by purchasing photographs.

1

3

5

2

4

SHINFIELD *MAP 5, SU76*

L'Ortolan

⊛⊛⊛ MODERN FRENCH  NOTABLE WINE LIST

0118 988 8500 | Church Lane, RG2 9BY

www.lortolan.com

A country-house style restaurant set in an elegant red-brick former vicarage with Gothic-style front door and bow-fronted windows, L'Ortolan is a name synonymous with modern British gastronomy since the 1980's. Now, talented young chef James Greatorex is the man in 'whites', delivering sophisticated, highly detailed, aspiring contemporary cooking via carte and tasting menus. Dishes come dressed to thrill, with flavour, texture, balance and precision to the fore; witness 'melting' citrus cured Cornish mackerel teamed with cucumber and buttermilk, or 'sparkling fresh' Cornish cod ballotine with clams, sea herbs and watercress. Fine-dining standards like canapés, bread, pre-desserts and petit fours round of a polished act, alongside professional and informed service

7

6

Chef James Greatorex **Seats** 58, Private dining 22

Closed 2 weeks Christmas to New Year

8

9

Prices from S £12.50, M £16, D £11 **Parking** 30

Notes No children under 3 years

11

10

How we assess for Rosettes

First introduced in 1956, our Rosette award scheme was the first nationwide scheme for assessing the quality of food served by restaurants and hotels. It has been a 5-tier system since 1992.

A consistent approach

The Rosette scheme is an award, not a classification, and although there is necessarily an element of subjectivity when it comes to assessing taste, we aim for a consistent approach throughout the UK. Our awards are made solely on the basis of a meal visit or visits by one or more of our hotel and restaurant inspectors, who have an unrivalled breadth and depth of experience in assessing quality. Essentially, it's a snapshot, whereby the entire meal, including ancillary items (when served) are assessed. Of all the restaurants across the UK, approximately 10% are of a standard worthy of 1 Rosette and above.

Rosette worthiness

For our inspectors, the top and bottom line is the food. The taste of a dish is what counts, and whether it successfully delivers to the diner the promise of the menu. A restaurant is only as good as its worst meal. Although presentation and competent service should be appropriate to the style of the restaurant and the quality of the food, they cannot affect the Rosette assessment as such, either up or down. The summaries opposite indicate what our inspectors look for, but are intended only as guidelines. We are constantly reviewing its award criteria, and competition usually results in an all-round improvement in standards, so it becomes increasingly difficult for restaurants to reach an award level.

The next level

Receiving a Rosette is a huge achievement and something not to be underestimated. We are often asked by chefs and proprietors: "What is the difference between 1 and 5 Rosettes and how can I get to the next level?" We answer that it's how well a chef manages to apply advanced technique while retaining maximum flavour, and assuming an appropriate quality of source ingredients.

While we endeavour to work with the industry and promote great cooking across the UK, it is of paramount importance for chefs to always serve their market first. We recommend they don't chase awards, but see them as something to celebrate when they come along. Where, however, the winning of Rosettes is an aspiration, the simple guidelines, shown opposite, may help. Experiencing our food tastings, enhanced food tastings or signing up to one of the AA Rosette Academies can also give further insight and guidance, but these are separate from the awards process and do not influence any assessments.

Announcements of awards

One and two Rosettes are awarded at the time of inspection. Three and four Rosette awards are announced twice during the year, but never at the time of inspection. Five Rosettes are awarded just once a year and never at the time of inspection.

One Rosette

These restaurants will be achieving standards that stand out in their local area, featuring:

- food prepared with care, understanding and skill
- good quality ingredients
- The same expectations apply to hotel restaurants where guests should be able to eat in with confidence and a sense of anticipation.

 Two Rosettes

The best local restaurants, which aim for and achieve:

- higher standards
- better consistency
- greater precision apparent in the cooking
- obvious attention to the selection of quality ingredients.

 Three Rosettes

These are outstanding restaurants that achieve standards that demand national recognition well beyond their local area. The cooking will be underpinned by:

- the selection and sympathetic treatment of the highest quality ingredients
- timing, seasoning and the judgment of flavour combinations will be consistently excellent
- these virtues will tend to be supported by other elements such as intuitive service and a well-chosen wine list.

 Four Rosettes

Among the top restaurants in the UK where the cooking demands national recognition. These restaurants will exhibit:

- intense ambition
- a passion for excellence
- superb technical skills
- remarkable consistency
- an appreciation of culinary traditions combined with a passionate desire for further exploration and improvement.

 Five Rosettes

The pinnacle, where the cooking compares with the best in the world. These restaurants will have:

- highly individual voices
- exhibit breathtaking culinary skills and set the standards to which others aspire, yet few achieve.

The top restaurants of 2022

Restaurants with 3, 4 or 5 Rosettes represent the best in the UK. They are often internationally recognised and serve cuisine of the highest standard. The restaurants in this year's list all had 3 or more Rosettes at the time of going to press.

ENGLAND

BERKSHIRE
The Fat Duck, Bray

BRISTOL
Casamia Restaurant, Bristol

CAMBRIDGESHIRE
Midsummer House Restaurant, Cambridge

CUMBRIA
L'Enclume, Cartmel

DEVON
Lympstone Manor Hotel, Exmouth

LANCASHIRE
Moor Hall Restaurant with Rooms, Ormskirk

LONDON
Restaurant Story, SE1
Marcus, SW1
Claude Bosi at Bibendum, SW3

Hélène Darroze at The Connaught, W1
Pollen Street Social, W1
Sketch (Lecture Room & Library), W1
Core by Clare Smyth, W11

NOTTINGHAMSHIRE
Restaurant Sat Bains with Rooms, Nottingham

OXFORDSHIRE
Belmond Le Manoir aux Quat'Saisons, Great Milton

SCOTLAND

EDINBURGH
The Kitchin, Edinburgh

WALES

CEREDIGION
Ynyshir Restaurant & Rooms, Eglwys Fach

ENGLAND

BERKSHIRE
Restaurant Coworth Park, Ascot

BUCKINGHAMSHIRE
The Hand & Flowers, Marlow

CORNWALL & ISLES OF SCILLY
Paul Ainsworth at No. 6, Padstow
Outlaw's New Road, Port Isaac

CUMBRIA
Forest Side, Grasmere
Hrishi at Gilpin Hotel & Lake House, Windermere

GLOUCESTERSHIRE
Le Champignon Sauvage, Cheltenham

GREATER MANCHESTER
Adam Reid at The French, Manchester
Mana, Manchester

LANCASHIRE
Hipping Hall, Cowan Bridge
Northcote Restaurant, Langho

LINCOLNSHIRE
Winteringham Fields, Winteringham

LONDON
Dinner by Heston Blumenthal, SW1
Muse, SW1
Seven Park Place by William Drabble, SW1
The Five Fields, SW3
Restaurant Gordon Ramsay, SW3
Alain Ducasse at The Dorchester, W1
Murano, W1
The Ritz Restaurant, W1

▲ Mana, Manchester

MERSEYSIDE
Fraiche, Oxton

NORFOLK
Morston Hall, Blakeney

NOTTINGHAMSHIRE
Alchemilla, Nottingham

OXFORDSHIRE
Orwells, Henley-on-Thames

RUTLAND
Hambleton Hall, Oakham

SUFFOLK
Tuddenham Mill, Newmarket

SURREY
Steve Smith at Latymer, Bagshot
Sorrel, Dorking

SUSSEX, WEST
Gravetye Manor Hotel,
  West Hoathly

TYNE & WEAR
House of Tides,
  Newcastle upon Tyne

WEST MIDLANDS
Hampton Manor, Solihull

WILTSHIRE
The Dining Room, Malmesbury

YORKSHIRE, NORTH
The Angel at Hetton, Hetton
The Black Swan at Oldstead,
  Oldstead

YORKSHIRE, WEST
The Man Behind The Curtain,
  Leeds

CHANNEL ISLANDS
JERSEY
Ocean Restaurant at
  The Atlantic Hotel, St Brelade
Tassili, St Helier

SCOTLAND
EDINBURGH
21212, Edinburgh
Number One, The Balmoral,
  Edinburgh
Restaurant Martin Wishart,
  Edinburgh

PERTH & KINROSS
Andrew Fairlie at Gleneagles,
  Auchterarder

WALES
ISLE OF ANGLESEY
Sosban & The Old Butcher's
  Restaurant, Menai Bridge

MONMOUTHSHIRE
The Whitebrook, Whitebrook

REPUBLIC OF IRELAND
DUBLIN
Restaurant Patrick Guilbaud,
  Dublin

COUNTY KILKENNY
The Lady Helen Restaurant,
  Thomastown

⊛⊛⊛
ENGLAND
BEDFORDSHIRE
Paris House Restaurant, Woburn

BERKSHIRE
The Hind's Head, Bray
The Waterside Inn, Bray
The Crown, Burchett's Green
The Vineyard, Newbury
The Woodspeen – Restaurant and
  Cookery School, Newbury
L'Ortolan, Shinfield

BUCKINGHAMSHIRE
The Artichoke, Amersham
The Coach, Marlow
Humphry's at Stoke Park,
  Stoke Poges
The Cliveden Dining Room,
  Taplow

**CORNWALL
& ISLES OF SCILLY**
Hell Bay Hotel, Bryher
Merchants Manor, Falmouth
The Seafood Restaurant,
  Padstow
Kota Restaurant with Rooms,
  Porthleven
Driftwood, Portscatho
Hotel Tresanton, St Mawes

CUMBRIA
Lake Road Kitchen, Ambleside
The Old Stamp House Restaurant,
  Ambleside
Rothay Manor Hotel, Ambleside
Allium at Askham Hall, Askham

The Cottage in the Wood,
  Braithwaite
Rogan & Co Restaurant, Cartmel
Pentonbridge Inn, Penton
The Samling, Windermere

DERBYSHIRE
Cavendish Hotel, Baslow
Fischer's Baslow Hall, Baslow
The Peacock at Rowsley, Rowsley

DEVON
Gidleigh Park, Chagford
Paschoe House, Crediton
The Old Inn, Drewsteignton
Great Western,
  Moretonhampstead
Àclèaf, Plymouth
The Elephant Restaurant
  by Simon Hulstone, Torquay

DORSET
The Ollerod, Beaminster
Summer Lodge Country
  House Hotel, Restaurant
  & Spa, Evershot

DURHAM, COUNTY
The Orangery, Darlington

ESSEX
Le Talbooth, Dedham
Haywards Restaurant, Epping

GLOUCESTERSHIRE
Buckland Manor, Buckland
The Greenway Hotel & Spa,
  Cheltenham
Lumière, Cheltenham
The Slaughters Manor House,
  Lower Slaughter
Wilder, Nailsworth
The Feathered Nest Inn,
  Nether Westcote
Lords of the Manor,
  Upper Slaughter

GREATER MANCHESTER
Where the Light Gets In,
  Stockport

HAMPSHIRE
The Terrace Restaurant at The
  Montagu Arms Hotel, Beaulieu
36 On The Quay, Emsworth
The Elderflower Restaurant,
  Lymington
Hartnett Holder & Co, Lyndhurst

HERTFORDSHIRE
THOMPSON St Albans, St Albans

KENT
The West House Restaurant with
 Rooms, Biddenden
ABode Canterbury, Canterbury
Fordwich Arms, Canterbury
Hide and Fox, Hythe
Thackeray's, Royal
 Tunbridge Wells

LANCASHIRE
The Barn at Moor Hall, Ormskirk
The Freemasons at Wiswell,
 Whalley

LEICESTERSHIRE
John's House, Mountsorrel

LONDON
Galvin La Chapelle, E1
Cornerstone by Chef
 Tom Brown, E9
Anglo, EC1
The Clove Club, EC1
Club Gascon, EC1
City Social, EC2
The Princess of Shoreditch, EC2
La Dame de Pic London, EC3
Odette's, NW1
Trivet, SE1
Peninsula Restaurant, SE10
Amaya, SW1
A. Wong, SW1
Céleste at The Lanesborough,
 SW1
Chutney Mary, SW1
The Goring, SW1
Ikoyi, SW1
Pétrus, by Gordon Ramsey SW1
Wild Honey, SW1
Elystan Street, SW3
Trinity Restaurant, SW4
Medlar Restaurant, SW10
Myrtle Restaurant, SW10
Chez Bruce, SW17
Les 110 de Taillevent, W1
The Betterment
 by Jason Atherton, W1
Corrigan's Mayfair, W1
Cut at 45 Park Lane, W1
Davies and Brook, W1
Galvin at Windows Restaurant &
 Bar, W1

Gauthier Soho, W1
Le Gavroche Restaurant, W1
The Grill at The Dorchester, W1
Hakkasan Mayfair, W1
Hide Above, W1
Kitchen Table, W1
KOL Restaurant, W1
Locanda Locatelli, W1
Mere, W1
The Ninth, W1
No. 5 Social, W1
Ormer, W1
Orrery, W1
Pied à Terre, W1
Portland, W1
Roka Charlotte Street, W1
Roka Mayfair, W1
Sketch (The Gallery), W1
Social Eating House, W1
SOLA, W1
Umu, W1
The River Café, W6
Kitchen W8, W8
Launceston Place, W8
Clos Maggiore, WC2
Frenchie Covent Garden, WC2
Frog by Adam Handling, WC2
Kerridge's Bar & Grill, WC2
The Northall, WC2

LONDON, GREATER
Chapter One Restaurant, Bromley
The Glasshouse, Kew
The Dysart Petersham, Richmond
 Upon Thames

NORFOLK
The Neptune Restaurant
 with Rooms, Hunstanton
Benedicts, Norwich
Farmyard, Norwich
Roger Hickman's Restaurant,
 Norwich
Titchwell Manor Hotel, Titchwell

NORTHAMPTONSHIRE
Tresham Restaurant, Kettering
Murrays, Whittlebury

OXFORDSHIRE
Shaun Dickens at The Boathouse,
 Henley-on-Thames
The Wild Rabbit, Kingham
Minster Mill, Minster Lovell
Two One Five, Oxford

SHROPSHIRE
Fishmore Hall, Ludlow
Old Downton Lodge, Ludlow
The Haughmond, Upton Magna

SOMERSET
The Bath Priory Hotel, Restaurant
 & Spa, Bath
The Dower House Restaurant, Bath
The Olive Tree at the Queensberry
 Hotel, Bath

STAFFORDSHIRE
The Boat Inn, Lichfield

SUFFOLK
The Bildeston Crown, Bildeston

SURREY
Stovell's, Chobham
Tony Parkin at The Tudor Room,
 Egham
Langshott Manor, Horley
The Clock House, Ripley

SUSSEX, EAST
etch. by Steven Edwards, Brighton
The Little Fish Market, Brighton

SUSSEX, WEST
Amberley Castle, Amberley
Restaurant Tristan, Horsham
The Lickfold Inn, Lickfold
Restaurant Interlude,
 Lower Beeding
AG'S Restaurant at Alexander
 House Hotel, Turners Hill

WARWICKSHIRE
The Cross at Kenilworth,
 Kenilworth
The Dining Room
 at Mallory Court Hotel,
 Royal Leamington Spa
Salt, Stratford-upon-Avon

WEST MIDLANDS
Adam's, Birmingham
Carters of Moseley, Birmingham
Purnell's, Birmingham
Simpsons, Birmingham

WILTSHIRE
Bybrook at The Manor House Hotel,
 Castle Combe
Restaurant Hywel Jones by
 Lucknam Park, Colerne
Red Lion Freehouse, Pewsey

WORCESTERSHIRE
The Back Garden, Broadway
MO, Broadway
Brockencote Hall
Country House Hotel,
Chaddesley Corbett

YORKSHIRE, NORTH
Yorebridge House, Bainbridge
The Burlington Restaurant,
Bolton Abbey
Goldsborough Hall, Goldsborough
Horto Restaurant, Harrogate
The Pheasant Hotel, Helmsley
Forge, Middleton Tyas
Shaun Rankin at Grantley Hall,
Ripon
The Hare, Scawton
The Bow Room Restaurant
at Grays Court, York
Roots York Restaurant, York

YORKSHIRE, SOUTH
Jöro Restaurant, Sheffield

YORKSHIRE, WEST
Box Tree, Ilkley

CHANNEL ISLANDS
JERSEY
Longueville Manor Hotel,
St Saviour

SCOTLAND
ABERDEENSHIRE
Douneside House, Tarland

ANGUS
Gordon's, Inverkeilor

ARGYLL & BUTE
Restaurant at Isle of Eriska,
Eriska
Airds Hotel and Restaurant,
Port Appin
Inver Restaurant, Strachur

AYRSHIRE, SOUTH
Glenapp Castle, Ballantrae

DUMFRIES & GALLOWAY
Knockinaam Lodge, Portpatrick

EDINBURGH
The Pompadour, Edinburgh

FIFE
The Cellar, Anstruther

▲ Inverlochy Castle, Scotland

The Peat Inn, Peat Inn
Road Hole Restaurant,
St Andrews

GLASGOW
Cail Bruich, Glasgow
The Gannet, Glasgow
Unalome by Graeme Cheevers,
Glasgow

HIGHLAND
Edinbane Lodge, Edinbane
Michel Roux Jr at Inverlochy
Castle, Fort William
The Cross, Kingussie
Kilcamb Lodge Hotel, Strontian
The Torridon 1887 Restaurant,
Torridon

LANARKSHIRE, SOUTH
Crossbasket Castle, Blantyre

PERTH & KINROSS
Fonab Castle Hotel & Spa,
Pitlochry

SCOTTISH BORDERS
Windlestraw, Walkerburn

SCOTTISH ISLANDS
Loch Bay Restaurant, Stein
The Three Chimneys
& The House Over-By,
Colbost

STIRLING
Roman Camp Country House
Hotel, Callander
Cromlix and Chez Roux, Dunblane

WALES
CONWY
Bodysgallen Hall and Spa,
Llandudno

GWYNEDD
Palé Hall Hotel & Restaurant, Bala

MONMOUTHSHIRE
The Walnut Tree Inn,
Abergavenny

PEMBROKESHIRE
The Fernery, Narberth

POWYS
Llangoed Hall, Llyswen

SWANSEA
Beach House Restaurant at
Oxwich Beach, Oxwich

NORTHERN IRELAND
BELFAST
Deanes EIPIC, Belfast
OX, Belfast

COUNTY ANTRIM
Galgorm, Ballymena

COUNTY FERMANAGH
Lough Erne Resort, Enniskillen

REPUBLIC OF IRELAND
COUNTY CLARE
The Dining Room at Gregans
Castle, Ballyvaughan

Moving on up

Despite an annus horribilis for the restaurant world during the pandemic, our inspectors' travels around the country resulted in plenty of reasons to celebrate. Here's a run-through of the 3- and 4-Rosette award winning restaurants from 2020 and 2021.

(The AA Restaurant Guide was not published in 2021 as the hospitality industry was closed due to restrictions during the pandemic. The restaurants listed below are those that achieved three- and four-Rosette awards in inspections carried out between 2019 and 2021)

Northern Powerhouse

When it comes to exceptional food, the North definitely holds its own. Leading the way with four Rosettes is Mana in Manchester with benchmark food that is fresh, surprising and ultra-modern. Out in Stockport, you can expect innovative, on-trend three-Rosette food at Where The Light Gets In. Cumbria has never been short of foodie destinations, and continues to hit the heights with a new four-Rosette award for Paul Leonard for his artful treatment of local produce at Forest Side in Grasmere, followed by three-Rosette awards for Chris Archer at Pentonbridge Inn, and Ryan Blackburn at The Old Stamp House, Wordsworth's former house in Ambleside followed by Three-Rosette awards to both. Three-Rosette delights also await at The Barn at Moor Hall, a boutique hideaway in Ormskirk. Yorkshire's dynamic culinary scene continues to wow with five newcomers - Goldsborough Hall in Harrogate, Shaun Rankin at Grantley Hall in Ripon and The Pheasant at Harome. If you're in York, head for the historic Bow Room at Grays Court or Roots, where Tommy Banks showcases superb produce from the family's farm.

Culinary Capital

London and the surrounding counties will always be the culinary magnet with a world-beating culinary reputation that attracts top talent to its restaurants, notably John Williams MBE, whose luxurious, classically-inspired food at The Ritz Restaurant, and Tom Aikens with intensely seasonal cooking at Muse has lifted them into the rarefied ranks of four-Rosette winners. To the list of new three-Rosette venues we can now add the Dorchester Grill, whose 26-year-old head chef Tom Booton is the youngest in the restaurant's history. Sofian Msetfi carries forward Shaun Rankin's legacy at Ormer. Other three-Rosette winners include Les 110 des Taillevent, The Betterment by Jason Atherton, Chutney Mary, The Corinthia Hotel, Davies & Brook at Claridge's, The Dysart, Frenchie Covent Garden, Hide Above, KOL, Myrtle, The Northall, Petersham, Pétrus by Gordon Ramsay, Princess of Shoreditch, SOLA and Trivet.

In Surrey, Steve Smith at Latymer in Pennyhill Park now holds four Rosettes

▲ Frenchie Covent Garden

for his thrillingly modern tasting menus, while thoroughbred contemporary cooking has elevated Clock House in Ripley to three Rosettes. If you're in Berkshire, top of the pile with three Rosette awards are The Vineyard in Newbury and L'Ortolan in Shinfield. In Kent, chef-patron Allister Barsby at Hide and Fox hits the peaks with superbly creative food coupled with expertly chosen wines on the edge of Romney Marsh. Tucked away in Leonardslee Gardens in West Sussex, Interlude creates epic three-Rosette tasting menus full of invention and excitement.

◀ *(opposite)* Forest Side

Heart of England & Cotswolds

Brum has long cemented its place on our national foodie map but there's plenty going on if you cast your net wider around the heart of England and Cotswolds. If you're up for top-drawer country house dining, flying high with three-Rosette awards are Minster Mill in Minster Lovell. Elsewhere, seek out The Feathered Nest Inn in Nether Westcote, Murrays in Whittlebury Hall near Silverstone, The Haughmond in Upton Magna, and The Boat Inn in Lichfield.

East Anglia

Blessed with fine East Anglian produce to work with, the meticulously-renovated Tuddenham Mill in Newmarket has come up trumps and joins the ranks of four-Rosette dining, while Farmyard in Norwich boasts three-Rosettes after our inspector enjoyed its knock out textures and innovative combinations. Both are well worth visiting when you're in the region.

West Country & Channel Islands

The West Country has never lacked for superb dining destinations, with Olly Pierrepont at Driftwood in Portscatho now added to the roster of three-Rosette winners. And what better reason to head for Jersey than showstopping four-Rosette cooking from chef Will Holland at the Ocean Restaurant at The Atlantic Hotel.

Scotland

Scottish produce is second to none and its restaurant scene doesn't lack for world-class chefs who know just what to do with it. Three more venues in the nation join the ranks of three-Rosette winners: the Roux dynasty delivers complex contemporary dishes in an opulent setting at Michel Roux Jr at Inverlochy Castle; for contemporary cooking in an Arts and Crafts villa, try Windlestraw in Walkerburn, or head to Glasgow for inventive Celtic cooking at Unalome by Graeme Cheevers.

Images clockwise from top left: Northall, The Haughmond, TuddenhamMill, Tuddenham Mill interior, Minster Mill and Ocean Restaurant ▶

▼ Inverlochy Castle

THE

Haughmond

A MODERN
COACHING INN

Welcome

Minster *Mill*

Meet the chefs

Ever wondered what it is that drives chefs onward to create spectacular food? Why they became chefs in the first place and why they keep doing it? Mike Pedley speaks to top-flight chefs and some rising stars to see what they love about their calling

I had never considered becoming a chef whilst at school but always had a passion for eating. Washing dishes at a local hotel, I realised how much I loved the kitchen buzz. I started helping with desserts, the chef gave me a set of whites and I haven't looked back since! Working in a restaurant with 3 Rosettes fired me on to the next level. This is where my career really began. I moved to Jersey to work with Shaun Rankin in Bohemia - this was a different class to what I had been doing. Working with Martin Burge at Whatley Manor, Martin changed the way I viewed food and how to work as a chef. Quay restaurant in Sydney gave me an insight into integrating Asian influences into my cuisine. My first head chef role was at The Tudor Room in Great Fosters where we gained the coveted four AA rosettes. I moved to the Grove Hotel in Narberth as executive chef where we won AA Hotel of the Year for Wales, 5 stars and three AA rosettes. I love the skill and love needed to prep and cook shellfish to let them shine. I also love working with vegetables and find elevating something like a simple potato or turnip into something sensational a really rewarding experience. Concentrating on sustainability and health is the way forward.

Douglas Balish

THE FERNERY, GROVE OF NARBERTH, NARBERTH, PEMBROKESHIRE, WALES
page 426

*"I have a streaky bacon, fried egg and avocado roll
from the village deli every Monday. Insanely tasty!"* DOUGLAS BALISH

Tom Booton

DORCHESTER GRILL,
LONDON W1
page 223

I fell in love with the hustle of the kitchen the moment I stepped through the doors at Le Talbooth in my home town Colchester, aged 15. I moved to London and worked for Alyn Williams at The Westbury, then L'Autre Pied under Andy McFadden, followed by restaurants in New York, Copenhagen and Iceland to experience how other cultures celebrate food and champion different types of produce. Back in the UK I worked for Ollie Dabbous then moved back to Alyn Williams as head chef. The manager of The Dorchester came for dinner, asked to meet the chef and that led to me taking over The Grill as head chef. My aim is to elevate the experience of The Grill, we just reopened our Pudding Bar and plan to collaborate more with that. My favourite ingredients? I'm a big fan of mushrooms, they are extremely versatile and I love the flavour. You can't beat a button mushroom!

"Alyn Williams was massive for my early career. I really admire Jason Atherton and what he has done with his business. He must never sleep!" TOM BOOTON

I have always had an interest in food, cooking and baking with my mum from an early age. Later, I loved the feeling of been part of a kitchen team, it got me hooked. Moving to London to work at Petrus was a huge eye opener to learn what it was going to take to work at the top level. Working with an absolute hero of mine, Andrew Fairlie at Gleneagles, was a finishing school for me - I learnt so much about how to run a kitchen. I took over my first kitchen at the Isle of Eriska and look back on the time there with fond memories. Forest Side has given me the chance to really focus on evolving a style. My style of cooking isn't too complex, it suits the Forest Side perfectly. I love fish and shellfish, prepping and cooking a nice John Dory - it's an unbelievable ingredient. I have big ideas for the menu and the way the kitchen works - we will continue to improve, growing and nurturing both food and our team.

Paul Leonard

FOREST SIDE,
GRASMERE, CUMBRIA
page 71

"Mana in Manchester was awesome - I love what Simon and his team have created there. I was lucky to go to Denmark before the pandemic for an unreal experience at Henne Kirkeby Kro, I have had the pleasure of cooking alongside Paul Proffitt - what a place!" PAUL LEONARD

Calum Montgomery

EDINBANE, ISLE OF SKYE,
SCOTLAND
page 410

I didn't know I wanted to be a chef until I stopped being one! I left my Job at a 2-AA Rosette restaurant to study business management and realised how much I missed and loved cooking. Coming back was the best decision I ever made. I love to work with the super-fresh shellfish available to us in Skye, from hand-dived scallops to creel-caught jumbo langoustines. A lot of our suppliers are my friends and relatives so it means that bit extra to me that we really look after the produce as soon as we get it in the kitchen. I'd love to open a small, sustainable seafood takeaway in my hometown of Portree one day, somewhere that captures our food ethos – to go!

"I'm a sucker for a takeaway from our local Chinese restaurant "The Fat Panda" - a name that could fairly sum me up on a Monday night. Favourite food? I love a good BBQ at my dad's house when he has the big grill on the go and the sun is out."

CALUM MONTGOMERY

I always liked cooking as a child and began going into my dad's industrial kitchen as a young boy. I really enjoyed the camaraderie of the team and liked watching ingredients being turned into dishes which made people happy. I decided to become a chef even though my parents did all they could to persuade me otherwise! I began my career at the Intercontinental, Hyde Park Corner under the late Peter Kromberg. It was a steep learning curve but I was lucky to experience different types of cuisine and that has stayed with me throughout. I worked for several well-known chefs in London then came to Cornwall to work with Rick Stein at The Seafood Restaurant once I realised that seafood was 'my thing'. I opened my first restaurant 'The Black Pig' in Rock when I was 25. I have had restaurants in London and Dubai but since lockdown have decided that Cornwall is really where I want to be so have now settled myself with the two I have in Port Isaac, Outlaw's New Road and Outlaw's Fish Kitchen. My main aim is for the restaurants to become as sustainable as they can. It's such an important issue and one that we need to embrace and encourage. I also want to build more relationships with small, local suppliers, fishermen and producers. It's really important to me to go looking for the best ingredients I can find and some of the smaller sources have amazing things to offer. I never fail to look at a lovely piece of fish without asking myself what I can I do to do it justice. The same applies to veggies. I love it when the first crop of anything comes into season, it's like a new breath of life in the kitchen.

Nathan Outlaw

OUTLAW'S NEW ROAD AND
OUTLAW'S FISH KITCHEN,
PORT ISAAC, CORNWALL
page 62

Richard Swale

ALLIUM, ASKHAM HALL,
CUMBRIA
page 68

I was brought up in a pub in North Yorkshire so there was never much chance of escaping it. I would spend hours watching my mum cook, so good food and fresh produce was always around me. I started at local hotel which had 2 AA Rosettes but I wanted to be right at the top end of cooking. So I got in touch with all the 5 AA Rosette places; John Burton Race at the Ortolan got in touch with me and I got the job. What I learned there set me up for the rest of my career. I spent a few more years in London with Anthony Demetre and then set sail to go abroad to France, Australia and placements around Europe. An opportunity came up working for the Lowther family who were looking to turn the family home (Askham Hall) into a small restaurant with rooms. We constantly try to grow new things and keep everything as local as possible, hopefully in future we will look into doing a farm shop where we can sell produce that we grow.

"The place that had the wow factor was Mark Birchall's Moor Hall - it was faultless, so much attention to detail" RICHARD SWALE

My mother was a pâtissier and always cooked at home using fresh produce. I also was incredibly lucky to have travelled extensively. My father made me try everything from Turkish coffee in Istanbul when I was 4 to baby octopus in Greece. These experiences have made me into the chef I am today. I always source fresh ingredients from producers who put the same attention to detail and dedication into their work as we do in our restaurant. Working with like-minded people is the key ingredient to any dish we serve. Our team has achieved so much in so little time and we don't want to stand still. There are some exciting developments planned within the next year, but you have to wait to see.

Michael Wignall

ANGEL AT HETTON,
HETTON,
NORTH YORKSHIRE
page 351

"Japanese culture and cuisine have certainly had an effect on me. Their detail when selecting ingredients is second to none, everything is carefully sought out and chosen for the best results." MICHAEL WIGNALL

To find out further fascinating facts about the chefs featured here, head to www.ratedtrips.com/restaurants for the full interviews.

Notable wines 2021–22

Every year, we highlight restaurants with wine lists that have impressed our inspectors. This year, with the period for assessment of lists very much curtailed, we have combined the results of the past two years to create the guide's notable wine recommendations.

What makes a wine list notable?

We look for lists that first and foremost feature well chosen, quality wines, that have been curated with much care and interest. Ranging from compact to epic lists, they will be well presented, clear and easy to navigate. They will often feature a diversity across grape varieties, countries and style, and the best individual growers and vintages. To reflect the demand of diners, there should be a good choice of varied wines available by the glass.

To be one of the current 270 highlighted in the guide, we look for a real passion for wine and service to match, which should come across to the customer. We also look for a fair pricing policy (depending on the style of the restaurant); interesting coverage (not necessarily a large list), which might include areas of specialism, perhaps a particular wine area; sherries, dessert wines or larger formats such as magnums.

It is really encouraging to see more and more restaurants championing English wine as both the quality and depth continues to grow. Wine flights and pairings to accompany menus are also a regular feature of many restaurants giving the opportunity for diners to experience a range of wines they may not have tasted before.

▼ The wine cellar at The Vineyard Hotel, Stockcross

ENGLAND

■ BEDFORDSHIRE

BOLNHURST   MAP 12, TL05

The Plough at Bolnhurst
◉ MODERN BRITISH
01234 376274 | Kimbolton Road, MK44 2EX
www.bolnhurst.com
The Plough is a whitewashed 15th-century country inn and the restaurant is a striking contrast: the airy extension features lofty oak-beamed ceilings while full-length windows flood the room with light. Top-quality produce is transformed into big-flavoured modern dishes on daily-changing menus.

HENLOW   MAP 12, TL13

The Crown
◉ MODERN BRITISH
01462 812433 | 2 High Street, SG16 6BS
www.crownpub.co.uk
The busy pub on the main road through the village functions as a quintessential rural hostelry, full of enthusiastic local custom in both bar and dining room. Despite modernisation it retains its pub ethos, and boasts a young, classically trained chef.

LUTON   MAP 6, TL02

Adam's Brasserie at Luton Hoo
◉ MODERN BRITISH ⬥ NOTABLE WINE LIST
01582 734437 | Luton Hoo Hotel, Golf & Spa, The Mansion House, LU1 3TQ
www.lutonhoo.co.uk
The extensive Luton Hoo Estate, with its golf course and magnificent gardens, is home to this spa hotel. Adam's Brasserie is found in the former stables, where high ceilings and large windows give a sense of space, and the menu is a roster of feel-good dishes.

Wernher Restaurant at Luton Hoo Hotel, Golf & Spa
◉◉ MODERN BRITISH *V* ⬥ NOTABLE WINE LIST
01582 734437 | The Mansion House, LU1 3TQ
www.lutonhoo.co.uk
When only the full stately-home extravaganza will do, the magnificent Wernher in Luton Hoo is hard to top, with its marble panelling, ornate chandeliers and opulent fabrics.

WOBURN   MAP 11, SP93

Paris House Restaurant
◉◉◉ MODERN BRITISH *V*
See pages 28-29

WYBOSTON   MAP 12, TL15

The Waterfront Restaurant at Wyboston Lakes
◉ TRADITIONAL BRITISH, EUROPEAN
0333 700 7667 | Great North Road, MK44 3BA
www.thewaterfronthotel.co.uk
The Waterfront Restaurant offers a relaxed and modern brasserie-style dining experience with views over the south lake. The breads are home made and served with tapenade as well as oil and balsamic vinegar. For dessert, tuck into tiramisù with Madagascan vanilla cream and biscotti.

■ BERKSHIRE

ASCOT   MAP 6, SU96

The Barn at Coworth
◉◉ BRITISH
01344 756784 | Blacknest Road, SL5 7SE
www.coworthpark.com

There's a fine-dining restaurant at this lavish country hotel, plus this converted barn where you can tuck into classy brasserie-style food. It looks great with its open-to-view kitchen, unbuttoned vibe and cheerful service team sporting orange polo tops, and there's a fabulous terrace, too.

Bluebells Restaurant

◎◎ MODERN EUROPEAN
01344 622722 | London Road, SL5 0PU
www.bluebells-restaurant.co.uk

Smartly traditional and uncluttered, Bluebells Restaurant has full length windows, and a dark green interior with rose highlights. Service is upbeat and friendly, but still very professional. Staff dress in black and white with pink ties to complement the decor. Menus feature a selection of appealing European dishes with some Asian influences.

Restaurant Coworth Park

◎◎◎◎ MODERN BRITISH 🍷 NOTABLE WINE LIST
01344 876600 | London Road, SL5 7SE
www.coworthpark.com

Coworth Park is an elegant Georgian mansion with an effortlessly stylishly Palladian frontage, set in 240 acres of parkland and lovely gardens in the heart of rural Berkshire. Public rooms are high-ceilinged and spacious, with thoughtful contemporary design enhancing the classic country-house feel. Work up an appetite by taking on some of the equestrian opportunities – there are horses for riders of all abilities – or something more sedentary in the state-of-the-art spa, before heading to the restaurant. It's a serene space, calmly minimalist with generous, immaculately presented double-clothed tables and views across the rose terrace. Service is formal but engaging, and a large copper ceiling sculpture, the oak leaf chandelier, is a gloriously autumnal and impressive centre piece. Head chef Adam Smith's menus change with the seasons and he finds inspiration for his precise, dextrous and often innovative take on country-house cooking in the hotel's beautiful surroundings and in locally produced ingredients of the highest order. Dishes are picture-perfect and every element is thoughtfully considered. Dinner is a set, four-course affair with a number of choices at each course, so a summer meal might bring one new season peas with Old Winchester waffle, egg yolk and lovage salad, say, or caviar tart with crab, yuzu, cucumber and cultured cream as a starting point, with a second course of poached cod with Wharf Valley rapeseed oil, wild garlic and lemon. A third course might bring Highland Wagyu beer-glazed short rib with English asparagus and smoked bone marrow, perhaps, or Kentish lamb sweetbread with artichoke, courgette, basil and pine nuts. A Dover sole 'Wellington' might appeal if there are two of you to eat it. Finish with the signature dessert of chocolate hazelnut, salted caramel, and milk ice cream, or the freshest of Kentish strawberries. You can have cheese from the trolley should you wish.

Chef Adam Smith Seats 66, Private dining 16 Open All Year Parking 100 Notes No children under 8 years

WOBURN

Paris House Restaurant

◉◉◉ MODERN BRITISH *V*

01525 290692 | London Road, Woburn Park, MK17 9QP

www.parishouse.co.uk

Impeccable contemporary cooking in a reassembled timbered house

The entrance to Paris House Restaurant certainly raises expectations as you pass through the grand gateway and cross the Duke of Bedford's deer park at his Woburn estate to reach this beautiful half-timbered Tudor-style building. It's all fake, of course: originally constructed in Paris for the 1878 International Exhibition, then taken apart, shipped across the Channel and reassembled here. Inside, it's another story as the door opens onto the 21st century in refined surroundings of impeccable contemporary taste, complete with modern chandeliers, sleek furniture, and artworks that include a wall of seasonally changing, food-related works. Phil Fanning's modern British food is equally in tune with both seasons and current thinking, deftly adding his unique stamp to an international cast of ingredients. Dipping creatively into global – particularly Japanese - influences, the output consists of six- and eight-

"Dipping creatively into global – particularly Japanese – influences..."

course tasting menus brimful with boldly inventive ideas. Start with perfectly timed brill pointed up ceviche-style with a leche de tigre citrus marinade, green tomato, chilli and sweet potato. Next up, black truffle and Parmesan raise humble gnocchi to another level, then it's a trip to Asia for succulent pork belly in a pillowy steamed bun, all fired up with gochujang. Timings and techniques are spot on in perfectly executed hamachi (Japanese amberjack), the rich, buttery texture of the fish combined with white miso, sea kale and a virtuoso workout of cauliflower in various guises. Slot in a plate of artisan cheeses as an optional extra, before thrillingly creative desserts bring a smoothly refined finish to a memorable meal. A reinvented carrot cake involving molasses-like kuromitsu sugar, mandarin, and carrot sorbet is a stunner, while white chocolate and hibiscus cheesecake is a dish of impressive intensity. Relaxed, knowledgeable and professional service is at hand to guide you through every stage, and wine pairings are assembled with expertise and imagination.

Chef Phil Fanning
Seats 37, Private dining 12
Closed 23 December – 5 January
Parking 24
Notes Children welcome

BRAY

MAP 6, SU97

Caldesi in Campagna

◉◉ TRADITIONAL ITALIAN

01628 788500 | Old Mill Lane, SL6 2BG

www.caldesi.com

Here, in an immaculate house on the edge of Bray, expect classic Italian stuff made with (mostly) British ingredients. Among antipasti, deep-fried courgette flowers are filled with ricotta and basil, and to finish, traditional desserts might include Sicilian lemon tart.

The Crown at Bray

◉◉ TRADITIONAL BRITISH

01628 621936 | High Street, SL6 2AH

www.thecrownatbray.com

Devotees of the British pub know The Crown is safe in Heston Blumenthal's hands. His third address in the village, this 16th-century inn offers real ales, a well-constructed wine list and a menu that owes much to pub traditions while honouring the Blumenthal name.

The Fat Duck

◉◉◉◉◉ MODERN BRITISH ❶ NOTABLE WINE LIST

01628 580333 | High Street, SL6 2AQ

www.thefatduck.co.uk

Heston Blumenthal's The Fat Duck, and its telegenic proprietor himself, have entered the modern pantheon of culinary legend with the four-hour marathon of idiosyncratic and inventive eating that is one of those bucket-list experiences that will stay with you forever. A foodie pilgrimage here has never come cheap – the entrance fee is above £300 these days - and that's before you bring jaw-droppingly expensive wine, sundry drinks and the service charge into the equation – but when you appreciate the work that goes into each dish - the craft, the passion, the time - the cost seems easier to justify, and the stellar staff can cope with eight or so languages to keep the international visitors informed as they go along. What follows consumes you as much as you consume it, as a parade of highly conceptualised dishes unfold, arriving on sandy beaches accompanied by gigantic seashells or perched on great white cushions floating in mid-air. Ice cream is crab flavoured, and rocket-shaped ice lollies taste of Waldorf salad. It's ultimately what great cooking is about: when all the theatrical ingenuity makes sense and has purpose delivering flavour, emotion and craftsmanship; something The Fat Duck always accomplishes.

Chef Heston Blumenthal **Seats** 42 **Closed** 2 weeks at Christmas **Notes** Children welcome

The Hind's Head

◉◉◉ BRITISH ❶ NOTABLE WINE LIST

01628 626151 | High Street, SL6 2AB

www.hindsheadbray.com

Heston Blumenthal may still be reinventing the gastronomic at The Fat Duck but there is plenty of culinary magic at his reimagined 15th-century pub nearby. A former royal hunting lodge, the oak panelling, heavy beams and real fires are in step with the building's heritage, as are the hearty British dishes served by unstuffy staff. A classic chicken liver parfait is paired with cherry jelly, nasturtium leaf and toasted brioche. For main course, a perfectly timed roast fillet of cod is accompanied by kale, mussels and cider butter sauce. Finish with cherry Bakewell tart topped with yogurt ice cream.

Chef Peter Gray **Seats** 82, Private dining 18 **Closed** 25 December **Parking** 40 **Notes** Children welcome

The Waterside Inn

◉◉◉ FRENCH 𝑉 ❶ NOTABLE WINE LIST

01628 620691 | Ferry Road, SL6 2AT

www.waterside-inn.co.uk

The little car park is a squeeze, so accept the valet parking – an elegant and sophisticated introduction to The Waterside, a renowned destination for refined dining. Floor-to-ceiling windows give views on to the little jetty and its moored boats, and here in the peaceable upper reaches of the Thames everything really is idyllic. The cooking, too, is all you could wish for, Alain Roux maintaining the formidable standards of the legendary late Michel Roux père. Pan fried lobster medallions come with a white port sauce and ginger flavoured vegetable julienne; main course grilled rabbit fillets are served on celeriac fondant, with glazed chestnuts and Armagnac sauce.

Chef Alain Roux **Seats** 75, Private dining 8 **Closed** 26 December to 30 January **Parking** 20 **Notes** No children under 9 years

BURCHETT'S GREEN
MAP 5, SU88

The Crown
◉◉◉ BRITISH, FRENCH
01628 824079 | SL6 6QZ
www.thecrownburchettsgreen.com

Not just your average 19th-century pub, The Crown is full of original features and understated country-chic furnishings. Chef-patron Simon Bonwick clearly has an impressive grasp of classic French techniques and an intuitive grasp of how ingredients work together in each dish, and his sharp, precise cooking provides intense, satisfying flavours. Menu descriptions underplay what arrives on the plate, with dishes like Cromer crab with apple, citrus and cashew, croustade of sorrel and spinach, asparagus and morels, or slow cooked veal cheek with 'rather nice' veal sauce all proving to be more than the sum of their parts.

Chef Simon Bonwick **Open** All Year **Notes** No children

COOKHAM
MAP 6, SU88

The White Oak
◉◉ MODERN BRITISH
01628 523043 | The Pound, SL6 9QE
www.thewhiteoak.co.uk

The team behind the White Oak reopened it in 2008 as a modern dining pub. Set in Stanley Spencer's beloved Cookham, it has splashy contemporary artwork, bare tables and generous washes of natural light from a skylight and patio doors onto the garden.

HUNGERFORD
MAP 5, SU36

Blandy's at Inglewood
◉ MODERN, CLASSIC BRITISH
01488 687010 | Templeton Road, Kintbury, RG17 9AA
www.blandysbistro.co.uk

Housed in a handsome Georgian mansion in extensive gardens, Blandy's is the epitome of English elegance, overlaid with a gently contemporary edge. High ceilings, chandeliers, ornate plasterwork and panelling set a grandiose tone in the dining room, where you can expect meticulous plates of seasonal, produce-driven, modern food with sound classical foundations.

HURLEY
MAP 5, SU88

Hurley House
◉◉ JAPANESE, INTERNATIONAL
01628 568500 | Henley Road, SL6 5LH
hurleyhouse.co.uk

The candlelit restaurant at Hurley House offers two main menus – Japanese (plus a takeaway version) and International, although dishes from both menus can be combined. The International lists chipotle lime cauliflower steak, whole grilled Dover sole and home-made fermented sourdough pizzas. A good wine list is expertly explained by the young team.

See advertisement on page 33

MAIDENHEAD
MAP 6, SU88

Fredrick's Hotel and Spa
◎◎ MODERN BRITISH

01628 581000 | Shoppenhangers Road, SL6 2PZ

www.fredricks-hotel.co.uk

On the fringes of Maidenhead, Fredrick's is a popular venue for spa pampering and weddings. The restaurant goes for a neutral, modern look involving off-white panelled walls enlivened by bright artworks and designer lighting. The kitchen team continue to produce uncomplicated contemporary cooking with an eye to seasonal produce.

NEWBURY
MAP 5, SU46

Donnington Valley Hotel & Spa
◎◎ MODERN BRITISH 🏅 NOTABLE WINE LIST

01635 551199 | Old Oxford Road, Donnington, RG14 3AG

www.donningtonvalley.co.uk

The Wine Press is the atmospheric and relaxed restaurant at Donnington Valley Hotel & Spa. Bright in the day, with intimate ambience in the evening, a laid-back jazz soundtrack, and a gallery level running above the main area. Menus are modern British, a collection of uncomplicated combinations, using top quality ingredients. The heavyweight wine list is well worth investigation.

The Vineyard
◎◎◎ MODERN BRITISH V 🏅 NOTABLE WINE LIST

01635 528770 | Stockcross, RG20 8JU

www.the-vineyard.co.uk

There's no vineyard at The Vineyard, although owner Sir Peter Michael's world-class Californian winery supplies some pretty remarkable wines in a cellar that runs to a staggering 30,000 bottles. In fact, the super-slick operation is a stylish and sybaritic celebration of the world of wine and gastronomy, with side orders of spa pampering, luxurious accommodation and chic public areas. On the food front, Orkney scallop with chicken, grapes and marigold delivers precision and innovation in equal measure, while Berkshire Downs lamb is matched with Savoy cabbage and smoked onion purée. Expert sommeliers guide the way through that astonishing cellar, starting with around 100 available by the glass.

Chef Tom Scade **Seats** 86, Private dining 140 **Open** All Year **Parking** 100 **Notes** Children welcome

The Woodspeen – Restaurant and Cookery School
◎◎◎ MODERN BRITISH

01635 265070 | Lambourn Road, RG20 8BN

www.thewoodspeen.com

Just outside Newbury, this restaurant and cookery school is the latest venture for much-lauded chef John Campbell. Housed in a restored farmhouse with picture windows framing the idyllic views, the vibrant dishes are constructed with a light touch and layers of dazzling complexity, as in a starter of scallops, crispy BBQ pork cheeks, peas and balsamic onions. Mains showcase pedigree meats and tip-top seafood, with both combining in a dish of chargrilled beef fillet and Cornish lobster raviolo, lobster beignet and bisque, truffled leeks and spinach. Finish with rhubarb fool, rhubarb jam, ginger cake and yogurt ice cream.

Chef Peter Eaton **Seats** 70, Private dining 12 **Open** All Year **Parking** 30 **Notes** Children welcome

H

HURLEY HOUSE
— HOTEL —

READING
MAP 5, SU77

Caprice Restaurant & Terrace
◉◉ MODERN BRITISH, AUTHENTIC INDIAN V
0118 944 0444 | Crowne Plaza Reading East,
Wharfedale Road, Winnersh Triangle, RG41 5TS
www.cpreading.co.uk
Located in the bustling Winnersh Triangle
Business Park, Caprice Restaurant is part of
Crowne Plaza Reading East, and the Terrace
overlooks landscaped podium gardens. The
restaurant is bright, modern and open plan, while
the menu is modern British and authentic Indian.
As well as offering outstanding flavours, the
kitchen does a great job with its imaginative
presentation.

See advertisement opposite

Chez Mal Brasserie
◉ MODERN EUROPEAN, INTERNATIONAL
0118 956 2300 | Malmaison Reading, Great Western
House, 18-20 Station Road, RG1 1JX
www.malmaison.com
By all accounts the world's oldest railway hotel,
the early Victorian property is a real charmer. Its
historic past is recognised in some decorative
touches, but this being a Mal, the overall finish is
glamorous and stylish. Settle into the Malbar for
a pre-dinner cocktail.

The French Horn
◉◉ TRADITIONAL FRENCH, BRITISH
0118 969 2204 | Sonning, RG4 6TN
www.thefrenchhorn.co.uk
The riverside setting is a treat, with the dining
room opening on to a terrace, at the family-run
French Horn, which is full of old-school charm
with slick and well-managed service. The menu
looks across the Channel for its inspiration, with
a classically based repertoire.

SHINFIELD
MAP 5, SU76

L'Ortolan
◉◉◉ MODERN FRENCH 🍷 NOTABLE WINE LIST
0118 988 8500 | Church Lane, RG2 9BY
www.lortolan.com
A country-house style restaurant set in an
elegant red-brick former vicarage with Gothic-
style front door and bow-fronted windows,
L'Ortolan is a name synonymous with modern
gastronomy since the 1980s. Now, talented young
chef James Greatorex is the man in 'whites',
delivering sophisticated, highly detailed, aspiring
contemporary cooking via carte and tasting
menus. Dishes come dressed to thrill, with
flavour, texture, balance and precision to the

fore; witness 'melting' citrus cured Cornish
mackerel teamed with cucumber and buttermilk,
or 'sparkling fresh' Cornish cod ballotine with
clams, sea herbs and watercress. Fine-dining
standards like canapés, bread, pre-desserts and
petit fours round of a polished act, alongside
professional and informed service

Chef James Greatorex **Seats** 58, Private dining 22
Closed 2 weeks Christmas to New Year
Prices from S £12.50, M £16, D £11 **Parking** 30
Notes No children under 3 years

THATCHAM
MAP 5, SU56

The Bunk Inn
◉ MODERN BRITISH, FRENCH
01635 200400 | Curridge, RG18 9DS
www.thebunkinn.co.uk
A short canter from Newbury Racecourse, this
convivial inn is still very much the village hub
where locals prop up the bar by the open fire
with a glass of ale and a packet of crisps, but its
confident modern cooking also attracts foodies.

WHITE WALTHAM
MAP 5, SU87

The Beehive
◉◉ BRITISH
01628 822877 | Waltham Road, SL6 3SH
www.thebeehivewhitewaltham.com
With the cricket ground opposite, The Beehive is
the epitome of the English village pub. A bar
menu, daily-changing lunch and dinner menus,
and a specials board reveal season-driven,
modern British dishes known for their gimmick-
free, 'less is more' simplicity. Start with Dorset
snails with garlic butter, gorgonzola and grilled
sourdough and follow with calves' liver, crisp
bacon, onions and mash.

WINDSOR
MAP 6, SU97

The Greene Oak
◉ MODERN BRITISH
01753 864294 | Oakley Green, SL4 5UW
www.thegreeneoak.co.uk
Very much a dining pub, The Greene Oak is a
charming old place with bright, homely decor and
cheerful staff who keep it all ticking along nicely.
The kitchen makes good use of local seasonal
ingredients, focusing on gently contemporary
British- and European-inspired ideas.

Caprice Restaurant

Discover the new 2 AA Rosette Caprice Restaurant, located in the exceptional new 4 Silver Star Crowne Plaza Reading East; The perfect spot to enjoy your meal in tranquil surroundings, with floor to ceiling windows and comfortable seating, all complimented by great service.

Monty's Bar Lounge and Terrace offers a fresh and quality modern British menu, as well as an extensive authentic Indian menu. Why not try some creative cocktails on the landscaped lawns and gardens.

The splendid Afternoon Teas are the finest in Berkshire. There is a fantastic terrace for al fresco dining. Our flexible dining alternatives, including private and corporate banqueting, as well as Christmas Parties and residential packages/offers, are also available upon request.

E: fb@cpreading.co.uk   T: 0118 944 0444   W: www.cpreading.co.uk
Wharfedale Road, Winnersh Triangle, Reading RG41 5TS

■ BRISTOL

MAP 4, ST57

Adelina Yard

◉◉ MODERN BRITISH

0117 911 2112 | Queen Quay, Welsh Back, BS1 4SL

www.adelinayard.com

Owner-chef couple Jamie Randall and Olivia Barry have made quite an impact on the local scene since opening this stylish restaurant at the end of 2015. Located on the water's edge in the city's revitalised harbourside area, the open-plan kitchen provides an informal setting.

Berwick Lodge

◉◉ MODERN BRITISH

0117 958 1590 | Berwick Drive, Henbury, BS10 7TD

www.berwicklodge.co.uk

The Victorian gent who built this manor house back in the 1890s picked a good spot, surrounded by 18 acres of gardens and woodland. The smart boutique restaurant, Hattua, is the perfect setting for creative modern dishes which look as good as they taste.

The Bird in Hand

◉ MODERN BRITISH

01275 395222 | Weston Road, Long Ashton, BS41 9LA

thebirdinla.co.uk

Just beyond Bristol's western limits, The Bird in Hand offers the charm you'd expect from a village pub, while here and there hinting at the South African origins of one of the owners. There's the country's national flag, of course, paintings and, on the menu, lamb Durban curry bunny chow, alongside modern British dishes and pub classics.

Casamia Restaurant

◉◉◉◉ MODERN BRITISH 𝄢 NOTABLE WINE LIST

0117 959 2884 | The General, Lower Guinea Street, BS1 6SY

www.casamiarestaurant.co.uk

Casamia's location in the redeveloped General Hospital overlooking Bathurst Basin in Bristol's docklands, is very different from the leafy suburb of Westbury-on-Trym, where self-taught chef Peter Sanchez-Iglesias opened it first time round. Passing through the monumental stone archway you enter a sleek, subtly monochrome interior with linen-clad tables, a tiled floor, and walls hung with periodically rotating arboreal pictures. In the open kitchen, a battalion of chefs works with calm concentration to produce driven-by-the-seasons tasting menus – a four-course (except Friday and Saturday evenings), and a longer version (Wednesdays to Sundays). Ingenious, novel and well-nigh flawlessly executed, they are undeniably aimed upmarket. The chefs themselves then bring them to the table and talk them through with diners, which is handy because the economically worded menus give little away; even their website reveals only 'what we're cooking at the moment', as in 'beef', 'lamb', 'hake'. You'd expect the carefully chosen wine pairings to complement the complex detail of each dish – and they do. Casamia, like many top restaurants today, requires payment on booking, with drinks and service added on the day.

Chef Peter Sanchez-Iglesias, Kelvin Potter **Seats** 30 **Closed** Christmas, New Year and bank holidays **Notes** Children welcome

Fish NEW

◉◉ MODERN FRENCH

0117 929 0704 | Welsh Back, BS1 4SB

fishbristol.co.uk

Formerly the Glassboat Restaurant, this converted 1920s barge has been moored in the heart of Bristol's Harbourside area since 1986. It's a handsome and appealing restaurant with walnut floors, a beautiful marble bar and lovely river views; the menu offers fish dishes (as per the new name!).

Hotel du Vin Bristol

◉ FRENCH, BRITISH 𝄢 NOTABLE WINE LIST

0117 925 5577 | The Sugar House, Narrow Lewins Mead, BS1 2NU

www.hotelduvin.com

In a former sugar warehouse close to the waterfront, the casual French-inspired bistro at the Bristol HdV is a buzzy and easy-going venue. Factor in the world-class wine list, and you've got a compelling package. The bilingual menu deals in classic stuff.

The Ivy Clifton Brasserie

⊚ BRITISH

0117 203 4555 | 42–44 Caledonia Place, BS8 4DN

www.theivycliftonbrasserie.com

Set in the heart of Clifton, just moments from the famous suspension bridge, this former bank has been tastefully converted into a must-visit restaurant in this area. Taking inspiration from her London big sister, it is a great casual dining all-day concept.

The Ox

⊚ MODERN BRITISH

0117 922 1001 | The Basement, 43 Corn Street, BS1 1HT

www.theoxbristol.com

Head down to the basement, a one-time bank vault, and you'll find a restaurant that the old boys of yesteryear would have admired, with its oak panels, ox blood leather seats and murals. They'd have appreciated the red-blooded menu too - steaks are their thing.

Paco Tapas

⊚⊚ ANDALUSIAN TAPAS

0117 925 7021 | 3A Lower Guinea Street, BS1 6SY

www.pacotapas.co.uk

Located directly on the docks at Bristol harbourside, this bustling tapas bar offers authentic dishes from the owners' Andalusian home. Much of the produce comes directly from the region while daily specials are added by way of fresh fish and seafood delivered daily from the Cornish coasts.

The Pump House

⊚⊚ MODERN BRITISH

0117 927 2229 | Merchants Road, Hotwells, BS8 4PZ

the-pumphouse.com

Set on Bristol's Floating Harbour, The Pump House is a Victorian former hydraulic pumping station housing a buzzy gastro pub and restaurant with a mezzanine seating area. As well as a wide selection of 'small plates', there are pub classics like fish and triple-cooked chips, and buttermilk fried chicken with aïoli.

riverstation

⊚ MODERN EUROPEAN

0117 914 4434 | The Grove, BS1 4RB

www.riverstation.co.uk

Being on the River Avon as it flows through the city's docks, the views from riverstation's terrace and balcony are outstanding. You can even arrive by boat — just ask your ferryman to dock at the restaurant's own pontoon. A seasonally changing menu offers fresh and inspiring modern British and European dishes, while the downstairs bar serves brunches, English classics and small plates.

Root

⊚ BRITISH, SHARING PLATES

0117 930 0260 | Unit 9, Cargo 1, Gaol Ferry Steps, BS1 6WP

www.eatdrinkbristolfashion.co.uk

Originating at the Queen Square Festival, Root is the restaurant venture of Eat Drink Bristol Fashion, and is stationed on the historic dockside at Wapping Wharf. In a vibrant, chattery atmosphere, with seating around the bar overlooking the kitchen, a menu of small sharing plates encompasses globally influenced cooking with plenty of attitude.

Second Floor Restaurant

⊚⊚ MODERN BRITISH ⚑NOTABLE WINE LIST

0117 916 8898 | Harvey Nichols, 27 Philadelphia Street, Quakers Friars, BS1 3BZ

www.harveynichols.com

Overlooking the old Quakers Friars Dominican friary in the heart of Cabot Circus shopping quarter, this gold and beige-hued, second-floor dining room is a supremely relaxing place. The kitchen turns out a menu of lively modern British and European food. There are interesting wines on offer too.

BRISTOL continued

The Spiny Lobster

◉ MEDITERRANEAN, SEAFOOD

0117 973 7384 | 128 Whiteladies Road, Clifton, BS8 2RS

www.thespinylobster.co.uk

Mitch Tonks' seafood brasserie and fish market maintains a rigorous commitment to freshness and simplicity, using fish and shellfish mostly landed by the Brixham boats. The dining room sports linen-clothed tables, staff are friendly, and top-class materials slapped onto a charcoal-burning Josper grill can't be beaten.

Tare Restaurant

◉◉ MODERN EUROPEAN *V*

0117 929 4328 | Unit 14, Museum Street, Wapping Wharf, BS1 6ZA

tarerestaurant.co.uk

Operating out of a converted shipping container in the up-and-coming Wapping Wharf harbourside development, Tare offers intimate, relaxed and modern dining. The carefully sourced top-quality produce contributes to the regular and seasonal menu updates including a five-course tasting menu. There are some interesting bottled beers and ciders too.

■ BUCKINGHAMSHIRE

AMERSHAM

MAP 6, SU99

The Artichoke

◉◉◉ MODERN EUROPEAN 🏅

01494 726611 | 9 Market Square, Old Amersham, HP7 0DF

www.artichokerestaurant.co.uk

Amersham's finest continues to set a regional standard for dazzling modern cooking delivered with engaging brio in an atmosphere enlivened by views of the kitchen pass. Laurie Gear offers a sheaf of tasting menus, as well as the standard prix-fixe, a set lunch and vegetarian options. He's the kind of chef unafraid to do the simplest things: a plate of just al dente risotto flavoured with parsley roots and dressed with melted Lancashire Bomb. For fish, there could be skate wing garnished with diced apple, sea beets and triple-cooked chips seasoned with powdered capers and vinegar, in a sauce of mussels and cider. Succulent venison sausage is partnered with a terrine of potato cooked in beef dripping, red cabbage purée and beetroot. To finish, there may be Cambridge burnt cream offset with poached rhubarb, blood orange and aerated white chocolate. Preliminaries include the unmissable Chiltern Black Ale bread with lamb-fat butter.

Chef Laurie Gear, Ben Jenkins **Seats** 48, Private dining 16 **Closed** 2 weeks at Christmas, 1 week April (from Easter Sunday), 2 weeks in August/September **Notes** No children under 8 years at dinner

Gilbey's Restaurant

◉◉ MODERN BRITISH

01494 727242 | 1 Market Square, HP7 0DF

www.gilbeygroup.com

Housed in Old Amersham's 17th-century former grammar school, the fully renovated Gilbey's offers the style and intimacy you'd expect with low ceilings and wood flooring. Cooking is traditional and simple with modern touches - expect dishes such as roasted red pepper soup with green tomato salsa followed by confit leg of duck with tomato and olive gnocchi.

Hawkyns by Atul Kochhar

◎◎ MODERN BRITISH, MODERN INDIAN
01494 721541 | The Crown, 16 High Street, HP7 0DH
www.hawkynsrestaurant.co.uk
Set within The Crown, a Tudor-style building in the pretty town of Amersham, Hawkyns is run by the celebrated Indian chef Atul Kochhar. Set against a backdrop of original wooden beams, stripped floorboards and brick fireplaces, the scrubbed farmhouse-style tables and mismatched chairs add an informal pub feel but the food is a combination of the best British and Indian cooking.

AYLESBURY
MAP 11, SP81

The Chequers Inn

◎◎ MODERN BRITISH
01296 613298 | 35 Church Lane, Weston Turville, HP22 5SJ
www.thechequerswt.co.uk

the chequers inn

Dating from the 16th century, its traditional bar features old beams and polished flagstone floors, while the restaurant is more contemporary. Home to chef/owner Dritan and his maître d' wife Ranka, their 11 years here have seen them turn it into a locally renowned establishment. Although not open to the public, the prime minister's Chequers is a few miles away.

Hartwell House Hotel, Restaurant & Spa

◎◎ MODERN BRITISH *V* ◢NOTABLE WINE LIST
01296 747444 | Lower Hartwell, Vale of Aylesbury, HP17 8NR
www.hartwell-house.com
One-time residence of the exiled Louis XVIII, this majestic stately home is set within 90 acres of parkland. Befitting the grand setting, everything looks good on the plate and flavours are nicely handled. Beef carpaccio might be followed by seared fillet of halibut, prawn dumpling, pickled mooli and Thai shellfish broth.

BEACONSFIELD
MAP 6, SU99

The Jolly Cricketers

◎ MODERN BRITISH
01494 676308 | 24 Chalfont Road, Seer Green, HP9 2YG
www.thejollycricketers.co.uk
A red-brick, wisteria-festooned Victorian pub, The Jolly Cricketers is the hub of village life. Inside it's a genuinely unspoilt and unreconstructed village local that has created a reputation strong enough to bring in diners from much further afield. Uncomplicated cooking shows good attention to detail and big hearty flavours from well-sourced ingredients. Pub classics as well as more contemporary ideas.

See advertisement on page 40

BRILL
MAP 11, SP61

The Pointer

◎◎ MODERN BRITISH
01844 238339 | 27 Church Street, HP18 9RT
www.thepointerbrill.co.uk
The Pointer's roots extend deep into its local community. As well as being a welcoming pub in the picturesque village of Brill near Aylesbury, it also encompasses a working organic farm and kitchen garden, and an adjacent butcher's shop for take-outs of its pedigree meats.

BUCKINGHAM
MAP 11, SP63

Duke's Restaurant & Bar
◉ MODERN BRITISH

01280 822444 | Buckingham Villiers Hotel, 3 Castle Street, MK18 1BS

www.villiers-hotel.co.uk

Overlooking a courtyard, the restaurant at the Villiers Hotel offers a range of booths and seating options. The kitchen focuses on tried-and-tested dishes, but more ambitious ideas are just as well handled, such as roasted rump of lamb, shepherd's pie, Merguez sausage, peas, samphire, courgette and lamb jus.

BURNHAM
MAP 6, SU98

Burnham Beeches Hotel
◉◉ MODERN BRITISH, EUROPEAN

01628 429955 | Grove Road, SL1 8DP

corushotels.com/burnham-beeches-hotel

Close to Windsor, this extended Georgian manor house is set in 10 acres of attractive grounds. The oak-panelled Gray's restaurant is a formal affair with white linen and views of the pretty garden. The gently contemporary dishes are based on classical themes and techniques.

CUBLINGTON
MAP 11, SP82

The Unicorn
◉ MODERN, TRADITIONAL BRITISH

01296 681261 | 12 High Street, LU7 0LQ

www.theunicornpub.co.uk

This 17th-century inn serves the local community well. It has a shop, opens for coffee mornings and afternoon teas on Friday and Saturday and serves bar snacks all day. Menus show interesting ways with seafood and meat is deftly handled too.

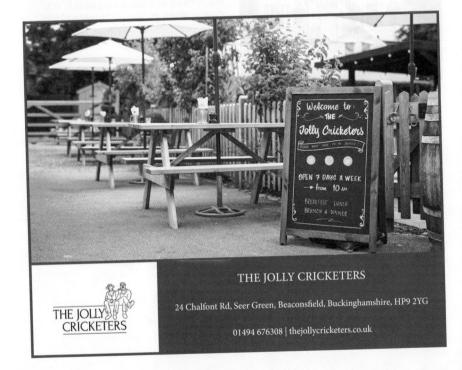

GERRARDS CROSS
MAP 6, TOO8

The Three Oaks
⊛⊛ MODERN BRITISH
01753 899016 | Austenwood Lane,
Chalfont St Peter, SL9 8NL
www.thethreeoaksgx.co.uk
Part of the draw at this attractive gastro pub is attentive service from a cheerful young team. There's a lovely garden for those balmy days, while inside, the place has a smartly updated look – a brick fireplace, bare wood tables and easy-on-the-eye colours. Expect to find accomplished contemporary cooking built on top-drawer produce.

GREAT MISSENDEN
MAP 6, SP80

Nags Head Inn & Restaurant
⊛ BRITISH, FRENCH
01494 862200 | London Road, HP16 0DG
www.nagsheadbucks.com
Only a 15-minute stroll from the enchantments of the Roald Dahl Museum in the High Street, the family-run Nags Head is a 15th-century country inn by the River Misbourne. Lightly modernised inside, it makes a relaxed, welcoming setting for creatively fashioned cooking, and dishes with the populist touch.

MARLOW
MAP 5, SU88

The Coach
⊛⊛⊛ FRENCH, BRITISH
3 West Street, SL7 2LS
www.thecoachmarlow.co.uk
The pint-sized Coach is a cosy, chic pub dominated by its stainless steel L-shaped bar, decked out with elbow-to-elbow leather bar stalls and tables with matching banquettes, while an open kitchen adds to the buzzy, uptempo action. Head chef Tom De Keyser turns out tapas-sized plates with in the same DNA as the garlanded Hand & Flowers – big on flavour and technical finesse. Divided between 'meat' and 'no meat' dishes, the menu reads like a roster of big-hearted modern pub food – think a rich wild boar lasagne with parmesan and lemon, or a towering burger with pulled pork and dill pickle, while the chips with béarnaise are made in heaven. From the 'no meat' side might come deep-fried brill with pease pudding and tartare sauce. The Coach doesn't take bookings, so turn up early. Serves breakfast too.

Chef Tom De Keyser, Tom Kerridge **Seats** 40
Closed 25–26 December **Notes** Children welcome

Danesfield House Hotel & Spa
⊛⊛ MODERN BRITISH
01628 891010 | Henley Road, SL7 2EY
www.danesfieldhouse.co.uk

Built in 1901, Danesfield House is set in 65 magnificent acres, just a hop from central London and a skip from Heathrow. As well as memorable views across the River Thames, the Orangery restaurant also offers interesting and innovative menus. The flavour is modern British but there's plenty of European influence.

Glaze Restaurant
⊛ MODERN BRITISH, INDIAN
01628 496800 | Crowne Plaza Marlow,
Fieldhouse Lane, SL7 1GJ
www.cpmarlow.co.uk/dine
Just outside Marlow is the Crowne Plaza Marlow, and its flagship restaurant. Glaze is a light-filled, stylish modern space, enjoying views over the hotel's lake in the grounds. Diners can choose from seasonally-changing menus of brasserie cooking or Indian cuisine, either of which always have something new and exciting to offer.

See advertisement on page 43

MARLOW continued

The Hand & Flowers

◉◉◉◉ FRENCH. BRITISH ⚑NOTABLE WINE LIST
01628 482277 | 126 West Street, SL7 2BP
www.thehandandflowers.co.uk

Tom Kerridge's career is about, above all, creating food that people want to eat, rather than baffling peculiarities they feel they ought to try. The nerve-centre remains the whitewashed country pub with its hanging baskets (plus its private dining space, The Shed, just up the road), where an atmosphere of endearing bonhomie prevails amid the bare tables and half-boarded walls. Marlow regulars doubtless appreciate the fact that the kitchen prides itself as much on producing a matchless roast beef and Yorkshire pudding for Sundays, as it does on working creative transformations on familiar ingredients. Beef toast and dripping comes with mustard butter, English asparagus and salad cream, while at main it's undoubtedly with pedigree meats that the principal emphasis rests. West End Farm pork belly with smoked cheek beignet, black pudding and gherkin ketchup vies for attention with Essex lamb 'bun' with sweetbreads and salsa verde. It's all pretty substantial, but don't even think of resisting the signature chocolate and ale cake with salt caramel muscovado ice cream.

Chef Tom Kerridge **Seats** 54, Private dining 9
Closed 24–26 December **Parking** 20 **Notes** Children welcome

The Vanilla Pod

◉◉ BRITISH, FRENCH ⚑NOTABLE WINE LIST
01628 898101 | 31 West Street, SL7 2LS
www.thevanillapod.co.uk

The culinary bar is set high in this stretch of the Thames Valley stockbroker belt, and The Vanilla Pod delivers a sure-footed take on modern British cooking, its roots clearly in the French classics. The setting is a handsome townhouse where TS Eliot once lived, and today the restaurant has a chic contemporary look in brown and cream.

STOKE POGES   MAP 6, SU98

Humphry's at Stoke Park

◉◉◉ MODERN BRITISH
01753 717171 | Park Road, SL2 4PG
www.stokepark.com

Stoke Park, including Humphry's, will be closed from August 2021 for a two-year refurbishment programme. The luxuriant acres of Stoke Park were turned into Britain's first country club in 1908, the domed and pillared mansion house at its centre surveying some of the grandest golf the nation had to offer. Since then, the place has played host to pro-am tournaments and rock concerts, as well as providing locations for British cinema from James Bond to Bridget Jones. The interiors are splendidly preserved, particularly in the magnificent marble-pillared, extravagantly corniced and deep-piled dining room, arrayed in sunny golds and pastel yellow and named in honour of Humphry Repton, who created the gardens.

Chef Chris Wheeler **Seats** 50, Private dining 146
Closed 24–26 December, 1st week in January
Parking 400 **Notes** No children under 12 years at dinner

TAPLOW   MAP 6, SU98

Berry's Restaurant and Terrace

◉◉ CLASSIC BRITISH
01628 670056 | Taplow House Hotel, Berry Hill, SL6 0DA
www.taplowhouse.com

The original Elizabethan manor was destroyed by fire, so today's house is a handsome piece of Georgian architecture instead, with suitably formal public rooms. The elegant Berry's Restaurant looks over the six acres of landscaped grounds, with huge French doors opening onto the terrace.

Continued on page 44

CROWNE PLAZA
MARLOW

Glaze Restaurant

he exceptional new AA Rosette Awarded Glaze Restaurant invites you to enjoy
r delicious British À la Carte or authentic Indian cuisine in superb surroundings.

lternatively, why not treat yourself to an indulgent Sparkling Afternoon Tea or a
reative cocktail or two in the Conservatory or Terrace, overlooking the stunning
lake and lawns.

Enjoy a BBQ feast on our terrace, the ideal way to bring friends and
family together for a special occasion.

To make a reservation please contact: Glaze Restaurant
T: 01628 496 800   E: Reservations@cpmarlow.co.uk
W: www.cpmarlow.co.uk/dine
Crowne Plaza Marlow, Fieldhouse Lane, Marlow, SL7 1GJ

TAPLOW continued

The Cliveden Dining Room

◉◉◉ MODERN BRITISH ⚑ NOTABLE WINE LIST

01628 668561 | Cliveden Estate, SL6 0JF
www.clivedenhouse.co.uk

Dripping with a history of high society scandal and lording it over a whopping 376-acres of National Trust estate, Cliveden belongs unquestionably in the premier league of England's stately homes. The dining experience is pretty special too, in an impeccably elegant, swagged and chandeliered restaurant with shimmering views over parterre gardens to the Thames. Paul O'Neill's dazzling cooking is more than a match for this luxurious setting. There are vegan and vegetarian menus as well as the standard á la carte, from which you might choose a perfectly-timed autumn truffle risotto, or English asparagus soup, followed by wild garlic gnocchi with peas and broad beans, or a deceptively simple dish of Jurassic Coast rose veal, with sweetbreads, carrot and black garlic. There's nowhere to hide here – so quality ingredients and sound technique are essential. At dessert, a pear soufflé with pear compôte and vanilla bean ice cream is a delightfully presented, elegant dish.

Chef Paul O'Neill **Seats** 78, Private dining 60 **Open** All Year **Parking** 60 **Notes** Children welcome

WADDESDON   MAP 11, SP71

The Five Arrows

◉◉ MODERN BRITISH

01296 651727 | High Street, HP18 0JE
fivearrowshotel.co.uk/restaurant

Part of the Rothschild Estate, this small Victorian hotel stands at the gates of Waddesdon Manor but has none of the airs and graces of the grand French château-style stately home. The relaxed restaurant sports a smart, contemporary look with wine-related prints on the walls.

WOOBURN   MAP 6, SU98

Chequers Inn

◉◉ BRITISH, FRENCH

01628 529575 | Kiln Lane, Wooburn Common, HP10 0JQ
www.chequers-inn.com

A 17th-century former coaching inn, there's no denying that the Chequers has moved with the times. The Anglo-French cooking in its chic and spacious restaurant delivers compelling flavour combinations. Eating out on the sunny patio in summer is a delight.

■ CAMBRIDGESHIRE

BARTLOW   MAP 12, TL54

The Three Hills

◉◉ MODERN BRITISH *V*

01223 890500 | Dean Road, CB21 4PW
www.thethreehills.co.uk

The Three Hills is a charming 17th-century, Grade II listed pub with a lovely garden leading down to a river. A collection of wicker bulls' heads on the oak-beamed orangery's white clapboard-style walls are a sign this is a restaurant that reflects its rural location.

CAMBRIDGE   MAP 12, TL45

Midsummer House Restaurant

◉◉◉◉◉ MODERN BRITISH *V* ⚑ NOTABLE WINE LIST

See pages 46–47

See advertisement on page 48

Quy Mill Hotel & Spa, Cambridge

◉◉ MODERN EUROPEAN, BRITISH, FRENCH

01223 293383 | Church Road, Stow-Cum-Quy,
CB25 9AF
www.cambridgequymill.co.uk

Dine in the historic Waterwheel Room, where the Quy water literally runs through the middle of the Grade-II listed original waterwheel, featuring modern British cuisine in a unique setting. Good wine list.

Restaurant 22

◉◉ MODERN BRITISH

01223 351880 | 22 Chesterton Road, CB4 3AX
www.restaurant22.co.uk

Backing onto the River Cam and Jesus Green, Restaurant 22 is a converted Victorian townhouse with an elegant and comfortable dining room in shades of grey and crisp white. Look out for the late 19th-century stained-glass windows. Choose between two tasting menus or a set menu for lunch, and expect unfussy cooking with layers of flavour.

FORDHAM
MAP 12, TL67

The White Pheasant
◎◎ BRITISH, EUROPEAN
01638 720414 | 21 Market Street, CB7 5LQ
www.whitepheasant.com
The White Pheasant is a modern foodie pub with simply decorated interior, log fires and plain wood tables, but chef-proprietor Calvin Holland's cooking sets it a cut above the average. The kitchen sources the very best materials from local producers.

HINXTON
MAP 12, TL44

The Red Lion Inn
◎ BRITISH
01799 530601 | 32 High Street, CB10 1QY
www.redlionhinxton.co.uk
With its timeless rustic cosiness, the timbered Tudor Red Lion's bar is a great spot for classic pub grub, but for contemporary cuisine head for the airy, oak-raftered restaurant, where there's an eclectic carte pitched just right for the kitchen's ambitions.

PETERBOROUGH
MAP 12, TL19

The Chubby Castor NEW
◎◎ MODERN BRITISH V
01733 380801 | 34 Peterborough Road, Castor, PE5 7AX
www.thechubbycastor.com
The Chubby Castor's 'civilised dining' focusses on modern British cooking and is located in a 17th-century building at The Fitzwilliam Arms in the beautiful rural village of Castor. Chef Patron, Adebola Adeshina, has previously worked at a range of highly established restaurants including being part of the Aubergine team under Gordon Ramsay and at Petrus under Marcus Wareing.

ST NEOTS
MAP 12, TL16

The George Hotel & Brasserie
◎◎ MODERN BRITISH
01480 812300 | High Street, Buckden, PE19 5XA
www.thegeorgebuckden.com
The Furbank family brought this old coaching inn back to life in 2003 by creating a cool and contemporary venue and respecting the integrity of the old building. The menu delivers feel-good flavours based on quality ingredients (including some stuff they grow themselves).

STILTON
MAP 12, TL18

The Bell Inn
◎◎ MODERN BRITISH
01733 241066 | Great North Road, PE7 3RA
www.thebellstilton.co.uk
Dating from 1642, this rambling village coaching inn has a contemporary outlook when it comes to cooking. The kitchen turns out bright ideas displaying a good balance of flavours. Perhaps open with chicken liver parfait, mango chutney and toasted brioche before Moroccan lamb loin, harissa-spiced couscous, bok choi and red pepper purée.

WISBECH
MAP 12, TF40

Crown Lodge Hotel
◎ MODERN, TRADITIONAL
01945 773391 | Downham Road, Outwell, PE14 8SE
www.thecrownlodgehotel.co.uk
A modern hotel kitted out to host conferences and meetings, Crown Lodge is a useful local resource. The flexible approach to dining means you can go for simple things like fish and chips or a burger, but there's also a more ambitious carte.

Midsummer House Restaurant

🌼🌼🌼🌼🌼 MODERN BRITISH *V* 🍴 NOTABLE WINE LIST

01223 369299 | Midsummer Common, CB4 1HA

www.midsummerhouse.co.uk

Modern fine dining elevated to the highest level

Since Daniel Clifford bought Midsummer House in 1998, he has turned this former private residence - and one-time dog breeding home - into a world class dining destination. Idyllically set in a handsome Victorian villa on the banks of the River Cam, the chic and light-filled conservatory dining room is a tranquil setting with its white linen tablecloths and slate and charcoal hues. Diners are separated from the kitchen by a window, through which Clifford and his head chef, Mark Abbott, can be observed at close quarters. They are supported by a talented team of studious and focused chefs creating elegant, precise and inventive modern British dishes showcased in a nine-course tasting menu and, from Wednesdays to Saturdays, a more compact set lunch menu. The concise menu descriptions are at odds with the intricacy of the food - each carefully sourced ingredient is

> "...each carefully sourced ingredient is treated with respect and is on the plate for a reason."

treated with respect and is on the plate for a reason. Flavours chime perfectly with the seasons, and a meal might begin with fresh water prawns, broad beans, English peas, sauce cocktail, before moving on to Suffolk tomatoes, aged parmesan, Nocellara olives, English basil, sauce gazpacho. Things remain light with hand-dived Orkney scallop, salt baked celeriac, Granny Smith apple and summer truffle before gaining in richness with roasted Norfolk quail, creamed shallots, duck liver, confit quail egg, Jerez vinegar, followed by slowly cooked Loch Duart salmon, white chocolate and caviar sauce and finger lime.

Another highlight is a dish of grass-fed Yorkshire beef, tenderstem broccoli, pickled anchovy and beurre rouge. Next up, a cheese course of truffled Baron Bigod, English yogurt, mushroom consommé and truffle honey might precede Cambridgeshire strawberries, ewe's yogurt and garden lovage. Baked passionfruit and crystallised orange tart might be a final flourish before coffee and a plate of delicate petit fours.

Chef Daniel Clifford
Seats 45, Private dining 12
Closed 2 weeks Christmas to New Year, 1 week at end of April, 2 weeks end of August to September

See advertisement on page 48

MIDSUMMER HOUSE

Midsummer House is located in the heart of
historic Cambridge. This Victorian Villa encapsulates
Daniel Clifford's vision for culinary perfection and
is home to some fresh innovative dishes.

Daniel Clifford has taken the restaurant
to another level over the past 23 years; his
cooking has a modern-focus which is underpinned
by classical French technique offering
seriously sophisticated food.

Upstairs there is a private dining room, a welcoming
lounge and terrace for after dinner drinks with river
views. The private dining room is the perfect location for
small weddings, lavish birthday celebrations, simple
family gatherings or corporate entertaining.

Midsummer Common, Cambridge CB4 1HA

Tel: 01223 369299 **Website:** www.midsummerhouse.co.uk

Email: reservations@midsummerhouse.co.uk

Instagram: @midsummer_house **Twitter:** @Midsummerhouse

Facebook: www.facebook.com/midsummerhouserestaurant

CHESHIRE

BROXTON
MAP 15, SJ45

Carden Park Hotel, Golf Resort & Spa
◉ MODERN BRITISH

01829 731000 | Carden Park, CH3 9DQ

www.cardenpark.co.uk

A country estate with a Jacobean core, Welsh mountain views and a three-acre vineyard. The cooking style encompasses Asian-style red mullet terrine with wakame seaweed and sesame salad; and pan-roasted chicken breast and leg crépinette with hay-smoked mash and roasted cauliflower. Chocolate mousse, salted caramel and milk ice cream is in there too.

BURWARDSLEY
MAP 15, SJ55

The Pheasant Inn
◉ BRITISH, EUROPEAN V

01829 770434 | Higher Burwardsley, CH3 9PF

www.thepheasantinn.co.uk

Midway along the Sandstone Trail in rural Cheshire, the far-reaching views from The Pheasant stretch as far as the Welsh hills. Pub classics done well rub shoulders with more contemporary ideas on their crowd-pleasing menu. Steamed Menai mussels followed by Italian-influenced pork saltimbocca then local Cheshire Farm ice cream is one way to go.

CHESTER
MAP 15, SJ46

Brasserie ABode
◉ MODERN CLASSIC FRENCH

01244 405820 | Grosvenor Road, CH1 2DJ

www.brasserieabode.co.uk/chester

The Cheshire outpost of the ABode hotel group occupies a shiny modern rotunda overlooking Chester racecourse. Its restaurant is on the fifth floor, with stellar views over the castle and lush countryside. There's a contemporary finish, with stylish fixtures and rather glam light fittings.

La Brasserie at The Chester Grosvenor & Spa
◉◉ MODERN EUROPEAN

01244 324024 | Eastgate, CH1 1LT

www.chestergrosvenor.com

La Brasserie offers commendable support to its superstar sibling the Simon Radley restaurant. With the swagger of an authentique Parisian outfit, it has black-leather banquettes, shimmering brass and a giant hand-painted skylight, plus a menu that builds confidently on classic ideas.

Palm Court
◉ BRITISH AND EUROPEAN V

01244 570560 | Grosvenor Pulford Hotel & Spa, Wrexham Road, Pulford, CH4 9DG

www.grosvenorpulfordhotel.co.uk/palmcourt

The sprawling red-brick hotel has a swish spa, luxe bedrooms and pretty gardens, but the main dining option Palm Court stands out with stucco paintwork, lots of palm trees and greenery. Expect modern brasserie food.

Restaurant 1539
◉ MODERN BRITISH

01244 304611 | The Racecourse, CH1 2LY

www.restaurant1539.co.uk

Part of the Chester Racecourse complex, 1539 was given a cool half-million's worth of upgrade in 2014. The full-drop windows of the restaurant are still a major feature, and if your heart isn't given to equestrianism, swivel round for an ambient view into the kitchen.

Simon Radley at The Chester Grosvenor
ROSETTES SUSPENDED MODERN FRENCH 🔔 NOTABLE WINE LIST

01244 324024 | Eastgate, CH1 1LT

www.chestergrosvenor.com

The Rosette award for this establishment has been suspended and reassessment will take place in due course.

The Chester Grosvenor has a prime spot within the ancient Roman walls of the city, next to the historic Eastgate Clock and is the undoubted epicentre of the city's culinary activity. The opulent dining room is rich with shades of gold and cream, with plush chairs to sink into, and a smart and well organised team on hand to service your needs. The dress code is smart, but this is the 21st century, and the mood is suitably buoyant.

Chef Ray Booker **Seats** 45, Private dining 14 **Closed** 25 December **Notes** No children under 12 years

CHESTER continued

The Sticky Walnut

◉◉ MODERN EUROPEAN

01244 400400 | 11 Charles Street, CH2 3AZ

www.stickywalnut.net

The Sticky Walnut is spread over two floors, with chunky wooden tables, blackboards and an open kitchen. With cracking desserts like a deconstructed lime cheesecake with pecan butter biscuits and chocolate sorbet, this is a kitchen that delivers real impact.

CONGLETON   MAP 16, SJ86

Pecks

◉ MODERN BRITISH

01260 275161 | Newcastle Road, Moreton, CW12 4SB

www.pecksrest.co.uk

Pecks' culinary expertise is greatly appreciated round here, especially its Dinner at Eight tasting menu, with waiting staff describing the ingredients, flavours and techniques used. Choices may include onion and thyme galantine of guinea fowl, and hot smoked salmon with sautéed samphire. On certain evenings you can bring your own wines, corkage free. Plat du Jour is popular at lunchtime.

See advertisement opposite

HANDFORTH   MAP 16, SJ88

Best Western Plus Pinewood on Wilmslow

◉ MODERN, TRADITIONAL

01625 529211 | 180 Wilmslow Road, SK9 3LF

www.pinewood-hotel.co.uk

This good-looking red-brick hotel is home to the thoroughly modern One Eighty restaurant, a sleek-looking space with darkwood tables and fashionably muted tones. The menu maintains the brasserie attitude and reveals keen creativity in the kitchen. Expect honest cookery produced with very good skill levels.

KNUTSFORD   MAP 15, SJ77

Cottons Hotel & Spa

◉ ITALIAN

01565 650333 | Manchester Road, WA16 0SU

www.cottonshotel.co.uk/food-drink

A large, modern hotel at the edge of town, Cottons' menu is an appealing Mediterranean brasserie-style package. Try the lemon and black pepper queenie scallops with chilli mayonnaise; chicken liver parfait, Armagnac prunes, baby leeks, pickled mushrooms and toasted brioche.

Mere Court Hotel & Conference Centre

◉ MODERN MEDITERRANEAN

01565 831000 | Warrington Road, Mere, WA16 0RW

www.merecourt.co.uk

Mere Court Hotel has bags of appeal. Dating from the turn of the 20th century, this imposing Arts and Crafts house has plenty of period swagger. The oak-panelled Arboretum Restaurant is an elegant spot with lake views, and is the setting for upbeat European-inspired cooking.

The Mere Golf Resort & Spa

◉◉ INTERNATIONAL

01565 830155 | Chester Road, Mere, WA16 6LJ

themereresort.co.uk

The Mere is a must for Cheshire's fairways fans, plus it's a good location for accomplished brasserie dining in the open-plan Browns. Linen tablecloths and relatively formal service are slightly at odds with the overall tone, but the food makes some good modern statements.

LYMM   MAP 15, SJ68

The Church Green British Grill

◉◉ MODERN BRITISH

01925 752068 | Higher Lane, WA13 0AP

www.thechurchgreen.co.uk

Chef-patron Aiden Byrne will be a familiar face to *MasterChef* fans, and his focus is on traditional British grill cooking, with excellent prime materials and touches of modern technique. On the menu might be a serving of home-made black pudding with a crispy poached egg (quite a feat) and caper and rocket salad, and comfort-pud finales like Bakewell tart with black cherry and Amaretto ice cream.

IF IT HAS TO BE SPECIAL.... THEN IT HAS TO BE PECKS

All of our dishes are freshly prepared with the best seasonal produce to deliver exciting menus that combine classic simplicity with unique originality. A blend of traditional favourites and modern culinary practices ensure that each dish is both original and exciting.

Pecks is also available for any special celebration. Weddings, birthday, baby showers, anniversary, private parties, business meetings and groups and organisations. Pecks can create a bespoke Menu for any occasion.

PECKS RESTAURANT, NEWCASTLE ROAD, MORETON,
Nr CONGLETON, CHESHIRE CW12 4SB
1260 275161   info@pecksrest.co.uk   www.pecksrest.co.uk

Please advise us if you have any specific dietary requirements, including allergens when booking.

Member of the Pear Hospitality and Retail Group.

AA Rosette
For Culinary Excellence

MOTTRAM ST ANDREW
MAP 16, SJ87

Mottram Hall
◎◎ MODERN BRITISH
01625 828135 | Wilmslow Road, SK10 4QT
www.champneys.com/hotels/mottram-hall
A dapper 18th-century pile, Mottram Hall's attractions stretch as far as golf, pampering in the spa, and modern country-house dining in the classy Carrington Grill. The food keeps step with the times and is well prepared from high-quality raw materials.

NANTWICH
MAP 15, SJ65

Rookery Hall Hotel & Spa
◎ MODERN BRITISH
01270 610016 | Main Road, Worleston, CW5 6DQ
www.handpickedhotels.co.uk/rookeryhall
Rookery Hall was built in 1816 by a Jamaican sugar plantation owner whose wealth is evident in the sumptuous interior. Cooking-wise, sound technique and accuracy are hallmarks. Try breast of Yorkshire grouse with creamed potato, bread purée, cabbage and bacon fricassée, watercress cream and wood sorrel.

WARMINGHAM
MAP 15, SJ76

The Bear's Paw
◎ MODERN EUROPEAN AND BRITISH
01270 526317 | School Lane, CW11 3QN
www.thebearspaw.co.uk
A Victorian pub given a modern makeover inside, with lots of light wood, and library shelves in the dining room. Local farmers supply the kitchen with quality northwest produce, with cheeses and ice creams also sourced from within a tight radius.

■ CORNWALL & ISLES OF SCILLY

BODMIN
MAP 2, SX06

Trehellas House Hotel & Restaurant
◎ TRADITIONAL
01208 72700 | Washaway, PL30 3AD
www.trehellashouse.co.uk
Trehellas House is a modern country hotel, its rooms spread between an inn and coach house. Its beamed, slate-flagged dining room makes a homely setting for bright Cornish cooking mixing innovation and tradition. Proximity to Camel Valley makes that vineyard's benchmark fizz the obvious aperitif.

BOSCASTLE
MAP 2, SX09

The Wellington
◎◎ MODERN BRITISH, FRENCH
01840 250202 | The Harbour, PL35 0AQ
www.wellingtonhotelboscastle.com
There's a traditional bar with real ales and blackboard menus and a charming restaurant with chandeliers at this 16th-century coaching inn with a castellated tower. The kitchen sources its materials from within the county and serves bright, modern ideas with their roots in the classics.

BRYHER (THE ISLES OF SCILLY)
MAP 2, SV81

Hell Bay Hotel
◎◎◎ MODERN BRITISH *V*
01720 422947 | TR23 0PR
www.hellbay.co.uk
Not nearly as alarming as it sounds, Hell Bay is actually an idyllic secluded cove embraced by gorse-laden hillocks. Reached by ferry, Bryher is small enough to get around on foot, and the unassuming Hell Bay Hotel is the perfect spot to set off from. There is much to love in its Cornish art-filled rooms and sea views, while on the food front Richard Kearsley's assured, confident cooking is a major draw. You're in the right place when it comes to fish and seafood, whether it's pan-roasted Cornish scallops, Newlyn hake with smoked haddock and mussel velouté or Bryher crab. There are meat and vegetarian options too if fish is not your thing, while for dessert maybe plump for the tangy lemon meringue pie.

Chef Richard Kearsley **Seats** 70, Private dining 14
Closed 1st November to 15th March **Prices from** S £7.50,
M £14, D £7.50 **Notes** Children welcome

FALMOUTH
MAP 2, SW83

Brasserie on the Bay
◉◉ MODERN MEDITERRANEAN, BRITISH

01326 312707 | St Michaels Resort, Gyllyngvase Beach, Seafront, TR11 4NB

www.stmichaelshotel.co.uk/dine/brasserie-on-the-bay

There's a stylishly upmarket vibe at this seaside hotel with its hip-looking bar and nautically themed restaurant. The panoramic view is inspiring, jaw dropping even. The kitchen buys materials solely from local producers, and its passion for cooking is palpable in well-executed modern dishes with a hint of the classics.

Falmouth Hotel
◉ BRITISH

01326 312671 | Castle Beach, TR11 4NZ

www.falmouthhotel.com

Nothing becomes a seaside town like a great white hotel, lording it over the waters from the headland. The elegant dining room has sweeping views over the bay and a menu that works its way round the seasonal calendar in both British and international modes.

The Greenbank Hotel
◉◉ MODERN BRITISH

01326 312440 | Harbourside, TR11 2SR

www.greenbank-hotel.co.uk

The house that became The Greenbank Hotel has occupied this spot since 1640, and in 2015 its restaurant received a top-to-toe facelift. The head chef delivers a please-all roster of classics and modern dishes with Cornish produce as a starting point for his menus.

Merchants Manor
◉◉◉ MODERN BRITISH

01326 312734 | 1 Weston Manor, TR11 4AJ

www.merchantsmanor.com

Merchants Manor, a white-fronted hill-top house, retains a pleasingly historic air, with its lofty-ceilinged interiors preserving much of their Edwardian splendour. Bright interiors create a cheery ambience and the Rastella dining room adds to an all-round feel of well-being with white linen and vintage candles. Local suppliers buttress the menus, as does the hard-working wood-fired oven and what emerges is a roster of smartly presented, modern dishes full of precision and inspiration. To start, there could be grilled halloumi with sweet chilli, followed by Newlyn lobster, or sharing platters of Cornish tapas or a West Country charcuterie board. Finish, perhaps, with yogurt parfait and berries.

Chef Hylton Espey **Seats** 64, Private dining 20 **Open** All Year **Parking** 30 **Notes** Children welcome

Penmorvah Manor
◉ CLASSIC BRITISH

01326 250277 | Penjerrick Hill, Budock Water, TR11 5ED

www.penmorvah.co.uk

The stone-built manor house has stood in its six acres of wooded gardens near Falmouth since 1872. The atmosphere is white-linened gentility, the culinary style is modern brasserie, with well turned-out dishes making an impact on both eye and palate.

The Restaurant - The Royal Duchy Hotel
◉◉ MODERN BRITISH

01326 313042 | The Royal Duchy Hotel, Cliff Road, TR11 4NX

www.royalduchy.co.uk

Overlooking Falmouth Bay, the Royal Duchy Hotel is home to a large, elegantly traditional restaurant decorated in dove grey and rich plum, with chandeliers and white Georgian moldings. Food is assured and purposeful, with a light, skilled touch that reflects the elegance of the restaurant. Modern British with Asian and Mediterranean influences.

See advertisement on page 54

HELSTON
MAP 2, SW62

New Yard Restaurant
◉◉ BRITISH

01326 221595 | Trelowarren Estate, Mawgan, TR12 6AF

www.newyardrestaurant.co.uk

On Cornwall's stunning Lizard peninsula, the New Yard Restaurant is at the heart of the historic Trelowarren Estate. Occupying the former stable yard, the distinctive interior sports a chequered floor, arched windows and bare wooden tables, while the open-plan kitchen produces punchy, seasonal cooking.

HUGH TOWN (THE ISLES OF SCILLY)   *MAP 2, SV91*

Spirit

◉ MODERN BRITISH

01720 422316 | St Mary's Hall Hotel, Church Street, TR21 0JR

www.stmaryshallhotel.co.uk

Local sourcing is key at the Spirit restaurant in this handsome townhouse hotel set in charming Mediterranean gardens. Served in a gently updated setting, rare breed meats come from the owners' farm, while fish and seafood are hauled in daily by local boats to form the bedrock of carefully prepared, fuss-free dishes.

LITTLE PETHERICK   *MAP 2, SW97*

Old Mill Bistro

◉ MODERN BRITISH *V*

01841 540388 | The Old Mill House, PL27 7QT

www.oldmillbistro.co.uk

Set in a 16th-century, former corn mill in a postcard-pretty hamlet, this homely family-run bistro comes with a full complement of beamed and stone-floored character. Service is warm

and informed, while the cooking is full of panache, with sharply defined flavours and confident combining of impeccably local and seasonal materials.

LIZARD   *MAP 2, SW71*

Fallowfields

◉◉ BRITISH, SEAFOOD, SEASONAL, *V*

01326 567500 | Housel Bay Hotel, Housel Bay, TR12 7PG

www.houselbay.com

On the spectacular Lizard peninsula, the granite-built Housel Bay Hotel dates back to Victorian times and the light and airy Fallowfields restaurant boasts stunning Atlantic views. As befits the coastal setting, local fish is a strength here, perhaps in a main of sea bass, tiger prawn, bisque, crab ravioli, cavolo nero and curry oil.

LOSTWITHIEL
MAP 2, SX15

Asquiths Restaurant
◉◉ MODERN BRITISH
01208 871714 | 19 North Street, PL22 0EF
www.asquithsrestaurant.co.uk
Its black and white decor, smartly set tables and elegant staff create positive impressions of this restaurant opposite the church, where food is taken seriously. Confit duck and beetroot pastilla is teamed with pomegranate molasses and couscous, with an alternative perhaps of kedgeree with a Scotch egg and pea cream. Fish gets a decent showing, maybe a well-timed roast hake fillet, curried cauliflower, a courgette bhaji and potato purée.

LOWER TOWN (THE ISLES OF SCILLY)
MAP 2, SV91

Cloudesley Shovell Restaurant
◉◉ MODERN, SEASONAL, SEAFOOD
01720 422368 | Karma St Martin's, TR25 0QW
www.karmastmartins.com
Admiral Sir Cloudesley Shovell's disastrous loss of 22 ships off the Scilly Isles in 1707 is remembered here in the Karma St Martin's Hotel. The restaurant overlooks the crystal-clear Atlantic - a source of fresh fish, crab and lobster which feature heavily on the menu. Alternatively simply order a Cornish pasty picnic and head for the beach.

See advertisement on page 57

MAWGAN PORTH
MAP 2, SW86

The Herring NEW
◉ MODERN
01637 861200 | TR8 4BU
www.bedruthan.com
The Herring is elegant, understated and contemporary, with stunning views out to sea. Unclothed tables and designer chairs give the room a real Scandi feel. The team are personable, engaging and genuinely eager to please. Dinner starts with a set of sharing plates, well-balanced and cohesive, and follows with a choice of main course. A fascinating food journey.

The Scarlet Hotel
◉◉ MODERN EUROPEAN ♠ NOTABLE WINE LIST
01637 861800 | Tredragon Road, TR8 4DQ
www.scarlethotel.co.uk
The Scarlet has impeccable eco credentials, but first and foremost it's about hedonistic pleasures - wining, dining and serious pampering. The kitchen team focuses on the West Country. Dessert of white chocolate mousse is surrounded by honeycomb shell, joined by pistachio cake and griottines cherries.

MAWNAN SMITH
MAP 2, SW72

Meudon Hotel
◉ CLASSIC
01326 250541 | TR11 5HT
www.meudon.co.uk
Bream Cove Restaurant presents an inviting space amid coastal gardens overlooking Falmouth Bay. The order of the day is modern cooking with a nod to classic cuisine, offering a true flavour of Cornwall and a sound helping of local wines.

Trelawne Hotel NEW
◉ MODERN BRITISH
01326 250226 | Maenporth Road, TR11 5HT
www.trelawnehotel.co.uk
Run by the same family for decades, the Trelawne Hotel has a light, airy dining room that enjoys stunning views across to Falmouth Bay. The style of cooking is utterly unpretentious here, with a very genuine team and an experienced chef. Dishes draw heavily on the local fish and seafood industries, as well as nearby farmers and butchers.

MEVAGISSEY
MAP 2, SX04

Trevalsa Court Hotel
◉◉ MODERN BRITISH
01726 842460 | School Hill, Polstreth, PL26 6TH
www.trevalsa-hotel.co.uk
Situated on a clifftop, there is a real sub-tropical feel to this handsome granite and slate house. When the sun shines, a table on the terrace with views across Mevagissey Bay is worth its weight in gold, but the view is special from inside, too.

MULLION
MAP 2, SW61

Mullion Cove Hotel
⊛⊛ MODERN BRITISH
01326 240328 | TR12 7EP
www.mullion-cove.co.uk
This solidly built white property on the Lizard Peninsula sits on the clifftop, giving uninterrupted sea and coast views. The kitchen is committed to local suppliers, with day boats providing seafood – an international element is evident in some dishes.

The Restaurant at Polurrian on the Lizard
⊛⊛ MODERN BRITISH, MEDITERRANEAN
01326 240421 | TR12 7EN
www.polurrianhotel.com
This one-time Victorian railway hotel has been reworked in smart contemporary style. From its perch on the cliffs of the Lizard Peninsula, the rather grand restaurant presents those wild, far-reaching coastal views as a backdrop to inventive modern cooking based on tip-top ingredients from local producers.

NEWQUAY
MAP 2, SW86

Dune NEW
⊛ MODERN V
01637 852221 | Esplanade Road, TR7 1PT
www.fistralbeachhotel.co.uk
Dune is well named, as it's all about the spectacular view of the relentless surf, with Newquay's surfers always at play amidst the foaming breakers. The elegant restaurant has a light, airy feel, with a relaxed atmosphere. The team are committed and focused, but not over attentive, allowing guests to take their time.

The Samphire Restaurant
⊛⊛ MODERN BRITISH
01637 872211 | The Headland Hotel and Spa, Fistral Beach, TR7 1EW
www.headlandhotel.co.uk
You'll likely find yourself distracted by the incredible views from The Headland's elegant dining room when you should be perusing the menu – you might even spot dolphins out in the bay. Inside, its smart and sharp – expect crisp linens and formal service.

Silks Bistro and Champagne Bar
⊛ MEDITERRANEAN, SEAFOOD
01637 839048 | Atlantic Hotel, Dane Road, TR7 1EN
www.atlantichotelnewquay.co.uk
Although it was built in 1892 this is no gloomy Victorian haunt. Silks is bright and modern, with zebra-patterned bar stools and sunburst-styled café chairs at linen-swathed tables. In the evenings, candlelight softens the scene. Save room for feel-good puddings.

The Terrace
⊛ CLASSIC BRITISH
01637 872211 | The Headland Hotel and Spa, TR7 1EW
www.headlandhotel.co.uk/eat/terrace-restaurant
Located just steps from the famous sands of Fistral Beach, The Terrace restaurant has floor to ceiling glass, wooden floors, and a laid-back beach vibe. The short bistro-style menu presents such starters as garlic prawns and harissa dip, or Cornish mussels. Enjoy the ocean views.

PADSTOW
MAP 2, SW97

Paul Ainsworth at No. 6
⊛⊛⊛⊛ MODERN BRITISH ≜ NOTABLE WINE LIST
See pages 58–59

See advertisement on page 60

The Restaurant at THE PIG at Harlyn Bay NEW
⊛ BRITISH ≜ NOTABLE WINE LIST
01841 550240 | Harlyn Bay, PL28 8SQ
www.thepighotel.com/at-harlyn-bay/eat-padstow
Evocative of the rustic past in a very reassuring way, The Restaurant at THE PIG at Harlyn Bay is an unpretentious and engaging dining environment. Comfortably mis-matched tables and chairs, and collected eclectic ephemera, combined with unfussy yet professional service mean that diners feel free to chat, making for a welcoming buzz. The cooking is simple and simply prepared, but also very good.

Continued on page 61

Paul Ainsworth at No. 6

◉◉◉◉ **MODERN BRITISH** ⚱NOTABLE
WINE LIST

01841 532093 | Padstow Townhouse, 6 Middle Street, PL28 8AP
www.paul-ainsworth.co.uk

Defining contemporary cooking in a pint-sized townhouse

Padstow is undeniably a shining beacon on the UK's gastronomic map, and Paul Ainsworth's townhouse restaurant, tucked down one of the narrow streets, just back from the harbour, has been a major player here since 2005. Paul has built a reputation for creating contemporary food focused on the regional produce that makes Cornwall such a culinary destination these days, while a healthy run of TV exposure via the BBC's *The Great British Menu* has certainly helped boost his public profile. The restaurant occupies a whitewashed Georgian townhouse split into three diminutive spaces on the ground floor and another upstairs, with the period charm of the spaces intact and bold artworks peppering the walls with visual entertainment. Ainsworth's cooking, interpreted here by Chris McClurg, has always tended towards the creatively sharp end of the modern British spectrum, with

technical pizzazz galore and eye-catching presentation. Prime materials of the finest and freshest to be found in Cornwall's seasonal larder are helped along by global goodies in dishes that deliver muscular layers of flavour and texture. Local scallops are hard to ignore at the best of times, and here they might be served raw and matched with kohlrabi rice and finger lime, or go for another seafood opener that delivers super-fresh, beautifully cured sea bass with vibrant sand shrimp slaw and the umami hit of dried and smoked tuna flakes in katsuobushi mayonnaise. Next up, turbot might star in a robust main course showing off the best of Cornish waters, alongside silky mashed potato and onion gravy, while fillet of beef could get a classical treatment with mushroom persillade and sauce bordelaise. Ingenious desserts are

> '..creatively sharp end of the modern British spectrum, with technical pizzazz galore and eye-catching presentation.'

equally hard to pass by – expect the likes of 75% chocolate 'vol au vent' with cep caramel, or the showpiece 'Fairground Tale', a true extravaganza built around a bitter chocolate soufflé.

Chef Paul Ainsworth, Chris McClurg
Seats 46, Private dining 8
Closed 24–26 December,
13 January to 6 February
Notes No children under 4 years

See advertisement on page 60

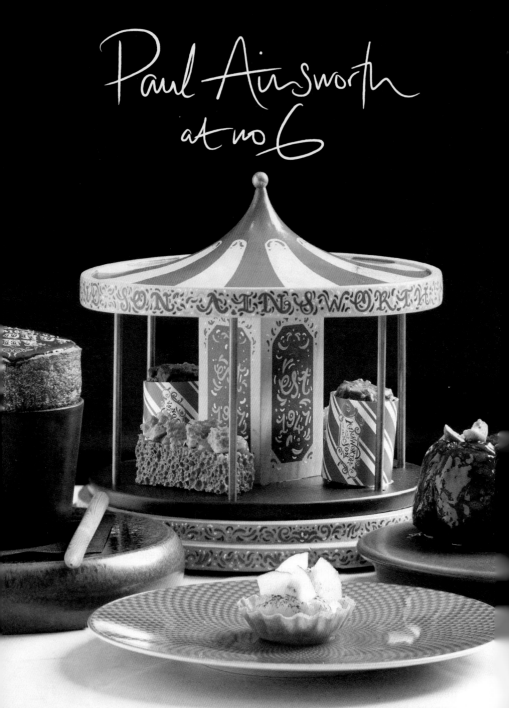

For reservations call 01841 532 093 or visit www. paul-ainsworth.co.uk

Paul Ainsworth at No6 | 6 Middle Street, Padstow

PADSTOW continued

St Petroc's Bistro

◎ MEDITERRANEAN, FRENCH

01841 532700 | 4 New Street, PL28 8EA

www.rickstein.com/restaurants/st-petrocs-bistro

The bistro is an informal and relaxing sort of place, with simple tables and chairs on worn wooden floorboards, modern paintings on plain white walls, and professional service from attentive staff. There's a cosy bar and a pleasant lounge for pre-dinner drinks.

The Seafood Restaurant

◎◎◎ INTERNATIONAL SEAFOOD ▲ NOTABLE WINE LIST

01841 532700 | Riverside, PL28 8BY

www.rickstein.com

Padstow may be rather different these days from the little fishing village of Rick Stein's youth, with great places to eat a dime a dozen, but this is still top of everyone's list, so book well ahead for the busy season. There's a sunny conservatory at the front, a roof terrace, views of the harbour, and a bright, friendly, informal air – seaside colours, comfortable seating, and an eclectic selection of modern art. Sit at the bar with a drink and you'll soon be keen to get cracking – literally, if you go for one of the magnificent fruits de mer platters. Otherwise, you could begin with the seared chipirones, beautifully tender squid stuffed with tuna, mackerel, salmon, prawns, ginger and spring onion, before moving on to Indonesian seafood curry, packed with delicious pieces of sea bass and hake, along with prawns and squid. A delicate floating island with salted caramel pistachios and Grand Marnier anglaise is the perfect finale.

Chef Stephane Delourme **Seats** 120 **Closed** 25–26 December **Notes** No children under 3 years

PENZANCE

MAP 2, SW43

Harris's Restaurant

◎ BRITISH, FRENCH, SEAFOOD

01736 364408 | 46 New Street, TR18 2LZ

www.harrissrestaurant.co.uk

The Harris family have run their appealing restaurant on a cobbled side street in the town centre for over 30 years, offering professionally prepared and freshly cooked quality produce (local meats, seafood from Newlyn, for instance), with the kitchen taking an unshowy line.

The Shore Restaurant

◎◎ FISH, SEAFOOD

01736 362444 | 13-14 Alverton Street, TR18 2QP

www.theshorerestaurant.uk

A paradise for seafood lovers, this smart little restaurant goes for a minimalist contemporary look of white walls, nautical art and unclothed tables. Local boats supply the fish each day, and it's handled with skill and precision by a chef who has a clear classical skill set and a sound grasp of how flavours work together.

The Tolcarne Inn

◎ SEAFOOD

01736 363074 | Newlyn, TR18 5PR

tolcarneinn.co.uk

Only the high sea wall separates The Tolcarne Inn from the crashing waves on the other side, adding considerable charm to this traditional pub next to Newlyn's fish market. Close links with local fishermen mean the day's catch dictates what appears on the chalkboard menu.

PERRANUTHNOE

MAP 2, SW52

Victoria Inn

◎◎ MODERN BRITISH

01736 710309 | TR20 9NP

www.victoriainn-penzance.co.uk

Smartly restored without sacrificing any of its traditional charm, the Victoria functions admirably as both a convivial country pub serving local ales and ciders, and a relaxed restaurant worth seeking out. The cooking is all about confident technique, sound local sourcing and lively ideas.

PORT GAVERNE
MAP 2, SX08

Pilchards
⦿ MODERN BRITISH
01208 880244 | PL29 3SQ
www.portgavernehotel.co.uk
The Port Gaverne is a traditional inn, set in a tiny cove on Cornwall's dramatic north coast, just five minutes' walk from Port Isaac. Pilchards is their café, slap-bang on the beach. It's relaxed and friendly, offering excellent snacky dishes as well as larger plates.

Port Gaverne
⦿ MODERN BRITISH, SEAFOOD
01208 880244 | PL29 3SQ
www.portgavernehotel.co.uk
Tucked away in a hidden cove, a hilly but short stroll from Port Isaac, this whitewashed village inn with its hanging baskets and outdoor tables is pretty as a picture, the slate-floored bar giving way to a pair of interlinked dining rooms. The traditionally-based cooking is inventive.

PORT ISAAC
MAP 2, SW98

Outlaw's Fish Kitchen
⦿⦿ MODERN BRITISH, SEAFOOD
01208 881183 | 1 Middle Street, PL29 3RH
nathan-outlaw.com
Nathan Outlaw is a big fish in Cornwall with two restaurants in Port Isaac. The Fish Kitchen, originally a 15th-century fisherman's cottage, is a rustic little place right on the harbour, with sea views. Serving up a fixed menu of small, original plates of fresh seafood, sourced from the local daily catch.

Outlaw's New Road
⦿⦿⦿⦿ MODERN BRITISH, SEAFOOD ⓐ NOTABLE WINE LIST
01208 880896 | 6 New Road, PL29 3SB
nathan-outlaw.com
Named literally for the road it sits on and located proudly at the top end of Port Isaac, this seafood restaurant is Nathan Outlaw's chance to return (after a short spell in London with Spirit at The Goring, cut short by the pandemic) to the cooking he loves. Expect simple seafood dishes, exquisitely presented. Immaculately fresh, every fine-tuned dish displays his affinity with the Cornish coasts where his centre of gravity undoubtedly remains. Covering lunch and dinner, there are only a handful of tables between the upstairs dining room and the downstairs bar seating, so booking ahead is essential. The set seafood menu is your only option, and you might start with raw bass with a pea and mint dressing, followed by a Port Isaac lobster salad, finishing with strawberry and champagne sorbet. You won't be disappointed; the quality is there in every touch – very highly recommended.

Chef Nathan Outlaw **Notes** No children under 10 years

Stargazy Inn NEW
⦿ MODERN
01208 811516 | The Terrace, PL29 3SG
www.stargazyinn.co.uk
Stargazy Inn is a Victorian villa with splendid views of the North Cornwall coastline. The destination dining rooms are unpretentious and comfortable, allowing the food to do the talking. Menus draw heavily on local produce, especially seafood, and offer well-balanced dishes prepared with accuracy and simplicity.

PORTHALLOW
MAP 2, SX25

Talland Bay Hotel
⦿⦿ MODERN INTERNATIONAL
01503 272667 | Porthallow, PL13 2JB
www.tallandbayhotel.co.uk
Close to the pretty Cornish towns of Looe and Fowey, the dining room offers lovely views over the gardens and across the bay. Arty knick-knacks add an eclectic touch to the boutique charm of the place and there are similar contemporary twists to the classic cookery.

PORTHLEVEN
MAP 2, SW62

Kota Kai
⦿ ASIAN FUSION
01326 574411 | Celtic House, The Shipyard, TR13 9JY
www.kotakai.co.uk
On the upper floor of Celtic House, Kota Kai is blessed with unbeatable views over the inner harbour of Porthleven, Britain's southernmost port. The menu, with its Asian bias, also rewards close attention, listing, for example, bao bun with hoisin sauce, kimchi, spring onions and peanuts.

Kota Restaurant with Rooms

◉◉◉ BRITISH, PACIFIC RIM, SEAFOOD

01326 562407 | Harbour Head, TR13 9JA

www.kotarestaurant.co.uk

Situated on the harbour head by Porthleven's shingle beach and the bay, Kota aims to bring a Pacific Rim seafood ethos to windblown Cornwall. With a pair of guest rooms on hand, it's a streamlined operation, centred on a tiled dining room under an old beamed ceiling. Jude Kereama hails from New Zealand and brings the Asian-influenced approach of the southern hemisphere to bear on his set menu, or the seven-course tasting menu (plus veggie version). This kicks off with Porthilly oysters, either tempura with baby gem and wasabi tartare, or natural with cucumber and rice wine granita. Next up, a choice between duck breast, beef sirloin, or the 'Spring Rockpool' - a vegetable dashi broth with hake, crab raviolo, Cornish mussels, tiger prawn and seaweed. A pre-dessert of blood orange cream with rhubarb is followed by either chocolate mousse with chocolate torte, or blue cheese ice cream with poached pear.

Chef Jude Kereama Seats 40 Closed January
Notes Children welcome

PORTLOE
MAP 2, SW93

The Lugger

◉◉ MODERN, CLASSIC

01872 501322 | TR2 5RD

www.luggerhotel.com

Dating from the 16th century, now a luxury inn, The Lugger overlooks the sea and tiny harbour of a picturesque village on the Roseland Peninsula, with a terrace outside the smart, spacious restaurant for summer dining. Local ingredients are the kitchen's linchpin, particularly seafood.

PORTSCATHO
MAP 2, SW83

Driftwood

◉◉◉ MODERN EUROPEAN

See page 64

ST AUSTELL
MAP 2, SX05

Carlyon Bay Hotel

◉ MODERN, TRADITIONAL BRITISH

01726 812304 | Sea Road, Carlyon Bay, PL25 3RD

www.carlyonbay.com

Perched on a clifftop, this large hotel, spa and golf course is an imposing presence above the bay. The huge windows allow maximum exposure to the rugged Cornish coast views. The kitchen keeps things simple and relies on the quality and provenance of its ingredients.

ST IVES
MAP 2, SW54

Porthminster Beach Restaurant

◉◉ INTERNATIONAL, SEAFOOD

01736 795352 | TR26 2EB

www.porthminstercafe.co.uk

Slap bang on stunning Porthminster Beach, this landmark white building occupies an enviable position. Whether you dine in the restaurant or on the terrace, the sea views are breathtaking. Vibrant pan-Asian dishes dominate the menu, which uses the best local seafood available.

Porthminster Kitchen

◉ INTERNATIONAL, PACIFIC RIM

01736 799874 | Wharf Road, TR26 1LG

www.porthminster.kitchen

A companion venue to the Porthminster Beach Restaurant just along the bay, the Kitchen also enjoys a bracing seaside location. Slick, stylish decor resists the indignity of seashells, and the menus deal in populist global cuisine with a Cornish accent.

PORTSCATHO

MAP 2, SW83

Driftwood

❀❀❀ **MODERN EUROPEAN**
01872 580644 | Rosevine, TR2 5EW
www.driftwoodhotel.co.uk

Independently owned, this beach-house-style hotel stands in seven acres on the Roseland Peninsula, an Area of Outstanding Natural Beauty. Standing above a private cove on the turquoise waters of Gerrans Bay, the restaurant is bright and airy with stunning coastal views. There's super-attentive service, with staff showing impressive knowledge, including excellent wine recommendations. The kitchen team have developed strong links with many local producers, so local materials star on the menu, with expressive seafood dishes a particular strength. One way to start is with a terrine of Cornish skate wing and smoked eel with cockle beignets, cucumber, horseradish and dill, followed by roast pheasant with crushed swede and carrot, pearl barley, trompettes and quince. To finish try poached apricots with Cornish honey, buttermilk pannacotta, fresh almonds and chamomile.

Chef Olly Pierrepont **Seats** 34 **Closed** early December to early February (subject to change) **Parking** 20 **Notes** No children after 6pm

ST MAWES
MAP 2, SW83

Hotel Tresanton
◉◉◉ MEDITERRANEAN, SEAFOOD V

01326 270055 | 27 Lower Castle Road, TR2 5BH

www.tresanton.com

A stunning cliffside location is the setting for this collection of cottages, transformed by Olga Polizzi into a supremely elegant and understated hotel. Superb views of the Cornish coast and laidback nautical chic contribute to an atmosphere of refined luxury. The calm, airy restaurant, with its mosaic tiled floor and shell-like lighting is classy, with simple table settings and engaging, responsive staff. If you're here in daylight it will be hard to drag yourself away from the views, so give yourself plenty of time for a long lunch. The cooking matches the environment with a pleasing simplicity; the uncluttered dishes have a refreshing Mediterranean influence. Kick off with a couple of Porthilly oysters or indulge with Exmoor Caviar. Follow with turbot with asparagus and hollandaise, a satisfying main course, and you can keep it simple at dessert with the classic Italian affogato using Tresanton's home-made ice cream.

Chef Paul Wadham **Seats** 60, Private dining 50 **Open** All Year **Parking** 30 **Notes** No children under 6 years at dinner

TRESCO (THE ISLES OF SCILLY)
MAP 2, SV81

The New Inn
◉ MODERN, TRADITIONAL

01720 422849 | TR24 0QQ

www.tresco.co.uk

The friendly and welcoming New Inn sits beside the water, right at the heart of this small community, where guests and islanders mix happily. The fine dining here is based around island produce (everything else has to be brought in by sea, don't forget).

Ruin Beach Café
◉◉ MODERN MEDITERRANEAN

01720 424849 | TR24 0PU

www.tresco.co.uk/eating-on-tresco/ruin-cafe

Next to the beach at New Grimsby, this former smugglers' cottage boasts stunning views. A contemporary space with bare wooden tables and cutlery laid out on crisp tea towels, the food has similarly clean lines. Excellent island ingredients and classic cooking techniques makes for strong flavour definitions here and the wood-fired oven is used to good effect.

TRURO
MAP 2, SW84

The Alverton Hotel
◉◉ MODERN BRITISH, EUROPEAN

01872 276633 | Tregolls Road, TR1 1ZQ

www.thealverton.co.uk

Dating from 1830, The Alverton is an impressive building designed by the same chap as Truro Cathedral. There is plenty of period charm and a contemporary sheen to the upmarket brasserie. The menu takes a modern European path with a good representation of Cornish ingredients.

Hooked Restaurant & Bar
◉ MODERN BRITISH, SEAFOOD

01872 274700 | Tabernacle Street, TR1 2EJ

www.hookedrestaurantandbar.co.uk

Tucked away down a quiet street just off the city centre, the open kitchen feeds into a lively buzz in this smart modern brasserie, with unclothed tables, exposed brickwork and high ceilings adding to the jaunty seaside feel. Seafood is the leading suit, with full-size and tapas dishes available daytime and evening.

Mannings Hotel
◉◉ MODERN, PACIFIC RIM

01872 270345 | Lemon Street, TR1 2QB

www.manningshotels.co.uk

Mannings is a classic-looking, solid-stone building – Grade II listed no less – but within it is all slick modernity and contemporary attitude. The restaurant has its own entrance, and an interior design spec that includes moody black-and-white photos, stainless steel, and trendy lights.

TRURO continued

Tabb's Restaurant

◎◎ MODERN BRITISH

01872 262110 | 85 Kenwyn Street, TR1 3BZ

www.tabbs.co.uk

The refurbished Tabb's occupies a white corner building that looks for all the world like a private dwelling. The kitchen's a busy place, producing everything in-house. Pigeon breast, soft-boiled egg, black pasta and sun-dried tomato dressing could be followed by tender roast pork belly, couscous, black olives, green lentils, battered courgettes and sauté potatoes.

VERYAN
MAP 2, SW93

The Dining Room Restaurant

◎ TRADITIONAL *V*

01872 501111 | The Nare, Carne Beach, TR2 5PF

www.narehotel.co.uk

The more traditional fine dining option at The Nare hotel on the beautiful Roseland peninsula, The Dining Room provides diners with magnificent panoramic sea views and local fish to match. Fresh Portloe crab rillettes could precede a grilled fillet of lemon sole, leek purée, capers, samphire, saffron Parmentier potatoes and champagne velouté.

The Quarterdeck at The Nare

◎◎ TRADITIONAL BRITISH ⬥ NOTABLE WINE LIST

01872 500 000 | Carne Beach, TR2 5PF

www.narehotel.co.uk/dining/the-quarterdeck

The Quarterdeck is a shipshape, yachtie-themed setting of polished teak, gingham seats and square rails. The kitchen produces modern dishes bursting with bold flavours and local fish and shellfish are a strong point too; perhaps choose a luxurious duo of pan-fried turbot and lobster medallion.

■ CUMBRIA

AMBLESIDE
MAP 18, NY30

Lake Road Kitchen

◎◎◎ *V*

015394 22012 | Susse House, Lake Road, LA22 0AD

www.lakeroadkitchen.co.uk

James Cross's restaurant is deeply rooted in the concept of 'the North', and that means an all-embracing passion for Lakeland and Scottish produce, as well as clear Nordic sensibilities, from the stark simplicity of its sauna-like, Scandi-style pine plank walls and bare tables to a fervour for pickling, foraging and fermenting. Daily-changing menus come in eight- and 12-course versions, and the self-styled 'cold climate cooking' brings remarkable combinations of taste and texture. A revelatory spring meal opens with slow-barbecued, smoky veal rib with a celeriac 'taco', yogurt, fermented cabbage, wild garlic and capers. Along the way, pine nut stew with garlic, parsley purée and oil accompany mussels cooked a la plancha, while gold-standard Skrei cod is simply poached and pointed up with parsley sauce. To finish, the richness of baked New York cheesecake is counterpointed by sea buckthorn sorbet. Home-baked sourdough is a superlative version with crunchy dark crust, served with hand-churned whey butter.

Chef James Cross **Seats** 21 **Open** All Year
Notes No children

The Old Stamp House Restaurant

◎◎◎ MODERN BRITISH

015394 32775 | Church Street, LA22 0BU

www.oldstamphouse.com

William Wordsworth was Cumbria's 'Distributor of Stamps' back in the 19th century, and this is where he plied his trade. Today, the organic and foraged ingredients on show make this is a thoroughly modern sort of restaurant and it has become quite the foodie destination. Situated below street level and accessed via a small set of stairs, chef Ryan Blackburn and his brother Craig, who works front of house, have created something special here. Dishes are explained as they are placed. Chefs normally make a point of bringing some of the dishes themselves – Ryan likes to present a personal appearance to his strong local following. Recommendations are freely made for both food and wine indicating a deep knowledge of the product. Cumbrian local produce leads the way, with 6 or 8-course tasting menus and a smaller lunch menu. The presentation is always thoroughly creative.

Chef Ryan Blackburn **Seats** 30, Private dining 8
Closed Christmas **Notes** Children welcome

Rothay Manor Hotel

◉◉◉ MODERN BRITISH ♦NOTABLE WINE LIST

015394 33605 | Rothay Bridge, LA22 0EH

www.rothaymanor.co.uk

Built by a Liverpool shipping merchant in 1823, Rothay Manor Hotel has kept many original Regency features. It's a great example of a traditional Lake District country-house hotel, standing in attractive landscaped gardens close to Ambleside. Recent investment has raised the bar, not least in the restaurant, which has a gently contemporary look that matches the adventurous, complex modern cooking with Japanese and Scandinavian influences. A sample à la carte starts off with scallop and kohlrabi with elderflower, dashi and sorrel, then moves on to halibut with mussel, allium, burdock root and sea aster. Chocolate with rice, miso, kaffir lime and cep is the finisher.

Chef Daniel McGeorge **Seats** 40, Private dining 20 **Closed** 2-20 January **Parking** 25 **Notes** Children welcome

APPLEBY-IN-WESTMORLAND   MAP 18, NY62

Appleby Manor Hotel & Garden Spa

◉◉ MODERN BRITISH

017683 51571 | Roman Road, CA16 6JB

www.applebymanor.co.uk

The outlook over Appleby Castle and the Eden Valley is a pastoral treat, and this Victorian sandstone house was put up by someone with an eye for a view. The 1871 Bistro delivers breezy feel-good dishes while the main restaurant takes a more refined approach.

ASKHAM   MAP 18, NY52

Allium at Askham Hall

◉◉◉ CONTEMPORARY BRITISH ♦NOTABLE WINE LIST

See page 68

BARROW-IN-FURNESS   MAP 18, SD26

Abbey House Hotel & Gardens

◉ TRADITIONAL BRITISH, FRENCH

01229 838282 | Abbey Road, LA13 0PA

www.abbeyhousehotel.com

This grand red-brick house in 14 acres of countryside is home to the charming and gently contemporary Oscar's restaurant. There's nothing stuffy about the place, with a relaxed (but professional) approach all round. The kitchen turns out modern dishes based on good regional produce.

BASSENTHWAITE   MAP 18, NY23

Lake View Restaurant

◉◉ BRITISH, FRENCH

017687 76551 | Armathwaite Hall Hotel and Spa, CA12 4RE

www.armathwaite-hall.com

Standing in 400 acres of grounds bordering Bassenthwaite, Armathwaite Hall has rich fabrics and acres of oak panelling. The Lake View Restaurant is a high-ceilinged room in rich golds and reds with formally-laid tables. The kitchen steers a course to keep both traditionalists and modernists happy.

Ravenstone Lodge Country House Hotel

◉ MODERN BRITISH

017687 76629 | CA12 4QG

www.ravenstonelodge.co.uk

Enjoying an enviable position near Bassenthwaite Lake, this country-house hotel has plenty going on, including a bar and bistro in the former stables. The Coach House restaurant is smartly turned out and the team in the kitchen uses quality regional ingredients.

BORROWDALE   MAP 18, NY21

Borrowdale Gates Hotel

◉◉ BRITISH, FRENCH

017687 77204 | CA12 5UQ

www.borrowdale-gates.com

Revered Lakeland Fells guidebook author Alfred Wainwright especially loved the Borrowdale Valley, where this classic country house turns out skilfully cooked modern dishes. Get going with Coronation chicken terrine and spiced chicken mini-nugget; then on to pan-fried sea bass, tiger prawn curry and coconut basmati rice, and end with rhubarb cheesecake, warm ginger cake and rhubarb sorbet.

Borrowdale Hotel

◉ MODERN BRITISH

017687 77224 | CA12 5UY

www.lakedistricthotels.net/borrowdalehotel

This handsome Victorian hotel has been in business since 1866. Gently made over for the modern world, the place marries contemporary good looks with original features, a formula which works equally well in the restaurant – the kitchen walks a path between tradition and uncontroversial modernity.

Continued on page 69

ASKHAM

MAP 18, NY52

Allium at Askham Hall

◉◉◉ **CONTEMPORARY BRITISH** ≗NOTABLE WINE LIST

01931 712350 | Askham Hall, Askham, CA10 2PF
www.askhamhall.co.uk

Askham dates from the 14th century and describes itself as 'an intimate, unpretentious home from home' – and you might very well wish your home was as lovely as this delightful place. Owned by the same family since the 1830s, it has a real feeling of authenticity and heritage. The restaurant, Allium, is the only modern addition and overlooks the gardens, with wonderful natural light. The modern British menu changes daily, as to what's available from the kitchen garden and farms on the estate. An autumn meal might begin with fresh white crab on a bright green lovage gel, given a sweet kick with blackcurrant and freshness from garden herbs. Accurately timed breast of salt-aged duck is accompanied by clean, crisp turnip fondant and purée, while pine-smoked sea trout has a subtly smoky flavour with texturally spot-on beetroot and fennel.

Chef Richard Swale **Seats** 30, Private dining 18 **Closed** Christmas, 3 January to mid February (excluding groups) **Parking** 50 **Notes** No children under 10 years

BORROWDALE continued

Hazel Bank Country House
◉◉ BRITISH
017687 77248 | Rosthwaite, CA12 5XB
hazelbankhotel.co.uk
Set amid four acres in the gorgeous Borrowdale Valley, this classic stone-built Lakeland hotel offers a daily-changing set menu, with a cheeseboard as an optional extra. High-end ingredients are given the modern British treatment with occasional Asian influences in dishes like a starter of teriyaki mackerel and roasted watermelon.

Lodore Falls Hotel
◉◉ MODERN BRITISH
017687 77285 | CA12 5UX
www.lakedistricthotels.net/lodorefalls
The Lodore Falls Hotel has enjoyed a magnificent setting on the shores of Derwentwater for over 200 years. The aptly named Lake View Restaurant, stylishly done out with modern furnishings and pristine white tablecloths, is the setting for equally stylish and thoughtfully constructed contemporary menus.

Mizu
◉ PAN-ASIAN
017687 77285 | Lodore Falls Hotel, CA12 5UX
www.lakedistricthotels.net/lodorefalls
A megabucks refurb of this luxe spa hotel overlooking Derwentwater brought the opening in 2018 of Mizu, a sleek, contemporary pan-Asian restaurant done out in cool, cosmopolitan style, with floor-to-ceiling windows and lake views. The chefs at work in the open kitchen provide culinary theatre, and there's also a heated riverside terrace.

BOWNESS-ON-WINDERMERE   *MAP 18, SD49*

Belsfield Restaurant
◉◉ MODERN, INTERNATIONAL
015394 42448 | Laura Ashley The Belsfield Hotel, Kendal Road, LA23 3EL
www.lauraashleyhotels.com/thebelsfield
This lovingly restored Windermere hotel is set in six acres of landscaped gardens. As you might expect from a hotel owned by the Laura Ashley brand, it's tastefully furnished, forming an elegant setting for a menu that fuses British dishes with inspiration from further afield.

The Ryebeck
◉◉ MODERN BRITISH
015394 88195 | Lyth Valley Road, LA23 3JP
www.ryebeck.com
Formerly known as Fayrer Garden, The Ryebeck is an appealingly isolated country house overlooking the shining expanse of Lake Windermere. The informal conservatory dining room serves up a delicious view and a modern British menu that shows off the technical skills of the team in the kitchen.

BRAITHWAITE   *MAP 18, NY22*

The Cottage in the Wood
◉◉◉ MODERN BRITISH
017687 78409 | Whinlatter Pass, CA12 5TW
www.thecottageinthewood.co.uk
Located at the top of the Whinlatter Pass, deep in the Lake District National Park, this restaurant with rooms is in a building that dates partly from the 17th century and is surrounded by forest; from the terrace and front half of the dining room there are wonderful views down the valley. The bare wood tables with round slate place mats prove the perfect foil for very pretty dishes, inspired by Cumbria's wonderful produce. There's a six-course tasting menu that takes you on a culinary journey through the woods and along the coastline of this stunningly beautiful region, while the well-balanced set-price menu is equally exhilarating. From the fabulous canapés and amuse bouches to the confident, joyful dishes on the menus – a carefully-constructed crab starter is both a thing of beauty and completely delicious – there's plenty of evidence here that the kitchen is really hitting its stride.

Chef Ben Wilkinson **Seats** 40 **Closed** January **Parking** 16 **Notes** No children under 10 years at dinner

BRAMPTON   *MAP 21, NY56*

The Cedar Tree Restaurant *NEW*
◉◉ MODERN BRITISH *V*
016977 46234 | Hallbankgate, BRAMPTON, CA8 2NG
www.farlamhall.co.uk
The Cedar Tree Restaurant at Farlam Hall Hotel offers seasonal dishes with rolling changes and a strong emphasis on local produce and the authenticity of it. You can expect some innovative dishes with some bold flavour combinations that work. There's a classical basis with the novel touches and methods that elevate the food to a modern interpretation.

CARLISLE
MAP 18, NY35

Crown Hotel
◉ MODERN BRITISH

01228 561888 | Station Road, Wetheral, CA4 8ES
www.crownhotelwetheral.co.uk

The Georgian hotel is in a picturesque village a few miles out of Carlisle, close to Hadrian's Wall. Its Conservatory Restaurant overlooks the landscaped gardens, and has a striking raftered ceiling and red quarry floor tiles. The kitchen favours a largely modern British approach.

CARTMEL
MAP 18, SD37

Aynsome Manor Hotel
◉ MODERN, TRADITIONAL BRITISH

015395 36653 | LA11 6HH
www.aynsomemanorhotel.co.uk

A charming, small country-house hotel in the untouched Vale of Cartmel with views south to the Norman priory, meadows and woods. The cooking shows accurate timings, judiciously considered combinations and clear flavours on short, daily-changing menus, with seasonal vegetables served separately.

L'Enclume
◉◉◉◉◉ MODERN BRITISH ⚑ NOTABLE WINE LIST

See pages 72–73

See advertisement opposite

Rogan & Co Restaurant
◉◉◉ MODERN BRITISH

015395 35917 | The Square, LA11 6QD
www.roganandco.co.uk

The understudy to L'Enclume sits cheek by jowl with its elder sibling in tranquil Cartmel, with a trickle of a river running alongside it. Behind the stone façade, a modern space has been fashioned, with zinc-topped tables under the gnarled old beams and a happy buzz of contented custom. The Rogan signature style of modernist treatments of gold-standard Cumbrian produce, some of it sourced from the proprietor's own farm in the surrounding valley, is capably expressed in menus that showcase a broad range of technique. Start with cured mackerel and an oyster, a bracing dish set alight with the contrasting sharpnesses of pickled vegetables and wasabi, before turning to a main

such as the Rogan farm's pork loin in its own broth with spiced cannellini beans. Cauliflower dressed in Red Leicester, or confit new potatoes with garlic and thyme, are certainly a cut above the side-dish norm.

Chef Simon Rogan, Tom Barnes **Seats** 40, Private dining 10 **Closed** 1st week January **Notes** Children welcome

CLIFTON
MAP 18, NY52

George and Dragon, Clifton
◉ BRITISH PUB FOOD *V*

01768 865381 | Clifton, CA10 2ER
www.georgeanddragonclifton.co.uk

Comfy sofas and little alcoves all characterise this popular inn, meticulously renovated by owner Charles Lowther, on his historic family estate. His ancestor, Lord Lonsdale, helped found the AA, which adopted yellow, his favourite colour, as its trademark. British cooking relies on the estate for pedigree Shorthorn beef, and pork from rare-breed stock, while game and most fish is also pretty local.

CROSTHWAITE
MAP 18, SD49

The Punchbowl Inn at Crosthwaite
◉◉ MODERN BRITISH

015395 68237 | Lyth Valley, LA8 8HR
www.the-punchbowl.co.uk/

A small country house in the Lyth Valley, The Punchbowl is one of Lakeland's homelier places, run with great civility by the hands-on team. A slate-topped bar and modern rustic furniture give the place a fresh look, and the menu shows plenty of fashion-conscious technique.

ELTERWATER
MAP 18, NY30

Stove at Langdale Hotel & Spa
◉ MODERN BRITISH

015394 37302 | The Langdale Estate, LA22 9JD
www.langdale.co.uk

The gastronomic action at this smart Lakeland resort is in Stove dining room, a contemporary space with an open kitchen with a wood-fired oven, and a mezzanine with valley views. The kitchen takes a broad-minded approach, producing good stuff that hits the comfort food brief nicely.

GLENRIDDING
MAP 18, NY31

Inn on the Lake
◉◉ MODERN EUROPEAN

017684 82444 | Lake Ullswater, CA11 0PE

www.lakedistricthotels.net

In 15 acres of grounds surrounding Ullswater, this hotel's main culinary action takes place in its Lake View Restaurant, the elegant dining room decorated with shades of lilac and fawn. The kitchen makes good use of regional ingredients to produce dishes of modernity and creativity.

GRANGE-OVER-SANDS
MAP 18, SD47

Clare House
◉ MODERN BRITISH

015395 33026 | Park Road, LA11 7HQ

www.clarehousehotel.co.uk

The Read family has owned this traditional hotel with secluded gardens overlooking Morecambe Bay since the 1960s, and their passionate care is evident wherever you look. In the two-roomed dining area, well-spaced tables dressed in crisp linen are attended by smartly turned-out, loyally long-serving staff.

GRASMERE
MAP 18, NY30

Forest Side
◉◉◉◉ MODERN BRITISH *V* 🍸 NOTABLE WINE LIST

015394 35250 | Keswick Road, LA22 9RN

www.theforestside.com

As the name suggests, Forest Side occupies a verdant setting and the spacious dining room celebrates views of both the garden and surrounding forest. Elegant but rustic, linen napkins and local pottery wares are a talking point, as are tables fashioned out of old floor boards. Paul Leonard's exciting modern approach includes 8- or 4-course tasting menus that evolve with the seasons. Expect solid technical skills and big flavours conjured from high quality local ingredients. Raw aged Cumbrian deer turns up with smoked fresh cheese, wood sorrel and swede before moving on to native lobster barbecued over forest pine with tomatoes, elder and fennel. Top drawer Lakeland Dexter beef appears with alliums from the garden and forest, with preserved raspberry, meadowsweet and custard a stand-out dessert. The carefully chosen wine list is full of interesting bottles and the knowledgeable sommelier is on hand should choices become too tricky.

Chef Paul Leonard **Seats** 40, Private dining 10 **Open** All Year **Parking** 44 **Notes** No children under 8 years

MAP 18, SD37

L'Enclume

◉◉◉◉◉ MODERN BRITISH 🍷 NOTABLE WINE LIST
015395 36362 | Cavendish Street, LA11 6PZ
www.lenclume.co.uk

Triumphant, dazzling dishes from one of the UK's best chefs

One of the UK's best-known sites of culinary pilgrimage, L'Enclume (that's 'anvil' in French – it's housed in the former blacksmith's) is set in the rather idyllic medieval village of Cartmel, which comes complete with narrow streets, foodie shops, and a priory (saved by the villagers during the Dissolution of the Monasteries). L'Enclume is in many ways the ultimate destination restaurant and you probably deserve to stay in one of the comfortable, classy bedrooms dotted round the village. Inside, the interior is plain – with beams, stone floors, unclothed tables, whitewashed walls, and windows overlooking a small but perfectly manicured garden. Table appointments are bespoke, with an array of stunning dishes and serving vessels designed to highlight the food. Many chefs these days are interested in keeping things local, but the level of control over the ingredients here is

> "L'Enclume is in many ways the ultimate destination restaurant..."

obsessive, with some coming direct from chef Simon Rogan's own organic farm while others are foraged from the surrounding fields, hedgerows and woods. The wine list is superb and recommendations come with real depth of knowledge, while the daily and seasonally changing menus are complex productions that you'll be guided through by the polished, switched-on staff. What you'll experience here is triumphant levels of skill and invention, very refined, dazzlingly contemporary cooking, every perfect miniature dish bursting with dynamism and creativity and allowing the tremendous quality of the ingredients to speak for themselves. A mere recitation of dishes will give the faintest hint of what you might expect, with lunch offering the likes of native lobster and gooseberry tart, with Cherry Belle radish and rosehips; fritter of Duroc pig and smoked eel, with lovage and fermented sweetcorn; Jersey Royal potatoes in onion ashes with pickled walnut and, melted Westcombe cheese; scallops from Orkney glazed in XO with salt baked Snowball turnips, smoked pork fat and nasturtium, and Cornish Texel Cross lamb loin with white Lisbon onions, ramson leaves and flowers. The signature 'Anvil' dessert is a caramel mousse with miso, apple and spruce.

Chef Simon Rogan, Paul Burgalieres
Seats 45, Private dining 6
Closed 25–26 December
Parking 7

See advertisement on page 71

GRASMERE continued

The Wordsworth Hotel & Spa

◉ MODERN BRITISH

015394 35592 | Stock Lane, LA22 9SW

www.thewordsworthhotel.co.uk

Just up-river from Grasmere, and once the Earl of Cadogan's hunting lodge, the Wordsworth Hotel is set in two acres of riverside gardens, with some great views of the lake. The Signature Restaurant is an airy conservatory, offering excellent, well-balanced dishes. Not just a hotel dining room, it's now quite a destination in itself.

See advertisement opposite

HAWKSHEAD
MAP 18, SD39

The Sun Inn

◉ TRADITIONAL BRITISH

015394 36236 | Main Street, LA22 0NT

www.suninn.co.uk

This listed 17th-century coaching inn, at the heart of the charming village of Hawkshead, is always popular with locals and visitors alike. Inside, low ceilings, open stonework and wooden floors hark back to former times. The kitchen sends out well considered and generous dishes.

KESWICK
MAP 18, NY22

Brasserie 31 *NEW*

◉ MODERN BRITISH

017687 72071 | Main Street, CA12 5BN

www.lakedistricthotels.net/skiddawhotel

Brasserie 31 is part of Keswick's popular Skiddaw Hotel, and a recent revamp has created a luxuriously comfortable space for fine Modern British dining. The table d'hote menu offers imaginative and well-executed dishes, such as artichoke and shredded jackfruit steamed suet pudding, or a marvellous sea trout loin poached in red wine.

Brossen Steakhouse

◉ MODERN BRITISH

017687 73333 | Inn on the Square, Main Street, CA12 5JF

www.innonthesquare.co.uk/brossen

The Inn on the Square is a revamped hotel with a contemporary edge and a restaurant that is all about prime protein cooked over coals. The dining room is a light, bright and casual space, with a view into the kitchen.

KIRKBY LONSDALE
MAP 18, SD67

Pheasant Inn

◉ MODERN BRITISH

015242 71230 | Casterton, LA6 2RX

www.pheasantinn.co.uk

An 18th-century coaching inn with a proper bar complete with real ales and snug. Grab a table by the fire in the bar, or head on through to the slightly more refined restaurant – the menu is the same throughout. Expect dishes that reflect the easy-going pub setting but don't lack ambition and flair.

Sun Inn Restaurant

◉◉ MODERN BRITISH

015242 71965 | 6 Market Street, LA6 2AU

www.sun-inn.info

Anyone with foodie inclinations should visit the white-painted, 17th-century Sun Inn, a proper pub with beams, log fires and real ales in the convivial bar, and a smart contemporary dining room. Reliable hands in the kitchen conjure up full-flavoured dishes using the best local and seasonal ingredients.

LEVENS
MAP 18, SD48

The Villa Levens

◉◉ MODERN, TRADITIONAL *V*

01539 980980 | Brettargh Holt, LA8 8EA

www.thevillalevens.co.uk

The nuns are long gone from this former Victorian convent, now the imposing Villa Levens hotel. Much survives from its early days, including wood panelling and a fireplace in the intimate dining room, where a contemporary British menu offers the likes of pan-seared scallops, and dry-aged fillet steak. The hotel also offers a brasserie menu.

See advertisement on page 76

LUPTON
MAP 18, SD58

The Plough Inn
MODERN BRITISH *V*

015395 67700 | Cow Brow, LA6 1PJ

www.theploughatlupton.co.uk

The Plough sports a clean-lined contemporary look without sacrificing the best of its pubby character. It's a classy act with leather sofas, and a Brathay slate-topped bar set against the cosiness of wooden floors, beams, real fires and the like. Comforting modern takes on classic dishes prevail.

NEAR SAWREY
MAP 18, SD39

Ees Wyke Country House
TRADITIONAL BRITISH

015394 36393 | LA22 0JZ

www.eeswyke.co.uk

Beatrix Potter spent her holidays in this white Georgian house. These days, on a scale small enough to unite guests, a four-course dinner menu is served at a single start time. A pair of choices is offered at most stages.

PENRITH
MAP 18, NY53

FYR
MODERN BRITISH

01768 868111 | North Lakes Hotel & Spa, Ullswater Road, CA11 8QT

fyrgrill.co.uk

Next to Wetheriggs Country Park, this Thwaites-owned hotel occupies an enviable position in Penrith at the edge of the Lake District. FYR restaurant features an impressive bespoke open-fire grill at the heart of the restaurant where guests can experience the theatre of their dishes being cooked in front of them.

PENTON

MAP 21, NY47

Pentonbridge Inn

◉◉◉ BRITISH, INTERNATIONAL *V*

01228 586636 | CA6 5QB

pentonbridgeinn.co.uk

Just on the English side of the border but closer to Scottish towns, this fully refurbished inn has built a sound reputation for good food. There's a blend of modern and traditional inside, with exposed brick, log burning stoves and a stylish decor. Much of the produce used for the imaginative menus comes from the owner's nearby estate and gardens. Solid technical skill underpins the dishes, which are big on flavour and precision presentation. Cornish crab with quail egg caviar and leek and potato foam might precede Cartmel Valley red deer, crispy haggis, neeps and tatties with bone marrow sauce.

Chef Christopher Archer **Seats** 26 **Open** all year **Prices** from S £12.75 M £25 D£8 **Parking** 36 **Notes** Vegetarian dishes, children welcome

See advertisement opposite

POOLEY BRIDGE

MAP 18, NY42

1863 Bar Bistro Rooms

◉◉ MODERN BRITISH

017684 86334 | High Street, CA10 2NH

www.1863ullswater.co.uk

Built in 1863 for the village blacksmith, what is now its contemporary dining room lives up to its bistro billing, with prime ingredients from Britain and beyond underpinning the modern British menu. Start with crapaudine beetroot and ragstone cheese, then move on to céviche-topped Cornish mackerel, and finish with Amalfi lemon parfait, ginger and meringue.

RAVENSTONEDALE

MAP 18, NY70

The Black Swan

◉◉ MODERN BRITISH

015396 23204 | CA17 4NG

www.blackswanhotel.com

Ravenstonedale is a pretty conservation village, and this smart Victorian inn has friendly bars and tranquil riverside gardens. There are two handsome restaurants, equally cosy and welcoming, where you can enjoy the seasonally-changing menus of modern dishes and pub classics. The team work closely with many local suppliers.

ROSTHWAITE
MAP 18, NY21

Scafell Hotel
◉◉ MODERN BRITISH
017687 77208 | CA12 5XB
www.scafell.co.uk
Surrounded by peaks and the lush greenery of the Borrowdale Valley, the Scafell Hotel is ideal for those seeking time in the great outdoors. The Riverside Bar and lounge bar offer informal dining, with the main restaurant a more formal option. Salmon is cured in-house.

SEDBERGH
MAP 18, SD69

The Black Bull Inn NEW
◉ BRITISH, GERMAN AND JAPANESE
01539 620264 | 44 Main Street, LA10 5BL
www.theblackbullsedbergh.co.uk
The Black Bull Inn's simple, understated restaurant offers food which is heavily influenced by the surrounding countryside, slow grown meat from local producers is delivered with a Japanese twist. Wabi Sabi – the Japanese 'art of imperfection' – is illustrated in elements of the older fabric of the building being untouched. Expect great hospitality and professional service in contemporary surroundings. The wine list has some unusual, but carefully chosen, offerings alongside more commercial and popular grape varieties with a heavily European influence.

SKELTON
MAP 18, NY43

The Dog and Gun Inn
◉◉ BRITISH, EUROPEAN
017684 84301 | CA11 9SE
www.dogandgunskelton.co.uk
Whatever you choose you can be sure a meal at this atmospheric little dining pub will feature local produce cooked with skill. There's an emphasis on generous portions and big flavours, and menus might feature a perfectly timed, light-as-a-feather, twice-baked Lancashire cheese and chive soufflé, to be followed, perhaps, by neatly presented glazed shoulder, braised leg and hot pot of Pringle House lamb with intensely flavoured roasted cauliflower purée and a fresh, bold salsa verde. Opening hours are limited, so booking is advised - this is a very popular spot.

WINDERMERE
MAP 18, SD49

Briery Wood Country House Hotel
◉◉ MODERN, TRADITIONAL
015394 33316 | Ambleside Road, Ecclerigg, LA23 1ES
www.lakedistrictcountryhotels.co.uk
Set in seven acres of grounds, Briery Wood is a charming, white-painted property, dating to the late 19th century. It's a cosy, relaxing place with an informal atmosphere. In the dining room you'll find attentive staff serving modern country-house style cooking.

Cragwood Country House Hotel
◉◉ BRITISH, FRENCH
015394 88177 | Ambleside Road, LA23 1LQ
www.lakedistrictcountryhotels.co.uk
Built in 1910 from stone quarried in its own 21 acres of grounds, Cragwood has views over Lake Windermere and bags of country-house charm. The two dining rooms have lovely views and smart furnishings. Things get rolling with three canapés and five types of bread.

Gilpin Spice
◉◉ PAN-ASIAN *V*
015394 88818 | Gilpin Hotel & Lake House, Crook Road, LA23 3NE
www.thegilpin.co.uk/eat-and-drink/gilpinspice
Adjacent to the main Gilpin Hotel building with its own entrance, this restaurant is a stunner – divided into three sections, each decorated differently in bright colours. There is an open kitchen with high, comfortable bar-stool seating directly facing the chefs at work. The pan-Asian menu is designed to offer lots of taster dishes rather than the traditional starter–main–dessert options; taster menus for two are available too.

Henrock NEW
◉◉ INTERNATIONAL
015394 88600 | Crook Road, LA23 3JA
leeucollection.com/UK/linthwaite-house
Henrock is set within the stunning Linthwaite House Hotel and features views across the Lake District National Park and Windermere. Simon Rogan's team operates here so expect a great deal of produce from his farm in Cartmel. There are small plates for starters and then more substantial mains and some sharing dishes. The restaurant itself is understated - three separate rooms decorated in muted, natural tones with a few splashes of colour - a very comfortable and thoroughly designed space.

Holbeck Ghyll Country House Hotel

◉◉ MODERN BRITISH

015394 32375 | Holbeck Lane, LA23 1LU

www.holbeckghyll.com

Holbeck Ghyll began life as a Victorian hunting lodge, when its eminent position overlooking Lake Windermere must have suggested itself as a suitable bolthole for country pursuits. Dining goes on in an austerely panelled room, where the window seats are literally that, rather than freestanding chairs, for those with their backs to the view. Additionally, there's a chef's table for up to 10 diners.

HRiSHi at Gilpin Hotel & Lake House

◉◉◉◉ MODERN BRITISH, ASIAN INFLUENCES V

See pages 80–81

See advertisement on page 82

Langdale Chase

◉◉ BRITISH

015394 32201 | Ambleside Road, LA23 1LW

www.langdalechase.co.uk/food-drink

This impressive Victorian building was 'the first residence in Windermere to have electricity installed' and it still boasts a fabulous late 19th-century interior, full of period details. Six acres of grounds lead down to the lake, and the terraces and reception rooms all enjoy wonderful views.

Lindeth Howe Country House Hotel & Restaurant

◉◉ CLASSIC FRENCH

015394 45759 | Lindeth Drive, Longtail Hill, LA23 3JF

www.lindeth-howe.co.uk

Beatrix Potter not only lived in this classic country house on a hillside overlooking Windermere and the mountains, but wrote some of her tales here. The word 'hillside' undersells what are in fact six acres of sweeping gardens, worth exploring before eating.

Merewood Country House Hotel

◉◉ MODERN BRITISH

015394 46484 | Ambleside Road, Ecclerigg, LA23 1LH

www.lakedistrictcountryhotels.co.uk/merewood-hotel

Built in 1812 from stone quarried in the hotel's grounds, Merewood is perfectly positioned to make the best of the views over Lake Windermere. There are 20 acres of woodland and gardens, and this Lakeland country house is equally on the money on the inside.

Porto

◉ MODERN BRITISH, EUROPEAN

015394 48242 | 3 Ash Street, Bowness, LA23 3EB

www.porto-restaurant.co.uk

The cool greys, blues and greens of Porto's comfortable dining room pick up those of the surrounding lakes, fells and mountains; tables are natural oak and framed retro prints line the walls. Modern and classic British food prevails, but you'll notice European and Asian influences too. Eating on the heated roof terrace or in the garden is also an option.

The Samling

◉◉◉ MODERN BRITISH ♨NOTABLE WINE LIST

015394 31922 | Ambleside Road, LA23 1LR

www.thesamlinghotel.co.uk

The Samling's contemporary dining room of Lakeland slate and floor-to-ceiling glass offers spectacular views of the hotel gardens and Lake Windermere. The colour palette of greys and neutrals is understated, and there's a hint of formality with tables covered in crisp white linen. Head chef Robby Jenks has created several menus, all featuring modern British cooking, such as the five-course tasting menu that might include turbot and mussels with watercress pesto, sea vegetables and radish, or duck with beetroot, turnip and apple. The impressive wine list is clearly curated by someone in the know, and the very knowledgeable sommelier has excellent recommendations.

Chef Robby Jenks **Seats** 40, Private dining 8 **Open** All Year **Parking** 40 **Notes** No Children

Storrs Hall Hotel

◉◉ MODERN BRITISH

015394 47111 | Storrs Park, LA23 3LG

www.storrshall.com

Within 17 acres of grounds on the shore of Lake Windermere, this Georgian villa provides a quintessential Lakeland country house setting. Overlooking the lawns and glorious scenery, the elegant restaurant makes for a relaxed backdrop to the modern cooking. The kitchen displays a sound skill set.

Continued on page 83

WINDERMERE

HRiSHi at Gilpin Hotel & Lake House

◉◉◉◉ MODERN BRITISH, ASIAN INFLUENCES V

015394 88818 | Gilpin Hotel & Lake House, Crook Road, LA23 3NE

thegilpin.co.uk/eat-and-drink/hrishi

Pin-sharp attention to detail and exciting contemporary cooking

A fabulously chic and luxurious bolthole set in 21 acres of woodland and gardens, Gilpin offers an air of sophisticated tranquillity. The main house may have begun life as an Edwardian lodge, but this isn't your average country house hotel. From the truly splendid detached suites, with their cedar cladding, floor-to-ceiling windows and amazing hot tubs, to the more traditional rooms in the main building, the attention to detail is reassuring and impressive, and the same can certainly be said of the food. The three dining rooms of the flagship HRiSHi (the nickname of head chef Hrishikesh Desai) is where you'll find the very best in contemporary British cuisine, subtly influenced by Desai's Asian heritage. There's a real sense that this is exciting, cutting-edge cooking, and dining here is a highlight of any stay. The thought and work that goes into every dish is clear – these creations may be infinitely Instagrammable

but you can be assured this is not a case of style over substance. Tables are set with fresh flowers, candles and crisp white linen, and the friendly and attentive staff provide perfect service. The depth of flavour in, for example, a starter of flame grilled Lancashire cauliflower, is remarkable, with a rich lime leaf 'moilee', black garlic ketchup, and tomato and cumin gel all contributing. A main course of roasted fillet of Shetland turbot might come with buttered mussels and cockles, saffron-braised fennel compôte, and jalapeño peppers 'two ways', the heat from the chilli successfully tempered by a rich Vermouth emulsion. Prepare for dessert with a tender vodka and orange gel with cranberry foam, before moving on to peanut semifreddo – a feather-light parfait

"...you'll find the very best in contemporary British cuisine, subtly influenced by Desai's Asian heritage."

with coconut milk, glazed banana and chocolate sorbet. The wine list offers an extensive and global selection at a range of prices.

Chef Hrishikesh Desai
Seats 56, Private dining 20
Open All Year
Parking 48
Notes No children under 7 years

See advertisement on page 82

WINDERMERE continued

The Wild Boar Inn, Grill & Smokehouse
@ TRADITIONAL BRITISH
015394 45225 | Crook, LA23 3NF
englishlakes.co.uk/the-wild-boar
The white-painted Wild Boar is a classic inn with
a host of stylish bedrooms, a smart bar, and a
restaurant with an open kitchen at its heart.
They even have an on-site microbrewery. The
dining area has oak beams and darkwood tables.

■ DERBYSHIRE

BAKEWELL
MAP 16, SK26

Piedaniel's
@ TRADITIONAL FRENCH, EUROPEAN
01629 812687 | Bath Street, DE45 1BX
www.piedaniels-restaurant.com
Piedaniel's is run with great personal warmth and
charm by a husband-and-wife team who keep
the town supplied with reliable bistro cooking.
Main courses nail their colours to the mast of
hearty prime cuts while fish gets a look-in too.

BASLOW
MAP 16, SK27

Cavendish Hotel
@@@ MODERN BRITISH *V*
01246 582311 | Church Lane, DE45 1SP
devonshirehotels.co.uk/cavendish-hotel-baslow
This stylish hotel dates back to the 18th century,
and the comfortable public areas are adorned
with paintings from the Duke's extensive art
collection. The Gallery restaurant is traditionally
decorated with a smart modern twist, and in
season menus feature lamb and game from the
estate. You might begin with cod loin and satay
sauce, cooled by coconut yogurt. A neatly plated,
colourful dish of Moss Valley pork belly comes
with home-made black pudding, sage mashed
potato, Swiss chard, broccoli and peppered
pineapple. 'Simple presentation and perfect
execution' sums up a dessert of banana, walnut
and caramel soufflé with silky dark chocolate
sorbet.

Chef Adam Harper Seats 50, Private dining 18 Open All
Year Parking 40 Notes Children welcome

Fischer's Baslow Hall
@@@ MODERN EUROPEAN *V*
See pages 84-85

The Prince of Wales, Baslow
@ MODERN BRITISH
01246 583880 | Church Lane, DE45 1RY
princeofwalesbaslow.co.uk

With its real fire, Peak District-brewed ales
and live music, this pub is very much the village
hub but the seasonal food draws diners from
afar. Local black pudding, crispy hen's egg,
pancetta and tomato salsa might lead on to
pan-seared rainbow trout, spring greens and wild
garlic sauce.

BEELEY
MAP 16, SK26

The Devonshire Arms at Beeley
@ MODERN BRITISH ★NOTABLE WINE LIST
01629 733259 | Devonshire Square, DE4 2NR
www.devonshirebeeley.co.uk
A night in one of the guest rooms would allow you
to say you'd stayed at Chatsworth, sort of, as this
stone-built village inn is situated in the heart of
the estate. Expect cask-conditioned ales and a
terrific wine list, and a menu offering
contemporary pub food.

BRADWELL
MAP 16, SK18

The Samuel Fox Country Inn
@@ MODERN BRITISH
01433 621562 | Stretfield Road, S33 9JT
www.samuelfox.co.uk
A stone-built inn near the Pennine Way named
after the Victorian steel magnate who invented
the folding ribbed umbrella. Breads of the day,
variously flavoured with treacle or with
Henderson's relish and onion, make an
encouraging prelude to tasty dishes.

BASLOW

Fischer's Baslow Hall

◎◎◎ **MODERN EUROPEAN** 𝑉
01246 583259 | Calver Road, DE45 1RR
www.fischers-baslowhall.co.uk

Meticulously-sourced modern country-house cooking near Chatsworth

Max and Susan Fischer took over Baslow Hall in 1988 and have since worked ceaselessly to cement its reputation as one of northern England's top-flight country house retreats. It's a fine Edwardian house, built in the style of a Stuart manor with protruding wings and mullioned windows, reached by a winding driveway lined with mature chestnut trees, not far from the Chatsworth Estate and the town of Bakewell, famed for its eponymous pudding. The immaculately turned-out dining room is a picture of elegance in its soft-focus palette of grey and blue, and the service team brings polished attentiveness to the whole experience. Those gorgeous gardens flanking the setting are not merely there to look pretty: Chef Nathan Wall's supply lines begin in Baslow's own kitchen garden and its glasshouse, which provides newly plucked herbs, so you can rest assured that the sourcing is meticulous,

> "...sourcing is meticulous, and ingredients are treated with the respect they deserve."

and ingredients are treated with the respect they deserve. The seasons loom large in the cooking, a sound foundation that applies equally whether you go for the five-course à la carte (also delivered in pescatarian and meat-free modes) or the tasting menu. Whichever path you take, subtle Nordic and Japanese influences are to the fore. Fish cookery is sensitive and accurate, perhaps pairing chalk stream trout with sea herbs, hot smoked oyster and yuzu gel, or a more classical styling of turbot with crab, courgette and onion. The intriguing,

on-trend approach extends to mains, which showcase pedigree meats such as Derbyshire lamb offset with the smoky note of barbecued asparagus and the herbal zip of salsa verde. A trolley of fine British cheeses awaits the savoury toothed, ahead of inventive desserts such as sweet potato with ice cream and furikake, or a revamped Brit classic - gypsy tart with Kentish apple and cobnut crumble.

Chef Nathan Wall
Seats 46, Private dining 8
Closed 25–26 December
Parking 25
Notes No children under 8 years in main dining room

CHESTERFIELD

Casa Hotel
◉◉ MODERN BRITISH, MEDITERRANEAN
01246 245990 | Lockoford Lane, S41 7JB
casahotels.co.uk
Casa's Cocina restaurant is an über-chic space with darkwood, white chairs and floor-to-ceiling windows. The menu has a selection of salads and tapas running from a board of Spanish charcuterie to a croquette of hake, cheese and chives with tartare dressing.

Peak Edge Hotel at the Red Lion
◉◉ MODERN BRITISH
01246 566142 | Darley Road, Stone Edge, S45 0LW
www.peakedgehotel.co.uk
A new-build stone edifice on the border of the Peak District National Park, the family-owned hotel is handy for Chatsworth and Haddon Hall. Next door is the Red Lion, a Georgian coaching inn that is home to the hotel's bar and bistro.

CLOWNE

Van Dyk by Wildes
◉ MODERN BRITISH
01246 387386 | Worksop Road, S43 4TD
www.vandykbywildes.co.uk
The white-fronted Van Dyk stands on the A619 not far from Chesterfield. Amid the surrounding ruggedness, it looks a little like a sugar-frosting confection, which only adds to its idiosyncratic character. There's a hint of old-school formality about the Chapel Restaurant.

DARLEY ABBEY

Darleys Restaurant
◉◉ MODERN BRITISH V
01332 364987 | Waterfront, Darley Abbey Mills, DE22 1DZ
www.darleys.com

This converted silk mill by the River Derwent is the setting for some bright, modern cooking making really excellent use of regional produce. The shady terrace makes the most of the riverside location, a great backdrop for the thoroughly contemporary menus. Desserts demonstrate real creativity.

FROGGATT

The Chequers Inn
◉ MODERN, TRADITIONAL
01433 630231 | S32 3ZJ
www.chequers-froggatt.com
The Tindalls' country inn in the Hope Valley charms, with a warm colour scheme, wooden pub-style furniture and a fireplace creating a relaxing atmosphere. The menu deftly steers between stalwarts and more modern offerings.

HARTINGTON

Biggin Hall Hotel
◉ MODERN BRITISH
01298 84451 | Biggin-by-Hartington, SK17 0DH
www.bigginhall.co.uk
Seventeenth century, 1,000 feet up in the Peak District National Park - what's not to like? There's more - oak beams, stone walls, flagstones and great views. Always cosy, the restaurant is full of character, with daily changing, modern British menus that acknowledge vegetarian tastes.

HATHERSAGE
MAP 16, SK28

The Plough Inn
⊛ MODERN EUROPEAN
01433 650319 | Leadmill Bridge, S32 1BA
www.theploughinn-hathersage.co.uk
Set in nine acres of grounds that slope gently to the River Derwent, the stone-built 16th-century Plough is welcoming and friendly. The courtyard's the place to be in summer, and the dining room is always smartly turned out, as is the cooking.

HIGHAM
MAP 16, SK35

Santo's Higham Farm Hotel
⊛ MODERN INTERNATIONAL
01773 833812 | Main Road, DE55 6EH
www.santoshighamfarm.co.uk
Santo Cusimano runs a highly individual rural retreat. With the rolling Amber Valley all about, it's in a prime slice of Derbyshire walking country, and has been fashioned from an old farmstead. Menus mobilise plenty of pedigree local produce and Italian influences are never distant.

MATLOCK
MAP 16, SK35

Stones Restaurant
⊛⊛ MODERN BRITISH
01629 56061 | 1 Dale Road, DE4 3LT
www.stones-restaurant.co.uk
Stones may be an intimate basement venue, but it has the best of both worlds on fine days, thanks to a stylish conservatory and tiled sun terrace perched above the Derwent. The decor is a mix of subtle earthy tones, to match a Mediterranean-inflected menu.

MELBOURNE
MAP 11, SK32

Amalfi White
⊛⊛ MODERN BRITISH, EUROPEAN
01332 694890 | 50 Derby Road, DE73 8FE
www.amalfiwhite.com

With a terraced garden plus a children's play area, this stylish brasserie has all the attributes needed to make a family-friendly venue all year round. Inside, there's a contemporary space in greys and silvers with a mixture of artwork in the softly-lit dining room.

The Bay Tree
⊛ MODERN BRITISH, NEW WORLD
01332 863358 | 4 Potter Street, DE73 8HW
baytreerestaurant.com
Set across different levels, the building was once home to several shops but beyond its stone façade is a contemporary restaurant with clean lines, decorated in very sophisticated shades of muted grey and beige. Menus are thoughtfully constructed, and feature complex but elegant dishes based on top-quality ingredients.

MORLEY
MAP 11, SK34

The Morley Hayes Hotel
⊛⊛ MODERN BRITISH
01332 780480 | Main Road, DE7 6DG
www.morleyhayes.com
Morley Hayes has been a dynamic hotel since the 1980s, and with its golf complex, conference facilities and popular wedding venue, it has most bases covered. The kitchen offers a roster of unpretentious modern dishes, with influences from around the globe adding vibrancy and colour.

REPTON
MAP 10, SK32

The Boot Inn
◉◉ MODERN BRITISH
01283 346047 | 12 Boot Hill, DE65 6FT
www.thebootatrepton.co.uk
Five miles from the National Brewery Centre, you
would expect beer to be a strong draw, especially
in a stylishly-appointed 17th-century coaching
inn. A range of evocatively-named ales from its
microbrewery is a plank of The Boot's huge
popularity. There's something on the menus to
suit everyone.

ROWSLEY
MAP 16, SK26

The Peacock at Rowsley
◉◉◉ MODERN BRITISH
See pages 90-91

See advertisement opposite

SANDIACRE
MAP 11, SK43

La Rock
◉◉ MODERN BRITISH
0115 939 9833 | 4 Bridge Street, NG10 5QT
www.larockrestaurant.co.uk
Hidden away down a side street in Sandiacre,
La Rock's sophisticated and contemporary
interior has exposed brick walls, wooden floors,
solid oak tables with granite centres and
sparkling glassware, and there's a glass-roofed
lounge area with inviting comfy sofas; soft music
plays in the background.

THORPE
MAP 16, SK15

The Izaak Walton Hotel
◉◉ MODERN, TRADITIONAL
01335 350981 | Dovedale, DE6 2AY
www.izaakwaltonhotel.com
This creeper-clad country house has glorious
views over the Dovedale Valley and the
Derbyshire peaks. Decorated in rich hues of red
and gold, the elegant Haddon Restaurant favours
a traditional candlelight-and-linen look, in
contrast to the up-to-date and creative menu.

TIDESWELL
MAP 16, SK17

The Merchant's Yard
◉◉ CONTEMPORARY, CLASSIC
01298 872442 | St John's Road, SK17 8NY
www.themerchantsyard.com

Once an actual merchant's yard, the property is
full of references to its past, and has a strong
industrial feel. This is softened by teal velvet
bench seating, and technical drawings of many
household items. The young and enthusiastic
staff are passionate and knowledgeable, while
the menus are always evolving, offering precise
cookery and showing a high level of skill.

WOOLLEY MOOR
MAP 16, SK36

The White Horse & The View
@ Woolley Moor
◉ MODERN BRITISH *V*
01246 590319 | Badger Lane, DE55 6FG
www.thewhitehorsewoolleymoor.co.uk
In the hamlet of Woolley Moor on the outskirts of
Ashover, this stone-built country inn sits on the
eastern edge of the Peak District National Park.
It's a glorious setting to enjoy modern British
dishes like blue cheese and walnut soufflé,
followed by crispy belly pork, spring onion mash
and smoked bacon sauce.

THE PEACOCK AT ROWSLEY

The Peacock at Rowsley is a cosy, chic boutique hotel, originally a manor house in the heart of the Peak District National Park and very close to Haddon Hall and Chatsworth House. Perfect for a countryside break with comfortable bedrooms including four posters and one of the best hotel suites in the region. Our award winning restaurant serves a delicious fine dining menu, crafted by Head Chef Dan Smith. Dan worked with notable chefs such as Tom Aikens before joining The Peacock. The atmospheric bar with open fire is a very convivial place to meet for lunch, dinner or just a drink – with its own menu of freshly cooked seasonal food. Treat yourself to a drink from the extensive cocktail menu. Sunday lunch at The Peacock is a local favourite. The hotel is famed for is excellent fly fishing on the Derbyshire Wye and River Derwent.

For further information or to make a booking please call **01629 733518** or email **reception@thepeacockatrowsley.com**. The Peacock at Rowsley, Derbyshire DE4 2EB

ROWSLEY   MAP 16, SK26

The Peacock at Rowsley

◉◉◉ **MODERN BRITISH**
01629 733518 | Bakewell Road, DE4 2EB
www.thepeacockatrowsley.com

Inventive modern take on country-house cooking

The Peacock was originally a manor house, built in 1652, and has been a hotel since the 1830s. It's part of the Haddon Hall Estate (make sure you visit Haddon while you're in the area, a truly fabulous Tudor building) and is the perfect size – just 15 bedrooms and a properly cosy, comfortable place. It's ideally situated between Matlock and Bakewell, handy for Chatsworth and the Peak District National Park. Interiors are comfortable, with plenty of polished wood and stone walls, period features and an intimate dining room. Here you'll find traditional portraits in oil and walls in dark plum and lime green for a slightly contemporary twist on the country-house look, with chunky, unclothed tables, crisp linen napkins, and quite a formal atmosphere, the setting for head chef Dan Smith's inventive modern British menus. These change seasonally, and are creative and technically nimble, making excellent

> "..excellent use of produce from the kitchen gardens as well as locally reared organic meats from nearby estates."

use of produce from the kitchen gardens as well as locally reared organic meats from nearby estates. The á la carte might offer starters of Isle of Wight tomatoes with watermelon, elderberry vinegar, and native lobster, or Norfolk quail and ham ballotine, girolles, artichoke and liver parfait on toast. A carrot salad, with walnut, nasturtium pesto, raisins and crème fraîche makes a good vegetarian alternative. Mains could take in local lamb, spiced aubergine, courgette, mint and pistachio dressing, or roast potato terrine with crispy egg, grilled onions, cheddar custard, Bakewell oyster mushrooms, tarragon and mushroom sauce. When it comes to dessert you might choose the warm raspberry financier, apricot, almond, Amaretto soft scoop, honey or maybe the cherry and chocolate semifreddo with caramelised white chocolate ice cream, Kirsch and vanilla cream. The wine list is short but well chosen, with a good choice by the glass.

Chef Dan Smith
Seats 56, Private dining 14
Open All Year
Parking 25
Notes No children under 10 years on Fridays and Saturdays

See advertisement on page 89

■ DEVON

ASHBURTON
MAP 3, SK77

The Old Library Restaurant
⊛ MODERN BRITISH

01364 652896 | North Street, TQ13 7QH
www.theoldlibraryrestaurant.co.uk
Housed at the back of the Ashburton library, facing the car park, Joe Suttie and Amy Mitchell's place is a valuable local resource. Happy locals crowd the chunky tables, overseen by a busy kitchen counter, for a short, punchy menu that changes every six weeks or so.

AXMINSTER
MAP 4, SY29

Tytherleigh Arms
⊛⊛ MODERN BRITISH

01460 220214 | Tytherleigh, EX13 7BE
www.tytherleigharms.com
This family-run, 16th-century coaching inn on the borders of Devon, Dorset and Somerset creates a welcoming atmosphere with its beamed ceilings, wooden floors, and a wood-burner ablaze in the winter months. Local produce drives the menus here, and the well-conceived dishes are prepared with sensitivity.

BAMPTON
MAP 3, SS92

The Swan
⊛⊛ MODERN BRITISH

01398 332248 | Station Road, EX16 9NG
www.theswan.co
The Swan is a smart country pub - warm colours, lots of oak, a few sofas, soft lighting - with a convivial atmosphere. The bar is the heart of the operation, but it's easy to see why the whole place can be full of diners.

BARNSTAPLE
MAP 3, SS53

The Arlington Restaurant
⊛ BRITISH

01271 345861 | The Imperial Hotel, Taw Vale Parade, EX32 8NB
www.brend-imperial.co.uk
Set in the Edwardian grandeur of the riverside Imperial Hotel, this elegant old-school restaurant offers plenty of period character with its chandeliers, paintings and fancy plasterwork. It's a fitting setting for gently modern, classically-based cooking that achieves satisfying results thanks to skilful technique and quality ingredients rather than outlandish ideas.

Seasons Brasserie
⊛ MODERN BRITISH

01271 372166 | The Park Hotel, Taw Vale, EX32 9AE
www.parkhotel.co.uk
Warm oak, gleaming marble, soft lighting and cheery service all combine to create a soothing ambience in this smart, contemporary restaurant overlooking Rock Park. The buzzy hub of the hotel, Seasons Brasserie fits the bill whether you're here for coffee and cakes, cocktails or a please-all roster of straightforward modern and traditional cooking.

BEESANDS
MAP 3, SX84

The Cricket Inn
⊛ MODERN, SEAFOOD

01548 580215 | TQ7 2EN
www.thecricketinn.com
Smack on the seafront overlooking the shingle beach, with stunning views across Start Bay, The Cricket enjoys an unrivalled location and retains every ounce of its identity as a former fisherman's pub. Blackboard menus advertise what has been freshly drawn from the bay.

BIDEFORD
MAP 3, SS42

The Pig on the Hill
⊛⊛ FRENCH, ENGLISH 𝑉

01237 459222 | Pusehill, EX39 5AH
www.pigonthehillwestwardho.co.uk
Created in a converted cowshed, The Pig on the Hill is a country pub with a modern restaurant that has an eclectic style – black and white chequered floor, feature 'rose' wall, Liberty-style lampshades and bare wooden tables. Large windows create an airy atmosphere and service is informal yet professional.

The Royal George NEW
⊛⊛ MODERN BRITISH

01237 424138 | Irsha Street, Appledore, EX39 1RY
www.trgpub.co.uk
Right on the water, complete with an ancient slipway that runs into the sea, The Royal George overlooks the Taw and Torridge Estuary. Inside the cosy dining room, the food is as fine as the view, drawing heavily on fresh fish and local venison and lamb. The roast venison loin with breaded shoulder is a real treat.

BIGBURY-ON-SEA
MAP 3, SX64

The Oyster Shack
@ SEAFOOD
01548 810876 | Stakes Hill, TQ7 4BE
www.oystershack.co.uk

Thirty years ago, The Shack was an oyster and mussels farm. Mollusc lovers flocked here, armed with a packed lunch, wine and a shucking knife. It now sub-titles itself 'That Seafood Place', fish and seafood being its stock in trade, with a few meat dishes for good measure. Ride the sea tractor to nearby Burgh Island.

BLACK TORRINGTON
MAP 3, SK49

The Blackriver Inn
@ TRADITIONAL
01409 231888 | Broad Street, Black Torrington, EX21 5PT
www.blackriverinn.co.uk

Apparently, The Blackriver Inn has been around since the early 1820s, and describes itself as a 'proper village pub'. In addition to options such as hearty home-made burgers there are a wide variety of 'small plates', many classic dishes presented in smaller form. This means you can experience more of the kitchen's diverse output.

BRIXHAM
MAP 3, SX95

The Bonaparte Restaurant
@ MODERN BRITISH
01803 853225 | Berry Head Hotel, Berry Head Road, TQ5 9AJ
www.berryheadhotel.com
Views of the bay are very much the feature here at the Berry Head Hotel's formal dining option. The daily-changing menu offers quality ingredients and traditional cookery. The cuisine is enjoyable and clearly popular with the locals.

Quayside Hotel
@ MODERN BRITISH
01803 855751 | 41-49 King Street, TQ5 9TJ
www.quaysidehotel.co.uk
The restaurant at the Quayside Hotel majors in seafood and what reaches the menu depends on the catch. They know how to treat this prime product with respect. It takes place in a candlelit dining room with harbour views and a refreshing lack of pretence.

BURRINGTON
MAP 3, SS61

Northcote Manor and Spa
@@ MODERN BRITISH
01769 560501 | EX37 9LZ
www.northcotemanor.co.uk
Northcote Manor and Spa is a gorgeous 18th-century country house that sits happily in 20 acres of beautiful Devon countryside. As you'd expect, its restaurant is reassuringly traditional, and makes the best use of locally sourced West Country ingredients. Service is as efficient and discreet as you'd expect at a red star hotel.

See advertisement on page 95

CHAGFORD
MAP 3, SX78

Gidleigh Park

◉◉◉ MODERN, CLASSIC ▲NOTABLE WINE LIST

01647 432367 | TQ13 8HH

www.gidleigh.co.uk

As wonderful as always, the stunning setting of Gidleigh Park, approached through winding Devon lanes until you glimpse the graceful old lady standing proudly looking down the beautiful valley. Surrounded by woodland with a babbling brook to the front, one very much gets a sense of privilege arriving here, but also a genuine feeling that you're at a true country house. The dining room is split into three rooms, all relatively understated with 1950s-style chairs, impeccably clothed tables and a simple and refined elegance throughout. There's a tangible sense of pride in Chris Eden's staff with a beautifully drilled team delivering a perfectly balanced blend of knowledge, interest and hospitality.

Chef Chris Eden Seats 45, Private dining 22 Open All Year Parking 45 Notes No children under 8 years at lunch and dinner

Mill End Hotel

◉◉ MODERN BRITISH V

01647 432282 | Dartmoor National Park, TQ13 8JN

www.millendhotel.com

The River Teign flows past this pretty white-painted hotel, where a Devon cream tea is just the ticket, with a lush pastoral backdrop. There's an air of genteel formality in the restaurant with its linen-clad tables, while the kitchen's output is modern, seasonal, and well-presented.

CHITTLEHAMHOLT
MAP 3, SS62

Highbullen Hotel, Golf & Country Club

◉◉ MODERN BRITISH

01769 540561 | EX37 9HD

www.highbullen.co.uk

The Devon View Restaurant at the Highbullen Hotel doesn't disappoint when it comes to the promised vista, and that is indeed the rolling Devon countryside you can see through the bank of windows. The restaurant makes this golfing and spa hotel a useful stopover.

CREDITON
MAP 3, SS80

The Lamb Inn

◉ CHARGRILL V

01363 773676 | The Square, Sandford, EX17 4LW

www.lambinnsandford.co.uk

A 16th-century former coaching house with open fires, low ceilings and a pretty, sheltered garden on three levels, this lovely village pub is unpretentious and welcoming. The accomplished cooking makes good use of quality, local produce, the seasonal menu changing daily. Leave room for comforting desserts.

Paschoe House

◉◉◉ FRENCH, BRITISH, PAN-ASIAN

01363 84244 | Bow, EX17 6JT

paschoehouse.co.uk

A luxurious Grade II listed house, set in 25 acres of grounds in a remote Devon valley with cooking that proves to be a creative, effective fusion of Asian and modern British elements. You'll find this perfectly illustrated by a starter of well-timed lemongrass prawns with pineapple and chilli, served with a beautifully made dim sum. A main of tender Creedy Carver duck is accompanied by a rich, smooth ballotine of foie gras, with blackberries proving an excellent counterpoint – a dish with bags of flavour. A dessert of 'apple, cider, oats' makes for an impressively presented and delicious finale. Excellent wine list.

Chef Craig Davies Seats 30 Open All Year Parking 40 Notes Children welcome

DARTMOUTH
MAP 3, SX85

The Angel Restaurant – Taste of Devon
◉◉ CONTEMPORARY FINE DINING V
01803 833488 | 2 South Embankment, TQ6 9BH
www.theangeldartmouth.co.uk

There has been a notable restaurant on this site since 1974 when Joyce Molyneux opened it as the legendary Carved Angel. Elly Wentworth continues the tradition of a female head chef at the stoves with elegant, seasonal dishes such as braised halibut, seaweed and crab raviolo, charred gem, smoked caviar and lettuce cream.

The Dart Marina Hotel
◉ MODERN BRITISH
01803 832580 | Sandquay Road, TQ6 9PH
www.dartmarina.com
The hotel is a contemporary paradise with neutral colour tones, tasteful and trendy furniture and a swish spa, and it's also home to the River Restaurant. Views of the river are guaranteed through floor-to-ceiling windows, while the menu features regional produce. Open only to hotel residents and annual berth holders.

The Seahorse
◉ MEDITERRANEAN, SEAFOOD ≗NOTABLE WINE LIST
01803 835147 | 5 South Embankment, TQ6 9BH
www.seahorserestaurant.co.uk
Located in the bustling strip along the Dart waterfront, this is an inviting evening venue, while big windows let in the Devon light on summer days. Local seafood, as you might imagine, features widely on the menus, but there's plenty for non-fish fans as well.

DODDISCOMBSLEIGH
MAP 3, SX88

The NoBody Inn
◉ MODERN BRITISH
01647 252394 | EX6 7PS
www.nobodyinn.co.uk
This characterful 17th-century inn has a good local reputation, built upon its stylish food, excellent local cheeses, hefty wine list and a 240-long list of whiskies. Reached via winding lanes, inside it has blackened beams, mismatched tables, and walls adorned with plenty of visual interest.

DREWSTEIGNTON
MAP 3, SX79

The Old Inn
◉◉◉ INTERNATIONAL
01647 281276 | EX6 6QR
www.old-inn.co.uk
Despite the narrow roads that lead into it on either side, Drewsteignton was once a major staging-post on the coach route from Exeter to Okehampton. A slip of a Dartmoor village to the modern eye, it boasts Duncan Walker's white-fronted, 17th-century inn, a contemporary restaurant-with-rooms that has made the place a destination. The ambience is homely, with striking modern artworks, and the menu of assured, classically based cooking offers a wealth of enticement. European notes could be as inimitably French as grilled sole fillets with morels and Madeira, followed by Dexter beef pot-au-feu, while quality shines forth from a fillet of halibut crusted in lemon and parsley, served with braised celery. Traditionally conceived desserts punch above their weight as in a textbook tarte Tatin, or a billowing apricot soufflé with vanilla ice cream. A compact wine list is impeccably chosen and complements the heartening simplicity of the approach.

Chef Duncan Walker **Seats** 16, Private dining 10 **Closed** 3 weeks in January **Notes** No children

ERMINGTON
MAP 3, SX65

Plantation House
◎◎ MODERN BRITISH
01548 831100 | Totnes Road, PL21 9NS
www.plantationhousehotel.co.uk
A boutique restaurant in a restored Georgian rectory, with great garden views. The dinner deal here is simple – three courses or five. The five-course option maybe starts with an appetiser, then lentil, leek and Yarg cheese terrine; fillet of turbot with mussels; medallion of fillet steak with smoked lardons; and hand-carved Serrano ham with cave-aged cheddar.

EXMOUTH
MAP 3, SY08

Lympstone Manor Hotel
◎◎◎◎◎ MODERN BRITISH ♨ NOTABLE WINE LIST
01395 202040 | Courtlands Lane, EX8 3NZ
www.lympstonemanor.co.uk
While Lympstone Manor is hardly 'new' – it's a creamy-white, Grade II, Georgian manor built by the Baring banking dynasty – it has been transformed by Michael Caines's vision and now stands proud - a gorgeous building with sublime views over the Exe estuary, set in 28 acres of grounds that were planted with a vineyard in 2018 to produce sparkling wine. The place delivers everything you'd hope from a country house given a stylish 21st-century twist: comfort and sheer class are delivered in equal measure throughout the public areas, the styling working a treat thanks to soft-focus hues, hand-painted wallpapers, designer chandeliers and modern artworks, and the mood is intimate and unbuttoned. Elegant and outstanding cuisine, augmented by a significant 600-bin wine list, underpin the Lympstone experience, served in three exquisite dining rooms, where the service tone is the same throughout, friendly, engaging and completely devoid of reverentially hushed tones. The cooking delivers a seamless blend of classical technique and precision with contemporary riffs on flavour and texture. All-in-all, its a superb experience.

Chef Michael Caines MBE, Dan Gambles **Seats** 60
Open All Year **Parking Notes** No children

Saveur
◎◎ MODERN EUROPEAN
01395 269459 | 9 Tower Street, EX8 1NT
www.saveursrestaurant.com

Hidden down a quiet pedestrianised street behind the church, this neighbourhood restaurant ticks all the right boxes when it comes to cosiness, informality and fine cooking. Meaning 'flavour', Saveur celebrates local seafood from Lyme Bay and Brixham as well as other, equally local produce.

HAYTOR VALE
MAP 3, SX77

Conservatory Restaurant NEW
◎ MODERN BRITISH
01364 661142 | The Moorland Hotel, TQ13 9XT
moorlandhoteldartmoor.co.uk
At the foot of Haytor in the heart of Dartmoor National Park, the spacious Conservatory Restaurant is set within The Moorland Hotel and offers far-reaching views. Locally sourced ingredients dominate the modern British menu, with typical offerings including a duo of smoked duck and liver parfait, followed by lemon sole, wilted spinach, samphire, crab bisque, crab croquette, lemon oil.

Rock Inn
◎◎ MODERN BRITISH, CLASSIC
01364 661305 | TQ13 9XP
www.rock-inn.co.uk
The rustic Rock Inn's pre-Victorian air provides a welcoming backdrop to the modern European culinary style on show in its candlelit dining room. A crisp-coated duck Scotch egg with chilli jam and salad leaves is listed among the well-executed starters.

HONITON
MAP 4, ST10

The Holt Bar & Restaurant
◉ MODERN BRITISH
01404 47707 | 178 High Street, EX14 1LA
www.theholt-honiton.com
The Holt's main dining area is upstairs: open-plan, with a wooden floor, simple decor, candlelight, and pleasant, efficient service. Food is a serious commitment here and standards are consistently high, with the menu a happy blend of the traditional and more à la mode.

THE PIG at Combe
◉◉ SEASONAL BRITISH ♦ NOTABLE WINE LIST
01404 540400 | Giltisham, EX14 3AD
www.thepighotel.com/at-combe
Set in an Elizabethan mansion of honeyed stone in 3,500 acres, any hint of starchy country-house formality is banished here, so dining is an informal affair in a rustic-chic setting, and the '25 Mile' menu reveals a kitchen that gets serious on sustainability and localism, with an abundant kitchen garden for seasonal supplies and minimal food miles.

ILFRACOMBE
MAP 3, SS54

Sandy Cove Hotel
◉◉ MODERN BRITISH
01271 882243 | Old Coast Road, Combe Martin Bay, Berrynarbor, EX34 9SR
www.sandycove-hotel.co.uk
With stunning views of both the bay and the wild landscape of Exmoor, Sandy Cove Hotel offers the best of both worlds. Positioned to maximise the vista with large windows (and a terrace when the weather allows), the restaurant offers a hypnotic view.

ILSINGTON
MAP 3, SX77

Ilsington Country House Hotel
◉◉ MODERN EUROPEAN
01364 661452 | Ilsington Village, TQ13 9RR
www.ilsington.co.uk
A substantial white property, Ilsington's diverse menu includes some divertingly appealing dishes. Accompaniments complement the main ingredients without swamping them, seen in main courses of roast chicken with maple and mustard gel, pommes Anna, pea purée, mushrooms, confit tomato and smoked beetroot.

KNOWSTONE
MAP 3, SS82

The Masons Arms
◉◉ MODERN BRITISH
01398 341231 | EX36 4RY
www.masonsarmsdevon.co.uk
In the idyllic village of Knowstone, this thatched 13th-century country inn is set deep in the lush countryside on the Devon and Somerset border. Chef-patron Mark Dodson once cooked under Michel Roux at Bray, which might explain the flair and precision evident in the kitchen.

LYNMOUTH
MAP 3, SS74

Rising Sun
◉◉ BRITISH, FRENCH
01598 753223 | Harbourside, EX35 6EG
www.risingsunlynmouth.co.uk
The Rising Sun rocks with good vibrations with its bar plus an atmospheric oak-panelled dining room. The food strikes a balance between hearty generosity and contemporary combinations, with plenty of seafood dishes. Start with seared king scallops with cauliflower cream and pancetta.

MORETONHAMPSTEAD
MAP 3, SX78

Great Western
◉◉◉ MODERN BRITISH ⚑ NOTABLE WINE LIST

01647 445000 | Bovey Castle, Dartmoor National Park, North Bovey, TQ13 8RE
www.boveycastle.com
Built in 1890 by stationery supremo WH Smith, Bovey Castle was reinvented as a 'golfing hotel' by the Great Western Railway back in 1930, an association acknowledged in its top dining venue, the Great Western restaurant. It's a grand old pile, big, bold and glamorous, with a spa and golf course to boot. The Great Western is an equally plush space, suitably romantic with art deco lines. Local lad Mark Budd leads the kitchen team, and his fondness for regional ingredients from land and sea looms large in good-looking contemporary dishes that reveal well-honed technical skills and sound classical roots – from starters like roasted veal sweetbreads, new season girolles, broad beans and summer truffle to mains such as Devonshire duck with roasted peach and white carrots. Aerated white chocolate, almond milk pannacotta is one way to round things off.

Chef Mark Budd **Seats** 120, Private dining 32 **Open** All Year **Parking** 100 **Notes** Children welcome

Smith's Brasserie
◉ BRITISH

01647 445000 | Bovey Castle, Dartmoor National Park, North Bovey, TQ13 8RE
www.boveycastle.com/eat/smiths-brasserie/
Built in 1890 by retailer W H Smith, Bovey Castle has two restaurants, of which Smith's Brasserie is the more informal - but smart all the same. With some dishes clearly Mediterranean inspired, choices include tapas-style snacks, Dover sole with poached oyster, and garden vegetable and rocket risotto. The terrace overlooks the River Bovey.

OKEHAMPTON
MAP 3, SX59

Lewtrenchard Manor
◉◉ MODERN BRITISH 𝑉

01566 783222 | Lewdown, EX20 4PN
www.lewtrenchard.co.uk
In a secluded valley beneath Dartmoor, this Jacobean manor dates back to the 17th century, as the wood-panelled restaurant attests with its ornate plasterwork and heavy-framed portraits. An emphasis on local meat and fish, as well as vegetables and fruits from the manor garden, drives the modern, ingredient-led menu.

PLYMOUTH
MAP 3, SX45

Àclèaf
◉◉◉ MODERN FRENCH
See pages 100-101

See advertisement on page 103

Artillery Tower Restaurant
◉ MODERN BRITISH

01752 257610 | Firestone Bay, Durnford Street, PL1 3QR
www.artillerytower.co.uk
A 16th-century circular gunnery tower on Plymouth waterfront - be sure to grip the handrail tight as you climb the spiral staircase. Arched windows that once served as gun emplacements in three-foot walls surround the dining space, where simple, modern bistro food is the drill.

Barbican Kitchen
◉ MODERN, INTERNATIONAL

01752 604448 | Plymouth Gin Distillery, 60 Southside Street, PL1 2LQ
barbicankitchen.com
The British, European and vegetarian-friendly dishes clearly appeal to the young evening crowd in Chris and James Tanner's colourful, loft-conversion-style restaurant. At lunchtime, though, the age range is wider. The brothers' place has stood the test of time in an area that survived wartime bombing to remind one of a much older Plymouth.

Continued on page 102

MAP 3, SX45

Àclèaf

◉◉◉ MODERN FRENCH, MODERN BRITISH
01752 344455 | Boringdon Hill, Plympton, PL7 4DP
www.boringdonhall.co.uk

Splendidly luxurious setting for inventively stylish British cooking

Boringdon Hall is a fabulously historic Tudor mansion, once given to the Earl of Southampton by none less than Henry VIII, and which can only be described as splendid. Nowadays it's a comfortably luxurious country house hotel, full of charm and elegance. There's a spa, and it's also a very popular wedding venue, as one might imagine. Àclèaf is the ultimate fine dining restaurant, with tables looking out over the wonderful Great Hall. It really does offer a tangible sense of the past, with age darkened beams and a plethora of period features, and the atmosphere is nicely balanced, giving a real sense of occasion without being overly formal, while staff are well informed and genuinely engaged. And what of the food? Well, no worries here that head chef Scott Paton won't be up to the task of providing dishes as impressive as the surroundings. The seasonally led menus showcase his stylishly inventive

British cuisine, where creative yet simple combinations can be seen in dishes such as a skilful, elegant and precisely cut duck terrine with quince, or sea bass served with a seafood tortellini and a sauce subtly and fragrantly flavoured with coconut and lemongrass, before a main course of 'turbot, garlic, parsley' where a fantastic piece of turbot is joined by plump, well-flavoured mussels and a thin garlic purée with bags of flavour. A palate cleanser before dessert plays on Black Forest gâteau, a rich chocolate ganache, sweet/sour cherry gel and a fresh-tasting vanilla ice cream, with meringue for texture. Finally, duck egg tart (a rich set custard with a razor thin caramelised top and hazelnut pastry base) is a precisely composed dish, with pear (fresh and

"The seasonally led menus showcase his stylishly inventive British cuisine, where creative yet simple combinations can be seen..."

compôte) delivering all the promised flavour, accompanied by a very good hazelnut ice cream. The vegetarian and vegan options are equally enticing, and wine pairings are available.

Chef Scott Paton
Seats 40, Private dining 26
Notes No children

See advertisement on page 103

PLYMOUTH continued

The Fig Tree @ 36
◉ MODERN BRITISH *V*
01752 253247 | 36 Admiralty Street, PL1 3RU
www.thefigtreeat36.co.uk

In an area on the up, menus here change frequently, with fish and meat given equal billing. The fish, locally caught of course, appears on the specials board soon after landing. The comfortable dining area contains a happy collection of mis-matched tables and chairs, while in a courtyard is the small fig tree after which the restaurant is named.

Rock Salt Café and Brasserie
◉◉ MODERN BRITISH
01752 225522 | 31 Stonehouse Street, PL1 3PE
www.rocksaltcafe.co.uk
Tucked away on a back street, Rock Salt Café and Brasserie has a relaxed, welcoming vibe. It used to be a pub, and extends over two floors, plenty of bare wood, friendly service with a smile and great artwork for sale on the walls. Food is packed with flavour, and the whole operation is underpinned with integrity and honesty.

ROCKBEARE
MAP 3, SY09
The Jack In The Green Inn
◉◉ MODERN BRITISH
01404 822240 | EX5 2EE
www.jackinthegreen.uk.com
This family-friendly roadside pub has gained a well-deserved reputation for its upmarket modern British food. With its low-beamed rooms, soft brown leather chairs and a wood-burning stove, the smart interior creates a contemporary atmosphere and innovative menus offer smart, thoughtful dishes with punchy flavours.

SALCOMBE
MAP 3, SX73
The Jetty
◉ MODERN, INTERNATIONAL
01548 844444 | Salcombe Harbour Hotel & Spa, Cliff Road, TQ8 8JH
www.harbourhotels.co.uk/hotels/salcombe
There are fabulous views over the estuary from The Jetty's prime position within the Salcombe Harbour Hotel. The hotel's spa facilities, and even a private cinema, offer many distractions, but time is never better spent than when sitting in the smart, contemporary restaurant.

Soar Mill Cove Hotel
◉◉ MODERN BRITISH
01548 561566 | Soar Mill Cove, Marlborough, TQ7 3DS
www.soarmillcove.co.uk
With the stunning cove below, this family-run hotel occupies a fabulous position with sweeping sea views. Needless to say, local fish and seafood get a strong showing in a kitchen that combines classical techniques with modern ideas. Thus, monkfish with boulangère potatoes, mussel and clam provençale with basil purée.

SAUNTON
MAP 3, SS43
Saunton Sands Hotel
◉◉ TRADITIONAL, MODERN BRITISH
01271 890212 | EX33 1LQ
www.sauntonsands.com
The location alone is a draw at this long white art deco hotel overlooking a three-mile stretch of unspoiled sandy beach. Watch the sun set from the terrace or soak up the maritime views from the large and stylish restaurant with original 1930s chandeliers.

SIDMOUTH
MAP 3, SY18
Hotel Riviera
◉◉ MODERN BRITISH
01395 515201 | The Esplanade, EX10 8AY
www.hotelriviera.co.uk
The spotless bow-fronted Riviera is a prime example of Devon's own seaside grandeur. Terrace tables make the most of the summer weather and the traditional, elegant dining room overlooks the bay. A seasonal menu of gently modernised British cooking, with an emphasis on fresh fish dishes, caters for most tastes.

Continued on page 104

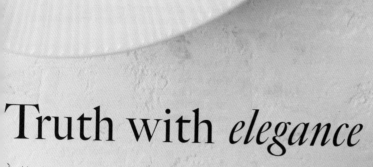

Truth with *elegance*

Àclèaf is a showcase of inventive British fare
by award-winning head chef, Scott Paton at
Boringdon Hall.

Book your table at acleaf.co.uk
or call 01752 344455

SIDMOUTH *continued*

The Salty Monk

◉◉ MODERN BRITISH *V* 🍷NOTABLE WINE LIST

01395 513174 | Church Street, Sidford, EX10 9QP

www.saltymonk.com

The name is not a reference to a seafaring friar, but rather to the building's 16th-century role as a store for the salt that the monks traded at Exeter Cathedral. The Garden Room restaurant makes a smart yet understated backdrop for the unpretentious cooking.

The Victoria Hotel

◉ TRADITIONAL

01395 512651 | The Esplanade, EX10 8RY

www.victoriahotel.co.uk

The setting at the end of the town's impressive esplanade is alluring, with the expansive bay offered up in all its shimmering glory. From the doorman to the pianist, The Victoria oozes old-world charm and what appears on the plate is generally classically minded.

SOUTH ZEAL
MAP 3, SX69

Oxenham Arms

◉ MODERN BRITISH

01837 840244 | EX20 2JT

www.oxdevon.com/

Set in deepest Dartmoor country, the historic Oxenham Arms is still the hub of village life. The place began in the 12th century as a monastery but today contemporary touches blend seamlessly with an ambience of gnarled beams, whitewashed stone walls and stone mullioned windows. A comfort-oriented menu of unfussy country inn food scores many hits.

TAVISTOCK
MAP 3, SX47

Bedford Hotel

◉ BRITISH

01822 613221 | 1 Plymouth Road, PL19 8BB

www.bedford-hotel.co.uk

Despite the castellated walls, this imposing Gothic building has always been about hospitality, and there is no lack of character or charm in the restaurant, with its moulded ceilings and panelled walls. The kitchen takes a more contemporary position, but a reassuringly gentle one.

The Horn of Plenty

◉◉ MODERN BRITISH

01822 832528 | Gulworthy, PL19 8JD

www.thehornofplenty.co.uk

With stunning views over the Tamar Valley, this charming, mid 19th-century country house hotel once belonged to the Duke of Bedford's mining chief. A team of six chefs creates award-winning cuisine, as in Creedy Carver duck terrine with slow-cooked duck egg and truffle dressing; pan-roasted hake with lobster ravioli, spinach and carrot purée; and treacle sourdough roll.

THURLESTONE
MAP 3, SX64

Thurlestone Hotel

◉◉ BRITISH

01548 560382 | TQ7 3NN

www.thurlestone.co.uk

The view across the golf course and sub-tropical gardens to the sea is a cracker, making The Trevilder restaurant a star attraction. The menu, including the daily-changing 'Market Dishes', makes good use of the region's produce in dishes that have classical foundations.

The Village Inn

◉ MODERN BRITISH

01548 563525 | Thurlestone Hotel, TQ7 3NN

www.thurlestone.co.uk

Among the original building materials of the 16th-century Village Inn are timbers from ships of the Spanish Armada wrecked off the Devon coast. It's all been sensitively spruced up, with plenty of light wood, a log burner, and an outdoor dining space by the pool.

TORQUAY
MAP 3, SX96

Cary Arms

◉ BRITISH, SEAFOOD

01803 327110 | Babbacombe Beach, TQ1 3LX

www.caryarms.co.uk

On a glorious summer's day, the terraced gardens leading to the water's edge are an unforgettable place to eat, but the whitewashed Cary Arms does have more than its fair share of good things: a beamed bar with stone walls and dreamy views.

The Elephant Restaurant by Simon Hulstone

◎◎◎ MODERN BRITISH

01803 200044 | 3–4 Beacon Terrace, TQ1 2BH

www.elephantrestaurant.co.uk

Simon Hulstone has built a well-established enterprise at this elegant venue close to Torquay marina. A split-level operation with an airy brasserie feel, service is unstuffy and the small brigade shows a maturity and confidence in its delivery of precise cooking with a purity of flavours on the plate. Orkney scallop with roasted onion, pancetta and sweetheart cabbage is an intelligent pairing and could lead on to Brixham hake, salt baked carrot, spiced croûtons, roasted carrot sauce and coriander. The innovation continues at the dessert stage with clementine cheesecake, BBQ satsuma, Thai basil ice cream and olive oil biscuit.

Chef Simon Hulstone Seats 75 Closed 1st 2 weeks in January Notes Children welcome

Grand Hotel

◎ MODERN EUROPEAN

01803 296677 | Torbay Road, TQ2 6NT

www.grandtorquay.co.uk

Occupying a prime position on Torquay's seafront, the Grand certainly has presence, built in Victorian times and expanding as the popularity of the English Riviera grew. The main dining option is the 1881 Restaurant, its genteel formality in keeping with its august past (Agatha Christie spent her honeymoon here). The menu sticks to traditional ideas with just enough contemporary thrust to satisfy both schools.

The Imperial Hotel

◎ MODERN BRITISH

01803 294301 | Park Hill Road, TQ1 2DG

www.theimperialtorquay.co.uk

The Imperial's Victorian founders couldn't have chosen a better spot for their hotel, whose clifftop position has wide-ranging views over the bay and Channel. The kitchen chooses its ingredients diligently, making good use of fish and local produce, and turns out well-considered, carefully-timed dishes.

Orestone Manor

◎◎ MODERN, EUROPEAN 𝒱

01803 897511 | Rockhouse Lane, Maidencombe, TQ1 4SX

www.orestonemanor.com

This handsome Georgian manor house occupies landscaped grounds overlooking Lyme Bay. The main restaurant is a relaxing space with wooden table tops and tartan accents – a suitable setting for the kitchen's ambitious à la carte menus. Classic French-accented technique delivers refined dishes with affordable set price menus.

Seasons

◎◎ MODERN BRITISH

01803 226366 | Belgrave Sands Hotel & Spa, Belgrave Road, TQ2 5HF

www.belgravesands.com

Set in the Belgrave Sands Hotel, just a stone's throw from the seafront, Seasons restaurant is a bright, comfortable space, with unclothed, dark wood tables and live music in the evenings. Contemporary British cooking features on the six-course menu, with particular attention paid to seasonality.

TOTNES

MAP 3, SX86

Gather NEW

◎ MODERN BRITISH

01803 866666 | 50 Fore Street, TQ9 5RP

www.gathertotnes.com/

Originally a pop-up, Gather now has permanent premises. The young, enthusiastic team trained together in the Michael Caines Academy at Exeter College and it's great to see them doing so well. The dining room is inviting, with big plate glass windows and an open kitchen, and the approach is genuine, with a particular interest in foraged and less well-known produce, making for light, elegant and flavour-driven dishes. One to watch.

The Riverford Field Kitchen

◎ MODERN BRITISH, ORGANIC

01803 762074 | Riverford, TQ11 0JU

www.riverford.co.uk

Wash Farm is the hub of the Riverford brand, delivering organically grown fruit and veg across the land. Hunker down here at communal tables for hearty organic food, a fixed deal of whatever is on-the-money that day – dishes are always teeming with superlative vegetable and fresh salad accompaniments.

TWO BRIDGES
MAP 3, SX67
Two Bridges Hotel
◉◉ MODERN BRITISH
01822 892300 | PL20 6SW
www.twobridges.co.uk
Deep in the Dartmoor National Park, the Tors restaurant in this character riverside hotel was refurbished in 2019. Local farmers and fishermen supply the kitchen with top notch produce for modern British dishes like Devon crab ravioli, bisque, brown shrimp and crayfish or Creedy Carver duck, red cabbage, pink peppercorn and pistachio praline.

WOOLACOMBE
MAP 3, SS44
Doyle's Restaurant
◉◉ MODERN BRITISH
01271 870388 | The Woolacombe Bay Hotel, South Street, EX34 7BN
www.woolacombe-bay-hotel.co.uk

Doyle's Restaurant, part of the mid-Victorian Woolacombe Bay Hotel, looks west across the sea. With its lofty ceilings, elegant columns and dark grey and pewter tones, the word 'striking' comes to mind. Particular dishes to note include pan-fried turbot, roasted rack of West Country lamb and, occasionally, Lundy Island lobster and crab. Five-course suppers are served from Thursday to Saturday.

Watersmeet Hotel
◉◉ TRADITIONAL BRITISH, EUROPEAN
01271 870333 | Mortehoe, EX34 7EB
www.watersmeethotel.co.uk
Surfers hang loose in the Atlantic below as diners enjoy the attentive, uniformed service of the hotel's clifftop Pavilion Restaurant. A frequently-changing menu of British cooking might suggest a three-course meal of wild mushroom and egg-yolk ravioli; halibut fillet with oyster emulsion and bacon; and vanilla pannacotta, cherry compôte and meringues.

■ DORSET

BEAMINSTER
MAP 4, ST40
Brassica Restaurant
◉ MODERN EUROPEAN V
01308 538100 | 4 The Square, DT8 3AS
www.brassicarestaurant.co.uk
On the main square, Brassica occupies a Grade II listed property overlooking the hubbub (or what passes for hubbub) of this small market town. Chef-director Cass Titcombe draws on a wealth of experience to deliver a daily-changing menu of local ingredients and broader European ideas.

The Ollerod NEW
◉◉◉ MODERN BRITISH
01308 862200 | 3 Prout Bridge, DT8 3AY
www.theollerod.co.uk
Ollerod is a dialect word for 'cowslip', and this charming, quirky building dates largely to the 13th century. Full of character, it offers plenty of period details, as well as contemporary furnishings and decor. Local art and photography can often be seen on display, and there's a real emphasis on the best local and seasonal produce, with fish and seafood from the Dorset coast. A summer menu might feature refreshing ajo blanco – a chilled almond soup with crab, mango and grapes, followed by an equally refreshing dish of salmon ceviche with avocado mousse. Finish with an elderflower cream with poached gooseberries and a mini doughnut.

Chef Chris Staines **Open** All Year

BOURNEMOUTH
MAP 5, SZ09
The Crab at Bournemouth
◉◉ MODERN BRITISH
01202 203601 | Park Central Hotel, Exeter Road, BH2 5AJ
www.crabatbournemouth.com
The epitome of a seafront venue, The Crab is part of the white-fronted Park Central Hotel, but functions as a restaurant in its own right, smartly done out in sandy hues. An array of fresh fish and shellfish is on the menu.

Cumberland Hotel

◎◎ MODERN BRITISH

01202 290722 | 27 East Overcliffe Drive, BH1 3AF

www.cumberlandbournemouth.co.uk

High up on Bournemouth's East Cliff, this art deco hotel boasts all the monochrome touches of that decadent period. Not that the cooking in the hotel's elegant Ventana Grand Café restaurant is stuck in the 1930s – the food is modern British to the core. As befits a hotel with panoramic sea views, fish gets a strong showing.

The Green House

◎◎ MODERN BRITISH

01202 498900 | 4 Grove Road, BH1 3AX

www.thegreenhousehotel.co.uk

The Green House is a striking-looking, centrally located property converted and run on sustainable principles. There are beehives on the roof, and the Arbor (Latin for 'tree' to further underline its green credentials) Restaurant deals in only organic, Fairtrade and farm-assured, mostly local produce.

Hermitage Hotel

◎ TRADITIONAL BRITISH

01202 557363 | Exeter Road, BH2 5AH

www.hermitage-hotel.co.uk

Hardy's Restaurant at the Hermitage, opposite the beach, is a large, traditionally styled room. The interesting menus serve local and sustainable ingredients and offer variety aplenty, as they must with residents eating here perhaps every evening.

No 34 at The Orchid Hotel

◎ EUROPEAN

01202 551600 | 34 Gervis Road, BH1 3DH

www.orchidhotel.co.uk

Close to the beach, No 34 is the flagship restaurant at The Orchid, a contemporary and secluded hotel in Bournemouth's lovely Eastcliff area. The kitchen cuts no corners when it comes to sourcing premium ingredients, much of it sourced from the region.

Roots

◎◎ MODERN EUROPEAN

01202 430005 | 141 Belle Vue Road, BH6 3EN

www.restaurantroots.co.uk

The food at Roots is simple, confident and effective. Service is charming, passionate and knowledgeable, and a key part of the experience. Monthly changing tasting menus, either 5- or 7-course, feature well-executed dishes with punchy flavours.

CHRISTCHURCH *MAP 5, SZ19*

Captain's Club Hotel & Spa

◎◎ MODERN EUROPEAN *V*

01202 475111 | Wick Ferry, Wick Lane, BH23 1HU

www.captainsclubhotel.com

A glass-fronted boutique hotel by the River Stour, where the kitchen serves up modern brasserie fare, fully in keeping with the attractive surroundings. Veggie possibilities include an Indian-spiced cauliflower risotto with coconut and coriander, and the desserts include some crowd-pleasing choices.

The Jetty

◎◎ MODERN BRITISH ♦NOTABLE WINE LIST

01202 400950 | Christchurch Harbour Hotel & Spa, 95 Mudeford, BH23 3NT

www.thejetty.co.uk

A dashing contemporary construction of glass and wood, The Jetty's culinary output is headed up by Alex Aitken. Provenance is everything here. In fine weather, grab a table on the terrace if you can, although floor-to-ceiling windows provide glorious views over Mudeford Quay. The kitchen turns out contemporary dishes taking inspiration from far and wide.

CHRISTCHURCH continued

The Lord Bute & Restaurant

◉◉ BRITISH, MEDITERRANEAN

01425 278884 | 179-181 Lymington Road,
Highcliffe-on-Sea, BH23 4JS

www.lordbute.com

In the grounds of 18th-century prime minister
Lord Bute's Highcliffe Castle, this hotel has
wonderful neighbours – east Dorset's golden
beaches. Among highlights on the classical
restaurant and orangery menu are fillet of
Jurassic Coast beef stuffed with mushrooms;
pan-seared halibut, king prawns, garlic and
chilli; and roasted vegetables, spinach,
asparagus and mozzarella.

Upper Deck Bar & Restaurant

◉ MODERN BRITISH

01202 400954 | Christchurch Harbour Hotel
& Spa, 95 Mudeford, BH23 3NT

www.christchurch-harbour-hotel.co.uk/upper-deck

Good views over the water are guaranteed, as is
a fine showing of regional produce. The Upper
Deck is pretty swanky, featuring a sleek,
contemporary bar and an upmarket seasidey
vibe, plus there's a terrace. The cooking takes a
modern British route through contemporary
tastes and, given the setting, plenty of locally-
landed fish.

CORFE CASTLE   MAP 4, SY98

Mortons Manor

◉◉ MODERN BRITISH

01929 480988 | 45 East Street, BH20 5EE

www.mortonsmanor.com

The restaurant at Mortons Manor is traditional in
style, an elegance without being too over
elaborate, and somewhere where guests are no
doubt looking forward to getting back to for a
satisfying dinner after a hard day walking the
coastal paths. Overall, a reassuring environment
with service also understated and sincere. Very
assured cooking here from a chef who knows the
market well. Expect quality produce very much at
the heart of the dishes.

EVERSHOT   MAP 4, ST50

The Acorn Inn

◉ BRITISH

01935 83228 | 28 Fore Street, DT2 0JW

www.acorn-inn.co.uk

Plumb in the middle of Thomas Hardy's favourite
stretch of England, the 16th-century coaching
inn makes an appearance in *Tess of the
d'Urbervilles* as the Sow and Acorn. The country-
style restaurant is a friendly spot to linger and
enjoy the seasonal dishes.

Summer Lodge Country House Hotel, Restaurant & Spa

◉◉◉ MODERN BRITISH 🔖NOTABLE WINE LIST

01935 482000 | Fore Street, DT2 0JR

www.summerlodgehotel.com

In the heart of Hardy's Dorset, picturesque
Summer Lodge Country House Hotel, Restaurant
& Spa prides itself on using as much local
produce as possible. Chef Steven Titman is
blessed to work with an abundance of
ingredients grown in the hotel's kitchen garden
and his 'field to fork' philosophy means he has
forged close links with local farmers and fish
suppliers who supply Dorset beef and Lyme Bay
mackerel. Grab a table in the refined restaurant
and light-filled conservatory (or al fresco on the
terrace in summer), and leave the rest to the
well-trained front-of-house team, for whom
nothing is too much trouble. The cooking here is
assured and based on solid technical
foundations. Portland crab, compressed mango,
avocado purée and natural yogurt is an opener
boasting harmonious flavours and textures. It
might be followed with loin of Dorset lamb, crispy
sweetbreads, confit new potatoes and wild garlic
aïoli. Valrhona Dulcey Crémeux Manjari Sorbet,
nibbed cocoa tuile and white chocolate 'Aero' is
an intricate and satisfying finale.

Chef Steven Titman **Seats** 60, Private dining 20 **Open** All
Year **Parking** 60 **Notes** Children welcome

MAIDEN NEWTON
MAP 4, SY59

Le Petit Canard

⊛ MODERN BRITISH, FRENCH

01300 320536 | Dorchester Road, DT2 0BE

www.le-petit-canard.co.uk

Le Petit Canard is a former coaching inn with low beams, a comforting ambience and strong local patronage. Ownership has been in the same hands for nearly 20 years, and the food offers honesty and integrity. Expect simple and uncluttered dishes that shine a spotlight on the excellence of fine Dorset produce. Front-of-house is engaging and affable.

POOLE
MAP 4, SZ09

Hotel du Vin Poole

⊛ MODERN BRITISH, FRENCH 🍷NOTABLE WINE LIST

01202 785578 | Mansion House, Thames Street, BH15 1JN

www.hotelduvin.com/locations/poole/

Hotel du Vin's Poole outpost is a bit of a landmark just off the quayside, a creeper-covered Georgian mansion. As expected, the kitchen deals in crowd-pleasing brasserie staples from over the Channel, all cooked just so. Start perhaps with escargots in garlic and herb butter.

Rick Stein Sandbanks

⊛ SEAFOOD 🍷NOTABLE WINE LIST

01202 283280 | 10-14 Banks Road, BH13 7QB

www.rickstein.com

The globetrotting Mr Stein needs no introduction and he's picked a promising spot in well-heeled Sandbanks for another outpost of the ever-expanding empire. The food bears the Stein imprint, nothing too elaborate, just light-touch treatment to let the quality of the produce strut its stuff.

SHERBORNE
MAP 4, ST61

The Green

⊛⊛ MODERN EUROPEAN

01935 813821 | 3 The Green, DT9 3HY

www.greenrestaurant.co.uk

The Green, a charming Grade II listed building in the centre of picturesque Sherborne, sets its sights on locally and ethically-sourced raw materials. Quality ingredients are evident throughout, and menus are thoughtfully constructed, offering contemporary dishes with classic roots, inspired by the seasons.

SHERBORNE continued

The Kings Arms
◉ MODERN BRITISH
01963 220281 | Charlton Herethorne, DT9 4NL
www.thekingsarms.co.uk
Sarah and Tony Lethbridge have given this stone-built inn, first licensed in the Regency era, a thoroughly modern makeover, though not to the detriment of its original charm. Sarah heads up the kitchen, capitalising on West Country produce, as well as drying and curing meats.

Seasons Restaurant at The Eastbury
◉◉ MODERN BRITISH V
01935 813131 | Long Street, DT9 3BY
theeastburyhotel.co.uk
Seasons Restaurant at the Eastbury overlooks the delightful walled garden, which has a dining pod for outdoor eating. However, the garden's not just for show, it's where the kitchen team grows much of the excellent produce they use. Despite the local focus of the ingredients, the menu is a bit of a globe-trotter, pulling influences and flavours from all over.
See advertisement opposite

STUDLAND *MAP 5, SZ08*

THE PIG on the Beach
◉◉ MODERN BRITISH ⚘NOTABLE WINE LIST
01929 450288 | The Manor House, Manor Road,
BH19 3AU
www.thepighotel.com
One of a litter of PIG hotels, this particular porker has its own kitchen garden, and raises its own chickens and quails, while fish and seafood are locally landed. A menu grouping dishes as Piggy Bits, Fishy Bits and so on, might feature crispy brawn, crab bake, New Forest celeriac risotto, and rhubarb and custard ice cream.

WEST BEXINGTON *MAP 4, SY58*

The Club House
◉ MODERN SEAFOOD
01308 898302 | Beach Road, DT2 9DF
www.theclubhousewestbexington.co.uk

Built in 1932, and previously a 'seaside cafe', the Club House has turned into a smart, relaxed venue that looks out onto Chesil Beach. Menus feature plenty of local seafood, along with an eclectic mix of other choices. Dishes change daily depending on the local catch, but many favourites endure. If you've got a helicopter, you can land it here.

WYKE REGIS *MAP 4, SY67*

Crab House Café
◉ BRITISH, SEAFOOD
01305 788867 | Ferrymans Way, Portland Road,
DT4 9YU
www.crabhousecafe.co.uk
Situated in a spruced up wooden hut overlooking Chesil Beach, the Crab House Café has natural charms aplenty. Simplicity and freshness is the name of the game, with oysters coming from their own beds and everything sourced from within a 40-mile radius. Rustic benches outside are a treat in the warmer months.

Time to Relax

THE EASTBURY

5 STAR ACCOMMODATION
AWARD WINNING SEASONS ⚫⚫ RESTAURANT
SHERBORNE, DORSET

Spa

LURY ROOMS | COTTAGE | BOUTIQUE SPA | FINE DINING | LOVELY GARDENS

Winner
Luxury Value Hotel"
in England
dé Nast Johansens
ders Awards 2020

CONDÉ NAST
johansens
Luxury Hotels · Spas · Venues
AWARD
WINNER
2020

"Two hours and a world away from London"
Country and Townhouse 2019
"...a friendly team of staff,
delicious food and walled garden"
Sawdays 2019
"Touch of class"
Dorset Living 2019

The Eastbury is a luxury Georgian country house style hotel with a unique boutique spa, country gardens and the award-winning Seasons ⚫⚫ restaurant. Set in the glorious Dorset countryside, adjoining the attractive ancient market town of Sherborne.

www.theeastburyhotel.co.uk   Tel: 01935 813131
relax@theeastburyhotel.co.uk

■ COUNTY DURHAM

BARNARD CASTLE
MAP 19, NZ01

The Morritt Country House Hotel & Spa
@@ MODERN FRENCH
01833 627232 | Greta Bridge, DL12 9SE
www.themorritt.co.uk
The arrival of transport by mail coach in the 18th century saw this former farm develop into an overnight stop for travellers between London and Carlisle. Charles Dickens probably stayed here in 1839, hence the fine-dining restaurant is named after him.

DARLINGTON
MAP 19, NZ21

The Brasserie
@ MODERN BRITISH
01325 729999 | Rockliffe Hall, Rockliffe Park, Hurworth-on-Tees, DL2 2DU
www.rockliffehall.com
The Brasserie at Rockliffe Hall is a modern space, very light with large windows down one side overlooking the garden. The colour scheme is grey and brown with all furniture dark wood and some banquette seating lining the walls. There's quite a relaxed atmosphere at lunch time, as it's also used for spa lunches. Expect seasonal menus and modern British cooking. Of course, there's also the Orangery for more formal dining.

The Orangery
@@@ MODERN BRITISH ♨NOTABLE WINE LIST
01325 729999 | Rockliffe Hall, Rockliffe Park, Hurworth-on-Tees, DL2 2DU
www.rockliffehall.com
Guests are spoilt for leisure pursuits at this impressive Georgian country mansion, from indulgence in the luxurious spa to tackling its 18-hole championship golf course, and a trio of restaurants. Cream of the crop is The Orangery, where gilded wrought-iron columns soar upwards to a glass roof in a romantic Gothic-inspired space, and a large wall of windows opens up sweeping views across the gardens and the action on the fairways. It's an exceedingly pleasant place to linger. Main courses might include salt-aged lamb, broccoli, ewes curd and tomato or poached turbot, alliums, mussels and buttermilk followed by English strawberry, miso, white chocolate and pistachio.

Chef Gary Duffy **Seats** 60, Private dining 20 **Open** All Year **Parking** 300 **Notes** Children welcome

DURHAM
MAP 19, NZ24

Fusion Restaurant
@ PAN-ASIAN, THAI
0191 386 5282 | Ramside Hall Hotel Golf & Spa, Carrville, DH1 1TD
www.ramsidehallhotel.co.uk
Surrounded by 350 acres of grounds including two 18-hole championship golf courses at Ramside Hall, the restaurant at the hotel's spa serves southeast Asian-inspired food throughout the day. Overlooking the spa's thermal suite, the Oriental-styled restaurant combines the dishes of Thailand, Japan and China including 'Make Your Own Bento Box'.

The Rib Room
@ INTERNATIONAL
0191 386 5282 | Ramside Hall Hotel Golf & Spa, Carrville, DH1 1TD
www.ramsidehallhotel.co.uk
Sprawling outwards from a largely Victorian house, is Ramside's glossy spa and health club. Culinary options run from straightforward carvery dishes to the menu in the brasserie-style Rib Room, a temple to slabs of locally-reared 28-day aged beef.

SEAHAM
MAP 19, NZ44

Seaham Hall - The Dining Room
@@ MODERN BRITISH ♨NOTABLE WINE LIST
0191 516 1400 | Seaham Hall, Lord Byron's Walk, SR7 7AG
www.seaham-hall.co.uk
Lord Byron was a former guest at Seaham Hall, an imposing building close to the cliffs. The interior design is stunning, displaying a commitment to the best of old and new. The restaurant has a similar ethic, with a mixture of semi-circular booths and individual tables. The menu is big on meaty modern British dishes.

See advertisement opposite

THE DINING ROOM

The Dining Room is where you can sample the best of modern British fare in a fabulous setting. With the rugged North Sea facing us and the glorious countryside all around, we have the finest ingredients right on our doorstep. Our seasonal menus draw inspiration from the region we love, and our dishes are varied, tasty and a little quirky.

AA
Rosette award for culinary excellence
2021

Seaham Hall
Lord Byron's Walk, Seaham, County Durham, England, SR7 7AG

0191 516 1400
hotel@seaham-hall.com
seaham-hall.co.uk

SEAHAM HALL

PRIDE OF BRITAIN HOTELS

SEDGEFIELD
MAP 19, NZ32

The Impeccable Pig NEW
◉ MODERN BRITISH
01740 582 580 | Front Street, TS21 3AT
www.impeccablepig.co.uk
With a mix of banquette seating, booths and deep, comfortable dining chairs you'll always be comfy eating at the Impeccable Pig, a Grade II listed building that's been transformed into an operation delivering great brasserie-style dining. Tables in the bar area have a view of the kitchen, where the chefs can be seen plying their trade. Josper grill cooking features heavily.

■ ESSEX

BRAINTREE
MAP 7, TL72

The Chophouse Braintree
◉ MODERN, CLASSIC BRITISH
01376 345615 | 34 New Street, CM7 1ES
www.thechophousebraintree.co.uk

Choose between bistro-style dining and a more formal experience here at The Chophouse Braintree. Service is just the right mix of relaxed and attentive, and the modern British menu offers simple, unfussy cookery, using ingredients sourced within a 30-mile radius where possible. Also a good spot if you like live music, particularly jazz.

BRENTWOOD
MAP 6, TQ59

Marygreen Manor Hotel
◉◉ MODERN EUROPEAN
01277 225252 | London Road, CM14 4NR
www.marygreenmanor.co.uk
Although the house is older than the 17th century, it was then that its owner named it 'Manor of Mary Green', after his young bride. Its many original features include exposed beams, carved panelling and the impressive Tudors Restaurant, where classic and traditional cooking holds sway, typically pork fillet and belly; and bouillabaisse.

CHELMSFORD
MAP 6, TL70

Samphire Restaurant
◉ BRITISH, MEDITERRANEAN
01245 455700 | County Hotel, 29 Rainsford Road, CM1 2PZ
countyhotelchelmsford.co.uk/food-drink/samphire-restaurant
The County Hotel has a cheery modern style, as typified in the Samphire Restaurant, where oak floors and leather seats in summery pastel hues of mustard, mint and tangerine add colour to the neutral, contemporary decor. Uncomplicated modern British and European cooking is the kitchen's stock-in-trade.

COGGESHALL
MAP 7, TL82

Ranfield's Brasserie
◉◉ MODERN BRITISH
01376 561453 | 4-6 Stoneham Street, CO6 1TT
www.ranfieldsbrasserie.co.uk
A fixture of the local dining scene for almost 30 years, its setting may be a 16th-century timbered house but there's nothing old about the approach. The mood is laid-back and cosmopolitan, and the decor akin to an eclectic art gallery with antique linen-clothed tables.

COLCHESTER
MAP 13, TL92

Church Street Tavern
◉◉ MODERN BRITISH ⌷NOTABLE WINE LIST
01206 564325 | 3 Church Street, CO1 1NF
www.churchstreettavern.co.uk
Just off the main shopping mayhem, the handsome Victorian former bank building has been repurposed as a trendy bar and first-floor restaurant full of light and artwork. Bare tables, banquettes and wood floors fit the smart-casual mood, and the seasonal menu is brim full of up-to-date ideas.

Cloisters

◎◎ MODERN BRITISH

01206 575913 | GreyFriars, High Street, CO1 1UG
www.greyfriarscolchester.co.uk
Cloisters restaurant is in the 20th-century part
of GreyFriars Hotel, once a Franciscan
monastery. Parquet floored with an art deco feel,
it's known for modern European dishes with a
British touch. Proving irresistible, perhaps, might
be a starter of oysters from Mersea Island nine
miles away.

DEDHAM
MAP 13, TM03

milsoms

◎ MODERN BRITISH *V*

01206 322795 | Stratford Road, CO7 6HN
www.milsomhotels.com
A contemporary brasserie in a creeper-covered
house in a pretty Essex village, the menu at
Milsoms offers everything from posh lunchtime
sandwiches to grilled steaks. Dressed crab and
Melba toast followed by fried buttermilk chicken
burger is one way to go. Leave room for the milk
chocolate and caramel mousse.

The Sun Inn

◎◎ MODERN BRITISH, MEDITERRANEAN ⚑NOTABLE
WINE LIST

01206 323351 | High Street, CO7 6DF
www.thesuninndedham.com
The Sun is a 15th-century village inn with open
fires, doughty timbers and panelling. Its culinary
leanings are distinctly Italian, with the kitchen
turning fresh produce and quality ingredients
such as cured meats, cheeses and oils into
uncomplicated, well-executed dishes.

Le Talbooth

◎◎◎ MODERN BRITISH *V* ⚑NOTABLE
WINE LIST

01206 323150 | Gun Hill, CO7 6HP
www.milsomhotels.com/letalbooth
The former toll house by the River Stour dates
from Tudor times, and the Milsom family have
pretty impressive staying power too, having run
this East Anglian stalwart for over half a century.
Sitting out on the canopy-shaded terrace
overlooking pretty gardens with the river running
by, what's not to like? Inside, the look is smartly
formal, setting white-linened tables and neutral,
contemporary shades against the period
character of leaded mullioned windows and bare
beams soaring to the roof. The kitchen stays
abreast of culinary trends, sending out modern
dishes full of precision and inspiration. Coffee
caramel and Jerusalem artichoke purée support

a duo of pan-seared scallops and pork belly, as a
prelude to a veal dish, the sirloin butter-roasted,
and sweetbreads served in open ravioli with wild
garlic, pommes soufflées and peppercorn sauce.
An inventive dessert teams a Black Forest soufflé
with Kirsch-soaked chocolate sponge, vanilla
Chantilly and black cherry sorbet.

Chef Andrew Hirst, Ian Rhodes **Seats** 80, Private
dining 34 **Open** All Year **Prices from** S £13, M £22.50,
D £9.50 **Parking** 50 **Notes** Children welcome

EPPING
MAP 6, TL40

Haywards Restaurant

◎◎◎ MODERN EUROPEAN *V*

See page 116

FEERING
MAP 7, TL82

The Blue Anchor NEW

◎ MODERN BRITISH

01376 571783 | 132 Feering Hill, CO5 9PY
www.theblueanchorfeering.co.uk
The Blue Anchor is a cosily welcoming converted
16th-century coaching inn, complete with plenty
of traditional features, including exposed brick
and beautiful ancient beams. A seasonally
changing modern British menu is the style here
– with classic combinations such as pan-fried
Barbary duck breast with five spice and honey
and soy ginger dressing and vanilla pannacotta
with poached rhubarb and caramelised apple.

GREAT TOTHAM
MAP 7, TL81

The Bull & Willow Room at Great Totham

◎ MODERN, TRADITIONAL BRITISH

01621 893385 | 2 Maldon Road, CM9 8NH
www.thebullatgreattotham.co.uk
This 16th-century village inn has an uncommonly
posh eating area, the Willow Room, where the
kitchen produces a repertoire of modern dishes.
Opt for a pub classic such as Atlantic prawn
cocktail or a plate of goats' cheese mousse,
blackberry poached pear and endive salad.

EPPING

Haywards Restaurant

⊛⊛⊛ MODERN EUROPEAN *V*
01992 577350 | 111 Bell Common, CM16 4DZ
www.haywardsrestaurant.co.uk

Occupying a converted coach house on the fringes of Epping Forest, this smart, family-run restaurant looks the rustic-chic part with its high vaulted ceiling, polished wooden tables and floors and tasteful, local photographs of Epping Forest. Service is attentive, and the focus here is high quality food that is imaginatively composed and isn't afraid to doff its cap to places further afield. The kitchen draws on regional ingredients to deliver a repertoire of sprightly ideas, kicking off with a complex dish of scallop, dashi, onion and oyster. Follow that with a succulent roasted venison fillet, radicchio, blackberries, potato and swede dauphinoise, swede and honey purée. Or, if fish is your thing, try the slow-cooked monkfish with parsley crumb, sweet potato purée and chorizo foam. Finish with a dessert simply called 'chocolate, hazelnut, milk' - an aerated chocolate and hazelnut mousse encased in a thin chocolate shell.

Chef Jahdre Hayward Seats 48, Private dining 14 Closed 26 December - 12 January Parking 24 Notes No children under 10 years

GREAT YELDHAM
MAP 13, TL73

The White Hart
◎◎ BRITISH, EUROPEAN
01787 237250 | Poole Street, CO9 4HJ
www.whitehartweddingvenue.co.uk
Dating back to the Tudor era, this is a classic timbered country inn set in extensive grounds. Crisp white napery and quality tableware confer distinctive class on the dining room, where the menu might offer salt marsh lamb stuffed with haggis alongside a pink noisette and a kidney.

HARWICH
MAP 13, TM23

The Pier at Harwich
◎◎ MODERN BRITISH, SEAFOOD V
01255 241212 | The Quay, CO12 3HH
www.milsomhotels.com
Right on the quayside, The Pier provides super-fresh seafood. You can dine in the first-floor brasserie and take the air on the balcony seating. Chargrilled Dedham Vale steaks are on offer, but Harwich crab and lobsters make for stiff competition.

HOWE STREET
MAP 6, TL61

Galvin Green Man
◎◎ MODERN BRITISH V
01245 408820 | Main Road, CM3 1BG
www.galvingreenman.com

Pulling in foodies from all over, Galvin Green Man is operated by Essex-born brothers, Chris and Jeff, and offers an outstanding modern British menu. It dates back to the 14th century, and has kept plenty of original features. The dining room is very smart, with a feature timber ceiling and glass roof, and the River Chelmer runs through the garden.

ORSETT
MAP 6, TQ68

The Garden Brasserie
◎ MODERN BRITISH
01375 891402 | Orsett Hall Hotel, Restaurant & Spa, Prince Charles Avenue, RM16 3HS
www.orsetthall.co.uk
The 17th-century Orsett Hall was rebuilt, phoenix like, following a fire a decade ago. Its floral-inspired Garden Brasserie is beautiful, with super views of the landscaped grounds, or if you just want a snack, Café Sartoria awaits.

SAFFRON WALDEN
MAP 12, TL53

The Cricketers Arms NEW
◎ MODERN BRITISH V
01799 619260 | Rickling Green, CB11 3YG
www.thecricketersarmspub.co.uk
The Cricketers Arms is exactly as you'd imagine. A pub overlooking the green, with relaxed dining throughout. There's a mixture of dining areas and seating, while service is informal, yet still attentive. The menu features plenty of top-quality, beautifully presented options, but the rump of lamb is really something special.

SOUTHEND-ON-SEA
MAP 7, TQ88

Holiday Inn Southend
◎ TRADITIONAL BRITISH
01702 543001 | 77 Eastwoodbury Crescent, SS2 6XG
www.hisouthend.com/dining
Calling all plane spotting foodies: both of your interests can be indulged in one fell swoop at the fifth-floor 1935 Restaurant overlooking the aviation action at Southend Airport. Naturally enough, soundproofing is of the highest order, and there's a real sense of occasion.

The Roslin Beach Hotel
◎◎ BRITISH
01702 586375 | Thorpe Esplanade, Thorpe Bay, SS1 3BG
www.roslinhotel.com
If you do like to be beside the seaside, The Roslin Beach Hotel has a sea-facing terrace, plus indoor space shielded by glass, so it is beach ready whatever the weather. The tables are dressed up in white linen and there's a buzzy ambience.

STOCK *MAP 6, T069*

Ellis's Restaurant
◉ MODERN BRITISH
01277 829990 | Greenwoods Hotel & Spa,
Stock Road, CM4 9BE
www.greenwoodshotel.co.uk
An appealing 17th-century, Grade II listed building
set in expansive landscaped gardens,
Greenwoods Hotel is just a few minutes from
Billericay town centre. Named after the manor
house's previous owner, the hotel's contemporary
Ellis's Restaurant offers a pleasing array of
innovative, fuss-free dishes.

The Hoop
◉ MODERN BRITISH
01277 841137 | High Street, CM4 9BD
www.thehoop.co.uk

The Hoop is an atmospheric, weatherboarded
pub between Basildon and Chelmsford, and the
restaurant is upstairs. Lots of exposed rafters
that were apparently salvaged from redundant
warships, and a menu of well-executed pub
classics with global influences that lean mostly
toward the French and Italian. Service is
relatively formal but still very friendly.

THORPE-LE-SOKEN *MAP 7, TM12*

Bell Inn Bistro NEW
◉◉ BRITISH
01255 861199 | High Street, CO16 0DY
www.bellinnbistro.com/
The Bell Inn Bistro is a refurbed high street pub
with an interesting history, and plenty of original
features. It's popular with the locals, but is also
something of a destination for foodies. A small
but committed team produces hearty and well-
executed meals. Almost everything on the
seasonal menu is gluten-free or has a gluten-
free option.

Harry's Bar & Restaurant
◉ MODERN BRITISH
01255 860250 | High Street, CO16 0EA
www.harrysbarandrestaurant.co.uk
It may be a long way from the original Harry's Bar
in Venice but this Essex village namesake offers
a similarly relaxed and stylish brasserie
ambience. The seasonally-changing menu
combines modern British dishes with more
global influences. The wine list covers the world's
best regions.

■ GLOUCESTERSHIRE

ALMONDSBURY *MAP 4, ST68*

The Curious Kitchen at Aztec Hotel & Spa
◉◉ MODERN BRITISH
01454 201090 | Aztec West, BS32 4TS
www.aztechotelbristol.co.uk/food-drink
Offering a full package of spa activities and
business facilities, the Aztec also has a
restaurant and bar which is worth a visit.
It's a contemporary alpine chalet-style space,
with a high-vaulted ceiling, leather seating
and a terrace for alfresco dining. The menu
takes a broad sweep through comfort-oriented
modern ideas.

BIBURY *MAP 5, SP10*

The Brasserie
◉ MODERN BRITISH
01285 740695 | Swan Hotel, GL7 5NW
www.cotswold-inns-hotels.co.uk
If you're already liking the sound of a former
coaching inn beside the River Coln, then throw in
the proposition of welcoming service and British
cooking with a European accent, and the
brasserie of the Swan Hotel is a shoo-in. Hearty,
no-nonsense cooking is the deal; especially hard
to resist is local Bibury trout fresh from the river.

BUCKLAND
MAP 10, SP03

Buckland Manor
◉◉◉ MODERN, CLASSIC BRITISH ⚑NOTABLE WINE LIST

01386 852626 | WR12 7LY

www.bucklandmanor.co.uk

Buckland Manor is a grand 13th-century manor house in 10 acres of beautiful, well-kept gardens with a stream and a waterfall. Public areas are furnished with fine antiques and rich fabrics, and log fires warm the lounges. The elegant dining room, with views over the Vale of Evesham, is where to enjoy cooking that's English at its core, maybe roast fillet of Longhorn beef with sweetcorn, girolles and Madeira, or Cornish sea bass with crab and garden verbena sauce. Fresh herbs are grown in the Manor's grounds and – only to be expected in such a house – there's a magnificent wine cellar.

Chef Will Guthrie **Seats** 40, Private dining 14 **Open** All Year **Parking** 20 **Notes** No children under 10 years

CHELTENHAM
MAP 10, SO92

Le Champignon Sauvage
◉◉◉◉ MODERN FRENCH

01242 573449 | 24–28 Suffolk Road, GL50 2AQ

www.lechampignonsauvage.co.uk

In its fourth decade of operations, Le Champignon Sauvage is a remarkable testament to the tenacity and dedication of David and Helen Everitt-Matthias. It has remained in the upper echelons of British gastronomy throughout, achieving its longevity without any attention-grabbing culinary stunts. The interior is prospect of blond wood and dove-grey, with striking artworks and trimly linened table, creates a civilised, discreet feel. The cooking, for all its modern ingredients and techniques, retains an underlying sense of classical French cuisine. You might begin with fillet of Cornish mackerel, kohlrabi, avocado purée and caviar, or Dexter beef tartare with corned beef, wasabi mayonnaise and pickled shimeji; perhaps followed by Brecon venison with parsnip purée, baby parsnips, black pudding and bitter chocolate, or red legged partridge with turnip choucroute, walnuts and quince. Delightfully creative desserts might include frozen bergamot parfait, orange jelly, liquorice cream, or blueberry cannelloni with wood sorrel cream and yogurt sorbet. A highly distinguished wine list completes the picture.

Chef David Everitt-Matthias **Seats** 40 **Closed** 10 days at Christmas, 3 weeks in June **Notes** Children welcome

The Curry Corner Est.1977
◉◉ BANGLADESHI, INDIAN

01242 528449 | 133 Fairview Road, GL52 2EX

thecurrycorner.com

Occupying a white Georgian townhouse on the edge of Cheltenham's main shopping area, the oldest Bangladeshi curry house in the UK has a chic, contemporary look, featuring ruby-red wall coverings as well as furniture designed by the chef and co-owner. Bangladeshi home cooking is the theme, with spices flown in from India, Morocco and Turkey.

The Greenway Hotel & Spa
◉◉◉ MODERN BRITISH, FRENCH

01242 862352 | Shurdington, GL51 4UG

www.thegreenwayhotelandspa.com

Set in Shurdington, on the verdant outskirts of leafy Cheltenham, The Greenway is an Elizabethan manor house of Cotswold stone, its façade half-hidden in clambering ivy. The Garden Restaurant is named after its soothing view, with a majestic stone fireplace and venerable oak panelling adding lustre. Marcus McGuinness is a model modern-day practitioner, overseeing a thriving kitchen garden, foraging and sourcing thoroughbred prime materials, before turning it all into elegant, eye-catching dishes. Start with gratin of Cornish crab and white port, with sea buckthorn and 'piggy cake', before moving on to poached and roast Cornish brill with pumpkin, hazelnuts, mussels and sage. Soufflés often feature at dessert – witness a fine dark chocolate version with coffee sorbet and whisky custard.

Chef Marcus McGuinness **Seats** 60, Private dining 22 **Open** All Year **Parking** 30 **Notes** Children welcome

Hotel du Vin Cheltenham
◉ FRENCH, EUROPEAN ⚑NOTABLE WINE LIST

01242 588450 | Parabola Road, GL50 3AQ

www.hotelduvin.com

The restaurant at the Cheltenham branch of this popular hotel chain follows the usual bistro look of wooden floor, unclothed tables, banquettes and a wine-related theme of empty bottles, prints and memorabilia. The menu goes along the expected bistro route.

Lumière
◉◉◉ MODERN BRITISH *V*

See pages 120–121

Continued on page 122

Lumière

◉◉◉ **MODERN BRITISH** *V*
01242 222200 | Clarence Parade, GL50 3PA
www.lumiere.cc

Enjoy modern British cuisine with plenty of bold flavours

The elegant Lumière, owned and run by the Howes, lies a little way off the leafy promenade for which Cheltenham is famous. The building may be an unassuming terrace, but indoors looks the very image of a modern dining room. It's an understated classy affair decorated in a soothing combination of cream and aubergine tones, statement mirrors and abstract artworks all adding up to a setting that says this is an operation of serious culinary intent. However, the capable hand of Helen Howe on the front-of-house tiller makes for a relaxing experience so nothing is too stiff or formal. Jon Howe's inventive British cooking delivers vibrant modern flavours, deploying plenty of technical wizardry showcased in tasting menus of six or eight courses. Another way to appreciate Lumière and see what it has to offer is to come for lunch on Friday or Saturday and try the four-course tasting

"..deploying plenty of technical wizardry showcased in tasting menus of six or eight courses."

menu. If you're coming for the full tasting menus, then things begin with a volley of snacks such as Cornish crab, pink grapefruit and viola or mac and cheese with black garlic and autumn truffle. The palate suitably primed, further courses might see diver-caught Orkney scallops matched with tomato, ponzu and basil. A mid-meal tequila shot with salt and lime clears the way for the meaty satisfaction of Stokes Marsh Farm beef fillet, hispi cabbage, onion and dill. Dessert creations are equally pleasurable, such as damson soufflé, yogurt and almond milk.

Vegetarians are well catered for too, with a tasting menu that's no mere afterthought and shows the same level of creativity in dishes such coronation cauliflower, apricot, crème fraîche and almond or butternut squash, moussaka, girolle mushrooms, broad beans, spinach and spiced orange. Some produce comes from the recently established kitchen garden.

Chef Jon Howe
Seats 20
Closed 2 weeks in winter and 2 weeks in summer
Notes No children under 8 years

CHELTENHAM continued

The Restaurant at Ellenborough Park

ROSETTES SUSPENDED MODERN BRITISH ⚑ NOTABLE WINE LIST

01242 545454 | Southam Road, GL52 3NH

www.ellenboroughpark.com

The Rosette award for this establishment has been suspended due to a change of chef and reassessment will take place in due course. Although the original house had been pottering along unexceptionably since the 1530s, Ellenborough really hit its stride when the first Earl of that ilk, erstwhile governor general of British India, moved himself and his wife into it 300 years later. The place itself is a sumptuous beauty in Cotswold honey, looking a little like an Oxford college, with a high-glitz panelled dining room at the centre of operations.

Notes Vegetarian dishes, No children under 12 years at dinner

CIRENCESTER   MAP 5, SP00

The Potager

◉◉ MODERN EUROPEAN 𝑉

01285 740000 | Barnsley House, Near Cirencester, GL7 5EE

www.barnsleyhouse.com

The restaurant at 17th-century Barnsley House is named The Potager, after the ornamental and vegetable garden designed in the 1950s by Rosemary Verey, which it overlooks. Typical of the dishes is perfectly cooked lamb sweetbreads in a noteworthy jus served with no more than morels and garden chard.

CLEARWELL   MAP 4, SO50

Tudor Farmhouse Hotel & Restaurant

◉◉ MODERN BRITISH ⚑ NOTABLE WINE LIST

01594 833046 | High Street, GL16 8JS

www.tudorfarmhousehotel.co.uk

The charm-laden grey stone building looks the rustic part but, once inside, its stone walls, beams, wood panelling and inglenooks are overlaid with lashings of boutique bolt-hole style. Nor is the kitchen stuck in the past – its 20-mile menus are full of fresh, up-to-date ideas.

COLEFORD   MAP 4, SO51

Verderers NEW

◉ MODERN BRITISH

01594 822607 | The Speech House Hotel, Speech House Road, GL16 7EL

www.thespeechhouse.co.uk

Part of The Speech House Hotel, Verderers is set within a 17th century former hunting lodge in the heart of the idyllic Royal Forest of Dean. In the beamed restaurant, modern British cooking sticks to the seasons with a starter of scorched mackerel, chive and cucumber salsa followed by rack of lamb, hazelnut rösti, asparagus and watercress.

DAYLESFORD   MAP 10, SP22

Daylesford Farm Café

◉ MODERN BRITISH

01608 731700 | GL56 0YG

www.daylesford.com

On the Gloucestershire farmland that spawned a mini-empire, the Daylesford Farmshop and Café occupies a smartly converted barn with a New England finish and an open-to-view kitchen. The food makes a virtue of simplicity, with quality ingredients allowed to shine.

EBRINGTON   MAP 10, SP14

The Ebrington Arms

◉◉ CLASSIC BRITISH

01386 593223 | GL55 6NH

www.theebringtonarms.co.uk

Still very much a pub in the heart of the village by the green, the Ebrington has served its community for several hundred years, as is evident from its copious oak beams and flagged floors. The menu takes a contemporary line of original modern dishes and has won awards for its organic content.

GLOUCESTER
MAP 10, SO81

Hatherley Manor Hotel & Spa
⊛ TRADITIONAL BRITISH
01452 730217 | Down Hatherley Lane, GL2 9QA
www.hatherleymanor.com
A stylish brick and stone-built 17th-century house, Hatherley Manor is popular as a wedding venue. The Dewinton Restaurant is a relaxed setting for contemporary dining, with rich gold drapes and upholstery and linen-clad tables.

Hatton Court
⊛ MODERN INTERNATIONAL
01452 617412 | Upton Hill, Upton St Leonards, GL4 8DE
www.hatton-court.co.uk
A country-house hotel not far from the M5, Hatton Court is smothered with climbing foliage, its little windows barely peeping through the green. The formal dining room is kitted out with linen-clad tables, wood panelling and full-drop windows at one end.

LOWER SLAUGHTER
MAP 10, SP12

The Slaughters Country Inn
⊛⊛ MODERN BRITISH
01451 822143 | GL54 2HS
www.theslaughtersinn.co.uk
This artfully modernised, 17th-century Cotswold-stone inn makes good use of its riverside terrace in this peaceful village. In the 1920s the building was a crammer school for Eton College, thus it now has Eton's Restaurant. The modern British menu also covers the bar.

The Slaughters Manor House
⊛⊛⊛ MODERN BRITISH ♨ NOTABLE WINE LIST
01451 820456 | GL54 2HP
www.slaughtersmanor.co.uk
Built from golden Cotswold stone, this comfortable manor house dates from the 17th century, and offers a stylish 21st-century interpretation of country living. Wonderful period features and the delightful formal gardens, rub shoulders with modern decorative touches and pale, soothing colours. The elegant dining room is an airy, light-filled space with nicely spaced, linen-clad tables. Dishes are often picture-perfect explorations of flavour

and texture, maybe starting with dressed Cornish crab, served with lemon verbena and cucumber, followed by Herdwick lamb, braised gem lettuce, mint and black garlic. Finish with macerated English strawberries, yogurt sorbet and long pepper.

Chef Nik Chappell **Seats** 48, Private dining 24 **Open** All Year **Parking** 30 **Notes** Children welcome

MORETON-IN-MARSH
MAP 10, SP23

Manor House Hotel
⊛⊛ MODERN BRITISH
01608 650501 | High Street, GL56 OLJ
www.cotswold-inns-hotels.co.uk/manor
This Cotswold-stone hotel might date from the reign of Henry VIII, but careful renovation and updating have brought it squarely into the 21st century. The Mulberry Restaurant has generously spaced tables, comfortable chairs and on-the-ball staff, while the kitchen produces appealing dishes without over-complicating things.

Redesdale Arms
⊛ MODERN
01608 650308 | High Street, GL56 0AW
www.redesdalearms.com
Dating from the 17th century, this inn has been sympathetically updated to give a contemporary edge. There are two dining rooms, one in a rear conservatory, the other overlooking the high street. A glance at the menu shows a kitchen seaming the modern British vein.

NAILSWORTH
MAP 4, ST89

Wilder

◉◉◉ MODERN BRITISH V

01453 835483 | Market Street, GL6 0BX

www.dinewilder.co.uk

The arty market town of Nailsworth is as quintessentially Cotswolds English as you could ask for. Wilder offers a neutral, decluttered and modern space where diners all settle in at 7pm for an imaginative, daily-changing, eight-course tasting menu. The kitchen hauls in whatever's best from the local larder as the basis for sharply seasonal cooking that applies careful attention to detail and well-thought-out flavour combinations. Global influences come thick and fast, as in white miso aubergine with baba ganoush, labneh, shimeji mushrooms and a salty-sweet miso and soy dresssing. Another idea sees perfectly pink duck breast and a crispy bonbon matched with roasted and puréed artichoke, caramelised onions and red wine sauce, while sweet courses include chocolate porter cake with chocolate ganache, ale jelly and malted milk ice cream.

Chef Matthew Beardshall **Seats** 18 **Open** All Year **Notes** Children welcome

NETHER WESTCOTE
MAP 10, SP22

The Feathered Nest Inn

◉◉◉ MODERN BRITISH V

01993 833030 | OX7 6SD

www.thefeatherednestinn.co.uk

The Feathered Nest is a born-again country hostelry that's seriously worth a detour. There's pretty accommodation, too, if you fancy staying the night. The Cotswold-stone building looks good inside and out, with a contemporary country-chic interior (stone walls, flagged floors and antique furniture), the feelgood factor ramped up by real fires in winter, and bucolic views from the terrace and garden. Expect a modern British menu that fizzes with good ideas and appealing combinations – Orkney scallops with pork cheek, caramelised apple, celeriac and crackling for starters, then a big-hearted main course of Cotswold fallow deer with salt-baked parsnips, black pudding hash, braised red cabbage, parsnip and vanilla.

Chef Matthew Weedon **Seats** 20, Private dining 25 **Open** All Year **Parking** 45 **Notes** Children welcome

NORTH CERNEY
MAP 5, SP00

Bathurst Arms *NEW*

◉◉ BRITISH

01285 832150 | GL7 7BZ

www.bathurstarms.co.uk

The Bathurst Arms is a beautiful old country pub with a menu that does all it can to spotlight local produce, and help organic farmers reach a larger audience. Wherever possible, everything is homemade, and obviously, organic. The serving approach is a kind of tapas style, so it's recommended that everyone order two small plates, then share it around.

PAINSWICK
MAP 4, SO80

The Painswick

◉◉ MODERN EUROPEAN V

01452 813688 | Kemps Lane, GL6 6YB

www.thepainswick.co.uk

The swish Calcot Manor group have sprinkled this grand Palladian mansion with a touch of contemporary boutique chic to go with its original Arts and Crafts features, and the result is a covetable bolthole that exudes relaxed luxury. The kitchen comes up with the modern European-accented dishes.

SELSLEY
MAP 4, SO80

The Bell Inn

◉◉ MODERN BRITISH

01453 753801 | Bell Lane, GL5 5JY

www.thebellinnselsley.com

Dating from the 16th century, The Bell Inn is a Cotswold pub through and through, with menus offering a range of classic and contemporary dishes, typically rich local game, rolled pork belly and beer-battered fish and chips. Ales from nearby Uley brewery keep drinkers happy, as does the choice of 70 gins.

See advertisement opposite

the
bell
at selsley

drink | food | beds

THE BELL AT SELSLEY

Set in the picturesque village of Selsley, The Bell Inn is a 16th century
Grade II listed Cotswold Inn. Your friendly country pub with rooms.
We are here to give you a true taste of the Cotswolds and all that it has
to offer, serving real ales, locally-sourced food and seasonal game.

Whether catching up with friends in our bar, settling down for a
traditional Sunday lunch or enjoying a delicious country escape –
come and soak up some country life with us.

AA

**Rosette award for
culinary excellence**

2021

The Bell at Selsley
Bell Lane
Selsley
Stroud
Gloucestershire
GL5 5JY

01453 753801

info@thebellinnselsley.com

thebellinnselsley.com

Lords of the Manor

⊛⊛⊛ **MODERN BRITISH** 🍷 NOTABLE WINE LIST
01451 820243 | GL54 2JD
www.lordsofthemanor.com

Intimate, refined dining in a splendidly historic setting

Upper Slaughter might not sound terribly charming but take it from us, it most definitely is. Set between the equally delightful Bourton-on-the-Water and Stow-on-the-World, this is a heart-stoppingly beautiful area, and if you're looking for honey-coloured Cotswold stone and all the charm of the English countryside you won't go far wrong in heading to Lords of the Manor, a 17th-century former rectory of immense charm.

There are mullioned windows, acres of manicured lawn, and plenty of period details like beams and plaster moulding. Decorated throughout with a cool and relaxingly tasteful elegance, there are fresh flowers everywhere and it looks as delightfully romantic in the snows of winter as when it basks in midsummer heat. The Atrium is the fine dining restaurant, a refined, intimate (just 14 covers, make sure you book ahead) and elegant space with a

dramatic roof light and chairs upholstered in silvery velvet. Dinner is served in one sitting, at 18.45, and is a theatrical experience that might begin with a tour of the lovely gardens. The seven-course tasting menu (plus a vegetarian alternative) changes with the seasons and what's available, with head chef Charles Smith admitting he's 'obsessed' with sourcing the very best ingredients. His cooking is ambitious and precise, reflecting that obsession in the confident choices made for every dish. You might begin with a fresh and vibrant dish of Isle of Wight heritage tomatoes, burrata and pickled celery, before another perfectly matched flavour combination in the form of tourchon of foie gras with peaches, sauternes and fresh almonds. Scottish langoustine soup with scallop dumplings and Australian black winter truffle is a real highlight with great depth of flavour. A delicate piece of steamed Cornish turbot might come with Wye Valley asparagus, seaweed butter sauce, while top-quality Belted Galloway beef is accompanied by hen of the wood mushroom and artichoke. Aged Cornish gouda with cured pork collar, preserved green tomatoes is up next, packed full of flavour and followed by 'quite simply delicious' verbena tea jelly with lime granita and caramelised honey. Summer berries with vanilla cream is a well judged, light and refreshing end to the meal.

Chef Charles Smith
Seats 50, Private dining 30
Open All Year
Parking 40
Notes No children under 7 years

STOW-ON-THE-WOLD

The Kings Head Inn
◉ BRITISH

01608 658365 | The Green, Bledington, OX7 6XQ

www.kingsheadinn.net

This mellow stone Cotswolds pub comes with a classic bar with wobbly floors, log fires and head-skimming beams. It's a textbook example of a switched-on village pub with cooking that's a definite notch or two up.

Number Four at Stow
◉◉ MODERN BRITISH

01451 830297 | Fosse Way, GL54 1JX

www.hotelnumberfour.com

With its wood-burning stove, exposed brickwork and muted tones, there are hints of country style in this split-level boutique hotel restaurant but also elements of modernity. From the seasonal modern British menu, try the pork belly and tenderloin, rhubarb, potato rösti, spring Savoy cabbage and pork pie sauce.

Old Stocks Inn
◉◉ MODERN BRITISH

01451 830666 | The Square, GL54 1AP

www.oldstocksinn.com

An appealing package of bright and funky modern decor, a fun ambience, an array of regionally-brewed craft beers and an inventive take on contemporary pub grub makes this revamped 17th-century Cotswolds inn worth checking out.

Wyck Hill House Hotel & Spa
◉ MODERN BRITISH

01451 831936 | Burford Road, GL54 1HY

www.wyckhillhousehotel.co.uk

Overlooking the Windrush Valley, Wyck Hill House is surrounded by 50 acres of grounds in the Cotswold Hills. The finely-tuned cooking on the seasonal menus takes provenance seriously. Start perhaps with heritage beetroot salad, goats' cheese and caramelised hazelnuts before oven-roasted Cornish hake, Jerusalem artichokes, salsify and chive cream sauce.

STROUD

The Bear of Rodborough
◉ BRITISH, INTERNATIONAL

01453 878522 | Rodborough Common, GL5 5DE

www.cotswold-inns-hotels.co.uk

This Cotswold hotel with its own vineyard is a handsome beast, its identity emphasised by two stuffed bears in reception. The dining room enjoys ravishing countryside views and a menu of thoroughgoing British modernism.

Burleigh Court Hotel
◉◉ BRITISH, MEDITERRANEAN

01453 883804 | Burleigh, Minchinhampton, GL5 2PF

www.burleighcourtcotswolds.co.uk/

Built of Cotswold stone early in the 19th century, this imposing, ivy-clad manor house overlooks Golden Valley and the River Frome. Its Georgian-style interior incorporates an oak-panelled lounge and a dining room decorated with scenes of the house's history, where large windows reveal a beautiful garden.

TETBURY

The Close Hotel
◉ MODERN BRITISH

01666 502272 | 8 Long Street, GL8 8AQ

www.theclose-hotel.com

The Close Hotel is a handsome 16th-century pile, boasting period details and contemporary elegance. There are two dining options in the form of a brasserie and fine-dining restaurant. The modern British menu strikes the right balance in this setting, with creative combinations proving very tempting.

The Conservatory at Calcot
◉◉ MODERN BRITISH

01666 890391 | Calcot, GL8 8YJ

www.calcot.co

Calcot is a boutique-style hotel of Cotswold stone with a health spa and a light-filled restaurant called The Conservatory. The kitchen works around a repertoire of imaginative modern dishes, and flavours have real punch. Expect modern twists to classic dishes.

Hare & Hounds Hotel
◉◉ MODERN BRITISH
01666 881000 | Westonbirt, GL8 8QL
www.cotswold-inns-hotels.co.uk
The Beaufort Restaurant is the culinary heart of
this Cotswold-stone hotel just outside Tetbury.
There's an excellent selection of home-made
breads (including a Guinness soda bread) to
accompany the meal, and ice rhubarb parfait
may be your choice of dessert.

THORNBURY   *MAP 4, ST69*
Ronnie's of Thornbury
◉◉ MODERN BRITISH
01454 411137 | 11 St Mary Street, BS35 2AB
www.ronnies-restaurant.co.uk
Ronnie's occupies a 17th-century building done
out with a smart contemporary look that
seamlessly blends stone walls, beamed ceilings,
wooden floors, and neutral hues pointed up by
paintings and photos by West Country artists. A
menu of satisfyingly unfussy and hearty modern
cooking satisfies all comers, with a keenly priced
set lunch for bargain hunters.

UPPER SLAUGHTER   *MAP 10, SP12*
Lords of the Manor
◉◉◉ MODERN BRITISH ♦NOTABLE WINE LIST
See pages 126–127

■ GREATER MANCHESTER

DELPH   *MAP 16, SD90*
The Old Bell Inn
◉ MODERN BRITISH
01457 870130 | 5 Huddersfield Road, OL3 5EG
www.theoldbellinn.co.uk
A traditional 18th-century coaching inn with a
thoroughly contemporary attitude to dining, this
pub holds a world record for its collection of
1,100 gins, displayed in the Gin Emporium. In the
modern restaurant, hearty, innovative food is
created using an abundance of local raw
materials.

The Saddleworth Hotel
◉ MODERN EUROPEAN
01457 871888 | Huddersfield Road, OL3 5LX
www.saddleworthhotel.co.uk
The Saddleworth feels like a real attempt to
create a country inn for the modern era. With
landscaped gardens, woodland, and sweeping
views over the Lancashire moorland, it's not far
from Oldham yet feels pleasingly remote from
anywhere.

DIDSBURY   *MAP 16, SJ89*
HISPI
◉◉ CONTEMPORARY BRASSERIE
0161 445 3996 | 1C School Lane, M20 6RD
www.hispi.net

Named after what has been called 'the trendiest
cabbage variety in British catering', this is serial
restaurateur Gary Usher's third crowd-funded
venture. What he gives Didsbury is minimalist
decor, an open kitchen and inviting,
contemporary food, exemplified by roast duck
with braised turnip, plum sauce and duck leg
pastilla. Gary clearly trains and inspires his
people well.

Continued on page 130

MANCHESTER *MAP 16, SJ89*

Adam Reid at The French

◉◉◉◉ MODERN BRITISH 𝘝 🍷

0161 235 4780 | The Midland, Peter Street, M60 2DS

the-french-manchester.co.uk

The Midland Hotel looks as grand as a city hall, in a city not short on municipal grandeur. It was constructed in the Edwardian decade to lure discerning travellers to Manchester and has been given fresh impetus in the most recent generation, not least by means of a dining room firing on all culinary cylinders. Adam Reid makes his presence felt with a fully up-to-the-minute operation that embraces small-plate dining while sitting at the kitchen counter, as well as grand tasting processions served in the glitzy French restaurant, a handsome room done in moody blue and grey beneath giant crystal globes. In the set menu expect energetic, precise combinations such as vibrant curried Cornish squid with spinach and potato, served with malted bread and fabulous beef and onion butter. Goosnargh duck with lentils, beetroot and sour cherry is a classy main, the duck meltingly tender, with textural interest coming from praline and sweet cubes of beetroot. An intense dish of forced Yorkshire rhubarb with baked English custard is a real highlight – served with a mint butter described as 'a revelation', the dish as a whole is truly stunning.

Chef Adam Reid **Seats** 28 **Closed** Christmas **Notes** No children under 8 years

Brasserie ABode

◉◉ EUROPEAN BRASSERIE

0161 247 7744 | ABode Manchester, 107 Piccadilly, M1 2DB

www.abodemanchester.co.uk

Relaxed, all-day dining with a menu that features plats du jour with a comfortingly, nostalgic nod and time-honoured classics. Generosity and value are at the heart of the Brasserie whether it's Sunday lunch, classic dishes with plentiful sides or cocktails with a side serving of nibbles.

Chez Mal Brasserie

◉ MODERN BRITISH, INTERNATIONAL

0161 278 1000 | Malmaison Manchester, Piccadilly, M1 3AQ

www.malmaison.com/locations/manchester

This prime piece of heritage industrial architecture is plumb in the city centre. The interior is boutiqued to the max, while cocktails and upscale brasserie food draw in the crowds. In The Smoak Bar & Grill, the open-to-view kitchen produces surprising versions of modern comfort food.

El Gato Negro Tapas

◉ SPANISH

0161 694 8585 | 52 King Street, M2 4LY

www.elgatonegrotapas.com

Set over three floors of a stripped-back, industrial-themed building in Manchester's busy city centre, this buzzy tapas bar has a charcuterie station and restaurant with an open kitchen. Chargrilled octopus with capers, shallots and aïoli; and pork belly, celeriac purée, straw potatoes and raisins marinated in PX sherry are among the menu highlights.

George's Dining Room & Bar

◉ MODERN BRITISH

0161 794 5444 | 17-21 Barton Road, Worsley, M28 2PD

www.georgesworsley.co.uk

The name of this gastro pub pays homage to Victorian architect Sir George Gilbert Scott, but this place does not look backwards. The setting is stylish, with tan leather banquettes and neutral creamy hues, and the food is very much what you'd expect of a 21st-century kitchen.

Greens

⊛ MODERN VEGETARIAN

0161 434 4259 | 43 Lapwing Lane, West Didsbury, M20 2NT

www.greensdidsbury.co.uk

TV chef Simon Rimmer's lively restaurant draws the crowds with exciting vegetarian cooking. Precisely flavoured dishes are the hallmark of the kitchen, with inspiration picked up from around the globe in a menu that bursts with bright and appealing ideas.

Harvey Nichols Second Floor Bar and Brasserie

⊛ MODERN INTERNATIONAL ♦NOTABLE WINE LIST

0161 828 8898 | 21 New Cathedral Street, M1 1AD

www.harveynichols.com/store/manchester/dining

The brasserie's high-gloss interior gives it a very modern look, while the views through its large windows include the city's few remaining old half-timbered buildings. Brunch is served from early until after lunch, with the brasserie's international carte on offer all day. A deli counter sells dry goods, wines and spirits, leaving the food hall temptations for the way out.

Hotel Gotham

⊛⊛ MODERN EUROPEAN

0161 413 0000 | 100 King Street, M2 4WU

www.hotelgotham.co.uk

The sleek art deco lines of a vintage bank building make a good setting for this hip restaurant in a glossy boutique hotel. Parquet floors, metal-topped tables and semi-circular windows all feed into the retro styling, while the menus are all about modern British and European combinations.

Kala Bistro NEW

⊛ BRITISH

0800 160 1811 | King Street, M2 4LQ

www.kalabistro.co.uk

The latest addition to Gary Usher's ever-increasing empire, and partly crowdfunded by his enthusiastic fans, Kala Bistro is a stripped back, stylish space bang in the city centre, surrounded by posh boutiques. The trademark open kitchen stretches the length of the back wall and the plate glass frontage ensures a light, airy setting for bold, simple, seasonal flavours. Maybe start with octopus braised in a fantastic chilli salsa, followed by smoked duck breast with confit tomatoes, lovage and duck fat croûtons. Banana bread with poached pineapple is a comforting old school finish.

The Lowry Hotel

⊛⊛ CLASSIC, TRADITIONAL

0161 827 4000 | 50 Dearmans Place, Chapel Wharf, Salford, M3 5LH

www.thelowryhotel.com

With floor-to-ceiling windows commanding spectacular views over the canal and the Lowry Bridge, The River Restaurant enjoys plenty of natural light, with glass and leather decor giving it a contemporary feel. The elegant surroundings are juxtaposed with informal, chatty service.

Mana NEW

⊛⊛⊛⊛ MODERN, NORDIC INFLUENCES

0161 392 7294 | 42 Blossom Street, M4 6BF

www.manarestaurant.co.uk

Situated on a cobbled street in Manchester, Mana has a minimalist look with high ceilings and picture windows. Dramatic darkwood tables are unclothed and an open island-style kitchen is populated by chefs sending out some highly accomplished Nordic-influenced cooking. Multi-course menus deliver dishes that are highly technical, intelligent and masterfully constructed to balance flavours and textures, with fermentation and fire contributing to the skills set. Expect to find the finest raw materials underpinning the likes of unpreserved caviar with sorrel and caramelised cream; a trimmed oyster with iced dill, English wasabi and macerated oyster leaf; 'fillets' of Devonshire blue mussel with garlic 'cooked for two months'; smoked Scottish sea trout with 'inoculated' grains, and 100% outdoor raised Dexter Beef with 'all the artichoke'. The sweet end of the menu brings wild fig soft serve with marigold and fermented honey, and 'still-hot' doughnut with Islay whisky custard.

Chef Simon Martin

MANCHESTER continued

WOOD - Manchester
◉◉ MODERN BRITISH *V*
0161 236 5211 | Jack Rosenthal Street, First Street, M15 4RA
www.woodmanchester.com

The flagship restaurant of the BBC's 2015 *MasterChef* winner, Simon Wood, WOOD - Manchester is close to the city's theatreland. It's got a real buzz and has accumulated quite a local following of foodies eager to settle down to some imaginative and innovative cooking. The offer is a five- seven- or 10- course tasting menu.

ROCHDALE
MAP 16, SD81

Nutters
◉ MODERN BRITISH NOTABLE WINE LIST
01706 650167 | Edenfield Road, Norden, OL12 7TT
www.nuttersrestaurant.co.uk

This grand old house is run as a family affair by the larger-than-life TV chef Andrew Nutter. The menu takes a modern British path, with plenty of flavours from Asia and regional ingredients providing a sense of place. There's a good value 'business lunch' menu with three courses and a six-course surprise menu.

STOCKPORT
MAP 16, SJ89

Where the Light Gets In
◉◉◉ MODERN BRITISH
0161 477 5744 | 7 Rostron Brow, SK1 1JY
www.wtlgi.co/restaurant
Where the Light Gets In occupies a hipster-friendly industrial-chic former warehouse that's fully in tune with contemporary sensibilities and the industrial heritage of the town. Music is loud, the vibe is casual and chefs deliver dishes hot-foot to tables. A procession of small dishes – up to 15 – takes in current trends for fermenting, pickling and sustainability. Along the way expect to encounter the likes of pickled kohlrabi with verbena leaves, butter curds and gooseberry compôte; preserved red mullet with tomato water and brown butter, and a hands-on taco-style dish of pork rump with fermented bread, miso and preserved cucumber.

Chef Sam Buckley **Seats** 30
Open Wednesday – Saturday, last booking 20:30

■ HAMPSHIRE

ANDOVER
MAP 5, SU34

Esseborne Manor
◉◉ MODERN BRITISH
01264 736444 | Hurstbourne Tarrant, SP11 0ER
www.esseborne-manor.co.uk
Esseborne Manor is a Victorian country house in an Area of Outstanding Natural Beauty. The ambience is traditional with white clothed, formally set tables and candlelight. A relaxed and enjoyable dining experience with formal but friendly service. Cooking is unfussy and straightforward, but packed with flavour. Good use is made of herbs from the Manor's own herb garden.

BARTON-ON-SEA
MAP 5, SZ29

Pebble Beach
◉ BRITISH, FRENCH, MEDITERRANEAN, SEAFOOD
01425 627777 | Marine Drive, BH25 7DZ
www.pebblebeach-uk.com
A clifftop perch gives this modern bar-brasserie a sweeping vista across Christchurch Bay to the Needles and the Isle of Wight. Inside is a buzzy split-level venue where high stools at the oyster bar allow views of the open-plan kitchen. The alfresco terrace is irresistible.

BASINGSTOKE
MAP 5, SU65

Audleys Wood Hotel
◉ MODERN BRITISH
01256 817555 | Alton Road, RG25 2JT
www.handpickedhotels.co.uk/audleyswood
This striking Victorian property stands in seven acres of grounds and woodland and has all the trappings of a luxury country-house hotel. The Conservatory Restaurant with its high vaulted ceiling and small minstrels' gallery serves a seasonally-changing menu.

Glasshouse Restaurant
◉◉ MODERN INTERNATIONAL
01256 783350 | Oakley Hall Hotel, Rectory Road, Oakley, RG23 7EL
www.oakleyhall-park.com
Jane Austen enthusiasts will find references to Oakley Hall in her work. As a young woman, she was a frequent visitor. The Glasshouse restaurant is the setting for classically based modern British menus that draw their raw materials from the kitchen garden.

BAUGHURST
MAP 5, SU56

The Wellington Arms
◉◉ MODERN BRITISH
0118 982 0110 | Baughurst Road, RG26 5LP
www.thewellingtonarms.com

Much of your meal in this long-standing, two-Rosette holder will come from its garden, polytunnel or local allotment; a flock of Jacob sheep graze in the field behind. Understandably some items, such as Lyme Bay king scallops, do have to travel. The pub sign displays the coat of arms of the Dukes of Wellington, whose estate is at Stratfield Saye.

BEAULIEU
MAP 5, SU30

The Drift Inn
◉ MODERN BRITISH
023 8029 3344 | Beaulieu Hotel, Beaulieu Road, SO42 7YQ
thedrift.newforesthotels.co.uk
Surrounded by New Forest heathland, The Drift Inn has a welcoming dog- and family-friendly attitude and an upmarket country inn ambience, with open fires adding to the overall sense of well-being. The kitchen stocks its larder with fine local bounty as the bedrock of a nifty menu of sturdy, up-to-date pub dishes.

The Master Builder's at Buckler's Hard
◉ MODERN BRITISH
01590 616253 | Buckler's Hard, SO42 7XB
www.themasterbuilders.co.uk
Named after the man who built ships for Nelson's fleet on the grassy areas running down to the Beaulieu River, the restaurant in this rustic 18th century hotel offers tranquil river views. The straightforward modern British cooking is underpinned by well-sourced local ingredients. Try the fillet of venison, pommes Anna, romanesco and glazed figs.

Monty's Inn
◉ TRADITIONAL BRITISH
01590 614986 | The Montagu Arms Hotel, Palace Lane, SO42 7ZL
www.montaguarmshotel.co.uk
Specialising in hearty, unpretentious food that doesn't try to punch above its weight, Monty's Inn goes for a clubby look involving wood-panelled walls, wooden floors and unclothed tables in a posh country pub setting. Kick things off perfectly with a home-made local pork Scotch egg.

BEAULIEU continued

The Terrace Restaurant at The Montagu Arms Hotel

◉◉◉ MODERN EUROPEAN

01590 612324 | Palace Lane, SO42 7ZL

www.montaguarmshotel.co.uk

The Montagu Arms is the quintessential wisteria-draped, 17th-century country hotel, set in a prime New Forest spot. The oak-panelled Terrace Restaurant has linen-swathed tables and French windows opening onto a sun-trap garden, setting the scene for some fine-tuned and innovative cooking from head chef Matthew Whitfield. You'll find the best available local produce on the menu, whether south coast hake or wild garlic from the Forest, the stars of dishes like Black Water pig belly with glazed hispi cabbage, smoked bacon ragù, turnip and Szechuan pepper, or chalk stream trout with Hampshire watercress, lime caviar, charred cucumber and beurre blanc.

Chef Matthew Whitfield **Seats** 60, Private dining 32 **Open** All Year **Parking** 50 **Notes** No children under 12 years at dinner

BRANSGORE   *MAP 5, SZ19*

The Three Tuns

◉ BRITISH, EUROPEAN

01425 672232 | Ringwood Road, BH23 8JH

www.threetunsinn.com

The picture-postcard 17th-century thatched inn deep in the New Forest is a delight in summer, festooned with flowers, and cosy in winter as blazing log fires warm the low beamed bar. The welcoming scene draws foodies and forest visitors for its charm and character.

BROCKENHURST   *MAP 5, SU30*

The Balmer Lawn Hotel

◉◉ MODERN BRITISH

01590 623116 | Lyndhurst Road, SO42 7ZB

www.balmerlawnhotel.com

This imposing pavilion-style Victorian hunting lodge in a charming New Forest setting does good business as a friendly, family-run operation with an excellent spa, sports and conference facilities. Expect modern cooking with a healthy showing of prime-quality, often local, materials.

Cambium

◉◉ MODERN BRITISH ⚜NOTABLE WINE LIST

01590 623551 | Careys Manor Hotel & SenSpa, Lyndhurst Road, SO42 7RH

www.careysmanor.com/restaurants/cambium

The Careys Manor Hotel is to be found in the New Forest, an environment its restaurant celebrates (Cambium is a technical botanical term for the inner tissue of plants or trees). The decor incorporates leafy screens and a central bare-twigged tree with purple flowers. Alastair Craig's cooking plays its part too, with plates that look pretty and deliver convincing natural flavours.

Rhinefield House Hotel

◉◉ CLASSIC, TRADITIONAL BRITISH

01590 622922 | Rhinefield Road, SO42 7QB

www.handpickedhotels.co.uk/rhinefieldhouse

The present house sprang up in the late Victorian era. A Tudor-Gothic hybrid architecturally, the interiors are awash with finely crafted mouldings, copperwork, and beautiful examples of the lavatorialist's art, and a room modelled on the Alhambra.

THE PIG

◉◉ BRITISH ⚜NOTABLE WINE LIST

01590 622354 | Beaulieu Road, SO42 7QL

www.thepighotel.com

This is a restaurant for our times, with cocktails served in jam jars and massages available in the old potting shed. Here, in the wilds of the New Forest, the passion is for home-grown and foraged ingredients. It's a buzzy place with a retro interior.

BURLEY
MAP 5, SU20

Burley Manor
◉◉ BRITISH, MEDITERRANEAN
01425 403522 | Ringwood Road, BH24 4BS
burleymanor.newforesthotels.co.uk
Burley Manor was built in 1852 by a magistrate and custodian of the surrounding New Forest. A hotel since the 1930s, this grand former home enjoys fabulous parkland views and a peaceful patio. In the restaurant, the menu has Mediterranean influences.

DOGMERSFIELD
MAP 5, SU75

Wild Carrot at Four Seasons Hotel Hampshire
◉◉ CONTEMPORARY BRITISH V
01252 853100 | Dogmersfield Park, Chalky Lane, RG27 8TD
www.fourseasons.com/hampshire/dining/
restaurants/wild-carrot
Set within the expansive acreages of the Dogmersfield Estate, the Four Seasons' dining options include a bistro and café, but the main event is the Wild Carrot restaurant, a light-filled dining space with French windows and an upscale, gently contemporary sheen.

EMSWORTH
MAP 5, SU70

36 on the Quay
◉◉◉ MODERN BRITISH, EUROPEAN
01243 375592 | 47 South Street, PO10 7EG
www.36onthequay.com
This charming and long-running restaurant-with-rooms has a wonderful setting, in a 17th-century building right on the harbour in this lovely little fishing village. It's a great place to watch the sun go down – have a drink outside in the courtyard before heading in to the bright, airy dining room. The menu delivers interesting, gently contemporary interpretations of classic dishes and flavour combinations, and tasting menus are available at both lunch and dinner. A neatly presented starter of salt-cured cod comes with black pudding, winter leeks, cod roe and honey mustard, while main course combines superb local South Downs venison with braised spelt, pumpkin in various guises, black fig, winter greens and a fathoms-deep jus. Dessert captures the astringent essence of the new season's forced rhubarb, appearing in poached, puréed and sorbet forms alongside creamy vanilla custard parfait and pistachio cake; otherwise, go for a tasting plate of six British cheeses.

Chef Gary Pearce **Seats** 45, Private dining 12 **Closed** 1st 2/3 weeks January, 1 week May, 1 week October, 25–26 December **Notes** Children welcome

Fat Olives
◉◉ MODERN BRITISH, MEDITERRANEAN
01243 377914 | 30 South Street, PO10 7EH
www.fatolives.co.uk
A few steps from the quayside of the pretty Emworth harbour, this 17th-century fishermen's cottage provides the setting for Lawrence and Julia Murphy's smart brasserie. The stripped-out interior of cream walls, wooden floors and unclothed tables is as unvarnished and honest as the food. Excellent ingredients do the talking on a menu that's an appetising fusion of modern, well-thought-through ideas.

FAREHAM
MAP 5, SU50

Solent Hotel & Spa
◉ MODERN BRITISH, EUROPEAN, INTERNATIONAL V
01489 880000 | Rookery Avenue, Whiteley, PO15 7AJ
www.solenthotel.co.uk/food-drink
A modern hotel with spa facilities among woodland, yet close by the M27, The Solent's Terrace Restaurant is a cheery contemporary space. Separated from the bar by an open fireplace, it offers cosy nooks and booths and an easygoing ambience. The wide-ranging menu aims to please all-comers with a roster of modern dishes.

FARNBOROUGH
MAP 5, SU85

Brasserie at Aviator
◉◉ MODERN INTERNATIONAL V
01252 555890 | 55 Farnborough Road, GU14 6EL
www.aviatorhampshire.com
The TAG timepiece manufacturer's aviation-themed hotel has landed on the Hampshire-Surrey border, in the vicinity of the celebrated air show at Farnborough. The uncomplicated, modern brasserie food has something to please all tastes including a repertoire of classic cuts of steak, done on the charcoal grill.

HORDLE
MAP 5 SZ29

The Old Mill
● MODERN BRITISH
01590 682219 | Silver Street, SO41 6DJ
www.gordletonmill.co.uk/
Whether you settle in the cosseting bar, the contemporary river-view restaurant or the orangery, this creeper-clad inn serves properly satisfying modern British food. From bread to soups, sauces, ice cream and puddings, it's all made in-house from scratch using local and organic ingredients from producers in the nearby New Forest.

LYMINGTON
MAP 5, SZ39

The Elderflower Restaurant
● ● ● MODERN BRITISH, FRENCH
01590 676908 | 4A Quay Street, SO41 3AS
www.elderflowerrestaurant.co.uk
Andrew and Marjolaine Du Bourg's welcoming restaurant occupies a Grade II listed building close to the quayside. Low black beams and bay windows add to the old-world charm but the interior is as contemporary as the modern European cooking. Whether it's the à la carte or tasting menus, expect well-balanced dishes with a real depth of flavour. Pork consommé, smoked bacon, greengage, coco beans and sun-dried tomato could precede roast crab cannelloni, crab foam, sweetcorn and pickled black mooli. End with a perfectly risen lemon meringue soufflé with lemon sauce, bouquet garni ice cream and organic pollen.

Chef Andrew Du Bourg Seats 40 Open All Year Notes No children under 12 years at dinner Friday, Saturday and Valentine's Day

LYNDHURST
MAP 5, SU30

1820 Grill & Brasserie
● ● MODERN BRITISH
023 8028 6129 | Forest Lodge Hotel, Pikes Hill, Romsey Road, SO43 7AS
www.newforesthotels.co.uk/forest-lodge-hotel
On the outskirts of Lyndhurst, this hotel's restaurant is a hugely stylish environment. The menu covers a lot of ground, from burgers and light bites to a well-conceived starter of quail three ways (poached breast, confit leg and a Scotch egg).

The Crown Manor House Hotel
● ● MODERN BRITISH
023 8028 2922 | High Street, SO43 7NF
www.crownhotel-lyndhurst.co.uk
The fireplace just inside the entrance once provided instant defrosting for travellers who had braved the horse-drawn carriage transfer from the railway station. Such is the Crown's history, which extends from 15th-century beginnings to a late Victorian makeover, its panelled dining room a refreshing space today for contemporary brasserie cooking.

Hartnett Holder & Co
● ● ● ITALIAN ▲NOTABLE
023 8028 7177 | Lime Wood, Beaulieu Road, SO43 7FZ
www.limewoodhotel.co.uk/food/hh-and-co
Lime Wood looks out over the peaceable expanses of the New Forest. The kitchen here is in the hands of Luke Holder, and overseen by Italian food superstar Angela Hartnett. The seasonal menus work indeed to an Italian template, with antipasti and primi before the main course, and a wealth of respectfully treated natural ingredients running through them. A serving of Cornish crab with smoked eel, radish and apple is the perfect palate-primer for a pasta dish such as guinea fowl agnolotti with lardo di Colonnata, onion and sage. At main, there could be one of the locally reared meats, perhaps Saddleback pork fillet with king cabbage and roasted Cox's apple. To close, a fragrant dessert such as saffron pannacotta with rosewater and pistachios.

Chef Angela Hartnett, Luke Holder Seats 70, Private dining 16 Open All Year Parking 90 Notes Children welcome

MILFORD ON SEA
MAP 5, SZ29

Verveine Fishmarket Restaurant
● ● MODERN, SEAFOOD
01590 642176 | 98 High Street, SO41 0QE
www.verveine.co.uk
Stylish, understated decor and fish-related artworks feed into the sense of a committed operation at this dinky fish restaurant tucked away, appropriately enough, behind a fishmonger's. It's an intimate, elegant dining room, reached via the open kitchen, and the deal is 3 to 10 courses of finely-honed cooking.

NEW ALRESFORD
MAP 5, SU53

Pulpo Negro
◉◉ MODERN SPANISH
01962 732262 | 28 Broad Street, SO24 9AQ
www.pulponegro.co.uk
Alresford - famous for its watercress, steam railway and clear-running chalk streams - has rather improbably added a sunny slice of the Med to its quintessentially English appeal with the arrival of Pulpo Negro. There's a smart-casual, modern feel-good vibe about the place, with its floorboards, café-style chairs, pews and wooden tables. On offer, an appealing tapas menu and well-selected Spanish wines.

NEW MILTON
MAP 5, SZ29

The Dining Room
◉◉ MODERN BRITISH ⚑NOTABLE WINE LIST
01425 282212 | Chewton Glen, Christchurch Road, BH25 6QS
www.chewtonglen.com
The cuisine at Chewton Glen is one of its highly regarded features. In the light, subtly hued Dining Room, modern British classics include pressed duck liver with almond, plum sake and toasted brioche; Isle of Gigha halibut with sticky chicken wings, aubergine, miso and lotus root; and Valrhona chocolate and orange mousse.

The Kitchen
◉ ITALIAN, AMERICAN
01425 282212 | Chewton Glen, Christchurch Road, BH25 6QS
www.chewtonglen.com/thekitchen
Staff are friendly and service is polished at this modern venue, purpose-built as a restaurant and cookery school. Take a seat in one of the deep burgundy leather chairs or banquettes at copper-topped tables and peruse the menu of crowd-pleasing dishes cooked up by chefs James Martin and Adam Hart.

OTTERBOURNE
MAP 5, SU42

The White Horse
◉ MODERN, TRADITIONAL BRITISH
01962 712830 | Main Road, SO21 2EQ
www.whitehorseotterbourne.co.uk
Seasonal menus list British-influenced food at this traditional village pub just south of Winchester. Friendly and welcoming staff serve dishes such as braised pork belly with bubble and squeak, and ale-battered fish and chips, but also Moroccan-style chickpea and kale stew, and Goan fish curry. Antique furnishings fill the interior, while the two large gardens incorporate a children's play area.

PORTSMOUTH
MAP 5, SU60

Restaurant 27
◉◉ MODERN EUROPEAN
023 9287 6272 | 27a South Parade, PO5 2JF
www.restaurant27.com

Family-run with a heartfelt passion for local materials, chef-proprietor Kevin Bingham's stylish restaurant is a high-ceilinged, modern space dressed up in grey, with unclothed tables, and walls hung with eclectic artworks. Two six-course tasting menus with veggie alternatives showcase the kitchen's modern European sensibilities. Expect ambitious, thoughtfully composed dishes delivering on-trend ingredients and well-defined flavours.

The Purefoy

◉◉ BRITISH V

01256 389514 | Alresford Road, RG25 2EJ

thepurefoyarms.co.uk

This classic red-brick Victorian pub opposite the village church proves a switched-on affair, from its country-modern interior and sunny-natured service to drawcard garden and adept cooking, it certainly ticks all the relevant 'destination' & 'local' boxes. Crowd-pleasing modern British cooking is the raison d'être, delivered via pub classics, carte and tasting menu dishes.

The Oak Room Restaurant

◉◉ MODERN BRITISH

01256 764881 | Tylney Hall Hotel, Ridge Lane, RG27 9AZ

www.tylneyhall.co.uk

The Oak Room at Tylney Hall remains one of Hampshire's exemplary country-house restaurants. What arrives in front of you will be a gently updated take on a traditional English or European classic, thus pan-seared scallops come with artichoke and miso caramel, and Herefordshire lamb loin with a harissa-spiced lamb cigar and roasted San Marzano tomatoes.

Blue Jasmine *NEW*

◉◉ ASIAN

023 8063 6387 | Unit 3-4 Alexandra Wharf, Maritime Walk, Ocean Way, SO14 3QS

Show-stopping, hotspot venue on the quayside at Ocean Village, with go-to terrace and super-stylish interiors to match its contemporary South-East Asian cooking. Every bit as well-dressed, the innovative cuisine comes perfect for sharing and flavour packed; witness signature Sarawak black pepper roasted duck to grilled Chilean sea bass with pomegranate glaze and soya-ginger crumble.

The Jetty

◉◉ MODERN

023 8110 3456 | Southampton Harbour Hotel & Spa, 5 Maritime Walk, Ocean Village, SO14 3QT

www.southampton-harbour-hotel.co.uk

The Jetty is part of the rather spectacular Southampton Harbour Hotel and enjoys panoramic views across Ocean Village Marina. There's a terrace for outdoor dining, surrounded by sunshine and yachts. It's chic and elegant, with a bright airy feel and cheery turquoise and yellow highlights.

The Greyhound on the Test

◉◉ MODERN BRITISH

01264 810833 | 31 High Street, SO20 6EY

www.thegreyhoundonthetest.co.uk

The Greyhound has no shortage of appeal, from upmarket, sumptuous bedrooms to a restaurant with that opened-up, country-chic vibe. The menu is a thoroughly up-to-date affair with regional produce at its heart. You're sure to go home happy after dark chocolate brownie with chocolate mousse.

The Peat Spade Inn

◉ MODERN BRITISH

01264 810612 | Village Street, Longstock, SO20 6DR

www.peatspadeinn.co.uk

A stolid-looking red-brick country inn where close-set tables add to the dining-room buzz. Rustic cooking with more than a soupçon of French influence proves abidingly popular, seen in the form of fried chicken livers on sourdough toast with charred sweetcorn in peppercorn sauce.

The Three Cups Inn

◉ MODERN & TRADITIONAL BRITISH

01264 810527 | High Street, SO20 6HB

www.the3cups.co.uk

This 16th-century coaching inn is still very much a pub offering local ales, but it's also a dining destination with low-ceilinged dining room and an orangery extension opening up to the garden. The kitchen makes good use of local foodstuffs. There are bedrooms, too.

WINCHESTER *MAP 5, SU42*

Avenue Restaurant at Lainston House Hotel

ROSETTES SUPENDED MODERN BRITISH ⚑ NOTABLE WINE LIST

01962 776088 | Woodman Lane, Sparsholt, SO21 2LT

www.exclusive.co.uk/lainston-house

The Rosette award for this establishment has been suspended due to a change of chef and reassessment will take place in due course.
The imposing red-brick manor house is of 17th-century vintage, with an avenue of mature lime trees leading to it. It's that arboreal feature that is referenced in the name of the dignified dining room, where varnished oak panels set with contemporary wall lights, a marble fireplace and simple modern table settings establish the mood. Open-air dining on the terrace will coax the sun-lovers out.

Seats 60 Private dining 120 **Closed** 25-26 December
Parking 100 **Notes** Vegetarian dishes, children welcome

The Black Rat

◉◉ MODERN BRITISH

01962 844465 | 88 Chesil Street, SO23 0HX

www.theblackrat.co.uk

In an inconspicuous white-fronted former pub on the edge of town, The Black Rat sets its sights firmly on culinary modernism. Lots of good technical skills and techniques – good flavours and consistency across all dishes and efficient service to boot.

The Chesil Rectory

◉◉ MODERN BRITISH

01962 851555 | 1 Chesil Street, SO23 0HU

www.chesilrectory.co.uk

A beautiful half-timbered building dating from 1450, The Chesil Rectory is the oldest house in Winchester. Enter through a low door to be greeted by a brilliantly preserved interior with low beams, charming inglenook fireplaces and exposed brickwork, updated with lime green banquettes and stylish chairs. The kitchen puts a gently modernised spin on classic French dishes.

Marwell Hotel

◉◉ MODERN EUROPEAN

01962 777681 | Thompsons Lane, Colden Common, Marwell, SO21 1JY

www.marwellhotel.co.uk

A pastoral retreat in the manner of an African safari lodge, Marwell Hotel is set in wooded grounds next door to a wildlife park, so the odd screech of a monkey is to be expected. The kitchen applies modern styling to mostly traditional dishes.

Running Horse Inn

◉ CLASSIC BRITISH

01962 880218 | 88 Main Road, Littleton, SO22 6QS

www.runninghorseinn.co.uk

The Running Horse is a revitalised village inn with a relaxed and informal dining environment: a wood-burning stove in a brick fireplace, some banquette seating, wooden tables and a mixture of artwork adorning the walls. The kitchen delivers stimulating full-flavoured dishes.

The Wykeham Arms

◉◉ MODERN BRITISH

01962 853834 | 75 Kingsgate Street, SO23 9PE

www.wykehamarmswinchester.co.uk

A coaching inn since the mid-1700s, The Wykeham Arms offers simple options, listed as 'Home Comforts' on the menu, but this is a kitchen that can turn out a starter as fashionable as boneless chicken wings with BBQ emulsion and blue cheese sauce.

■ HEREFORDSHIRE

AYMESTREY
MAP 9, SO46

The Riverside at Aymestrey
◉◉ CLASSIC BRITISH
01568 708440 | The Riverside Inn, HR6 9ST
www.riversideaymestrey.co.uk
Close to Ludlow and Hereford on the edge of
Mortimer Forest, this 16th-century black and
white timber-framed inn features a kitchen that
is serious about its food, with produce from their
own garden. The menu changes daily and dishes
are simple and honest.

LEDBURY
MAP 10, SO73

Feathers
◉ MODERN BRITISH
01531 635266 | High Street, HR8 1DS
www.feathersledbury.co.uk/
The heavily timbered Feathers is a wonderful
slice of Tudor England, its oak-panelled
venerability thrown into relief by a modern
brasserie named after the hop variety Fuggles,
and an upmarket dining room, Quills. Sirloins and
fillets of local beef are a big draw.

ROSS-ON-WYE
MAP 10, SO52

Conservatory Restaurant
◉ BRITISH V
01989 763174 | King's Head Hotel, 8 High Street,
HR9 5HL
www.kingshead.co.uk
Dating from the 14th century, the King's Head is
woven into the historic high street's fabric and
comes with all the fireplaces and oak beams
you'd hope for in an inn of this vintage. The
cooking takes a modern tack, letting prime local
materials do the talking in flavour-led dishes.

Glewstone Court Country House
◉◉ TRADITIONAL BRITISH, EUROPEAN
01989 770367 | Glewstone, HR9 6AW
www.glewstonecourt.com
With pleasant views over the surrounding
countryside, the restaurant at Glewstone Court
family-owned Georgian retreat makes very good
use of local and high quality produce. The Cedar
Tree Restaurant offers seasonal fare with
regularly changing tasting menus also available.
The taster menu with wine flight is a very popular
choice here.

SYMONDS YAT [EAST]
MAP 10, SO51

Saracens Head Inn
◉ BRITISH
01600 890435 | HR9 6JL
www.saracensheadinn.co.uk
In a stunning location on the River Wye, The
Saracens Head can be reached by its own ferry,
operated by hand, just as it has for the past 200
years. There's a relaxed atmosphere throughout
this 16th-century inn, from the dining room to
two terraces.

■ HERTFORDSHIRE

BERKHAMSTED
MAP 6, SP90

The Gatsby
◉ MODERN FRENCH
01442 870403 | 97 High Street, HP4 2DG
www.thegatsby.net
In what locals call Berko, the art deco, former
Rex cinema is now a modern brasserie providing
not just modern European cuisine but also piano
accompaniment. Honey-roast ham hock rillettes
and celeriac remoulade is one way to start, with
pavé of Loch Duart salmon, tiger prawns and
squid ink risotto to follow.

BISHOP'S STORTFORD
MAP 6, TL42

Down Hall Hotel & Spa
◉ CONTEMPORARY BRITISH
01279 731441 | Hatfield Heath, CM22 7AS
www.downhall.co.uk
The house originally dates from the 1300s, but its
impressively grand Italianate exterior shows the
mark of a Victorian makeover. With period
details such as ornate cornices and white-
painted columns, the dining room has a vibe
reminiscent of an upmarket French brasserie.

CHANDLER'S CROSS
MAP 6, TQ09

The Stables Restaurant at The Grove
◉ MODERN BRITISH
01923 807807 | WD3 4TG
www.thegrove.co.uk/dining/the-stables/
The stable block of the Georgian mansion is now
an informal eatery with pared-back and sleek
decor reaching to the rafters. The open-to-view
kitchen is equipped with a wood-fired oven and
chargrill, but the menu has more going for it than
pizzas and steaks.

THOMPSON
St Albans

Set Lunch Menu
2/3 courses, £25/£29.50

Midweek Treat
4 courses, £42.50

Tasting Menus
5/7 courses, £69/£79

Allotment Tasting Menus
5/7 courses, £69/£79

Tasting Menu Wine Pairing
5/7 courses, £49/£59

Children's Menu
2/3 courses, £18/£21

Conservatory & Terrace
Dining Availability

f *thompsondining*
𝕏 *@thompsondining*
◎ *thompsondining*
www.thompsonstalbans.co.uk

ST ALBANS   MAP 6, TL10

THOMPSON St Albans

◉◉◉ **MODERN BRITISH** *V*
01727 730777 | 2 Hatfield Road, AL1 3RP
www.thompsonstalbans.co.uk

Fine dining, contemporary cooking with interesting combinations

Set in a row of four cottages predating the Second World War in the town centre, Phil Thompson's restaurant has put St Albans firmly on the gastronomic map with cooking that goes from strength to strength. Inside, it's a notch or two up from your average eatery, the dining room in subtle shades of grey, with white linen tables, and local artworks adding class to the walls (for sale, if anything catches your eye). Thompson's output is nothing if not inclusive, appealing to the local constituency with his seasonal and allotment inspired, plant based tasting menus, a children's menu, mid-week set lunch and 4 course mid-week treat options are an absolute steal. Whichever tempts you in, it's all underpinned by sound classical technique and is all about sharply judged flavours, vivid combinations of on-trend ingredients and gorgeous presentation. Inspired starters might

showcase citrus cured salmon gravlax, with pickled radish and avocado purée. Sure-footed and technically astute cooking is also a hallmark of main courses, bringing on the likes of confit belly of Blythburgh pork, served with roast onion and oregano purée, grelot onions and onion oil, while fish-based ideas might see roast fillet of grey mullet matched with buttered courgette, samphire and brown shrimp. Vegetarians will be delighted to see that meat-free dishes are no mere afterthought. There's a vegetarian (and a vegan) version of the tasting menus. Look for broad bean mousse, with goats' curd, garden shoots and croûtons or charred king oyster mushroom with spring onion, mushroom ketchup and pine nuts. Desserts show the same feel for astute flavour and

> "...is all about sharply judged flavours, vivid combinations of on-trend ingredients and gorgeous presentation."

texture combinations, with a well-conceived composition involving Sauternes and orange poached rhubarb, served with cream cheese mousse and meringue providing a tasty finisher. An intelligently compiled wine list delivers a global spread of bottles at sensible prices.

Chef Phil Thompson
Seats 90, Private dining 50
Notes Children welcome

See advertisement on page 141

DATCHWORTH
MAP 6, TL21

The Tilbury
◉◉ MODERN BRITISH 🔖
01438 815550 | Watton Road, SG3 6TB
www.thetilbury.co.uk

The Tilbury's kitchen is driven by quality, starting with carefully-sourced produce. A pub menu lists the likes of cottage pie or fish and chips with mushy peas and tartare sauce. Alternatively, move up a gear with pan-fried turbot paired with girolles, baby onions, kale and mash.

FLAUNDEN
MAP 6, TL00

Bricklayers Arms
◉ BRITISH, FRENCH
01442 833322 | Black Robin Lane,
Hogpits Bottom, HP3 0PH
www.bricklayersarms.com

The Bricklayers is a cheery Georgian pub with a cosy atmosphere, rustic oak beams, log fire and brick bar, with a garden and terrace. Food is a serious commitment, the kitchen sourcing locally and seasonally, supplementing the main menus with daily fish and vegetarian specials.

HEMEL HEMPSTEAD
MAP 6, TL00

Aubrey Park Hotel
◉ MODERN EUROPEAN
01582 792105 | Hemel Hempstead Road,
Redbourn, AL3 7AF
www.aubreypark.co.uk

It stands in nine acres of rolling countryside, dates back to 1287 and has an Iron Age hillfort in the grounds. Old in parts indeed, but Aubrey Park's interiors are contemporary, particularly the light, bright Brasserie, where friendly staff serve bistro classics.

HITCHIN
MAP 12, TL12

The Conservatory Restaurant NEW
◉◉ MODERN BRITISH, SEAFOOD 𝑉
01438 729500 | The Farmhouse at Redcoats,
Redcoats Green, SG4 7JR
www.farmhouseatredcoats.co.uk

Located within the original farmhouse and with lovely garden views, there is a homely feel to this restaurant. The modern British cooking has strong local provenance, with produce grown in the garden and at a sister property. Roasted Barbary duck breast, potato rösti, king oyster mushroom, pickled kohlrabi, mushroom ketchup and charcoal roasted hispi cabbage is a typical main course.

ST ALBANS
MAP 6, TL10

Chez Mumtaj
◉◉ FRENCH, ASIAN
01727 800033 | Centurion House, 136-142 London Road, AL1 1PQ
www.chezmumtaj.com

Maybe it's the subtle lighting, leather banquettes and wood panelling, but there's a touch of the gentlemen's club about this spacious restaurant, where pan-Asian and French cooking sometimes get quite neighbourly. Concise lunch, dinner and Asian tapas menus list Malaysian-style buttered black tiger prawns; corn-fed tandoori chicken with curly kale, saffron basmati; and sweet potato-stuffed beignets.

THOMPSON St Albans
◉◉◉ MODERN BRITISH
See pages 142-143

See advertisement on page 141

WELWYN
MAP 6, TL21

Auberge du Lac
◉◉ MODERN BRITISH
01707 368888 | Brocket Hall Estate, Brocket Road, AL8 7XG
www.aubergedulac.co.uk

In Brocket Hall's former hunting lodge, the Auberge takes its name from its lakeside setting overlooking the neoclassical Hall itself. The view alone might well prompt a daytime visit for a modern British lunch, maybe with ingredients foraged by the kitchen team on the magnificent 543-acre estate. A seven-course tasting menu is offered with optional paired wines.

The Wellington
◉ MODERN BRITISH
01438 714036 | High Street, AL6 9LZ
www.wellingtonatwelwyn.co.uk

The Wellington, on Welwyn's pretty high street, is an old coaching inn with rustic-chic exposed brick walls, real fires and a bar stocked with proper beers. The focus is firmly on the gastro side of the pub spectrum, with a simple, unpretentious menu.

The White Hart
◉ MODERN BRITISH
01438 715353 | 2 Prospect Place, AL6 9EN
whitehartwelwyn.co.uk
Beside the river in the village of Welwyn, this
17th-century coaching inn is owned and run by
brothers James and Tom Bainbridge, it's an inn
that oozes charm, from the cosy bar to the
flagstoned restaurant with its inglenook
fireplace. The thoroughly modern brasserie-style
menu has something for everyone.

WELWYN GARDEN CITY   MAP 6, TL21
Tewin Bury Farm Hotel
◉◉ MODERN BRITISH
01438 717793 | Hertford Road (B1000), AL6 0JB
www.tewinbury.co.uk
A complex of barns on a working farm has been
skilfully converted into this characterful modern
hotel. The restaurant is a handsome room with a
beamed ceiling above rafters, mustard-yellow
banquettes, and a boarded floor. Many of the
kitchen's raw materials are produced on site.

WILLIAN   MAP 12, TL23
The Fox
◉◉ MODERN BRITISH, SEAFOOD 𝒱
01462 480233 | SG6 2AE
www.foxatwillian.co.uk
If you lived in a village with just the one pub,
you'd hope for it to be a stylish gastro pub such
as this, its bar bristling with real ales, an open-
plan dining room and 25-seat conservatory, plus
a kitchen whose ambition goes beyond pub grub.

■ ISLE OF WIGHT

NEWPORT   MAP 5, SZ48
Thompsons
◉◉ MODERN EUROPEAN
01983 526118 | 11 Town Lane, PO30 1JU
www.robertthompson.co.uk
Robert Thompson has long been an ambassador
for the island and his eponymous restaurant has
a genuine buzz to it. An open-plan kitchen
ensures proper engagement with guests in the
uncluttered dining room, and shows a serious
commitment to island produce. Dishes are
eloquently executed.

SEAVIEW   MAP 5, SZ69
Seaview Hotel
◉◉ MODERN BRITISH
01983 612711 | High Street, PO34 5EX
www.seaviewhotel.co.uk
In the picturesque fishing village of Seaview, on
the island's north-east coast, this long-
established hotel is just 50 metres from the sea
that supplies much of the fish on the menu. The
cooking is refined with classic techniques letting
tip-top ingredients speak for themselves.

VENTNOR   MAP 5, SZ57
The Royal Hotel
◉◉ MODERN BRITISH
01983 852186 | Belgrave Road, PO38 1JJ
www.royalhoteliow.co.uk
The Royal is a handsome slice of Regency
grandeur on the Isle of Wight's south-east coast.
Inside, is a classic English tableau fully loaded
with crystal chandeliers, parquet floors and
decorative ironwork. The island's own
Gallybagger cheese opens proceedings in a
soaring soufflé.

Smoking Lobster
◉ BRITISH, PAN-ASIAN
01983 855938 | Esplanade, PO38 1JT
www.smokinglobster.co.uk

Bleached wooden floorboards, unclothed tables
and a minimal white decor jazzed up with
monochrome images of fish set a suitably
maritime mood in this easygoing eatery. As its
name suggests, fish and seafood are king, and
the pocket-sized galley kitchen sends out a nice
line in Asian-accented dishes to go with the
glorious sea views.

KENT

BIDDENDEN *MAP 7, TQ83*

The West House Restaurant with Rooms

◎◎◎ MODERN EUROPEAN ▮NOTABLE WINE LIST

01580 291341 | 28 High Street, TN27 8AH

www.thewesthouserestaurant.co.uk

This charming, tile-hung, 16th-century weaver's cottage in the picture-perfect village of Biddenden, The West House has all the twisty beams and interesting nooks and crannies you could possibly wish for. This is a family business, with husband and wife team Graham and Jackie Garrett running the kitchen and front-of-house respectively. There's a relaxed, friendly atmosphere in the dining room, with fresh flowers on the unclothed tables and fantastically seasonal dishes on the menu. Graham is a passionate and enthusiastic advocate of using the best possible produce in the most interesting ways, with an emphasis on simplicity and depth of flavour. A beautiful piece of main-course turbot is set on smoothly rich and creamy potato purée with crunchy pickled cucumber running through, along with light horseradish sauce that adds further complexity. Finish with mango cheesecake, accompanied by a divine mango sorbet and a refined and punchy mango salsa with a gentle kick of chilli.

Chef Graham Garrett **Seats** 32 **Closed** 24–26 December, 1 January **Parking** 7 **Notes** Children welcome

CANTERBURY *MAP 7, TR15*

ABode Canterbury

◎◎◎ MODERN EUROPEAN

01227 766266 | High Street, CT1 2RX

www.abodecanterbury.co.uk

An ornate arched portico announces the Canterbury branch of the go-ahead gastronomic hotel chain, which offers a champagne bar for that indispensable aperitif, and an expansive dining room with varnished floor, white walls and an appealing modern brasserie feel. There is also a chef's table, where up to a dozen inquisitive types can keep a beady eye on the kitchen flurry. The name of the game is well-balanced, technically accomplished cooking with much use of Kentish produce, and there's a tasting menu if you fancy it. Start with braised pig's cheek with pickled lotus root and crispy shallot, or crab with lime confit, mooli, and peanut chilli caramel.

Main courses might include sea bass with Jerusalem artichoke, smoked artichoke and chorizo sauce, or fillet of Kentish beef with salsify, oyster mushrooms and lovage. Dessert could be black sesame brûlée with honey and nutmeg ice cream, or go for the local cheeses with home-made chutney.

Chef Catalin Jauca **Seats** 76, Private dining 12 **Open** All Year **Parking** 40 **Notes** Children welcome

The Corner House *NEW*

◎◎ MODERN BRITISH

01227 780793 | 1 Dover Street, CT1 3HD

www.cornerhouserestaurants.co.uk

A 16th-century former coach house overlooking Canterbury's city walls, this stylish restaurant deals in no-nonsense modern favourites. Mains include chicken supreme, wild garlic, gnocchi, asparagus, leeks and wild mushrooms, or confit pork belly, black pudding, purple sprouting broccoli, mash and cider jus. Leave room for stout cake and coffee ice cream.

Fordwich Arms

◎◎◎ BRITISH ▮NOTABLE WINE LIST

01227 710444 | 1647 King Street, Sturry, CT2 0DB

www.fordwicharms.co.uk

The 1930s country boozer with a terrace and garden looking over the River Stour was begging for a makeover, and that's just what it got when high-flying young chef-patron Dan Smith took the helm in 2018 and immediately turned the place into a foodie destination. The updated stripped-back style looks the part without detracting from the period charm of its oak-panelled dining room, cosy open fires and 1930s-vintage bar. Smith's cooking is firmly in the new-wave modern British camp, allying sharp technique with intriguing combinations of first-class materials. Spitfire ale sourdough and rye bread with smoked pork fat and braised onions is a storming start, before poached Whitstable oysters that come pointed up with diced apple, caviar and light creamy sauce. Main-course venison of buttery tenderness is served as fillet and confit with celeriac, damson, smoked bone marrow and a full-throttle jus. For dessert, perhaps, baked St Clements cheesecake with Cointreau granita.

Chef Daniel and Natasha Smith **Seats** 60, Private dining 36 **Closed** 25 December **Parking** 12 **Notes** Children welcome

The Goods Shed

◉ BRITISH

01227 459153 | Station Road West, CT2 8AN
www.thegoodsshed.co.uk

In a split-level space overlooking the bustle of the indoor farmers' market stalls next to Canterbury West station, this easygoing restaurant has chunky pine tables with views through majestic arched windows over the railway. Straightforward treatments allow the sheer quality of local and seasonal market produce to shine; the menu changes daily.

THE PIG at Bridge Place NEW

◉◉ CLASSIC BRITISH ꩜NOTABLE WINE LIST

01227 830208 | Bourne Park Road, Bridge, CT4 5LF
www.thepighotel.com/at-bridge-place

This elegant 16th-century manor house has a notable rock 'n' roll history, as Pink Floyd and Led Zeppelin were among bands who performed here in the 1970s. Now part of THE PIG litter of boutique hotels, seasonal produce stars in dishes like beetroot and bacon soup followed by fillet of day-boat cod, salad onions and cockles.

CRUNDALE
MAP 7, TR04

The Compasses Inn

◉◉ MODERN BRITISH

01227 700300 | Sole Street, CT4 7ES
www.thecompassescrundale.co.uk

Run by Rob and Donna Taylor, this inn in a quiet hamlet is brimming with classic country pub rustic charm - all low beams, hopbines and walk-in fireplaces. The Compasses has become a real foodie hotspot, such is the growing reputation for Rob's accomplished cooking - expect muscular food that satisfies with gutsy flavours wrought from excellent seasonal produce.

DARTFORD
MAP 6, TQ57

Rowhill Grange Hotel & Utopia Spa

◉◉ MODERN EUROPEAN

01322 615136 | Wilmington, DA2 7QH
www.alexanderhotels.co.uk

A substantial 18th-century manor in acres of grounds that include a pond, Rowhill Grange is now an upmarket boutique hotel. RG's is the serious dining option, where roast hare (a welcome appearance) is served with textures of cauliflower and beer onions, for instance.

DEAL
MAP 7, TR35

Dunkerleys Hotel & Restaurant

◉◉ MODERN BRITISH

01304 375016 | 19 Beach Street, CT14 7AH
www.dunkerleys.co.uk

Considering this is a seafront restaurant with a maritime theme, it's no surprise that Dunkerleys Hotel & Restaurant has a strong focus on local seafood, delivered in fuss-free dishes by the friendly down-to-earth chef owner. It's practically on Deal Beach and the pier's just a short walk away, if you fancy catching some of your own seafood.

FAVERSHAM
MAP 7, TR06

Read's Restaurant

◉◉ MODERN BRITISH

01795 535344 | Macknade Manor, Canterbury Road, ME13 8XE
www.reads.com

Chef-patron David Pitchford's Georgian manor house has long been a Kentish destination for those in the know. Set in lush and peaceful grounds, it feels like a country retreat, and is run with the friendly, grown-up affability we hope to find in such places.

FOLKESTONE
MAP 7, TR23

Rocksalt

◉◉ MODERN BRITISH V

01303 212070 | 4-5 Fishmarket, CT19 6AA
www.rocksaltfolkestone.co.uk

Sitting on the harbour with a curving terrace cantilevered out over the water, a huge sliding glass wall to capitalise on the view and a classy, well-designed interior with oak floors, Rocksalt's menu has seafood at its heart. Save room for baked egg custard tart though.

GRAFTY GREEN
MAP 7, TQ84

Who'd A Thought It

◉◉ BRITISH

01622 858951 | Headcorn Road, ME17 2AR
www.whodathoughtit.com

A champagne and oyster bar with rooms in a Kentish village not far from the M20 designed with racy opulence. As well as a menu of modern classics, shellfish platters and thermidor will please seafood purists, as will sticky toffee pudding with butterscotch sauce for those with a sweet tooth.

HAWKHURST
MAP 7, TQ73

The Queen's Inn

◉ MODERN BRITISH

01580 754233 | Rye Road, TN18 4EY
www.thequeensinnhawkhurst.co.uk

Rejuvenated by its dynamic owners, this inviting pub offers an appealing line in hearty food. Inside, there is rustic-chic charm, pleasingly fuss-free service and a menu of unpretentious cooking that supports local producers. A separate dining room serves charcoal-grilled meat and fish dishes, plus pizzas from a wood-burning oven.

HYTHE
MAP 7, TR13

Hide and Fox *NEW*

◉◉◉ MODERN BRITISH

See page opposite

Hythe Imperial

◉ MODERN, TRADITIONAL

01303 267441 | Princes Parade, CT21 6AE
www.hytheimperial.co.uk

This elegant hotel stands looking out across the Channel from its prominent position on the seafront. Dishes are served on the finest tableware, in keeping with the grandeur of the setting, and menus include tried and tested favourites with an eye on seasonal produce.

KILNDOWN
MAP 6, TQ73

The Small Holding

◉◉ BRITISH *V*

01892 890105 | Ranters Lane, TN17 2SG
thesmallholding.restaurant

What was once a run-down village pub has been given a fresh lease of life here. The acre of land that came with the pub is now home to chickens, pigs and two polytunnels (hence the name) and dishes contain as much of their own produce as possible. The style is daily-changing tasting menus – 5 or 8 courses of small, rustic tasting plates plus vegetarian and vegan menus.

LENHAM
MAP 7, TQ85

Chilston Park Hotel

◉◉ MODERN BRITISH

01622 859803 | Sandway, ME17 2BE
www.handpickedhotels.co.uk/chilstonpark

Secluded in 22 acres of sublime landscaped gardens and parkland, Chilston Park brims with enough period authenticity, antiques and oil paintings that you might be inspired to dress as Mr Darcy or Elizabeth Bennet for dinner in the unique, sunken Venetian-style Culpeper's restaurant. The food is right up-to-date though.

Continued on page 150

Hide and Fox NEW

◎◎◎ MODERN BRITISH
01303 260915 | The Green, Saltwood, CT21 4PS
www.hideandfox.co.uk

Tucked away in the Kent coastal hinterlands near the edge of Romney Marsh, Hide and Fox is reason enough to venture off the beaten path. The venue occupies an old general store on Saltwood village green – a charming space of unshowy elegance in shades of blue and cream, with antique wood floors, all dominated by a beautifully crafted antique spice cupboard. The team behind it all have form: chef-patron Allister Barsby has served his time in stellar kitchens around the UK, while partner Alice Bussi's formidable experience as a sommelier means you can be sure the wines are up to scratch. Seasonal Kentish produce is the bedrock of the five- and eight-course tasting menus. Expect the likes of a ravioli filled with confit chicken and egg yolk on a base of lyonnaise onions and deeply flavoured chicken broth, or simply stunning Kentish lamb loin and pressed belly with artichoke purée, leek and mint gel. To finish, Nashi pear comes poached and as a sorbet, supported by white chocolate mousse, butterscotch and salted granola.

Chef Allister Barsby Open All year Seats 26
Prices from S £10 M£24 D£9
Notes Vegetarian dishes, no children in evenings

LEYSDOWN-ON-SEA
MAP 7, TR07

The Ferry House Inn
⊚ MODERN BRITISH

01795 510214 | Harty Ferry Road, ME12 4BQ

www.theferryhouseinn.co.uk

The Ferry House, a country inn alongside the Swale Estuary, has put the Isle of Sheppey on the culinary map. It's possible to eat in the bar, but the majority of diners book into the raftered Barn Restaurant. The kitchen's style is modern British.

MAIDSTONE
MAP 7, TQ75

Fish on the Green
⊚⊚ BRITISH, FRENCH

01622 738300 | Church Lane, Bearsted Green, ME14 4EJ

www.fishonthegreen.com

The pretty village green setting can be described as quintessentially English, and Fish on the Green has netted a strong local fan base with its fresh, unpretentious interior, clued-up staff, and excellent fish and seafood from a kitchen that treats super-fresh materials with intelligent simplicity. If you don't fancy fish, there are always appealing meat and veggie dishes in the mix.

MARGATE
MAP 7, TR37

The Ambrette
⊚ MODERN INDIAN

01843 231504 | 10 Fort Hill, CT9 1HD

www.theambrette.co.uk

Overlooking the sandy bay and the Turner Contemporary gallery, Dev Biswal's cheery eatery combines modern British and Indian flavours into an exciting fusion, amid a bright and neutral contemporary decor that is more Anglo than Asian. The presentation of dishes is also more akin to European mode and there's bags of flavour and plenty of Kentish produce to boot.

Angela's NEW
⊚ BRITISH

01843 319 978 | 21 The Parade, CT9 1EX

www.angelasofmargate.com

In a great setting close to the seafront, Angela's originally opened as a café in the fifties. It's undergone some changes since then, but the name remains. Everything that can be is recycled or reused, and they're making every effort to produce zero plastic waste. It's a small place, with just 20 seats in two rooms and an open kitchen. The blackboard menu changes daily, according to what fresh fish is available, and dishes are presented and cooked with pleasing simplicity.

Buoy and Oyster – Margate
⊚⊚ MODERN BRITISH, SEAFOOD

01843 446631 | 44 High Street, CT9 1DS

www.buoyandoyster.com

Overlooking the beach in Margate's up-and-coming Old Town, Buoy and Oyster is an inviting fish and seafood-oriented restaurant. Bare brickwork, an open kitchen and local artwork work a maritime look; beach views, outdoor tables, and well-tuned modern British food with an emphasis on fish and seafood seal the deal.

MINSTER
MAP 7, TR36

The Corner House
⊚⊚ BRITISH

01843 823000 | 42 Station Road, CT12 4BZ

www.cornerhouserestaurants.co.uk

Opposite the church in the tranquil village of Minster, The Corner House restaurant-with-rooms makes good use of its rural location by showcasing locally sourced ingredients. Expect the likes of garden pea pannacotta, Broadstairs crab mayo and Granny Smith apple followed by roasted duck breast, confit carrot, braised cavolo nero, mash and orange sauce.

ROYAL TUNBRIDGE WELLS   *MAP 6, TQ53*

Hotel du Vin Tunbridge Wells

⊛ BRITISH, FRENCH 🍷 NOTABLE WINE LIST

01892 526455 | Crescent Road, TN1 2LY

www.hotelduvin.com

A Grade II listed Georgian mansion is home to HdV's operation in Tunbridge Wells and the enormous wine lists remain an integral part of the attraction of this hotel chain. The cooking continues on a solid French bistro basis, as well as more Anglo comfort-food.

The Kentish Hare

⊛⊛ MODERN BRITISH

01892 525709 | 95 Bidborough Ridge, Bidborough, TN3 0XB

www.thekentishhare.com

The Kentish Hare is a stylish weatherboarded village inn that offers a real welcome. Chunky oak tables, fresh flowers, bare bricks, wood floors, and lots of hares scattered around in the fabrics and decor. There's also a large terrace area out back. The cuisine is modern British using excellent produce, and demonstrating real cooking skills that shine through.

Thackeray's

⊛⊛⊛ MODERN EUROPEAN 🍷 NOTABLE WINE LIST

01892 511921 | 85 London Road, TN1 1EA

www.thackerays-restaurant.co.uk

Once home to the novelist William Makepeace Thackeray, author of *Vanity Fair*, this lovely, white-weatherboarded old building dates back more than 300 years. Inside, it's full of delightful period details – sloping ceilings, odd little corners, uneven steps – a fine setting, with bags of character. The dining room is a great combination of ancient and modern, with stylishly up-to-date touches and smart table settings. The food, too, is elegantly contemporary and intelligently constructed, with precise presentation and refined, intricate re-workings of classic combinations. Service hits all the right notes of friendliness and professionalism. Begin with maple-glazed roasted veal sweetbreads with orzo pasta and flaked osso bucco, girolles and winter truffles, before moving on to cannon of lamb with roast pear, braised neck fillet, toasted almonds, and potato and thyme terrine. Bring things to a close with roast banana soufflé with white chocolate and lime crème anglaise and kalamansi sorbet.

Chef Pat Hill **Seats** 70, Private dining 16 **Open** All Year **Notes** Children welcome

The Twenty Six

⊛⊛ MODERN BRITISH

01892 544607 | 15a Church Road, Southborough, TN4 0RX

www.thetwenty-six.co.uk

When it comes to the number of seats there are for diners in this cosy restaurant from Scott Goss, the clue is in the name. To keep things interesting for visitors and staff, the menu changes every day but innovative dishes stick rigidly to the seasons.

Zagatos Brasserie

⊛ MODERN, TRADITIONAL BRITISH

01892 520331 | The Spa Hotel, Mount Ephraim, TN4 8XJ

www.spahotel.co.uk

This grande dame of the elegant Georgian hotels in Tunbridge Wells continues to capitalise on the spa business. The Zagatos brasserie presents a rather more contemporary face, with crowd-pleasing modern cooking to boot, while the sumptuous Chandelier Restaurant provides something rather more refined for a special occasion.

STALISFIELD GREEN   *MAP 7, TQ95*

The Plough Inn

⊛⊛ MODERN BRITISH V

01795 890256 | ME13 0HY

www.theploughinnstalisfield.co.uk

High up on the North Downs, with far-reaching views, stands this 15th-century, timber-framed, Wealden hall house. Dining takes place in both a cosy pubby area, where an impressive list of past landlords is displayed, and a second space, more restaurant-like, yet still informal.

TENTERDEN

The Swan Wine Kitchen
◎◎ EUROPEAN
01580 761616 | Chapel Down Winery, Small Hythe Road, TN30 7NG
www.swanchapeldown.co.uk

This striking, bare timber and galvanised steel building lies in the grounds of Chapel Down Winery, one of England's leading winemakers. Both the bar and terrace offer delightful countryside views, while from the open-plan kitchen comes a short but appealing choice of modern European dishes.

WEST MALLING

The Swan
◎◎ MODERN BRITISH
01732 521910 | 35 Swan Street, ME19 6JU
www.theswanwestmalling.co.uk
The Swan started life as a coaching inn back in the 15th century and it still draws the crowds. Inside, you'll find brasserie-style menus on offer, showcasing high-quality Kentish farm produce in carefully-constructed dishes inspired by global flavours and techniques.

WHITSTABLE

The Sportsman
◎◎ MODERN BRITISH
01227 273370 | Faversham Road, Seasalter, CT5 4BP
www.thesportsmanseasalter.co.uk
The Sportsman has a distinctly rustic, unpretentious look, with scuffed floorboards and plain walls hung with pictures above half-panelling. Everything is made in-house, including the butter. You might choose to start with an appetiser of super-fresh oysters topped with warm chorizo.

WINGHAM

The Dog at Wingham
◎◎ MODERN BRITISH
01227 720339 | Canterbury Road, CT3 1BB
thedog.co.uk
Close to Canterbury, this lovely village pub once formed part of a former monastery dating from the 13th century. A boutique makeover has lent the place a sympathetic 21st-century sheen, with mismatched furniture adding a rustic-chic edge to the cosy wood-panelled restaurant. Seasonal British ingredients drive the inventive cooking.

WROTHAM

The Bull
◎◎ MODERN BRITISH ♦ NOTABLE WINE LIST
01732 789800 | Bull Lane, TN15 7RF
www.thebullhotel.com

Lying just below the North Downs, The Bull is a 14th-century country inn that was first licensed in 1495 and still has plenty of original features creating an atmospheric and relaxed setting. There are plenty of food options but meats from the on-site smokery are a specialty and include chicken, beef and pork.

WYE

Wife of Bath
◎◎ MODERN SPANISH
01233 812232 | 4 Upper Bridge Street, TN25 5AF
www.thewifeofbath.com
Part of Mark Sargeant's growing collection of pubs and restaurants, The Wife of Bath has been a restaurant here since the 1960s. The dining room's wood floors and grey wash walls give the place a cool Nordic look but the menus take their inspiration from northern Spain.

■ LANCASHIRE

BLACKBURN
MAP 18, SD62

The Millstone, Mellor
⊛ MODERN BRITISH
01254 813333 | Church Lane, Mellor, BB2 7JR
www.millstonehotel.co.uk
Owned by Thwaites Brewery, whose ales are at the pumps, it's not all about beer at this old coaching inn. It also deals in feel-good menus that offer up pub classics, lunchtime sandwiches, locally sourced steaks cooked on the grill, and a few global flavours.

BURNLEY
MAP 18, SD83

Bertram's Restaurant
⊛⊛ BRITISH
01282 471913 | Crow Wood, Royle Lane, BB12 0RT
bertramsrestaurant.com/
Crow Wood, a modern hotel with extensive spa and leisure facilities, is set in 100 acres of woodland. Bertram's Restaurant, a stylish space with unclothed dark wood tables and smartly upholstered chairs, is popular with locals and guests alike. Prosecco cocktails get a meal of wide-ranging options off to a good start.

Fence Gate - Brasserie *NEW*
⊛ MODERN BRITISH
01282 509555 | Wheatly Lane Road, Fence, BB12 9EP
www.fencegate.co.uk
Booking is strongly advised for a table at the popular Fence Gate Brasserie. Notable are the small gin bar, and the meat ageing room, that specialises in 35-day dry aged beef ribs. Expect friendly and attentive service, hearty portions and a convivial atmosphere. Menus display a confident combination of quality pub dishes alongside more refined modern British offerings.

White Swan at Fence
⊛⊛ MODERN BRITISH
01282 611773 | 300 Wheatley Lane Road, Fence, BB12 9QA
www.whiteswanatfence.co.uk
Retaining all that makes the British pub such a national asset, while applying the highest standards in every department, the team at the White Swan create something special. It's a pub all right, but there's home-made damson vodka, and a chef delivering powerful flavours.

Wilfreds *NEW*
⊛ MODERN BRITISH, INTERNATIONAL
01282 471913 | Royle Lane, BB12 0RT
wilfredsrestaurant.com
Although it's set in a brand new, modern building, Wilfred's has a rich, plush, sophisticated appeal, almost like 1940s New York. Seating is comfortable, staff are friendly and attentive, and the whole place has a real buzz. The cooking claims an Italian theme, but the reality is more eclectic, offering a modern twist on many ethnic flavours.

CLITHEROE
MAP 18, SD74

Coach and Horses *NEW*
⊛⊛ MODERN BRITISH
01200 447331 | Main Street, Bolton by Bowland, BB7 4NW
www.coachandhorsesribblevalley.co.uk
The Coach and Horses is a large country inn in a picture perfect country village. The large bar with clubby blue decor with an open fire for colder days. The flagged floor restaurant is a brightly decorated space and has a wood burning stove and along one wall is entirely glassed looking into the onsite microbrewery. The staff are very friendly but still professional. Expect evolving seasonal menus in a modern British style – it's thoughtful and composed dining with flavours and ingredients that are very local.

COWAN BRIDGE
MAP 18, SD67

Hipping Hall
◉◉◉◉ MODERN BRITISH ▲NOTABLE WINE LIST

015242 71187 | LA6 2JJ

www.hippinghall.com

The word 'hipping' is an old term for the stepping-stones that cross the Broken Beck stream running through the hall's delightful gardens. Built in the 17th and 18th centuries, the pocket-sized country house is in a beautiful spot on the borders of Lancashire, Yorkshire and Cumbria, and is done out with a classical elegance, and offers a real draw in its stylish restaurant, where boarded floors, walls done in local pigments, soaring oak beams and a rustic fireplace feel rooted into the area. The restaurant is a 15th-century hall with tapestries and a minstrels' gallery that is as impressive as it is intimate. Expect modern, innovative cuisine with old flavours rooted in local produce and countryside. The service is personal and knowledgeable and a real asset to the whole set-up.

Seats 34, Private dining 14 **Parking** 20 **Notes** No children under 12 years

GREAT ECCLESTON
MAP 18, SD44

The Cartford Inn
◉◉ MODERN BRITISH

01995 670166 | Cartford Lane, PR3 0YP

www.thecartfordinn.co.uk

On the banks of the River Fylde, this ever-evolving 17th-century coaching inn is enlivened by the owners' own artwork and creative eye. The menu revels in Lancashire's fine produce, bringing it together in imaginative ideas that aim to comfort rather than challenge.

LANCASTER
MAP 18, SD46

Wagon & Horses NEW
◉◉ MODERN BRITISH

01524 846094 | 27 St Georges Quay, LA1 1RD

www.wagonandhorseslancaster.co.uk

Set on St George's Quay, overlooking the River Lune, the Wagon and Horses is a pub that presents an excellent modern British dining menu alongside some upgraded pub favourites. Service is very friendly, knowledgeable and attentive, and food flavours are both considered and balanced. Look out for their pork fillet or Scottish loch trout with mussels.

See advertisement opposite

LANGHO
MAP 18, SD73

Northcote Restaurant
◉◉◉◉ MODERN BRITISH *V* ▲NOTABLE WINE LIST

See pages 156–157

LOWER BARTLE
MAP 18, SD43

Bartle Hall Hotel
◉ MODERN BRITISH

01772 690506 | Lea Lane, PR4 0HA

www.bartlehall.co.uk

Between Blackpool and Preston, Bartle Hall is conveniently positioned for the M6 and the Lake District. Set within extensive gardens, this former private residence can be traced back to the 16th century although these days it's a comfortable modern hotel and wedding venue.

LYTHAM ST ANNES
MAP 18, SD32

Bedford Hotel
◉ MODERN BRITISH

01253 724636 | 307–313 Clifton Drive South, FY8 1HN

www.bedford-hotel.com

The Bedford is a welcoming, family-run Victorian hotel with lots going on. Its Cartland Restaurant has plenty of period charm, with decorative plasterwork, warm pastel tones, black-and-white prints of film stars and neatly laid tables. The cooking steers sensibly clear of left-field flavours.

Clifton Arms Hotel
◉ BRITISH

01253 739898 | West Beach, Lytham, FY8 5QJ

www.cliftonarmslytham.com

The present red-brick building dates from early Victorian times and is on the site of what was a small inn. Chic table settings with good napery and floral adornments look the part against the neutral hues of the main dining room, where bay windows give wide sea views. The kitchen delivers contemporary cooking that moves with the seasons.

WAGON & HORSES

RELAXED - QUALITY

TO BOOK PLEASE VISIT OUR WEBSITE
WWW.WAGONANDHORSESLANCASTER.CO.UK
OR CALL ON 01524 846094

Wagon & Horses
27 St. Georges Quay, Lancaster. LA1 1RD

f WagonAndHorses

Northcote Restaurant

⊛ ⊛ ⊛ ⊛ **MODERN BRITISH** *V* 🍷 NOTABLE WINE LIST
01254 240555 | Northcote Road, BB6 8BE
www.northcote.com

Sophisticated modern cooking at a long-established northern gem

As well as enjoying beautiful setting in the Ribble Valley, with fabulous views of the Forest of Bowland from the terrace – an ideal place for pre-dinner drinks – Northcote is justly famous as one of the best places to eat in the North. The original manor is red-brick and Victorian, much extended over the years, and is comfortably decorated in a relaxed modern style, with contemporary art works and elegant furnishings. It's a lovely place to stay and the highlight, of course, is the food. Lisa Goodwin-Allen is a staple of *The Great British Menu* and as executive chef she oversees a kitchen that takes its inspiration from the best of local ingredients (including some from Northcote's own kitchen garden), her years of experience and technical know-how are clear to see in sophisticated interpretations of classic dishes with a definite Lancashire accent. At lunch there's

a very reasonably priced seasonal three-course offering, while dinner presents a five-course tasting option, along with a vegetarian version. You might begin an early summer meal with refined and delicate Yorkshire asparagus with sheep's curd, sourdough and sorrel. Next up, an Orkney scallop is surrounded by a burst of colour and flavour with Isle of Wight tomato and basil, while the next courses offer knockout wild turbot, followed by Norfolk poussin, hen of the woods, garlic and alliums. Later in the year there might be chalk stream trout with mussel butter and charred yellow courgette, and 75-day aged Lake District beef with smoked marrowbone, slow-cooked onion and watercress. Vegetarians will be delighted by dishes such as young courgette with

> "..sophisticated interpretations of classic dishes with a definite Lancashire accent."

crispy flower, cucumber, dill and potato Lyonnaise. End on a high note with a stunning take on Amalfi lemon, bursting with sweet and tangy limoncello. Accompanying it all is one of the region's outstanding wine lists, its glories dispensed with engaging knowledgeability by a fine sommelier.

Chef Lisa Goodwin-Allen
Seats 70, Private dining 60
Closed Late January - early February (Obsession Food & Wine Festival)
Parking 60
Notes Children welcome

MORECAMBE
MAP 18, SD46

Best Western Lothersdale Hotel
◉ MODERN BRITISH

01524 416404 | 320-323 Marine Road, LA4 5AA

www.bfhotels.com

Run by the same family for more than 50 years, the seafront Lothersdale Hotel on the promenade in Morecambe has a separate bar and tapas area with an outside terrace area providing wonderful views across the bay to the Lakeland fells.

NEWTON-IN-BOWLAND
MAP 18, SD65

Parkers Arms
◉ MODERN BRITISH

01200 446236 | BB7 3DY

www.parkersarms.co.uk

Once the coach house of next-door Newton Hall, the white-fronted Parkers Arms hides in a Ribble Valley village near the Trough of Bowland. Inside, are stone floors and low ceilings, with a conservatory feel in the dining area. Nearly all produce is sourced within 30 miles.

ORMSKIRK
MAP 15, SD40

The Barn at Moor Hall
◉◉◉ BRITISH V

01695 572511 | Prescot Road, L39 6RT

www.moorhall.com

In five-acre grounds with a lake and accompanied by one of the UK's top restaurants in a glass-walled modernist extension, this boutique hideaway already has enough going for it. But if you're not up for the full-works, culinary virtuosity of the main attraction, this little sibling is no slouch, serving up sharp contemporary food in a casual, beamed setting. Start with perfectly timed smoked haddock with red lentil dhal, cumin foam, coriander and puffed rice, then move on to a full-bore plate of pork belly with heavenly crisp crackling alongside smoked apple, morels and roasted foie gras.

Chef Mark Birchall (Chef Patron) and Nathan Cornwell
Seats 65 **Closed** 2-26 January **Parking** 40
Notes Children welcome

Moor Hall Restaurant with Rooms
◉◉◉◉ MODERN BRITISH V 🏆

See pages 160-161

See advertisement opposite

THORNTON
MAP 18, SD34

Twelve Restaurant and Lounge Bar
◉◉ MODERN BRITISH

01253 821212 | Marsh Mill Village, Fleetwood Road North, FY5 4JZ

www.twelve-restaurant.co.uk

Twelve Restaurant's edgy design ethic embraces stripped-back bare bricks, exposed air ducts and roof beams, alongside sleek designer furniture and graffiti portraits of 20th-century cultural icons. The feel is definitely 'art space'. Staff are skilled, knowledgeable and well drilled, but still spontaneous and friendly. Food's in the modern city neighbourhood restaurant style. Simple things done well, with bold flavours.

WHALLEY
MAP 18, SD73

Breda Murphy Restaurant
◉ MODERN BRITISH AND IRISH

01254 823446 | 41 Station Road, BB7 9RH

www.bredamurphy.co.uk

After a top-to-toe makeover in 2017, this vibrant enterprise now comprises a contemporary restaurant, a gin bar and a casual daytime deli/café. Sitting cheek by jowl with the landmark Whalley Viaduct, it's ideally placed for friendly get-togethers accompanied by unfussy bistro dishes with hearty Irish and British accents.

Continued on page 162

MOOR HALL
RESTAURANT WITH ROOMS

...ot Road, Aughton, Lancashire L39 6RT • Tel: 01695 572511 • enquiry@moorhall.com • www.moorhall.co...

Moor Hall is a stunning grade II* listed building that is steeped in history dating back to the 13th century. Open since March 2017, *Moor Hall* has already been awarded 2 Michelin Stars, 5 AA Rosettes, ranked #1 restaurant in the UK at the *National Restaurant Awards*, ranked Number 11 in *Good Food Guide UK* Top 50 restaurants, named *GQ Newcomer of the Year* and also winning *Restaurant of The Year* at the *Lancashire Life Food & Drink Awards 2017*.

Set in five acres of breathtaking gardens overlooking a beautiful lake, 2 Michelin starred *Moor Hall Restaurant with Rooms* is in an idyllic setting to enjoy the delicate, produce driven menus inspired by our exceptional natural surroundings and talented chef patron Mark Birchall.

Moor Hall has 7 luxurious guest bedrooms, each one stunningly unique. 5 are located in the main Hall with a further 2 in the gatehouse by the lake. Each of the bedrooms within the Hall has a wonderful view of the lake or gardens.

Following the huge success of *Moor Hall*, Mark Birchall has also opened a casual dining restaurant *e Barn at Moor Hall* on the same 5 acre site and it promises great things! Achieving a Michelin Bib Gourmand, 3 AA Rosettes and winning *Lancashire Life Newcomer of the Year*, The Barn menu ranges from 35 day aged rib eye steaks to a full vegetarian menu, delicious side dishes, children's menu and puddings galore. The Barn has something for everyone including a fantastic selection of hand crafted cocktails, bottled and draught beers.

To make a reservation visit www.moorhall.com or call our reservations team on 01695 572511.

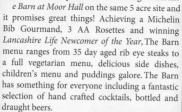

Moor Hall Restaurant with Rooms

⊛⊛⊛⊛⊛ MODERN BRITISH *V* ⬥NOTABLE WINE LIST
01695 572511 | Prescot Road, L39 6RT
www.moorhall.com

Breathtaking destination restaurant and dynamic modern food

Aughton is just outside Ormskirk, and Moor Hall, set in five acres of beautiful gardens, is Grade II* listed and dates back to the mid-16th century. Since taking over in 2015, Andy and Tracey Bell have worked hard here, overseeing a multi-million pound renovation, and, along with head chef Mark Birchall, they've created a stunning destination restaurant with rooms. The house itself is warmly traditional, with oak beams and floorboards and open fires, beautifully decorated and furnished with wonderful attention to detail. This focus can also be seen in the modern, glass-walled extension that houses the restaurant and state-of-the art open kitchen. Everything, from staff uniforms to light fittings, chairs and table settings, has been carefully chosen. Many of the vegetables in summer dishes are grown in the impressive kitchen gardens and the constantly evolving menus.

The eight-course taster, served at both lunch and dinner, and a four-course lunch option are dynamically modern with pin-sharp contemporary interpretations, influenced by Birchall's time at Simon Rogan's L'Enclume. You can expect extremely thoughtful, often virtuoso cooking, running from baked carrots with Doddington cheese, chrysanthemum and sea buckthorn, through turnip and crab with anise hyssop and green almond, before taking in Scottish langoustine with smoked marrow, tomato and rosehip, wild Cornish sea bass with mussel, courgette and sea greens, and honey roast Sladesdown duck with girolle, sweetcorn and beans, ragout and whey onion, liver and truffle. Eve's Delight is a dessert of strawberries, cream cheese, sweet cicely and rye, and Merchant cherries are enhanced by flavours of woodruff, almond,

> "...constantly evolving menus are dynamically modern with pin-sharp contemporary interpretations..."

sorrel and muscovado. The wine list is impressive, with a clear focus on food matching and a dedicated sommelier team to support it.

Chef Mark Birchall
Seats 50, Private dining 14
Closed 2-26 January; 31 July to 17 August; 25-26 December
Parking 40
Notes No children under 12 years at dinner

See advertisement on page 159

WHALLEY continued

The Freemasons at Wiswell

☺☺☺ MODERN BRITISH ☝ NOTABLE WINE LIST

01254 822218 | 8 Vicarage Fold, Wiswell, BB7 9DF
www.freemasonsatwiswell.com

A cream-painted inn on a lane in well-heeled Wiswell, The Freemasons has a pleasantly bucolic air, with small carpets thrown over the flagged floor, stressed bare tables and rolled-up kitchen cloths for napkins. The preference for rustic flavours such as those that pickling produces means that pub food meets cutting-edge gastronomy halfway, and Steven Smith plays his part with appetisers of Lancashire cheese tartlets topped with pickled mushrooms, before a first course like planched foie gras on toast with smoked eel and Yorkshire rhubarb in beer vinegar. Fortifying main dishes are the norm, as in slow-cooked suckling pig with crispy belly, sticky cheek and black pudding, alongside silky sweet potato purée in fish-savoury XO sauce, or cod poached with seaweed, served with salt cod cannelloni and wild mushrooms in buttery chicken stock sauce. Finish with Cluizel dark chocolate mousse, served with pineapple poached in PX sherry with raisins and razor-sharp passionfruit sorbet.

Chef Steven Smith, Matthew Smith Seats 70, Private dining 14 Closed from 2 January for 2 weeks Notes Children welcome

WREA GREEN   MAP 18, SD33

The Spa Hotel at Ribby Hall Village

☺☺ MODERN, TRADITIONAL

01772 674484 | Ribby Hall Village, Ribby Road, PR4 2PR
www.ribbyhall.co.uk/the-spa-hotel

As its name makes clear, there are some pretty swanky spa facilities at this classy adult-only retreat in 100 acres of Lancashire countryside. The Brasserie and its Orangery extension are another string to its bow, done out with orange and lime leather seats.

THE VILLA WREA GREEN

This 19th century 4 star country house hotel is set amidst rolling parkland in the wonderful surroundings of the Lancashire countryside.

Enjoy a culinary delight in our 2 AA Rosetted Restaurant open to non-residents all year round!

Ideally located off the M55 close to the Lytham St Annes and Blackpool, this hidden gem is a must-try!

The Villa Wrea Green, Moss Side Lane, Preston, Lancashire, PR4 2PE
T: 01772 80 40 40 E: reception@thevilla.co.uk W: www.thevillawreagreen.co.uk

The Villa Country House Hotel
⊛⊛ CLASSIC BRITISH *V*
01772 804040 | Moss Side Lane, PR4 2PE
www.thevilla.co.uk
The Villa restaurant's oak panelling is but one original feature of this Victorian gentleman's carefully restored and decorated former mansion, near Lytham St Anne's. No doubt he would be pleasantly surprised by its light, relaxed atmosphere and the simple, modern British food with classic flavours, such as duck breast, and wild sea bass, served by the friendly staff.

See advertisement opposite

■ LEICESTERSHIRE

ANSTEY *MAP 11, SK50*

Sapori Restaurant & Bar
⊛⊛ ITALIAN
0116 236 8900 | 40 Stadon Road, LE7 7AY
www.sapori-restaurant.co.uk

Sapori Restaurant is a classy, understated place, with its own cocktail bar. Set on the edge of Leicester, it has a clean-cut modern interior with cream and grey tones, and low-lighting for a nicely intimate ambience. The kitchen offers menus dedicated to presenting the best in Italian cuisine, from classics to dishes with an imaginative, contemporary spin.

LONG WHATTON *MAP 11, SK42*

The Royal Oak
⊛ MODERN BRITISH
01509 843694 | 26 The Green, LE12 5DB
www.theroyaloaklongwhatton.co.uk
The 21st-century incarnation of this thriving gastro pub is seen in a smart interior, some natty bedrooms and a focus on food. That said, real ale is part of the plan, and a few pub classics remain. The kitchen turns out some lively stuff.

MARKET HARBOROUGH *MAP 11, SP78*

Three Swans
⊛ MODERN, INTERNATIONAL
01858 466644 | 21 High Street, LE16 7NJ
www.threeswans.co.uk
Dating from the reign of Henry VIII, the Three Swans is on the High Street and has played host to various crowned heads over the generations. The interior has a clean modern look that respects the original features, and smartly attired, tuned-in staff run the dining room with inspiring confidence.

MELTON MOWBRAY
MAP 11, SK71

Stapleford Park
◎◎ MODERN INTERNATIONAL, BRITISH 🍷NOTABLE WINE LIST

01572 787000 | Stapleford, LE14 2EF

www.staplefordpark.com

Stapleford's lineage can be traced back to medieval times, the estate being owned by successive generations of the Earls of Harborough for nearly 500 years. Impeccable staff keep the elevated tone buoyant, and the cooking aims high too.

MOUNTSORREL
MAP 11, SK51

John's House
◎◎◎ MODERN BRITISH

01509 415569 | 139–141 Loughborough Road, LE12 7AR

www.johnshouse.co.uk

John Duffin has food in his DNA: after working up an impressive CV in some of London's stellar kitchens, he returned to his roots by opening his own restaurant on the family farm where he grew up. Bare beams and brick walls, wooden floors and tables all add up to a rustic feel, but think again if you're expecting food in a similar vein. Sure, Duffin is committed to a 'farm to plate' philosophy – much of the produce comes from his family's land, after all – but the cooking is ambitious, precise and full of contemporary verve. Marinated heritage tomatoes bursting with flavour are nimbly partnered with almond gazpacho and fresh mint, while main-course pork belly comes with the balanced flavours of sweetcorn purée, hen of the woods mushrooms and gremolata. A clever dessert of meringue encasing yuzu curd alongside elderflower sorbet and white chocolate rounds things off nicely.

Chef John Duffin **Seats** 30 **Closed** Christmas and 2 weeks in August **Notes** Children welcome

NORTH KILWORTH
MAP 11, SP68

Kilworth House Hotel & Theatre
◎◎ MODERN BRITISH

01858 880058 | Lutterworth Road, LE17 6JE

www.kilworthhouse.co.uk

A top-to-toe restoration overseen by the eagle eyes of English Heritage means period authenticity runs seamlessly through this Italianate 19th-century mansion. The Wordsworth Restaurant is the fine-dining option: a posh setting indeed, but the kitchen team certainly rises to the occasion.

QUORN
MAP 11, SK51

The Shires
◎ MODERN BRITISH

01509 415050 | Quorn Country Hotel, Charnwood House, 66 Leicester Road, LE12 8BB

With manicured gardens and oak-panelled interiors, the Quorn Country Hotel has a 17th-century house at its heart. The Shires restaurant begins its modern brasserie path with seared king scallops, parsnip purée and pancetta, then continues with guinea fowl supreme with tarragon, and on to the finish with egg custard tart and clotted cream.

SHAWELL
MAP 11, SP58

The White Swan
◎◎ MODERN EUROPEAN

01788 860357 | LE17 6AG

www.whiteswanshawell.co.uk

Fresh flowers on every restaurant table are good to see in this tastefully renovated pub, particularly in the light flooding through the conservatory-style ceiling. The talented guys in the kitchen produce dishes such as marinated quail breast, beef Wellington, roasted turbot and plenty more in the modern British style, but often with a small detour of their own.

WYMESWOLD
MAP 11, SK62

Hammer & Pincers
◎◎ BRITISH, EUROPEAN
01509 880735 | 5 East Road, LE12 6ST
www.hammerandpincers.co.uk

Having trained at The Savoy, this restaurant's owners know a thing or two about hospitality in the grand manner, but the mood here is decidedly more cutting edge. This is Stilton country, so Cropwell Bishop with quince paste might look appealing.

■ LINCOLNSHIRE

GRANTHAM
MAP 11, SK93

Harry's Place
◎◎ CLASSIC FRENCH
01476 561780 | 17 High Street, Great Gonerby, NG31 8JS

Now in its fourth decade of operations, Harry and Caroline Hallam's place retains the 1980s ethos with which it began: a domestic dinner-party feel in their converted farmhouse, from the era when nobody knew what a website was. The short, handwritten menu has been built of long-standing dishes honed to a pitch of straightforward but effective refinement.

GRIMSBY
MAP 17, TA21

Pig & Whistle *NEW*
◎◎ MODERN BRITISH
01472 884544 | Healing Manor Hotel, Stallingborough Road, Healing, DN41 7QF
www.healingmanorhotel.co.uk

A traditional pub, the Pig & Whistle adjoins the picturesque, ivy-clad Healing Manor Hotel and offers poshed-up pub grub with carefully-considered dishes made from ingredients such as plump, juicy scallops and excellent quality duck breasts, sitting alongside the more conventional sausage and mash and fish and chips. Justifying their dog-friendly claim, there's even a menu just for your canine companions.

HORNCASTLE
MAP 17, TF26

Magpies Restaurant with Rooms
◎◎ BRITISH, EUROPEAN
01507 527004 | 73 East Street, LN9 6AA
www.magpiesrestaurant.co.uk/

In a terrace of 200-year-old cottages, Magpies has decor of duck-egg blue, with mirrors, candlelight and drapes over the bay windows. After enjoyable savoury courses, if you've got room, finish with a trio of desserts: chocolate mousse, espresso crème brûlée and dark chocolate fondant.

HOUGH-ON-THE-HILL
MAP 11, SK94

The Brownlow Arms
◉◉ BRITISH
01400 250234 | High Road, NG32 2AZ
www.thebrownlowarms.com
This Lincolnshire village inn has come up in the world, being as elegantly appointed as an interiors magazine country house, with tapestry-backed chairs and gilt-framed mirrors in a panelled dining room. Meanwhile, attentive, friendly service puts everyone at their ease.

LACEBY
MAP 17, TA20

Best Western Oaklands Hall Hotel
◉ MODERN BRITISH
01472 872248 | Barton Street, DN37 7LF
www.thecomfyduck.com
The balustraded red-brick mansion, built in 1877, sits in five acres of landscaped parkland between the Wolds and the Humber and makes a pleasant spot for the full country-house experience. Dining takes place in the Comfy Duck Bistro, which goes for a modern brasserie look and delivers inventive modern British comfort food.

LINCOLN
MAP 17, SK97

The Lincoln Hotel
◉ MODERN BRITISH
01522 520348 | Eastgate, LN2 1PN
www.thelincolnhotel.com
Just a stone's throw from Lincoln's 12th-century cathedral, The Green Room has a striking, design-led interior, with candles and fresh flowers adding a nice homely touch. The atmosphere is relaxed but the small restaurant retains an air of formality.

The Old Bakery
◉◉ MODERN INTERNATIONAL
01522 576057 | 26-28 Burton Road, LN1 3LB
www.theold-bakery.co.uk
Ivano and Tracey de Serio's restaurant with rooms is a homely place, with the feel of a farmhouse kitchen. A five-course taster menu offers a comprehensive tour, and desserts include white chocolate and pistachio ganache with vanilla pannacotta and delicately flavoured star anise ice cream.

Washingborough Hall Hotel
◉◉ MODERN BRITISH
01522 790340 | Church Hill, Washingborough, LN4 1BE
www.washingboroughhall.com
Set in three acres of a sleepy Lincolnshire village, with a garden to provide herbs for the kitchen, Washingborough delivers all you would hope for in a Georgian manor turned country-house hotel. The smart Dining Room exudes quietly understated class.

The White Hart
◉ MODERN BRITISH *V*
01522 563290 | Bailgate, LN1 3AR
www.whitehart-lincoln.co.uk
The old hotel is a feature of the historic quarter of Lincoln, with splendid views of one of England's greatest cathedrals, and the castle not far off. Inside, a suave contemporary look brings wood flooring and large mirrors to the Grille restaurant and bar, where dark wood tables look the part.

MARKET RASEN
MAP 17, TF18

The Advocate Arms
◉◉ MODERN EUROPEAN, BRITISH
01673 842364 | 2 Queen Street, LN8 3EH
www.advocatearms.co.uk
The 18th-century restaurant with rooms in the centre of town has a contemporary finish and aims to impress with boutique styling and an open-plan interior. In the main restaurant, the output is broadly modern British, with some inventive combinations and plenty to satisfy any traditionalists.

SCUNTHORPE
MAP 17, SE81

San Pietro Restaurant Rooms
◉◉ MODERN MEDITERRANEAN
01724 277774 | 11 High Street East, DN15 6UH
www.sanpietro.uk.com
Pietro Catalano, who hails from Sicily, has created a restaurant with rooms in a former windmill that combines the best of Italian hospitality with a touch of boutique swagger. A first course dish of ballotine of rabbit and foie gras shows ambition.

SLEAFORD
MAP 12, TF04

The Bustard Inn & Restaurant
◉ MODERN BRITISH
01529 488250 | 44 Main Street, South Rauceby,
NG34 8QG
thebustardinn.co.uk

The bar, with an open fireplace, flagstones and real ales, is the hub of this Grade II listed inn. A typical main might be two ways with beef (fillet and rillette), accompanied by Madeira sauce, a fricassée of greens, pommes Anna and wild mushrooms.

SOUTH FERRIBY
MAP 17, SE92

The Hope and Anchor Pub
◉◉ MODERN BRITISH
01652 635334 | Sluice Road, DN18 6JQ
www.thehopeandanchorpub.co.uk
Tucked amidst creeks and moorings, the panoramic views from the patio and restaurant encompass the waterways and nearby Humber Bridge. An appealingly, updated 19th-century inn, with exposed brickwork and a log-burning stove, this is a popular stop not only for birdwatchers and dog-walkers but those seeking good bistro-style food.

STAMFORD
MAP 11, TF00

The Bull & Swan at Burghley
◉ TRADITIONAL BRITISH
01780 766412 | High Street, St Martins, PE9 2LJ
www.thebullandswan.co.uk
The old stone inn used to be a staging post for coaches on the Great North Road and is nowadays an informal dining pub. Within are beams, stone walls, rugs on dark wood floors and caramel-coloured leather dining chairs. Regional produce is the backbone.

The Oak Room
◉◉ TRADITIONAL BRITISH ♦ NOTABLE WINE LIST
01780 750750 | The George of Stamford, 71 St Martins, PE9 2LB
www.georgehotelofstamford.com
History seeps from the pores of every mellow stone of this venerable coaching inn, which once fed and watered passengers on the Great North Road. The oak-panelled restaurant is a magnificent room with an old-world feel, and its menus are steadfastly traditional too.

The William Cecil
◉◉ MODERN BRITISH
01780 750070 | High Street, St Martins, PE9 2LJ
www.thewilliamcecil.co.uk
The hotel is an interesting amalgam of three Georgian houses built at different times, named after the Elizabethan statesman otherwise known as Lord Burghley. It's a clever blend of old and new, the panelling done in lighter colours, with booth seating in the restaurant.

WINTERINGHAM
MAP 17, SE92

Winteringham Fields
◉◉◉◉ MODERN BRITISH, EUROPEAN ♦ NOTABLE WINE LIST
See page 168

WOODHALL SPA
MAP 17, TF16

Petwood
◉ MODERN BRITISH V
01526 352411 | Stixwould Road, LN10 6QG
www.petwood.co.uk
Once home to the famous 617 Squadron, known as 'The Dambusters', the original Squadron Bar still exists in this Tudor-style hotel, surrounded by gardens newly restored to their early 20th-century state. In the classy restaurant look for chilled crab cannelloni, seabass fillet and pies of the day. The bar looks out on to a refurbished terrace.

Winteringham Fields

◉◉◉◉ MODERN BRITISH, EUROPEAN ⚑NOTABLE WINE LIST
01724 733096 | 1 Silver Street, DN15 9ND
www.winteringhamfields.co.uk

Deep in the Lincolnshire countryside, six miles west of the Humber Bridge, Winteringham Fields is the hub of this well-heeled village. Chef Colin McGurran has created something quite magical here with farm outbuildings converted into accommodation and a high class restaurant. A rabbit warren of rooms and private dining areas with a mix of slate tiles and wood makes for a rustic setting for the contemporary ingredient-driven cooking. An eight-course tasting menu changes most days depending on what arrives in the kitchen but a typical meal might kick off with chicken taco, fermented cabbage, lime and herb emulsion followed by slow-poached Arlington White egg, celeriac, Morteau sausage and ham fat dressing. Inventive flavour combinations continue with BBQ teriyaki short rib Wagyu beef, English peas, buttermilk and wasabi. End with a delicate brown sugar tart teamed with banana salsa and rum malt.

Chef Colin McGurran Seats 60, Private dining 12 Closed 2 weeks Christmas Parking 20 Notes Children welcome

LONDON

Index of London Restaurants

This index shows Rosette restaurants in alphabetical order, followed by their postal district or Greater London location, plan/map references and page number in the guide. London plans are found on pages 176–187 and regional maps are at the back of the guide.

London Plan 1

London Plan 5

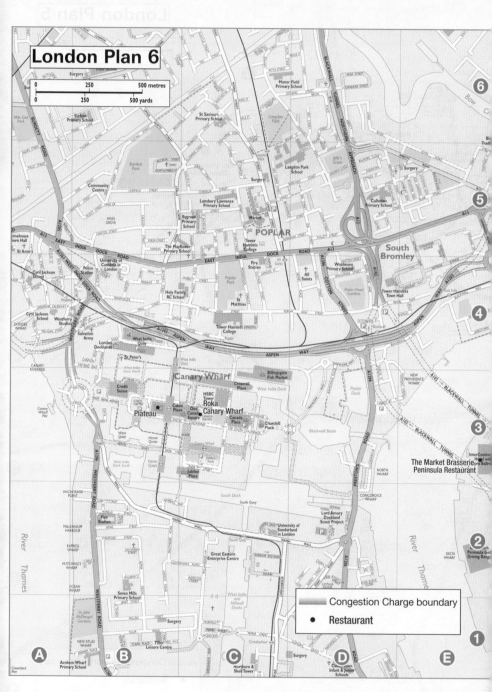

London Plan 6

0 — 250 — 500 metres
0 — 250 — 500 yards

POPLAR

South Bromley

Canary Wharf

Roka

Canary Wharf

Plateau

The Market Brasserie,
Peninsula Restaurant

River Thames

River Thames

Congestion Charge boundary
● Restaurant

Ⓐ Ⓑ Ⓒ Ⓓ Ⓔ

① ② ③ ④ ⑤ ⑥

Kerridge's Bar & Grill

■ LONDON

LONDON E1

BRAT
PLAN 3, J4

◉◉ BRITISH

First Floor, 4 Redchurch Street, E1 6JL

www.bratrestaurant.com

The USP of this high-flying restaurant up on the top floor of a former boozer is simple: source the finest ingredients and cook them with pinpoint precision on a wood-fired grill. The results are terrific, and it all takes place in a wood-panelled, shabby-chic room with the roaring grill taking centre stage amid the hubbub of enthusiastic diners.

The Buxton NEW
PLAN 3, J3

◉ BRITISH

0207 392 2219 | 42 Osbourn Street, E1 6TD

www.thebuxton.co.uk

Located in the heart of London's Brick Lane, this compact pub-with-rooms serves a concise menu of produce-driven British and European dishes. The menu changes frequently but you might catch the gnocchi, wild mushroom and rosemary cream sauce or the fish of the day teamed with mussels and fregola. Leave a space for frangipane tart with clotted cream.

Canto Corvino
PLAN 3, H3

◉◉ MODERN ITALIAN

020 7655 0390 | 21 Artillery Lane, E1 7HA

www.cantocorvino.co.uk

Canto Corvino ('song of the raven') brings modern Italian style to Spitalfields, with artwork on rough-hewn walls, comfortable chairs at well-spaced tables, soft lighting and a lively atmosphere. The menu is as fashionable as the surroundings, divided into eight sections of modestly portioned dishes.

The Culpeper
PLAN 3, J2

◉ TRADITIONAL, BRITISH

020 7247 5371 | 40 Commercial Street, E1 6LP

www.theculpeper.com

This lively gastro pub occupies a handsome Victorian boozer rejuvenated in hipster-friendly post-industrial style with bare-brick walls and a healthy dollop of period detail. The jam-packed ground-floor bar does an appealing line in switched-on modern food, while the first-floor Kitchen restaurant offers home-grown and European flavours on a thoroughly modern menu.

Galvin Bistrot & Bar
PLAN 3, H3

◉◉ MODERN FRENCH

020 7299 0404 | 35 Spital Square, E1 6DY

www.galvinrestaurants.com

In trendy Spitalfields, Galvin HOP has reinvented itself and now takes a modern bistro approach. The buzzy venue has kept its burnished copper tanks above the bar brimming with Czech Pilsner whilst giving the place a facelift with brightly colourful seating and pale wood tables. The traditional three-course lunch format segues to a repertoire of small and larger sharing plates.

Galvin La Chapelle
PLAN 3, H3

◉◉◉ FRENCH, EUROPEAN *V* ▲ NOTABLE WINE LIST

020 7299 0400 | 35 Spital Square, E1 6DY

www.galvinrestaurants.com

Sweeping stone archways, marble pillars and arched windows soaring 30 metres to the roof rafters of the converted red-brick Victorian St Botolph's girls' school provide a suitably jaw-dropping setting for the Galvin brothers' high-flying City venue. The cooking rises to the occasion, conforming immaculately to the Galvin genre: polished classical French cuisine buffed up with a light, modern gloss. Uncluttered, fine-tuned and pretty on the plate it is too – a fish cake of cod brandade poshed up with the luxury of lobster chunks and bisque foam being a case in point. Main course is another winner, matching roast suprême of Landes chicken with heavenly buttery mash, fresh peas and chard, crisp onions, trompette de mort mushrooms and a fathoms-deep jus, while fish dishes could see Cornish red mullet teamed with celeriac and wasabi, apple consommé, razor clam and hazelnut. To finish, top-drawer pastry skills distinguish a roast provençal apricot tart served with elderflower and rosemary custard.

Chef Jeff Galvin **Seats** 110, Private dining 16 **Closed** 24–26 December and 1 January **Notes** Children welcome

Lyle's
PLAN 3, J4

◉◉ MODERN BRITISH

020 3011 5911 | Tea Building, 56 Shoreditch High Street, E1 6JJ

www.lyleslondon.com

Lyle's coolly austere warehouse good looks – think whitewashed brick walls, subway tiles and industrial pendant lights – have made it a must-visit outfit since it first opened. The food certainly delivers on expectations, with some lesser-used gutsy cuts of meat and innovative combinations.

Super Tuscan
PLAN 3, H3

◉ ITALIAN

020 7247 8717 | 8a Artillery Passage, E1 7LJ

www.supertuscan.co.uk

The cheery Italian enoteca in a Dickensian Spitalfields' alley is a hang-loose setting for inspired classic Italian home cooking. Antipasti sharing platters of salamis and/or cheeses are obvious ways to pique the appetite. Expect hearty mains such as chargrilled veal chop with rosemary-spiked potatoes.

LONDON E2

Brawn
PLAN 3, K5

◉◉ TRADITIONAL EUROPEAN ⚑ NOTABLE WINE LIST

020 7729 5692 | 49 Columbia Road, E2 7RG

www.brawn.co

Set among a strip of artisanal shops, the corner-sited restaurant is a hard-edged, pared-back neighbourhood outfit. The trendy interior goes for an unadorned look of whitewashed brickwork, high ceilings, and plain café tables and retro chairs, plus the de rigueur open kitchen.

Marksman
PLAN 3, K6

◉◉ MODERN BRITISH

020 7739 7393 | 254 Hackney Road, E2 7SJ

www.marksmanpublichouse.com

What was once a run-down boozer, this was taken over by chefs Tom Harris and Jon Rotheram, both of whom previously worked at influential London restaurant St John. Restored to its former glory as a traditional pub downstairs, the first-floor restaurant is of a minimalist style.

LONDON E8

Pidgin
PLAN 1, G4

◉◉ MODERN BRITISH

020 7254 8311 | 52 Wilton Way, E8 1BG

www.pidginlondon.com

Hidden away on a Hackney backstreet, Pidgin is the epitome of latter-day dining. It's a dinky, spartan venue with little more than twigs on the walls by way of adornment, and bentwood chairs at café tables. Working in a pocket-sized galley, the kitchen team craft weekly-changing menus of creative food in complex, sometimes radical combinations.

LONDON E9

Cornerstone by Chef Tom Brown
PLAN 1, G4

◉◉◉ MODERN BRITISH, SEAFOOD

020 8986 3922 | 3 Prince Edward Road, E9 5LX

www.cornerstonehackney.com

A highly-talented young chef with an impressive CV choosing edgy Hackney Wick for his first solo venture might sound a little left-field, but Tom Brown (a Nathan Outlaw protégé and previous head chef of Outlaws at the Capital) has done exactly this, a fact that only makes Cornerstone all the more fascinating. This seafood joint is making big waves. The vibe is super cool, light and relaxed; a handsome monochrome, industrial look with retro bow-back chairs and black tabletops and dominant central-hub kitchen. Confidently exposed, Brown's team turns out dazzling seafood sharing-plates in the simple but brilliantly executed genre, backed by standout ingredients, flavour and balance. Take a sensational opener of pickled oyster served with celery, dill and subtle kick of horseradish, followed perhaps by headlining whole, sparkling-fresh John Dory (on the bone), again simply delivered with a silky roast chicken butter sauce. Round-off proceedings with a classy dark chocolate fondant, orange and whisky. Bubbly, informed service hits a high note too.

Chef Tom Brown, Christian Sharp
Notes Children welcome

The Empress
PLAN 1, G4

◉◉ MODERN BRITISH

020 8533 5123 | 130 Lauriston Road, Victoria Park, E9 7LH

www.empresse9.co.uk

This Victorian tavern fits right into its buzzy Victoria Park location. Red chesterfields, fashionable retro lighting and bare-brick walls are suitably à la mode, and when it comes to food, the kitchen (headed up by an ex L'Ortolan man) delivers honest stuff made with quality ingredients.

LONDON E14

Plateau
PLAN 6, B3

◉ MODERN FRENCH ⚑ NOTABLE WINE LIST

020 7715 7100 | 4th Floor, Canada Place, Canada Square, Canary Wharf, E14 5ER
www.plateau-restaurant.co.uk
Bag a window table to enjoy the incredible view over Canary Wharf from this fourth-floor restaurant with minimalist decor and an open-plan kitchen. A skilful pastry cook is behind a crisp pastry case for salted caramel and chocolate tart with raspberry coulis.

Roka Canary Wharf
PLAN 6, C3

◉◉ JAPANESE ⚑ NOTABLE WINE LIST

020 7636 5228 | 1st Floor, 40 Canada Square, E14 5FW
www.rokarestaurant.com
A cool, ultra-modern interior of natural woods befits the setting in Canada Square. Contemporary Japanese robatayaki cuisine is the deal, based on the robata grill (diners sitting alongside can watch the chefs silently working), with first-class fresh produce the kitchen's stock-in-trade.

LONDON EC1

Anglo
PLAN 3, D3

◉◉◉ MODERN BRITISH 𝑉

020 7430 1503 | 30 St Cross Street, EC1N 8UH
www.anglorestaurant.com
The anonymous grey frontage and stripped-back interior neutrality of bare tables, pendant lights and concrete floor are very much of the moment at this high-flying venue near Hatton Garden. Mark Jarvis's approach is all about celebrating splendid British ingredients - the clue's in the name - so expect cooking that matches contemporary creativity with a colourful, high-impact look on the plate. If time is tight at lunch, slot in the three-course option, otherwise settle in for one of the tasters. Home-made sourdough with yeasted butter and punchy intros of smoked haddock on a nori cracker and a cone of duck liver parfait and walnut get the tastebuds dancing for cured salmon with fish broth and croûtons. Main course brings premium Goosnargh chicken with chestnut and celeriac, its richness lifted by pickled trompette mushrooms to produce something remarkable. A pre-dessert of cheese and onion on malt loaf leads on to a grand finale of sticky toffee pudding with lightly smoked caramel.

Chef Anthony Raffo **Seats** 16 **Closed** 20 December - 3 January **Notes** No children

Le Café du Marché
PLAN 3, E3

◉ FRENCH

020 7608 1609 | Charterhouse Mews, Charterhouse Square, EC1M 6AH
www.cafedumarche.co.uk
The popularity of this classic cross-Channel country auberge-style venue remains undiminished. Bare-brick walls, French posters and candlelit tables set the tone in the rustic-chic converted Victorian warehouse. Food-wise, expect unreconstructed French provincial dishes on an ever-changing carte backed up by daily specials - honest, peasant cooking built on fresh, well-sourced materials.

Chez Mal Brasserie
PLAN 3, E3

◉ MODERN BRITISH

020 3750 9402 | Malmaison Charterhouse Square, 18-21 Charterhouse Square, Clerkenwell, EC1M 6AH
www.malmaison.com/locations/london
Like other hotels in the group, this branch is done out in best boutique fashion, with dramatic crimson and purple interiors, a sultrily lit bar and a brasserie in deep brown tones. The order of the day is lively modern British cooking with interesting variations.

The Clove Club
PLAN 3, H5

◉◉◉ MODERN BRITISH

020 7729 6496 | Shoreditch Town Hall, 380 Old Street, EC1V 9LT
www.thecloveclub.com
The Victorian pomp of old Shoreditch Town Hall has been reinvented as an arts venue and this rather chic, trend-conscious eatery. In step with the hipster-central location, the place goes for a pared-back look - white walls, wooden floors and tables, and a tiled open kitchen in a white, high-ceilinged space have a certain elegance still, but it's the cutting-edge production of the kitchen that creates most notice. A multi-course taster is the principal business, though there's also a shorter six-course option, and an entry-point four-course lunch, all bursting with clever ideas realised with top-flight technical skill. Flame-grilled mackerel comes pointed up with yogurt and kafir lime, then Cornish Thornback ray with cedrat lemon and sauce maltaise. On the meat front, pork jowl is matched with tart bursts from cider vinegar gel and apple balsamic. If you're not up for wine pairings, try a selection of soft drinks or ambient teas to go with the dishes.

Chef Isaac McHale, Oli Williamson **Seats** 55 **Closed** 2 weeks at Christmas and New Year **Notes** Children welcome

Club Gascon

PLAN 3, E3

⊚⊚⊚ FRENCH ▲ NOTABLE WINE LIST

020 7600 6144 | 57 West Smithfields, EC1A 9DS

www.clubgascon.com

The former Lyons tea room on a corner in the Smithfield district has been home to Pascal Aussignac's innovative restaurant for over 20 years. Dealing in a contemporary small-plate dining version of the culinary heritage of the chef-patron's native south-west France, it was a trail-blazer when it opened, and still manifests plenty of energy amid the rather sedate marbled walls and formal service of the setting. Start with a cylinder of pressed foie gras in a layer of concentrated crab jelly with piperade dip and a savoury crab canelé. Even more bewitching is a serving of monkfish with garnishes in camouflage colours, fashioned from truffles, parsley and beetroot, as well as brittle pork crackling, alongside a bowl of pork and fish stock consommé. Sweet things run from sublime prune jam with orange Armagnac cream to peach soufflé in a cup dusted with Earl Grey with cleansing lime and mint sorbet.

Chef Pascal Aussignac Seats 42, Private dining 10 Closed Christmas, New Year, bank holidays Notes Children welcome

Comptoir Gascon

PLAN 3, E3

⊚ TRADITIONAL EUROPEAN

020 7608 0851 | 61–63 Charterhouse Street, EC1M 6HJ

www.comptoirgascon.com

Comptoir deals in the gutsy food of south-west France, delivering simple comfort-driven cooking with full-on flavours. The decor fits the bill with its modern-rustic vibe; exposed brickwork and ducting, dinky elbow-to-elbow wooden tables, while the miniscule deli counter offers supplies to take away.

The Green

PLAN 3, D4

⊚ TRADITIONAL BRITISH

020 7490 1258 | 29 Clerkenwell Green, EC1R 0DU

www.thegreenclerkenwell.com

The corner-sited Green conforms to the trendy gastro pub template with its mismatched tables and chairs, art-laden walls and battery of real ales at the bar. Light streams in through big windows upon a lively crew whose attention is focused on the perky menu of fuss-free dishes that impress with their big flavours.

Luca

PLAN 3, E4

⊚ ITALIAN

020 3859 3000 | 88 St John Street, EC1M 4EH

www.luca.restaurant

Another sizeable venue on the bustling entrepôt of St John Street, Luca is that quintessentially millennial proposition, a restaurant using regional British produce in menus that look to Italy. Sharing plates for mixing and matching, and a boisterous, well-stocked bar are also on trend.

The Modern Pantry Clerkenwell

PLAN 3, E4

⊚⊚ MODERN, FUSION

020 7553 9210 | 47–48 St John's Square, Clerkenwell, EC1V 4JJ

www.themodernpantry.co.uk

Set in two listed Georgian townhouses on St John's Square, this breezy all-day eatery is an intimate, relaxed backdrop for a lively trek through the world of fusion cooking. Expect influences from around the globe, delivered in inspired combinations and stimulating contrasts of flavour and texture.

The Montcalm London City at The Brewery

PLAN 3, G4

⊚ TRADITIONAL BRITISH

020 7614 0100 | 52 Chiswell Street, EC1Y 4SB

www.themontcalmlondoncity.co.uk

Samuel Whitbread built up one of the UK's foremost beer brands on this spot, and part of his one-time Georgian brewery has been converted into this swanky hotel. There are a couple of dining options in situ, all entirely in keeping with the Georgian setting.

Moro

PLAN 3, D4

⊚ MEDITERRANEAN, NORTH AFRICAN

020 7833 8336 | 34–36 Exmouth Market, EC1R 4QE

www.moro.co.uk

Taking its cue from Spain via North Africa to the eastern Mediterranean, Sam and Samantha Clark's Moorish-inspired food draws in hordes who spill out onto pavement tables in fine weather. You can perch at the bar washing down tapas with splendid sherries or sink into a harem-style bolster cushion at one of the closely-packed tables. Friendly staff keep it all together, while inventive menus deliver colourful dishes of big flavours.

St John
PLAN 3, E3

◉◉ BRITISH

020 7251 0848 | 26 St John Street, EC1M 4AY

www.stjohnrestaurant.com

St John has earned its reputation as a pilgrimage spot for British foodies. In business for a quarter of a century in a stark, functional space in a former Georgian smokehouse by Smithfield Market, the 'nose-to-tail' eating philosophy championing unglamorous, lesser-used cuts has inspired a generation of chefs to this robust, gutsy style of cookery.

Smiths of Smithfield, No.3 Restaurant & Terrace
PLAN 3, E3

◉◉ EUROPEAN

020 7251 7950 | 67-77 Charterhouse Street, EC1M 6HJ

www.smithsofsmithfield.co.uk/no3

Smack opposite Smithfield Market, Smith's top-floor venue offers rooftop views of the City skyscrapers from its long, light-filled room through full-drop sliding glass doors and dream-ticket, fine-weather terrace. White linen, designer chairs, semi-circular leather banquettes and unstuffy service are spot on, while the kitchen produces light, modern, dishes of flair and flavour.

LONDON EC2

Aviary Restaurant
PLAN 3, G4

◉ MODERN BRITISH

020 3873 4000 | Montcalm Royal London House, 22-25 Finsbury Square, EC2A 1DX

www.montcalmroyallondoncity.co.uk

Ten floors above Finsbury Square in the heart of the City, this ultra-modern restaurant with a centralised bar and excellent roof terrace features two stuffed peacocks and sundry birdcages, which explain the restaurant's name. The main draw, of course, is the British brasserie-style food.

Boisdale of Bishopsgate
PLAN 3, H3

◉ TRADITIONAL BRITISH, FRENCH, SCOTTISH

020 7283 1763 | Swedeland Court, 202 Bishopsgate, EC2M 4NR

www.boisdale.co.uk

Down a Dickensian alley near Liverpool Street station, this Boisdale occupies an atmospheric vaulted basement. The soundtrack is live jazz, and the cooking is simple stuff founded on thoroughbred – often Scottish – meats and seafood, so starters include smoked salmon, or roast Blackface haggis.

City Social
PLAN 3, H2

◉◉◉ MODERN EUROPEAN ⚜NOTABLE WINE LIST

020 7877 7703 | Tower 42, EC2N 1HQ

www.citysociallondon.com

A dedicated lift whisks you up to the 24th floor of Tower 42 for wraparound views of the cityscape, taking in the Gherkin, the Cheesegrater and the Shard. The setting is no slouch either - a glamorous contemporary art deco-inspired space with rosewood panelling, horseshoe booths, leather banquettes, mirrored ceiling and brass table lamps. The food is equally spectacular - inventive, detailed and bursting with entertaining combinations of taste and texture - courtesy of Paul Walsh, who brings intelligence and top-flight technical craftsmanship to the classically founded modern European cooking. An opener of pig's trotter croquettes with crispy black pudding, apple textures and Madeira sauce sets the bar high, but it's easily upstaged by a staggeringly fine plate of rabbit saddle, wrapped in Parma ham, stuffed with trompette mushrooms and tarragon, and pointed up with spelt and silky purées of lovage and black garlic. At the end, a sensational raspberry soufflé comes with white chocolate ice cream is worth waiting for.

Chef Jason Atherton, Paul Walsh, Daniel Welna
Seats 90, Private dining 24 Closed 25 December, 1 January Bank Holidays Notes Children welcome

Coq d'Argent
PLAN 3, G2

◉◉ FRENCH

020 7395 5000 | 1 Poultry, EC2R 8EJ

www.coqdargent.co.uk

A stylish, modern, sharp-suit confection that comes properly dressed for the accomplished, big-flavoured French cooking and City skyscraper views. Menus boast bags of luxury for City high rollers; from oysters, lobster or caviar to deep-wallet mains like slabs of prime beef.

Duck & Waffle
PLAN 3, H2

◎◎ BRITISH, EUROPEAN

020 3640 7310 | 110 Bishopsgate, EC2N 4AY

www.duckandwaffle.com

The view from the 40th floor of the City's Heron Tower is pretty amazing, and Duck & Waffle can sort you out for breakfast, lunch, dinner, cocktails, a late supper, in a casual space open 24/7. Food takes a broad sweep through contemporary European ideas.

Eastway Brasserie
PLAN 3, H3

◎ EUROPEAN

020 7618 7400 | Andaz London Liverpool Street, 40 Liverpool Street, EC2M 7QN

eastwaybrasserie.com

There are numerous eating places to choose from here, including this take on a New York brasserie, with its own entrance, an open-to-view kitchen and massed ranks of tables. Open all day from breakfast to dinner, the carte offers up a wide selection of classic dishes.

Leroy
PLAN 3, H4

◎◎ EUROPEAN *V*

020 7739 4443 | 18 Phipp Street, EC2A 4NU

www.leroyshoreditch.com

The formula is on-trend – a spartan room of neutral hues and bare wood with an open kitchen and a short menu that reads like a shopping list of good things. Leroy's attraction is its simple approach to food – high quality produce, cooked precisely and no frills presentation in a buzzy, tightly-packed venue with switched-on service.

Manicomio City
PLAN 3, F2

◎ MODERN ITALIAN

020 7726 5010 | Gutter Lane, EC2V 8AS

www.manicomio.co.uk/city

The city branch of Manicomio occupies a Sir Norman Foster-designed glass building with a buzzy ground-floor terrace and café-bar (open from breakfast) and a sleek first-floor restaurant dressed up with a decor as sober as the suited-and-booted city types at its tables. Light and fresh contemporary Italian cooking that pays due respect to the provenance, seasonality and quality of its ingredients is the deal here.

Miyako
PLAN 3, H3

◎ JAPANESE

020 7618 7100 | Andaz London Liverpool Street, 40 Liverpool Street, EC2M 7QN

www.hyattrestaurants.com/en/dining/uk

Miyako is within the Andaz London hotel, although it has its own entrance where queues form at lunchtime for takeaway boxes. The restaurant itself has a cool, uncluttered look, thanks to large windows, walls veneered in pale wood and bamboo, and black-lacquered tables and chairs.

Popolo Shoreditch
PLAN 3, H5

◎◎ ITALIAN, MEDITERRANEAN

020 7729 4299 | 26 Rivington Street, EC2A 3DU

www.popoloshoreditch.com

A fashionable and young crowd are drawn to this small, modern restaurant that's spread over two levels. The service is informal but the staff are very knowledgeable, and you can sit at the bar to view the chefs producing excellent regional Italian tapas-style dishes.

The Princess of Shoreditch NEW
PLAN 3, H4

◎◎◎ MODERN BRITISH

020 7729 9270 | 76–78 Paul Street, EC2A 4NE

theprincessofshoreditch.com

From the 'short – but very good' wine list to the spot-on, sharply seasonal cooking, The Princess certainly lives up to her dreams of being 'the best pub in Shoreditch'. Dating from the 18th century, the building has plenty of atmosphere, and the upstairs dining room is a comfortable place, simply decorated with exposed floorboards and a stripped back look in shades of blue. Head chef Ruth Hansom brings a focus on seasonal British produce with dishes like a stunning piece of south coast hake with confit artichoke, pickled grapes, toasted almond and chervil. Service is relaxed and friendly, with staff easy to spot in their long green aprons.

Chef Ruth Hansom

SAGARDI London
PLAN 3, H4

◉ BASQUE

020 3802 0478 | Cordy House building, 95 Curtain Road, EC2A 3BS

www.sagardi.co.uk

Specialising in the cooking of the Basque country, Sagardi features a glass-walled meat-hanging room, wood-fired grilling and a copiously stocked wine wall. Steaks and pintxos (Basque tapas), plus fish from northern Spanish waters, comprise a menu replete with flavourful protein. The signature desserts include pastel vasco, a densely textured, crisp-shelled cake.

SUSHISAMBA London
PLAN 3, H2

◉◉ JAPANESE, BRAZILIAN, PERUVIAN ▮ NOTABLE WINE LIST

020 3640 7330 | 110 Bishopsgate, EC2N 4AY

www.sushisamba.com

The glass lift whizzes up to the 38th floor of Heron Tower in a few queasy seconds, but Sushisamba offers nothing but pleasure to the digestion. Japan, Brazil and Peru provide inspiration for a fusion of straight-up sushi and all-day grazing plates of high-quality ingredients.

LONDON EC3

Caravaggio
PLAN 3, H2

◉ MODERN ITALIAN

020 7626 6206 | 107–112 Leadenhall Street, EC3A 4AF

caravaggiorestaurant.co.uk

Ornate ceilings, art deco light fittings and an imposing staircase leading to a mezzanine gallery lend a 1930s sense of vitality and glamour to this Italian restaurant in a former banking hall. The pace is full-on at lunch, while evenings are more chilled. This is food of simplicity and flavour.

Chamberlain's Restaurant
PLAN 3, H2

◉ MODERN BRITISH, SEAFOOD

020 7648 8690 | 23–25 Leadenhall Market, EC3V 1LR

www.chamberlainsoflondon.co.uk

Spread over several floors amid the Victorian splendour of Leadenhall Market, Chamberlain's buzzes with the power-lunch crowd from the city skyscrapers. There's an all-weather terrace beneath the market's glass roof, while windows in the buzzy dining room and more intimate mezzanine make for good people-watching.

La Dame de Pic London
PLAN 3, H1

◉◉◉ FRENCH *V* ▮ NOTABLE WINE LIST

020 3297 3799 | Four Seasons Hotel London at Ten Trinity Square, 10 Trinity Square, EC3N 4AJ

www.ladamedepiclondon.co.uk

Anne-Sophie Pic's base in London is a sleek space done out with leather, wood and mirrors in this swanky Four Seasons Hotel, and her fine-tuned culinary imagination produces some powerful and unexpected flavour combinations. The cooking is really on song in a starter of Cornish crab, steamed with sobacha and dill pannacotta, with a fab Corsican clementine jelly. John Dory meunière with a purée of coco de paimpol haricot beans, sage and coffee-infused dashi is a beautifully constructed main course, and it is followed by an impressive and elaborate dessert of smooth blackberry coulis, sorbet and fresh blackberry.

Chef Anne-Sophie Pic, Marc Mantovani **Seats** 50, Private dining 12 **Open** All Year **Notes** Children welcome

Fenchurch Restaurant
PLAN 3, H1

◉◉ MODERN EUROPEAN

0333 772 0020 | Sky Garden, 1 Sky Garden Walk, EC3M 8AF

skygarden.london/fenchurch-restaurant

Up on the 37th floor of the Walkie Talkie tower, wraparound city views are a real draw at this sleek contemporary restaurant cantilevered over the tourist-magnet Sky Garden. Happily, the food is no mere afterthought, thanks to the high-level craft and creativity that goes into an appealing menu of modern European cooking.

The Fortnum's Bar & Restaurant at Royal Exchange
PLAN 3, G2

◉ CLASSIC AND MODERN BRITISH

020 7734 8040 | The Courtyard, The Royal Exchange, EC3V 3LR

www.theroyalexchange.co.uk/restaurants/the-fortnums-bar-and-restaurant

Surrounded by glittering boutiques in the neoclassical majesty of the Royal Exchange building, this glossy outpost of Fortnum's offers an all-day menu replete with luxurious ingredients, as well as an easygoing line-up of classic and modern British dishes. Take a seat at the central island bar counter or go for a table in the roped-off area.

Mei Ume
PLAN 3, H1

◉◉ JAPANESE, CHINESE *V*

020 3297 3799 | Four Seasons Hotel London at Trinity Square, 10 Trinity Square, EC3N 4AJ

www.meiume.com

Mei Ume is an impossibly chic Asian restaurant, showcasing dishes from China and Japan. Part of the incredibly impressive Ten Trinity Square hotel, the high-ceilinged dining room, with its pillars and curved banquettes, is a suitable venue for authentic dishes with a modern slant.

LONDON EC4

Bread Street Kitchen
PLAN 3, F2

◉◉ BRITISH, EUROPEAN

020 3030 4050 | 10 Bread Street, EC4M 9AJ

www.breadstreetkitchen.com

At this cavernous, high-decibel, high-octane city-slicker operation, courtesy of Gordon Ramsay Holdings, expect a soaring, warehouse-like space that mixes retro and modern looks with art deco references and the feel of a film set from Fritz Lang's Metropolis. Battalions of servers dressed in black ricochet to and fro, all friendly, engaging and on the ball, delivering quick-fire dishes from a lengthy all-day roster.

Ekte
PLAN 3, G1

◉◉ NORDIC

020 3814 8330 | 2-8 Bloomberg Arcade, EC4N 8AR

ektelondon.co.uk

Ekte's Nordic kitchen – with its chilled-out Scandi good looks, upbeat service and healthy values – stands out from the corporate crowd. The light, cosily minimalist space includes some communal tables so maybe kick off with a few plates of smørrebrød (open sandwiches; perhaps curried herring served with celery, apple and boiled egg). Also open for breakfast.

LONDON N1

12:51
PLAN 1, F4

◉◉ BRITISH

07934 202269 | 107 Upper Street, Islington, N1 1QN

www.1251.co.uk

James Cochran won *Great British Menu* in 2018 and his restaurant, 12:51, can be found not far from Islington Green. It may look unassuming, spread across two floors of pale tables and white walls, with candy-pink banquettes upstairs, but it's loud and buzzy, and the small-plate menus, divided into snacks, garden, sea and land sections, are driven by seasonal produce with some fixed signature dishes. The name 12:51, by the way, is a song by The Strokes.

Frederick's Restaurant
PLAN 1, F4

◉ MODERN BRITISH

020 7359 2888 | 106-110 Islington High Street, Camden Passage, Islington, N1 8EG

www.fredericks.co.uk

Celebrating its 50th birthday in 2019, the Victorian façade of this much-loved restaurant opens up into a smart bar and capacious conservatory dining area done out with painted and plain brick walls and clothed tables; statement abstract art on the walls adds to the stylish ambience. The wide-ranging roster of light, modern pan-European dishes is a real crowd pleaser.

Hicce
PLAN 1, F4

◉◉ BRITISH, SCANDINAVIAN, MEDITERRANEAN

020 3869 8200 | 102 Stable Street, Coal Drops Yard, King's Cross, N1C 4DQ

www.hicce.co.uk

Part of the Coal Drops Yard development in King's Cross, this second-floor restaurant occupies a reinvented Victorian warehouse with bare brick walls and high-beamed roof. From the vast open kitchen with its BBQ grills, modern European dishes emerge – perhaps cured salmon, wasabi and apple, followed by octopus, peperonata, cured egg yolk and almonds.

Prawn on the Lawn
PLAN 1, F4

@ SEAFOOD, TAPAS

020 3302 8668 | 292–294 St Paul's Road, N1 2LH

prawnonthelawn.com

You can almost smell the sea at this no-frills temple to fish – a bright and breezy space with subway tiles, exposed brick, big windows and paper-clothed tables. Choose the freshest fish you could ask for listed on a daily-changing small plate blackboard, or fish sourced from day boats and West Country markets from the fishmonger's counter.

Radici
PLAN 1, F4

@@ ITALIAN

020 7354 4777 | 30 Almeida Street, Islington, N1 1AD

www.radici.uk

Francesco Mazzei's restaurant is located opposite the Almeida Theatre, so it's a great spot to pop into before or after the theatre. It's a big room with a large bar and busy open kitchen that creates a great atmosphere. Service is attentive without being stuffy.

St Pancras by Searcys
PLAN 3, B6

@ BRITISH

020 7870 9900 | Grand Terrace, Upper Concourse, St Pancras International, N1C 4QL

stpancrasbysearcys.co.uk

With Eurostar trains outside the windows, you might expect the menu to give a nod to their destinations, but no. British place names proliferate, as in Portland crab cake, Scottish sherry-soaked salmon, Lake District beef cheek, Cornish plaice fillet and grilled Goosnargh chicken breast. And unquestionably British too is blackberry fool for dessert.

Smokehouse
PLAN 1, F4

@ MODERN AMERICAN

020 7354 1144 | 63–69 Canonbury Road, Islington, N1 2DG

www.smokehouseislington.co.uk

The Smokehouse is an old Islington boozer reborn as a temple to the elemental, Fred Flintstone principle of subjecting hunks of meat to fire and wood-smoke. In the yard are three giant smokers, and global culinary influences add punch, fire and spice.

Trullo
PLAN 1, F4

@@ ITALIAN

020 7226 2733 | 300–302 St Paul's Road, N1 2LH

www.trullorestaurant.com

Highbury's go-to Italian, Trullo is a lively, relaxed, cracking little neighbourhood trattoria that rocks; the setting for serious, unfussy, ingredient-driven Italian cooking with full-bore flavours and a menu that changes with every sitting. Modern, stripped-back trappings, spot-on service and all-Italian wines add to its street cred, likewise, home-made pasta (pappardelle with beef ragù) to skate wing, braised fennel and salsa verde.

LONDON NW1

Michael Nadra Primrose Hill
PLAN 1, E4

@@ MODERN EUROPEAN

020 7722 2800 | 42 Gloucester Avenue, NW1 8JD

www.restaurant-michaelnadra.co.uk

Nadra cooks on-the-money dishes of global cuisine, a reach that extends from tuna tartare and salmon céviche, through Ibérico presa (shoulder steak) and belly, wild mushrooms and mash in Madeira jus, to an apple and pear version of kataifi, the Greek shredded pastry dish.

Odette's
PLAN 1, E4

@@@ MODERN BRITISH, EUROPEAN

020 7586 8569 | 130 Regent's Park Road, NW1 8XL

www.odettesprimrosehill.com

The quintessential neighbourhood restaurant, Odette's has been a Primrose Hill stalwart since the late 1970s. With its open-air terrace and cosy dining room, this is a restaurant for all seasons and its surrounding greenery creates a decidedly rural feel. For the past 14 years, Odette's has been under the stewardship of Bryn Williams whose seasonal bistro food is simple, ingredient-driven and immaculately presented. Roast Scottish scallop, Welsh lamb belly, cauliflower and raisin is a perfectly poised starter and might lead on to Goosnargh chicken, Morteau sausage, sweetcorn and girolles. End with jaffa cake, milk sorbet and nibbed cocoa.

Chef Bryn Williams, Tom Dixon **Seats** 70, Private dining 20 **Closed** 2 weeks from 24 December **Notes** Children welcome

Pullman London St Pancras
PLAN 3, A5

⊚ MODERN EUROPEAN

020 7666 9000 | 100–110 Euston Road, NW1 2AJ

www.pullmanlondonstpancras.com

This sleek hotel restaurant continues the cross-Channel link by refuelling Eurostar travellers at St Pancras International, five minutes away. This is a clean-cut 21st-century space constantly thrumming with activity. An open kitchen and Josper grill turn out an eclectic repertoire of uncomplicated modern European dishes.

The Winter Garden
PLAN 2, F3

⊚⊚ MODERN EUROPEAN

020 7631 8000 | The Landmark London, 222 Marylebone Road, NW1 6JQ

www.landmarklondon.co.uk/dining/winter-garden

The Winter Garden is open all day, and the mood changes with the hour (and the weather), for it is in the heart of the eight-storey atrium that forms the nucleus of The Landmark London. It's an impressive spot for classically minded modern food drawing ideas from the Continent.

LONDON NW8

Soutine *NEW*
PLAN 2, E6

⊚ FRENCH

020 3926 8448 | 60 St John's Wood High Street, NW8 7SH

www.soutine.co.uk

From restaurateurs with the Midas touch, Jeremy King and Christopher Corbin, Soutine brings the atmosphere of the Parisian boulevard cafés to upscale St John's Wood. Bags of art nouveau styling, banquette seating, a glitzy bar and skylit rear dining room deliver that go-to vibe. From the all-day menu, think escargots à la bourguignonne to crème brûlée.

LONDON NW10

Parlour
PLAN 1, D4

⊚ MODERN BRITISH

020 8969 2184 | 5 Regent Street, Kensal Green, NW10 5LG

parlourkensal.com

The former Grey Horse has been reinvented as an on-trend food-oriented pub for a switched-on young crowd. Open for business from brunch to lunch and dinner, the place sports a shabby-chic look with white-tiled walls, painted panelling and banquette seating. Food-wise, expect a mix of heartily reworked British classics and creative dishes with a European accent.

LONDON SE1

The Anchor & Hope
PLAN 5, E5

⊚ BRITISH, EUROPEAN

020 7928 9898 | 36 The Cut, SE1 8LP

www.anchorandhopepub.co.uk

Rock up at this rollicking Waterloo gastro pub and try your luck for a table in the dining area. Every bit a proper no-frills boozer, food at The Anchor & Hope fits the no-nonsense mood, with wine served in tumblers and big-hearted dishes on a menu that changes each session.

Brasserie Joël
PLAN 5, C5

⊚⊚ MODERN FRENCH

020 7620 7200 | Park Plaza Westminster Bridge London, SE1 7UT

www.brasseriejoel.co.uk

Park Plaza's dining options centre on a French venue called Brasserie Joël, a monochrome space with a large tree in the middle and funky music filling the air. A mix of traditional and lightly modernised French dishes brings plenty of lustre to the brasserie-style menu.

Chino Latino London
PLAN 5, C3
◉◉ MODERN PAN-ASIAN, PERUVIAN
020 7769 2500 | Park Plaza London Riverbank,
18 Albert Embankment, SE1 7TJ
www.chinolatino.eu/london
Part of an international chain, Chino Latino
London is located in Park Plaza London, south of
Lambeth Bridge. The design is like a high-tech
movie set, but the menu is all about pan-asian
food with Latin inflections, as the name implies.
Check out the sushi and sashimi, the tempura
dishes and the marinated blow-torched salmon.

Florentine Restaurant
PLAN 5, D4
◉ BRITISH, ITALIAN
0845 450 2145 | Park Plaza London Waterloo,
6 Hercules Road, SE1 7DP
www.florentinerestaurant.co.uk
A short walk from the South Bank's attractions
and London Waterloo, this all-day contemporary
restaurant and bar is a buzzy and informal
setting for crowd-pleasing Mediterranean
brasserie-style food. Flatbreads come freshly
baked from the wood-fired oven, while the open
kitchen deals in straight-up steaks and an
appealing roster of uncomplicated, fresh and
vibrant dishes.

Hutong
PLAN 5, G6
◉ NORTHERN CHINESE
020 3011 1257 | Level 33, The Shard,
31 St Thomas Street, SE1 9RY
www.hutong.co.uk
The view from the 33rd floor of The Shard is
stunning, particularly at night with the
shimmering lights below. The room is a bit of a
looker itself, with red lanterns and an open-to-
view wood-fired oven where ducks are cooking
and drying, ready for the classic two-stage
Peking-style presentation.

Oblix
PLAN 5, G6
◉ MODERN INTERNATIONAL
020 7268 6700 | Level 32, The Shard,
31 St Thomas Street, SE1 9RY
www.oblixrestaurant.com
It goes without saying: the views from the
32nd floor of The Shard are somewhat
distracting. But prise your eyes from the
cityscape and you'll see the food at Oblix is no
mere afterthought. Delivered in a slick, brasserie
ambience, the team in the open kitchen sends
out vibrant cooking that's driven by the grill and
Josper oven.

The Oxo Tower Restaurant
PLAN 3, D1
◉◉ MODERN BRITISH 🌶NOTABLE WINE LIST
020 7803 3888 | 8th Floor, Oxo Tower Wharf, Barge
House Street, SE1 9PH
www.oxotowerrestaurant.com
On the eighth floor of the old Oxo building, this
bar, brasserie and restaurant overlooks the river
and St Paul's Cathedral, a world-class vista which
never fails to impress. The cooking is modern
British with a bit of globetrotting into Asian
territory. Afternoon tea and cocktails too.

Park Plaza County Hall London
PLAN 5, C5
◉ MODERN ITALIAN
020 7021 1919 | 1 Addington Street, SE1 7RY
www.parkplazacountyhall.com
Inside the snazzy modern hotel next to County
Hall on the South Bank, L'Italiano restaurant is on
a mezzanine level and has bags of style,
including great views through the large glass
wall. The heart of the culinary action is a wood-
fired oven.

Pizarro
PLAN 5, H4
◉◉ TRADITIONAL SPANISH
020 7378 9455 | 194 Bermondsey Street, SE1 3TQ
www.josepizarro.com/restaurants/pizarro
Whole hams hanging at a Spanish tile-frieze bar,
warm wood textures, and chefs at an open
plancha are a nod to an Iberian mood, while a
stripped back aesthetic appeals to local
trendsters. At Pizarro, the tapas formula has
evolved into gutsier regional fare.

Le Pont de la Tour
PLAN 5, J6

◎◎ MODERN FRENCH

020 7403 8403 | The Butlers Wharf Building,
36d Shad Thames, SE1 2YE

www.lepontdelatour.co.uk

The name translates as Tower Bridge, and that's what lies before you, a blue-chip view framed by the City skyscrapers, whether you're sitting out on the riverside terrace or indoors soaking up the vista through floor-to-ceiling windows in the sleek art deco-style dining room. The well-executed food is rooted in the French classics and doesn't stint on luxury ingredients.

Restaurant Story
PLAN 5, J5

◎◎◎◎◎ MODERN BRITISH ▲ NOTABLE WINE LIST

020 7183 2117 | 199 Tooley Street, SE1 2JX

www.restaurantstory.co.uk

Restaurant Story's simple-yet-refined look provides polished concrete floors, tablecloths and a ceiling adorned with bird mobiles. It's a bijou space, where full-drop windows flood the place with light, and chefs do their thing in an open kitchen. It's one of the capital's more intensively experimental places to eat and, as the name suggests, everything tells a story, and while the menu concept isn't applied too thickly, you can expect hyper-modern food full of revelatory twists, turns and outstanding technique. Menu descriptions reveal little of the highly worked detail in every dish. For a main dish, you might expect a plump roasted langoustine keeping company with a rich bisque and burnt apple purée, while the principal meat dish matches tender pigeon with ratte potato purée, rainbow chard and a punchy pigeon sauce with walnuts. 'Paddington Bear' is a transition from savoury to sweet, uniting marmalade pain perdu with cardamom parfait, grated foie gras and Sauternes, before various desserts conclude with variants of almond (cream, ice cream, butter, caramelised nuts) deftly aromatised with dill snow. The drinks list is equally of the moment, championing fragrantly botanical cocktails, modern wines and rare gin brands.

Chef Tom Sellers **Seats** 35 **Closed** August Bank Holiday weekend, 2 weeks Christmas **Notes** No children under 6 years

Roast
PLAN 5, G6

◎ BRITISH

020 300 66111 | The Floral Hall, Borough Market,
Stoney Street, SE1 1TL

www.roast-restaurant.com

Lording it above the global gourmet paradise of Borough market, Roast occupies the ornate Victorian Floral Hall, relocated from the old Covent Garden and, with pigeon's-eye views of the market, St Paul's Cathedral and The Shard, it's a fantastic setting. In true market fashion, it's open for breakfast too.

Skylon
PLAN 5, C6

◎ MODERN BRITISH

020 7654 7800 | Royal Festival Hall,
Southbank Centre, SE1 8XX

www.skylon-restaurant.co.uk

Skylon always rocks, thanks to the show-stopping Thames-side views through floor-to-ceiling windows. The Southbank set up incorporates a hotspot centre-stage bar, eye-catching chandelier-style lighting, dramatic flower displays and low-slung contemporary seating. The kitchen speaks with a simple modern-British accent; classic fish and chips (haddock, tartar sauce and peas) to dry-aged beef fillet with black garlic, parsnips and bone marrow. (There's a separate bar menu.)

Swan, Shakespeare's Globe
PLAN 3, F1

◎◎ MODERN BRITISH

020 7928 9444 | 21 New Globe Walk, South Bank,
SE1 9DT

www.swanlondon.co.uk/restaurant

Offering camera-clicking views across the Thames to St Paul's, the smart Swan has a hit on its hands. Sitting above its bustling ground-floor bar, the more formal restaurant is a light-filled room dominated by its lead-light Thames-side windows. Here, modern British cooking is underpinned by classic French references.

Ting
PLAN 5, G6

🟢🟢 BRITISH, EUROPEAN, ASIAN **1**

020 7234 8008 | Shangri-La Hotel at The Shard, London, 31 St Thomas Street, SE1 9QU

www.ting-shangri-la.com

The Shangri-La occupies the 34th to 52nd floors of The Shard, so the full-drop windows in Ting, the restaurant on level 35, pack quite a punch. The dining room is elegant, with a Chinoiserie feel, and the modern European menu has Asian influences.

Tom Simmons – Tower Bridge NEW
PLAN 5, J6

🟢🟢 BRITISH

020 3848 2100 | 2 Still Walk, SE1 2RF

www.tom-simmons.co.uk

Located within the new One Tower Bridge development, just a stone's throw from the bridge itself, the restaurant is found on the ground floor of a new residential building. Modern in style, with glass walls, the space divided between two levels, with some tables on the ground floor and the majority on the mezzanine level. The menu changes seasonally, the head chef champions Welsh produce, and cooking is accomplished. A starter of Orkney king scallops with confit pork belly is a simply presented, vibrant dish, while a wild garlic Kiev made with Pembrokeshire chicken is well executed and delicious.

Trivet NEW
PLAN 5, H5

🟢🟢🟢 MODERN BRITISH

020 3141 8670 | 36 Snowsfields, Bermondsey, SE1 3SU

trivetrestaurant.co.uk

When a new restaurant is opened by a former head chef (Jonny Lake) and master sommelier (Isa Bal) of the Fat Duck, it's bound to garner attention and high expectation. Trivet, tucked away opposite Bermondsey's historic Guinness Trust building, is however, refreshingly understated. The modern, clean-lined glass-fronted space features a marble bar (with separate bar menu) and two dining rooms with a focal-point open kitchen, while light, Nordic-style woods and pastel shades add warmth and keep things smack on-trend. The kitchen's carte-format menu bristles with appeal, with Lake's clean, confident, innovative and flawless cooking bringing ingredients to life. Take salt-steamed

turbot teamed with crosnes, Jerusalem artichoke and tarragon oil, while a baked potato mille feuille dessert (with sake and white chocolate mousse, and butter and sake gelato) catches the foodie attention. Service is relaxed, cheery and informed, while Bal's unique wine list – presented following the journey of early wine makers – starts at 7,000BC.

Chef Jonny Lake **Open** Tuesday evenings and Wednesday to Saturday

Union Street Café
PLAN 5, E6

🟢🟢 ITALIAN, MEDITERRANEAN

020 7592 7977 | 47–51 Great Suffolk Street, SE1 0BS

www.gordonramsay.com/union-street-cafe

This café's casual, urban-chic warehouse sheen, with funky lighting, buffed concrete, striking artwork and an open kitchen, is a big hit, as is the cooking, driven by the best market produce. Skilled simplicity and a confident, light, modern touch keep the food high on flavour.

LONDON SE10

The Market Brasserie
PLAN 6, E3

🟢 MODERN INTERNATIONAL

020 8463 6868 | InterContinental London - The O2, 1 Waterview Drive, SE10 0TW

www.iclondon-theo2.com

Views of the curving River Thames and bright lights of Canary Wharf skyscrapers through full-drop windows provide a big-city backdrop for dining in this stylish cosmopolitan brasserie. Expect prime British produce to form the backbone of hearty grills and modern European dishes prepared with a touch of culinary theatre in the open kitchen.

Peninsula Restaurant
PLAN 6, E3

🟢🟢🟢 MODERN EUROPEAN

020 8463 6868 | InterContinental London - The O2, 1 Waterview Drive, SE10 0TW

www.peninsula-restaurant.com

It's all happening on the Greenwich Peninsula, which has gradually been transformed into a smart London quarter with its own cultural milieu, and a swish InterContinental Hotel to boot. The Peninsula Restaurant on the second floor has views of the whole district, with Canary Wharf hovering behind it, and amid the sleek contemporary design, a menu of cutting-edge cooking completes the picture. The influences are from modern and classic European cuisines and this has created a menu reflective of the spice, exotic fruit and fresh fish trade that passed through East London's docks to be sold at London's Billingsgate. Highlights of the menu include excellent melt-in-the-mouth and flavoursome Wagyu beef with a silky-smooth celeriac purée and black garlic. The service is very well managed – there's a good team in place offering diligent service with good knowledge and recommendations offered throughout.

Chef Aurelie Simon **Seats** 60, Private dining 24
Closed Bank holidays, for private hire **Parking** 220
Notes Children welcome

LONDON SE23

Babur
PLAN 1, G2
◉◉ MODERN INDIAN
020 8291 2400 | 119 Brockley Rise, Forest Hill, SE23 1JP
www.babur.info
In business since the mid-1980s, Babur is a pioneer of modern Indian cuisine. Outside there's a life-sized model tiger on the roof, while inside is an upmarket, contemporary, brasserie-style space decorated with Indian artworks. Ingredients are never less than excellent, and they're put to good use in exciting, original cooking. Well-chosen, spice-friendly wine list.

See advertisement on page 203

LONDON SW1

Amaya
PLAN 4, G4
◉◉◉ MODERN INDIAN 🍷NOTABLE WINE LIST
020 7823 1166 | Halkin Arcade, Motcomb Street, SW1X 8JT
www.realindianfood.com
Discreetly tucked away in exclusive Belgravia, hot-ticket Amaya is part of the avant-garde Indian restaurant movement that has brought glitz, pizzazz and sophistication to the cooking of the subcontinent. From sleek cocktail bar to seductive dining room, there's an in-place vibe and high-glam good looks; think glittering lighting, black granite, leather seating, and vivid artworks and terracotta statues to catch the eye. But, it's the big drawcard theatre kitchen that delivers the real wow, the cooking built around

traditional grilling - in the tandoor, on the flat griddle and over the oven flame. The fashionable grazing menu features small-plate sharing dishes; perhaps adraki chicken tikka (juicy boneless chicken with warming spices and ginger) or knockout spinach tikki with spiced fig to chargrilled flaky fresh sea bass fillet (with coconut, curry leaf and chilli), while luxury might also see foie gras get the tandoori treatment. The more traditional finish is provided by a handful of grandstand curries (spicy Kerala prawn) and biryani (green herb chicken made with mature basmati rice), while spot-on service and a classy wine list (plus inventive cocktails) also hit the high-gloss stakes.

Chef Sanchit Kapoor **Seats** 99, Private dining 14
Open All Year **Notes** No children under 10 years at lunch Monday to Friday, no age restriction at dinner but must vacate table by 8pm

Aquavit
PLAN 2, K1
◉◉ NORDIC
020 7024 9848 | St James's Market, 1 Carlton Street, SW1Y 4QQ
www.aquavitrestaurants.com
Everything feels polished and image conscious, glossy and golden with a posh, contemporary Scandi sheen in London's sibling to New York's award-garlanded namesake. The handsome, double-height space comes bedecked with marble floors, pale oak panels, tan leather, striking all the right notes for upmarket dining on inventive Nordic cuisine.

Avenue
PLAN 4, J6
◉◉ MODERN BRITISH, AMERICAN
020 7321 2111 | 7-9 St James's Street, SW1A 1EE
www.avenue-restaurant.co.uk
With its chic big-city attitude, Avenue's long bar sets a classy tone, while the glam restaurant spreads out around a 'wine-glass' chandelier and decanting bar, delivering a cool cosmopolitan look. The kitchen deals in lively contemporary Asian-accented ideas with a light, clean-flavoured touch, while not neglecting those who fancy a slab of New York strip loin from the robata grill.

A. Wong
PLAN 4, J3

◉◉◉ CHINESE

020 7828 8931 | 70 Wilton Road, Victoria, SW1V 1DE

www.awong.co.uk

Andrew Wong points out informatively that China has no fewer than 14 national borders, a phenomenon that has seen it absorb disparate culinary traditions throughout its own vast gastronomic history, and which informs the energetic and thrilling experimentation going on at his smart Victoria venue. Squeeze in at the bar if you're too late for a table. Appetisers extend to a crumbed crab claw filled with garlic butter teamed with a cured scallop and wasabi, and a lacy shrimp dumpling with its ruff of shellfish foam. The steamed dumplings Shanghai-style are tender and savoury, dressed in ginger vinegar, the umami-rich Peking duck roll is presented with a flourish of tableside theatre, but the showstopper has to be the glorious Wagyu beef with wafer-thin crispy noodles. Desserts have a more restrained aspect, as when coconut ice, intense enough in itself, is served with dried berries and yogurt with a little mochi.

Chef Andrew Wong **Seats** 65, Private dining 12 **Closed** 23 December to 8 January **Notes** No Children under 8 years

Café Murano
PLAN 4, J6

◉◉ NORTHERN ITALIAN

020 3371 5559 | 33 St James's Street, SW1A 1HD

www.cafemurano.co.uk

Angela Hartnett's eatery is anything but a 'café', rather a sophisticated, albeit relaxed, take on a pop-in-every-day Italian. The slim room is a looker, from its marble-topped bar to wooden floors, brown banquettes and eye-catching lighting. The cooking is equally on cue, with a northern Italian menu of simple, rustic (if refined, well-executed and well-presented) lightly portioned dishes.

Caxton Grill
PLAN 4, K4

◉◉ MODERN EUROPEAN

020 7227 7777 | St Ermin's Hotel, 2 Caxton Street, St James Park, SW1H 0QW

www.caxtongrill.co.uk

Set in the Victorian splendour of St Ermin's Hotel, Caxton Grill is all soothing colours, striking modern art and designer furniture. Although there's plenty to choose from, the Josper grill is the focus, offering prime British steaks, pork and more. A lot of the veg comes from their own kitchen garden, and honey comes from the bees on the roof.

See advertisement on page 205

Celeste at The Lanesborough
PLAN 4, G5

◉◉◉ FRENCH, INTERNATIONAL 🍷 NOTABLE WINE LIST

020 7259 5599 | Hyde Park Corner, SW1X 7TA

www.oetkercollection.com/hotels/the-lanesborough

A grand old mansion on Hyde Park Corner, The Lanesborough's world-class level of luxury and service is not as inaccessible as you might think if you go for the set-price menu du jour – beneath a glass-domed ceiling and shimmering chandeliers. The cooking is in the modern French style, blending classic techniques with a contemporary eye for light, fresh flavours in supremely elegant dishes that celebrate first-class British ingredients: exquisite halibut is matched with a riot of Jerusalem artichoke – crushed, puréed, crispy skin, and in a truffle-dusted bon bon. Caramelised red apple, green apple sorbet, pine nut crumble and elderflower mousse provide a classy finish.

Chef Steeven Gilles **Seats** 100, Private dining 12 **Open** All Year **Parking** 25 **Notes** Children welcome

Chutney Mary
PLAN 4, J6

◉◉◉ MODERN INDIAN 🍷 NOTABLE WINE LIST

020 7629 6688 | 73 St James's Street, SW1A 1PH

www.chutneymary.com

New meets old at this stylish St James's restaurant with its hybrid of classical and modern décor. The smart doorman sets the tone at this classy venue, likewise the glittering Pukka Bar for cocktails. But its main dining room is the real jewel in the crown complete with mirrored columns and soft lighting. The creative Indian cuisine runs to inspiring combinations with luxurious touches and well-dressed presentation. Baked venison samosas, tamarind and date chutney might precede halibut tikka with dill and green chilli. A dark chocolate 'bomb' filled with milk chocolate mousse and passionfruit sauce is a skilful dessert.

Chef Achal Aggarwal **Seats** 112, Private dining 32 **Open** All Year **Notes** Vegetarian dishes, No children under 10 years at lunch Monday to Friday, 4–10 years at early dinner, must leave by 8pm

Continued on page 204

smart,
omfortable,
pace with
antastic food

babur

119 Brockley Rise, Forest Hill, London SE23 1JP
020 8291 2400
www.babur.info   mail@babur.info
www.facebook.com/BaburRestaurant   www.twitter.com/BaburRestaurant

LONDON SW1 continued

The Cinnamon Club
PLAN 5, A4

◉◉ MODERN INDIAN

020 7222 2555 | The Old Westminster Library, 30-32 Great Smith Street, SW1P 3BU

www.cinnamonclub.com

If you're fond of a splash of empire pomp, try combining it with some exciting new-wave Indian cuisine in the Cinnamon Club. Set in the old Westminster Library with its handsome book-lined galleries and high-end feel, there's a real sense of occasion to go with classy modern Indian cooking that draws on Asian and European techniques to great effect.

Colbert
PLAN 4, G3

◉ FRENCH

020 7730 2804 | 50-52 Sloane Square, Chelsea, SW1W 8AX

www.colbertchelsea.com

Inspired by the grand boulevard cafés of Paris, the Colbert is a very popular Sloane Square destination and bustles with a wonderful feel-good vibe from breakfast to late evening. The lengthy all-day menu offers something for every occasion. The essence of the cooking is clean simplicity, defined by premium ingredients and flavour. The street-side alfresco tables are a hot ticket.

Curry Room NEW
PLAN 4, H4

◉ INDIAN

020 7834 6600 | The Rubens at the Palace, 39 Buckingham Palace Road, SW1W 0PS

rubenshotel.com/dining-and-drinks

You'll find the opulent Curry Room in the Rubens at the Palace hotel, all rich jewel colours, Rajasthani hand embroidery, and dark red leather seating. Table settings sparkle and staff are relaxed but attentive and happy to help you through the menu. Traditional dishes are freshly made, vibrant, and very well spiced.

Dinner by Heston Blumenthal
PLAN 4, F5

◉◉◉ BRITISH ⚫NOTABLE WINE LIST

020 7201 3833 | Mandarin Oriental Hyde Park, 66 Knightsbridge, SW1X 7LA

www.dinnerbyheston.co.uk

Within the Mandarin Oriental Hotel in Knightsbridge, a surprisingly unelaborate dining room is kitted out with unclothed tables, with views over Hyde Park as well as a centrally sited kitchen with open frontage allowing diners occasional glimpses behind the scenes. What Heston Blumenthal has created here is the culinary equivalent of a research institute, with dishes from British history. The starter known as Rice and Flesh dates from the troubled reign of Richard II and is in essence a painstakingly timed saffron risotto topped with mouthfuls of tender calf's tail richly glazed in red wine. Then perhaps pause at the late Georgian era for 21-day-aged Hereford beef with mushroom ketchup and thrice-fried chips, perhaps followed by a gloriously elaborate raspberry tart lathered with Jersey cream, its sponge injected with olive oil, topped with corpulent raspberries filled with lovage cream and a pebble of gorgeously intense raspberry sorbet. A classic tipsy cake is garnished with a strip of sticky spit-roasted pineapple for a touch of exotic climes.

Chef Ashley Palmer-Watts **Seats** 110, Private dining 12 **Closed** late August **Notes** No children under 4 years

Continued on page 206

LONDON SW1 continued

The English Grill
PLAN 4, H4

◉◉ MODERN BRITISH

020 7834 6600 | The Rubens at the Palace, 39 Buckingham Palace Road, SW1W 0PS
www.redcarnationhotels.com

This elegant dining room is part of a hotel that has been run by the same family since 1912. Banquette seating along one wall provides views of large glass doors into the kitchen, where classic cooking techniques are employed for a menu that appeals to all.

Enoteca Turi
PLAN 4, G2

◉◉ MODERN ITALIAN ◖NOTABLE WINE LIST

020 7730 3663 | 87 Pimlico Road, SW1W 8PH
www.enotecaturi.com

Run by the same family since 1990, Enoteca Turi has put its roots down in Chelsea. The focus is on regional Italian flavours, with the menu highlighting the origins of each dish - Campania, Piedmont etc. The whole place buzzes with life and the wine list champions Italian wines.

Estiatorio Milos
PLAN 4, K6

◉◉ GREEK, MEDITERRANEAN, SEAFOOD

020 7839 2080 | 1 Regent Street, St James's, SW1Y 4NR
www.estiatoriomilos.com

The august surroundings of deep windows with voile coverings, frosted-glass globe lighting and white linen here make a handsome backdrop for its modern Greek food. The cooking is full of both sea-fresh savour and hearty meaty robustness.

The Game Bird at The Stafford London
PLAN 4, J6

◉◉ CLASSIC BRITISH *V* ◖NOTABLE WINE LIST

020 7518 1234 | 16–18 St James's Place, SW1A 1NJ
www.thegamebird.com

Tucked away in a discreet street near Green Park, The Stafford is a luxurious St James's address that is worth tracking down. The kitchen takes top-notch British produce, subjects it to contemporary treatments and comes up with ambitious dishes glowing with Mediterranean colour.

GBR (Great British Restaurant)
PLAN 4, J6

◉◉ BRITISH *V*

020 7491 4840 | DUKES LONDON, 36 Little St James's Street, SW1A 1NY
www.dukeshotel.com

Buttoned banquettes, mirrored walls, herringbone parquet and high leather stools at the marble-topped bar add up to a glam setting in this classy all-day Mayfair eatery. The initials stand for Great British Restaurant, and that's a clear pointer to the kitchen's inventive and up-to-date style of cooking.

The Goring
PLAN 4, H4

◉◉◉ TRADITIONAL BRITISH ◖NOTABLE WINE LIST

020 7396 9000 | Beeston Place, SW1W 0JW
www.thegoring.com

Run by the Goring family since 1910, this Edwardian treasure remains one of London's most luxurious and impeccably English hotels. Inside, the restaurant boasts David Linley furnishings and floating Swarovski blossom-like chandeliers that change colour with the light from outside. It's state of the art meets classic traditionalism, and as you'd expect service is polished, professional and elegant. Start with watercress Acquerello risotto with smoked eel, pickled cucumber and English wasabi, then move on to Norfolk baby chicken, with charred baby leeks, artichoke and a vin jaune sauce. For a delicious dessert try chocolate cremeux with Alphonso mango, passionfruit and sea salt.

Chef Richard Galli **Seats** 70, Private dining 50 **Open** All Year **Parking** 7 **Notes** Children welcome

Ikoyi
PLAN 2, K1

◉◉◉ MODERN WEST AFRICAN
020 3583 4660 | 1 St James's Market, SW1Y 4AH
www.ikoyilondon.com
Set in the St James's Market development just
south of Piccadilly, Ikoyi is named after an
affluent Lagos neighbourhood in Nigeria. Chef-
patron Jeremy Chan presents highly innovative,
intriguing small plates that deliver his translation
of West African cuisine, punctuated by heat, bold
flavour and high-skill and unusual ingredients.
Blind tasting menus might include the signature
'plantain and smoked scotch bonnet' with
raspberry salt, or perhaps 'hake and velouté'
served with ground elder, spring greens, sorrel
and kelp oil. To finish, 'wild rice (ice cream),
mango' and fonio biscuit. Inventive cocktails
catch the eye along the way too. The well-
informed service hits just the right note.

Chef Jeremy Chan **Notes** No children

Kahani
PLAN 4, G3

◉◉ MODERN INDIAN
020 7730 7634 | 1 Wilbraham Place, SW1X 9AE
www.kahanidining.com

Just off Sloane Square, this upmarket and chic
restaurant uses prime British ingredients for its
contemporary Indian dishes. The innovative style
is typified by a samosa platter of Punjabi aloo,
kolhapuri chicken and chettinad venison to start.
For mains, there's grilled stone bass coated with
brown garlic and sundried tomato purée
alongside a sweet and smoky sauce.

Lorne Restaurant
PLAN 4, J3

◉◉ MODERN BRITISH, EUROPEAN
020 3327 0210 | 76 Wilton Road, SW1V 1DE
www.lornerestaurant.co.uk
If you're looking to enjoy excellent cuisine in a
relaxed atmosphere in central London, Lorne
makes a fine choice. The restaurant has a bright
and airy feel, with calming decor. Sommelier
Katie Exton has created a wine list for
enthusiasts of every taste and pocket.

Marcus
PLAN 4, G5

◉◉◉◉◉ MODERN EUROPEAN, BRITISH ◢NOTABLE WINE LIST
020 7235 1200 | Wilton Place, Knightsbridge,
SW1X 7RL
www.marcusrestaurant.com
Located in Knightsbridge's Berkeley Hotel since
2008, Marcus has proved itself eminently capable
of punching above its weight, even for such a top
establishment. The dining room's contemporary
styling is an amalgam of rich, greyish patterned
carpets, muted light glowing off burnished wood
panelling, trendy prints, and tables laid with crisp
white cloths, on which burn small tealights in
smart opaque white glass bowls. Dining options
are flexible, with a range offering light lunch up
to eight-course tasting menus. The seasonal
Taste of Spring tasting menu might feature slow-
cooked egg with wild garlic and Mr Little's
Yetholm Gypsy potato (named for the man who in
1899 allegedly introduced it to the Scottish
Borders town); then skate roasted on the bone
with chicken butter and sea vegetable; smoked
pork cheek with piccalilli, and bacon broth; and
mango, meadowsweet and yogurt. Wine flights
come in two levels: Sommelier's Selection and,
for an additional outlay, the Prestige Selection,
both of course fully bearing out the AA's Notable
Wine List award. The management makes a point
of warning that, while there is no formal dress
code, sportswear is unacceptable.

Chef Marcus Wareing **Seats** 90, Private dining 16
Notes No children under 8 years

Muse *NEW*

PLAN 4, G4

◎◎◎◎ MODERN BRITISH

020 3301 2903 | 38 Groom Place, Belgravia, SW1X 7BA

www.musebytomaikens.co.uk

Tucked away close to Belgrave Square, Muse sees Tom Aikens' return to the capital's fine-dining scene, offering a multi-course tasting menu inspired by childhood memories and moments and key people form his celebrated career. A bijou, 25-cover space, Muse splits over two floors of a character mews house; there's a few seats for cocktails and a cold kitchen downstairs, while upstairs the main action takes place, with high chairs at the marble-topped kitchen counter and dining tables and curving banquette behind. It's intimate but relaxed, softly lit and decorated in warming pastel tones. Friendly staff and chefs bring out a succession of strikingly presented dishes to talk through, with names like 'Conquering the Beech Tree' or 'Playing with fire' supported by evocative menu descriptions, while ingredients are listed minimally ('langoustine, pork fat, burnt apple' or 'Beef, Norfolk grains, Barsham stout). This is fine-tuned cooking from a flavoursmith; innovative, story-telling dishes full of flavour, balance, finesse and artistry.

Chef Tom Aikens

One Twenty One Two Restaurant

PLAN 5, B6

◎ MODERN BRITISH

020 7451 9333 | 2 The Royal Horseguards Hotel, SW1A 2EJ

www.guoman.co.uk

This grand old pile was home to the Secret Service in World War I, and now makes an upmarket base when visiting London's attractions. Its posh restaurant comes kitted out with plush banquettes and deals in appealing modern brasserie-style food with its roots in French classics.

Osteria Dell'Angolo

PLAN 5, A4

◎ ITALIAN

020 3268 1077 | 47 Marsham Street, SW1P 3DR

www.osteriadellangolo.co.uk

The neutral tones of this Westminster Italian bring an air of Mediterranean sophistication to Marsham Street. Leather seating and white linen add class, and large windows fill the space with light, while a glass-panelled wall offers a glimpse of the chef in action as staff deliver regional classics and inventive modern interpretations, with simplicity and flavour to the fore.

Petrichor Restaurant

PLAN 4, J6

◎◎ MODERN EUROPEAN

020 7930 2111 | The Cavendish London, 81 Jermyn Street, SW1Y 6JF

www.thecavendish-london.co.uk

The Cavendish sits in a prime spot among the gentlemen's outfitters of St James's. The food in its Petrichor Restaurant cuts quite a dash too with its modern British styling and well executed dishes delivered by a skilled kitchen team that draws on thoroughbred suppliers for its materials.

Pétrus by Gordon Ramsay

PLAN 4, G5

◎◎◎ MODERN FRENCH ⚑ NOTABLE WINE LIST

020 7592 1609 | 1 Kinnerton Street, Knightsbridge, SW1X 8EA

www.gordonramsay.com/petrus

Pétrus by Gordon Ramsay is very much a fine dining environment with service of the highest order. The dining room has a circular dynamic with a glass wine cellar in the middle. It's comfortable, modern and light; think leather chairs and white linen, and pastel tones jazzed up by splashes of claret. All crockery, cutlery and glassware is of the highest standard. The menu may start with an organic egg with sweet corn, bacon and black truffle, continue to Cornish cod with violet artichoke, pine nuts, courgette and olive, and wind up in a delicious hazelnut soufflé with salted caramel ice cream. Outstanding wine list.

Chef Gilad Peled, Ben Waugh **Seats** 55 private dining 8 **Closed** 26-28 December **Notes** Children welcome

Quaglino's
PLAN 4, J6

◉ EUROPEAN

020 7930 6767 | 16 Bury Street, SW1Y 6AJ

www.quaglinos-restaurant.co.uk

Once the favoured watering-hole Evelyn Waugh and the future Edward VIII, Quaglino's is a masterpiece of art deco style on the cruise-ship scale, complete with golden-lit staircase to tempt out your inner Gloria Swanson. Flavours simply shine from the plate.

Quilon
PLAN 4, J4

◉◉ INDIAN, SOUTHWEST COASTAL 𝒱 ⓘ NOTABLE WINE LIST

020 7821 1899 | 41 Buckingham Gate, SW1E 6AF

www.quilon.co.uk

Quilon is part of St James' Court Hotel, but has its own entrance and feels like a stand-alone restaurant. Decor is sleek and ultra-modern, and the separate areas in the L-shaped space make it feel quite intimate. Cuisine is south-west Indian from Kerala and Goa, a mix of straightforward traditional dishes and more modern ideas, all based on top-class produce.

The Rex Whistler Restaurant
PLAN 5, B3

◉◉ MODERN BRITISH, EUROPEAN ⓘ NOTABLE WINE LIST

020 7887 8825 | Lower Floor, Tate Britain, Millbank, SW1P 4JU

www.tate.org.uk/visit/tate-britain/rex-whistler-restaurant

Tate Britain's restaurant is certainly a one-off thanks to Rex Whistler's wraparound mural 'The Expedition in Pursuit of Rare Meats' covering all four walls – a pleasant distraction as you tackle the thoughtfully composed, well executed dishes. Like the art collections within the galleries, the wine list is also something of a national treasure for oenophile art fans.

Sake No Hana
PLAN 4, J6

◉◉ MODERN JAPANESE ⓘ NOTABLE WINE LIST

020 7925 8988 | 23 Saint James's Street, SW1A 1HA

www.sakenohana.com

Part of the Hakkasan stable, this sleek Japanese restaurant is a striking L-shaped space with a wood lattice ceiling, bamboo columns and windows hung with screens. Perch at the sushi counter, or sit at low-slung leather banquettes for a menu offering both contemporary and traditional dishes.

Santini Restaurant
PLAN 4, H4

◉ TRADITIONAL ITALIAN

020 7730 4094 | 29 Ebury Street, SW1W 0NZ

www.santinirestaurant.com

The traditional values of a family-run Italian restaurant underpin this glossy Belgravia darling, and Latin style runs all the way from the sleek and bright interior to the waiters and the wine list. Impeccably sourced seasonal ingredients treated with a light touch are at the core.

Seven Park Place by William Drabble
PLAN 4, J6

◉◉◉ MODERN FRENCH ⓘ NOTABLE WINE LIST

020 7316 1600 | St James's Hotel and Club, 7–8 Park Place, SW1A 1LP

www.stjameshotelandclub.com

Tucked away in St James's, the eponymously titled five-star hotel and club is home to one of London's most seductive dining opportunities, where the incomparable William Drabble has been producing dynamic and creative modern French cuisine since 2009. The dining room is a gem, small but perfectly formed, shimmering with rich, warm colours and bold contemporary artworks. The set lunch is a great introduction to William's work for anyone on a budget (two choices at each course), with an all-conquering Menu Gourmand at the other end of the spectrum (including a choice of three wine flights or a juice pairing). First-rate ingredients from trusted suppliers lead the way on the à la carte menu. The technical virtuosity on display is impressive from start to finish, with attention to texture, flavour and temperature. The wine 'book' excels in France and does more than justice to the rest of the world.

Chef William Drabble **Seats** 34, Private dining 35 **Open** All Year **Notes** No children

Wild Honey
PLAN 4, K6

◉◉◉ FRENCH

020 7968 2900 | Sofitel London St James, 6 Waterloo Place, SW1Y 4AN

www.wildhoneystjames.co.uk

Wild Honey's move from Mayfair to the Sofitel London St James has resulted in an airy, high-ceilinged dining room with enormous windows draped in grey linen, black walls, impressive lighting, and beautiful pale blue velvet banquettes. This is a slick operation, serving up the simple, contemporary French-based seasonal cooking for which the restaurant is so well known. Kick off with the earthy flavours of roast heritage beetroot, rich black pudding purée and cured wild boar cheek. A highly successful main of perfectly cooked Welsh lamb comes with roast salsify, fresh sheep's ricotta and Italian greens, while dessert might be a classic English custard tart.

Chef Matt Greenwood **Seats** 84, Private dining 20 **Open** All Year **Notes** Children welcome

Zafferano
PLAN 4, F4

◉◉ MODERN ITALIAN

020 7235 5800 | 15 Lowndes Street, SW1X 9EY

www.zafferano.co.uk

Zafferano has remained part of the capital's dining establishment since Gorgio Locatelli opened here as head chef back in 1995. Inside a bar, striped banquettes, exposed brick and handsome flower displays add exclusivity, while the kitchen gives classic Italian dishes a sophisticated spin; think linguini with lobster, chilli and fresh tomato to veal Milanese. Deep-wallet prices, and a hotspot pavement terrace.

LONDON SW3

Claude Bosi at Bibendum
PLAN 4, E3

◉◉◉◉ MODERN FRENCH ❶ NOTABLE WINE LIST

0207 581 5817 | Michelin House, 81 Fulham Road, SW3 6RD

www.bibendum.co.uk

This fabulous post-art nouveau building in Chelsea was once the UK headquarters of the French tyre company, Michelin, and Bibendum himself (featuring in the exuberant stained glass of the dining room) is their famously pneumatic mascot. The ornate pillared entrance leads into the ground-floor, all-day Oyster Bar (offering spectacular seafood platters as well as the eponymous mollusc), while upstairs you'll find the beautiful dining room, surely one of the airiest and most elegant in London. Home to Claude Bosi's modern French cooking since 2016, classical techniques and seasonal ingredients underpin reassuringly precise presentation, and perfectly timed dishes deliver every promised flavour with elegant simplicity. Most meals begin with a 'Bibendum egg' – a white eggshell in a beautiful silver eggcup, filled perhaps with artichoke purée topped with creamy coconut foam and a dusting of vanilla powder. Lunch might offer new season girolles with peanut, sesame and crème fraîche, before Cornish cod white miso and English peas, followed by black leg chicken with black olive and feta. To finish, something from the ice cream trolley with warm madeleines and honey. If your whole party is willing, you might choose the 'taste of the season' or 'Classics' menu, and feast on Orkney scallops with brown butter dashi and lemon caviar, or Cornish turbot à la Grenobloise. The impressive wine list is mainly French and Italian.

Chef Claude Bosi **Closed** 23-26 December, 1-7 January, 14-22 April **Notes** Children welcome

Le Colombier
PLAN 4, D2

◉ TRADITIONAL FRENCH

020 7351 1155 | 145 Dovehouse Street, SW3 6LB

www.le-colombier-restaurant.co.uk

Le Colombier is the epitome of the old-school neighbourhood French restaurant, its blue-canopied terrace is a hot ticket, while the dining room is an equally sunny confection of cream and blues. Unfussy, unashamedly classic French brasserie-style dishes are so familiar they hardly need their translations.

Elystan Street
PLAN 4, E3
◎◎◎ MODERN BRITISH ♨NOTABLE WINE LIST
020 7628 5005 | 43 Elystan Street, Chelsea, SW3 3NT
www.elystanstreet.com
An expansive, light-flooded space with chairs in two colours at bare-topped tables is the location for Phil Howard's Chelsea operation, a sophisticated take on informal contemporary eating. His cooking, as befits his many years at The Square, displays a level of fine-tuned attention to detail in every element of a dish, from the skin-thin pasta of chicken and butternut ravioli with hazelnut pesto in chicken jus to the gently caramelised Orkney scallops that garnish a roasted fillet of sea bream with puréed broccoli and glazed salsify. Meat is of a high order too, perhaps Cumbrian rib-eye with a stuffed field mushroom, puréed shallots and potato galette in red wine. Peppered vanilla and bayleaf ice cream makes an assertive accompaniment to properly glutinous pear Tatin, while the Brillat-Savarin cheesecake is already legendary, its Seville orange glaze adding tang, its ice cream humorously flavoured with toast.

Chef Philip Howard, Toby Burrowes Seats 64, Private dining 14 Closed Christmas Notes Children welcome

The Five Fields
PLAN 4, F3
◎◎◎◎ MODERN BRITISH V ♨NOTABLE WINE LIST
See page 212

Hans' Bar & Grill
PLAN 4, F3
◎ MODERN BRITISH
020 7730 7000 | 164 Pavilion Road, Chelsea, SW1X 0AW
www.hansbarandgrill.com
Part of a luxury townhouse hotel on a Chelsea square, Hans' has its own entrance and slots in comfortably among the upscale shops on Pavilion Road. The place has smart contemporary looks - bare brickwork, low-slung banquettes and tasteful hues - and food to match on an appealing all-day menu of modern British dishes.

Kutir NEW
PLAN 4, F3
◎◎ PAN-INDIAN V
020 7581 1144 | 10 Lincoln Street, Chelsea, SW3 2TS
kutir.co.uk
An elegant townhouse in the heart of Chelsea is home to this stylish Indian restaurant. A series of intimate rooms, with panelling in a variety of colours and beautiful details, including a fabulously patterned bar, it's a discreet, pleasurable dining experience. Menus provide an innovative and refined exploration of the ingredients and dishes of India's many regions and cultures.

The Restaurant at The Capital
PLAN 4, F5
◎◎ BRITISH, SEAFOOD
020 7591 1202 | Basil Street, Knightsbridge, SW3 1AT
www.capitalhotel.co.uk
Located in the Capital Hotel in the heart of Knightsbridge you will find a smart, tall-ceilinged dining room with tall windows offering street views. British-inspired cuisine, using local and seasonal ingredients sourced from trusted suppliers, is produced from the kitchen with a touch of elegance. Service is attentive.

Restaurant Gordon Ramsay
PLAN 4, F1
◎◎◎◎ FRENCH ♨NOTABLE WINE LIST
020 7352 4441 | 68 Royal Hospital Road, SW3 4HP
www.gordonramsayrestaurants.com
The flagship of the Gordon Ramsay global empire remains a strong contender in London's high-end dining scene. The dining room is surprisingly intimate - just 45 or so seats - with clean-lined, art deco-influenced looks and plush, pastel-hued tones giving a sophisticated sheen to the space. As for the kitchen team, Matt Abé has been running things here for more than a decade. What keeps this venue in the premier league is its rejection of pointless experimentation and tawdry effects: what you get is superb ingredients, harmoniously combined and executed with pin-sharp precision. The fixed-price lunch menu is the best entry point for anyone looking for the RGR experience on a budget (relatively speaking). Pitch-perfect service is supervised by Jean-Claude Breton, and sommelier James Lloyd and his team steer the way through a roll-call of the world's best producers.

Chef Matt Abé Seats 45 Closed 1 week at Christmas Notes Children welcome

Continued on page 213

The Five Fields

◎◎◎◎ MODERN BRITISH 𝑉 ⚑ NOTABLE WINE LIST

020 7838 1082 | 8-9 Blacklands Terrace, SW3 2SP
www.fivefieldsrestaurant.com

The Five Fields might be billed as a 'neighbourhood restaurant' but that's where any illusions of a cheap and cheerful local hangout end. Befitting its swanky SW3 postcode, this is the very essence of Sloane Square finesse and style. Chef-patron Taylor Bonnyman, head chef Marguerite Keogh and the team deliver intuitive and exciting modern dishes centred around top-drawer ingredients. Expect exquisite looking plates of precise, inventive food, whether you go for the eight-course tasting at dinner or the slightly shorter lunchtime offering. A starter of lobster - roast tail and chopped claws - might arrive with kohlrabi, peas and summer cabbage. Meltingly tender beef short rib is braised with girolles and flanked by bone marrow and baby artichoke as well as a mini cottage pie. Finish with fig leaf ice cream and caramelised almonds. Well-drilled, polished service and an intelligently curated wine list complete the package.

Chef Taylor Bonnyman, Marguerite Keogh
Seats 40, Private dining 10 **Closed** Christmas, 2 weeks January, 2 weeks August
Notes No children

LONDON SW4

Bistro Union
PLAN 1, E2

◉◉ BRITISH

020 7042 6400 | 40 Abbeville Road, Clapham,
SW4 9NG

www.bistrounion.co.uk

This is exactly the sort of easy-going
neighbourhood eatery we'd all like on our patch.
You can perch on wooden bar stools, choosing
from a menu of on-trend nibbles hand-written
onto a roll of brown paper. What leaves the
kitchen is built with British-led ingredients.

Sorella
PLAN 1, F2

◉ ITALIAN

020 7720 4662 | 148 Clapham Manor Street, Clapham,
SW4 6BX

www.sorellarestaurant.co.uk

Chef-restaurateur Robin Gill of The Dairy fame
has relaunched his former The Manor into this
cracking little neighbourhood Italian that
genuinely celebrates the Mediterranean attitude
to cooking, eating and socialising. Tucked away
off the main drag, its stripped back, casual look
is right on-trend. Expect uncomplicated,
produce-led dishes big on flavour and generosity.

Trinity Restaurant
PLAN 1, E2

◉◉◉ BRITISH, EUROPEN ⚑ NOTABLE WINE LIST

020 7622 1199 | 4 The Polygon, Clapham, SW4 0JG

www.trinityrestaurant.co.uk

In the Old Town, just a short stroll from Clapham
Common tube, Adam Byatt's stellar
neighbourhood restaurant is a good reason to
move to SW4. The outdoor terrace and cool,
understated tones inside, complete with open-
to-view kitchen, are very much what modern
London dining is about, watched over by a slick
service team who are all wised-up about the
menu and maintain a relaxed mood throughout
proceedings. The inventive modern European
cooking has its feet firmly grounded in French
classicism, with careful balanced dishes that
impress with their invention and satisfy with
their deceptive simplicity.

Chef Adam Byatt **Seats** 50 **Closed** 24–27 December and
1–2 January **Notes** No children under 10 years

Tsunami
PLAN 1, F2

◉ JAPANESE

020 7978 1610 | 5–7 Voltaire Road, SW4 6DQ

www.tsunamiclapham.co.uk

This branch of Tsunami appeals to crowds of
thirty-somethings eager for first-class sushi and
sashimi and slick modern Japanese fusion food.
Okay, the open-planned space may be hard-
edged and high-decibel, but it's really sociable,
with the kitchen delivering fresh, skilful, smart-
looking classic-meets-contemporary dishes
designed for sharing and grazing.

LONDON SW5

Cambio de Tercio
PLAN 4, C2

◉◉ MODERN SPANISH

020 7244 8970 | 163 Old Brompton Road, SW5 0LJ

www.cambiodetercio.co.uk

Folding full-length glass windows open Tercio up
to the street, while inside there's a dark, intimate
feel – black slate floors, mustard yellow and
fuchsia pink walls hung with striking modern
artworks. The food is equally colourful and good
looking, ranging from traditional tapas to more
innovative dishes.

Capote y Toros
PLAN 4, C2

◉ SPANISH

020 7373 0567 | 157 Old Brompton Road, SW5 0LJ

www.cambiodetercio.co.uk

A few doors away from sibling Cambio de Tercio,
Capote y Toros describes itself as a tapas, ham
and sherry bar. It has vivid decor with
photographs of matadors and hams hanging
from the ceiling above the bar. Live flamenco
music adds to the fun.

LONDON SW6

The Harwood Arms
PLAN 1, E3

◉◉ BRITISH

020 7386 1847 | 27 Walham Grove, Fulham, SW6 1QR

www.harwoodarms.com

On an unassuming backstreet in trendy Fulham,
the stylish Harwood Arms is one of Britain's top
gastro pubs. Inside, you could almost forget
you're in London, with photos of outdoor country
pursuits hung on grey and cream walls, and
rustic wooden tables. On the menu, first class,
carefully-sourced English produce that's cooked
with confidence.

LONDON SW7

190 Queen's Gate by Daniel Galmiche
PLAN 4, C4

⊛⊛ BRITISH, FRENCH

020 7584 6601 | The Gore, 190 Queen's Gate, SW7 5EX

www.gorehotel.com

Close to the Royal Albert Hall, this venerable venue features a wood-panelled cocktail bar where the launch party for the Rolling Stones' *Beggars Banquet* album was held. French maître Galmiche oversees proceedings in the chandeliered, gilt-mirrored dining room, where modernised classic English dishes are served.

Bombay Brasserie
PLAN 4, C3

⊛⊛ INDIAN

020 7370 4040 | Courtfield Close, Courtfield Road, SW7 4QH

www.bombayb.co.uk

This glamorous South Ken institution (first opened back in 1982) still packs in the crowds for its authentic, melting-pot Mumbai (one-time Bombay) pan-Indian cuisine. Reworked modern interiors evoke that Raj-era spirit. The kitchen deals in freshly-ground, lightly toasted spices to impart maximum flavour.

Brunello
PLAN 4, C5

⊛ MODERN ITALIAN

020 7368 5700 | Baglioni Hotel London, 60 Hyde Park Gate, Kensington Road, Kensington, SW7 5BB

www.baglionihotels.com

The opulent restaurant at the Baglioni Hotel facing Kensington Gardens is a haven of Italian chic, done in parquet and monochrome tiles, with chairs in lemon leather, and giant mirrored baubles suspended from the ceiling. Classic Italian cooking is what this international chain trades in.

Sette NEW
PLAN 4, F5

⊛⊛ MODERN ITALIAN 𝒱

020 7151 1025 | 4 Knightsbridge Green, SW1X 7QA

www.settelondon.co.uk

The first thing you notice in Sette is how gleamingly contemporary the whole place is. All mirrors, metal surfaces, high ceilings and remarkable lighting. The food is authentic modern Italian, based on Manhattan's Scarpetta restaurant family. The term 'scarpetta' comes from the Italian tradition 'fare la scarpetta,' which means to indulge in a meal down to the very last taste.

The Townhouse NEW
PLAN 4, D3

⊛ BRITISH

020 7589 6300 | The Kensington, 109–113 Queen's Gate, SW7 5LP

www.doylecollection.com

With its high ceilings, oak floors, pastel hues and luxurious fabrics, there is certainly a grand feel to the restaurant within the well-positioned Kensington Hotel. The food in The Townhouse dining room is just as impressive, from English asparagus, mushroom duxelles, aged parmesan and pea shoots to grilled mixed fish with squid ink risotto.

Zuma
PLAN 4, F5

⊛⊛ MODERN JAPANESE

020 7584 1010 | 5 Raphael Street, Knightsbridge, SW7 1DL

www.zumarestaurant.com

An effortlessly cool playground of the beau monde, super glossy Zuma appeals to lovers of contemporary Japanese food and slick design. The vibe is high octane, buoyed by the buzzing front bar-lounge offering 40 different sakes. A lengthy roster of in-vogue sharing plates feature; the sushi is exemplary.

LONDON SW8

FIUME
PLAN 4, H1

⊛⊛ ITALIAN

020 3904 9010 | Circus West, Battersea Power Station, SW8 5BN

www.fiume-restaurant.co.uk

This modern restaurant within the Battersea Power Station redevelopment offers a stripped-back decor with industrial decor plus an open-plan kitchen with a pizza oven that takes centre stage. The seasonally changing menus offer Italian dishes from Sardinia with a modern twist. A full wine list, well-stocked bar and a cocktail menu back it all up.

LONDON SW10

Maze Grill Park Walk
PLAN 4, C1

⊛ MODERN AMERICAN, JAPANESE

020 7495 2211 | 11 Park Walk, SW10 0AJ

www.gordonramsayrestaurants.com/maze-grill-park-walk

On one side of the room at Maze Grill Park Walk is a neat line of marble tables at olive-green banquettes, on the other is a long bar. The place takes inspiration from Manhattan grill rooms, so beef is king here.

Medlar Restaurant   PLAN 4, D1

◉◉◉ MODERN EUROPEAN ⬥NOTABLE WINE LIST

020 7349 1900 | 438 King's Road, Chelsea, SW10 0LJ

www.medlarrestaurant.co.uk

A welcoming restaurant at World's End, Medlar radiates a smart feel and relaxed ambience. Colourful modern art, antique mirrors and mint-green banquettes add to the elegant setting and pavement tables are highly prized when the weather is kind. The precise modern European dishes are rooted in classic French technique and flavours are well defined. Crab raviolo with samphire, brown shrimps, fondue of leeks and bisque sauce might precede roast veal sweetbread and tongue with confit onion, rainbow chard, sorrel and sherry vinegar caramel. Round things off with chocolate delice, griottine cherries, roasted almond ice cream and cocoa nib tuile.

Chef Joe Mercer Nairne Seats 85, Private dining 28 Closed Christmas and 1 January Notes Children welcome

Myrtle Restaurant NEW   PLAN 1, E3

◉◉◉ MODERN EUROPEAN, IRISH

020 7352 2411 | 1a Langton Street, Chelsea, SW10 0JL

www.myrtlerestaurant.com

First solo venture from Irish-born chef Anna Haugh (known to a wider audience from her TV appearances on the BBC's 'Morning Live' or 'Saturday Kitchen'), Myrtle sees her deservedly step out into the limelight after working in some of London's top kitchens for celebrated chefs like Philip Howard, Shane Osborne and Gordon Ramsay. Small, two-floored light-filled and relaxed, Myrtle speaks with a soft, endearing Irish accent, with Haugh's intelligently simple yet refined, elegant dishes driven by top-notch Irish produce: witness, Clonakilty black pudding wrapped in crispy string potato with Bramley apple and pearl barley, and to follow, oat-crusted hake with smoked mackerel chowder and spinach.

Chef Anna Haugh Closed Mondays and Sundays

LONDON SW11

London House   PLAN 1, E3

◉◉ MODERN BRITISH

020 7592 8545 | 7-9 Battersea Square, Battersea Village, SW11 3RA

www.gordonramsayrestaurants.com/london-house

Smack on the corner of lovely Battersea Square, Gordon Ramsay's neighbourhood restaurant and bar is just the outfit everyone would love on their doorstep. The kitchen's creative modern British brasserie-style repertoire displays the same unmistakeable gloss; think simplicity, precision, flavour and flair.

LONDON SW14

Rick Stein, Barnes   PLAN 1, D2

◉ SEAFOOD

020 8878 9462 | 125 Mortlake High Street, Barnes, SW14 8SN

www.rickstein.com/eat-with-us/barnes

The Stein empire's first foray into London sees bottle-green banquettes and brass edged tables add class to the conservatory-style space. The globetrotting menu parades fish and seafood dishes inspired by Rick Stein's TV travels: simple, light-touch treatments that let the top-class ingredients do the talking.

LONDON SW17

Chez Bruce   PLAN 1, E2

◉◉◉ MODERN BRITISH ⬥NOTABLE WINE LIST

020 8672 0114 | 2 Bellevue Road, Wandsworth Common, SW17 7EG

www.chezbruce.co.uk

Overlooking leafy Wandsworth Common, the discreet aubergine-coloured frontage of Bruce Poole's high-flying neighbourhood restaurant sits discreetly in a parade of shops. A beacon of top-notch culinary achievement since 1995, the place doesn't need a celebrity chef, a social media storm or a glossy West End location to bring in the punters, preferring the unshouty approach of a white-walled dining room hung with tasteful art, furnished with linen-clad tables on herringbone parquet floors. It's a setting that suits Poole's unfussy but highly classy cooking to perfection, the roots of the modern European menu deeply imbedded in France and the Mediterranean.

Chef Bruce Poole, Matt Christmas Seats 75, Private dining 16 Closed 24-26 December and 1 January

LONDON SW19

The Fox & Grapes
PLAN 1, D2

⊕ TRADITIONAL BRITISH

020 8619 1300 | 9 Camp Road, Wimbledon, SW19 4UN

www.foxandgrapeswimbledon.co.uk

On the edge of Wimbledon Common, the 18th-century Fox & Grapes has morphed into a contemporary gastropub with an airy open-plan interior split into two areas by its central bar. Its kitchen surprisingly speaks with modern European accent; think black ink tagliolini, with squid, mussels, clams, king prawns and San Marzano tomato sauce to desserts like affogato al caffè.

Hotel du Vin Wimbledon
PLAN 1, D1

⊕ MODERN BRITISH, EUROPEAN

020 8879 1464 | Cannizaro House, West Side, Wimbledon Common, SW19 4UE

www.hotelduvin.com/locations/wimbledon

Located in Cannizaro House, a rather posh late-Georgian mansion, this Bistro du Vin occupies an expansive orangery-style space with soaring floor-to-ceiling glass walls looking over the park. From the menu you can expect the HdV house style of classic French bistro cooking based on well-sourced seasonal materials.

The Light House Restaurant
PLAN 1, D1

⊕ MODERN INTERNATIONAL, EUROPEAN

020 8944 6338 | 75-77 Ridgway, Wimbledon, SW19 4ST

www.lighthousewimbledon.com

The Light House is a beacon of fresh seasonal cooking just a short stroll from Wimbledon Common. Appealing menus of fresh, modern bistro-style dishes are the deal, with plenty of sunny, Mediterranean flavours being cooked up in the open kitchen.

The White Onion
PLAN 1, D1

⊕⊕ CONTEMPORARY FRENCH

020 8947 8278 | 67 High Street, Wimbledon, SW19 5EE

www.thewhiteonion.co.uk

This smart-casual bistro fits the bill for its well-heeled neighbourhood. With a sleek look of deep teal blue and white walls, bright modern artworks, buttoned leather banquettes and bare wood tables, it's a suitable setting for sparkly confident modern French cooking that gives star billing to excellent seasonal ingredients.

LONDON W1

10 Greek Street
PLAN 3, A2

⊕⊕ MODERN BRITISH, EUROPEAN

020 7734 4677 | W1D 4DH

www.10greekstreet.com

A Soho bistro reinvented for the present age, the lively cooking at number 10 has plenty to say for itself. Fish dishes in two sizes, such as gurnard with Jerusalem artichokes and black pudding, or mackerel chermoula with pomegranate and pistachio, indicate a flexible approach.

Les 110 de Taillevent NEW
PLAN 2, H2

⊕⊕⊕ MODERN FRENCH

020 3141 6016 | 16 Cavendish Sq, W1G 9DD

www.les-110-taillevent-london.com

Ornate high ceilings, tall windows, dark-green banquettes and a showpiece bar give this classy, low-lit wine-based outfit a romantic, high-end gloss. Sibling of much-worshipped Parisian restaurant with the same moniker, it offers diners 110 by-glass wines as part of its corking list that tops 1,500 bottles. Each dish is offered with four different wine pairings, in four different price brackets and measures (70ml or 125ml). Stellar chef Ross Bryans' modern French roster comes underscored by a classical French theme and delivers in well-dressed, perfectly executed plates clean on flavour. High skill, flair and balance shine in dishes like sea-fresh Cornish turbot teamed with Jerusalem artichoke, peacock kale and headlining sauce Albufera, while a blackcurrant soufflé, with speculoos biscuit ice cream, wows with theatre and flavour. Charming service underpins all.

Chef Ross Bryans

116 at The Athenaeum
PLAN 4, H6

⊕⊕ MODERN, CLASSIC BRITISH

020 7640 3333 | 116 Piccadilly, W1J 7BJ

www.athenaeumhotel.com

The Athenaeum Hotel's restaurant is another outpost in London chefs Chris and Jeff Galvin's empire. For the first time they've stepped away from their trademark French-inspired menus in favour of an array of menus including afternoon tea and private dining, and feature a modern take on classic British dishes.

Alain Ducasse at The Dorchester
PLAN 4, G6

◎◎◎◎ CONTEMPORARY, MODERN FRENCH **V** ⚑NOTABLE WINE LIST

020 7629 8866 | The Dorchester, 53 Park Lane, W1K 1QA

www.alainducasse-dorchester.com

The Dorchester has long been a London landmark, its Grill Room famous as the luxurious setting for opulent dining. Its current incarnation is as sharply, calmly elegant as you could wish for, the merest hint of a modern take of the deco feel found elsewhere in the hotel. The room is immaculately set for guests; polished silver, crisp linen napkins, elegant table appointments, smart staff and superb, highly polished gueridon trolleys. A wall of shining copper pans reflect the light, and the seasonally-changing menus offer a characterful take on the very best classical French cooking. Executive chef Jean-Phillippe Blondet supervises an endlessly accomplished list of reassuringly constant, technically precise dishes. You can expect the very best seasonal produce from British and French producers – witness a lunch of marinated courgette, shellfish, citrus and dill, followed by pork loin, purple artichokes and Tropea onion, before a delightfully refreshing dessert of strawberries with Madagascan vanilla and rocket sorbet.

Chef Jean-Philippe Blondet, Thibault Hauchard, Alberto Gobbo **Seats** 82, Private dining 30 **Closed** 1st week in January, Easter weekend, 3 weeks in August **Parking** 20 **Notes** No children under 10 years

Amaranto at Four Seasons Hotel London at Park Lane
PLAN 4, G6

◎◎ ITALIAN

020 7319 5206 | Hamilton Place, Park Lane, W1J 7DR

www.fourseasons.com/london/dining/restaurants/amaranto_restaurant

Four Seasons stands in modern grandeur at Hyde Park Corner, a distinctly plutocratic node of London. In the restaurant, carefully-crafted Italian dishes embrace the simplicity that everyone seeks in Italian food. The garden terrace is just the ticket in the summer.

Antidote
PLAN 2, J2

◎ MODERN EUROPEAN

020 7287 8488 | 12a Newburgh Street, W1F 7RR

www.antidotewinebar.com

Tucked away in a fashionably 'off-the-radar' cobbled lane behind Carnaby Street, Antidote offers the perfect fix for organic/biodynamic wine lovers and foodies alike. Upstairs, above its bustling wine bar, the dining room is a relaxed oasis and the kitchen delivers seasonal modern ideas that work thanks to great ingredients and a light touch.

Aqua Kyoto
PLAN 2, J2

◎◎ CONTEMPORARY JAPANESE

020 7478 0540 | 240 Regent Street, W1B 3BR

www.aquakyoto.co.uk

With a dining room that shimmers with contemporary style and a rooftop terrace – set five floors up above Regent Street – Aqua Kyoto is a go-to destination. The open kitchen delivers with equal razzmatazz, sending out innovative, visually striking modern Japanese cuisine of top-draw ingredients and some umami-rich flavour bombs; witness slow-cooked aka miso and garlic pork belly with shiso green apple.

Aqua Nueva
PLAN 2, J2

◎◎ MODERN SPANISH

020 7478 0540 | 5th Floor, 240 Regent Street, W1B 3BR

www.aquanueva.co.uk

A lift whizzes you up from ground-floor street life to jet-set high life at this slick fifth floor restaurant where people come to see and be seen while grazing on contemporary renditions of tapas based on top-class Spanish ingredients. Pick from a bilingual menu.

Arros QD *NEW*
PLAN 2, J2

◎◎ MODERN SPANISH, INTERNATIONAL

020 3883 3525 | 64 Eastcastle Street, W1W 8NQ

www.arrosqd.com

Spanish celebrity chef Quique Dacosta (famed for his avant-garde gastronomy and flagship restaurant near Alicante) elevates humble paella to star billing in this classy new operation in Fitzrovia. Start upstairs in the sleek cocktails bar, then grab a counter seat at the open kitchen for ringside views of the chefs cooking over flaming open grills.

Chef Quique Dacosta

Barrafina Dean Street
PLAN 2, K2

◉◉ SPANISH

020 7813 8016 | 26–27 Dean Street, W1D 3LL
www.barrafina.co.uk
Tapas is the name of the game here at this bustling plate-glass corner site. The no booking policy means queues are likely but, once in, you perch elbow-to-elbow at the marble counter and tuck into rapid-fire small plates bursting with flavour. The maximum group size is four.

Bellamy's
PLAN 2, H1

◉ FRENCH

020 7491 2727 | 18–18a Bruton Place, W1J 6LY
www.bellamysrestaurant.co.uk
Bellamy's effortlessly classy good looks and slickly professional service epitomise the chic, timeless French brasserie genre. Leather banquettes, tasteful French artworks, white linen and staff in bow ties and waistcoats add to the authentic look. The kitchen excels in simple, clear-flavoured dishes. Fabulous all-French wines, an afternoon oyster bar and a chic evening cocktail bar complete the experience.

Benares Restaurant
PLAN 2, H1

◉◉ MODERN INDIAN 🍷 NOTABLE WINE LIST

020 7629 8886 | 12a Berkeley Square, W1J 6BS
www.benaresrestaurant.com
In the heart of Mayfair, this restaurant has the buzz of a glamorous nightclub but takes a serious approach when it comes to dining. Combining high-end British ingredients with spices and aromatics the Anglo-Indian cooking always excites with its innovative ideas, precise technique and enticing presentation.

Bentley's Oyster Bar & Grill
PLAN 2, J1

◉ BRITISH, IRISH 🍷 NOTABLE WINE LIST

020 7734 4756 | 11–15 Swallow Street, W1B 4DG
www.bentleys.org
Now over a hundred years old, the illustrious oyster bar is a highly popular, feel-good rendezvous, its canopied terrace a hot ticket for slithering-fresh fish and seafood on a balmy day. Prices lean toward West End scary, but then the ingredients are second to none, the service slick and the wines a superb bunch.

Berners Tavern
PLAN 2, J2

◉◉ MODERN BRITISH 🍷 NOTABLE WINE LIST

020 7908 7979 | The London EDITION, 10 Berners Street, W1T 3NP
www.bernerstavern.com
This palatial space with a magnificent plaster ceiling, chandelier, and walls crowded with pictures, is nothing like a tavern. Jason Atherton oversees the cooking, which is in his contemporary brasserie style. Restyled classics such as lobster and prawn cocktail get things going nicely.

The Betterment by Jason Atherton NEW
PLAN 2, G1

◉◉◉ MODERN BRITISH

020 7629 9400 | The Biltmore, Mayfair, 44 Grosvenor Square, W1K 2HP
thebettermentmayfair.com
The Betterment is the Mayfair branch of Jason Atherton's London operations, occupying a glamorous setting in the ultra-luxurious Biltmore Hotel in Grosvenor Square, so this is not one for tight budgets. It's the sort of glitzy spot for putting your glad rags on in anticipation of some big-hitting dishes that tease out every molecule of flavour from pedigree ingredients. Roasted Orkney scallop with braised girolles and creamy parmesan sauce opens in fine style, while short rib with Montgomery cheddar and bone marrow is lifted by the textures of croûtons and diced apple. Almond financier with caramelised white chocolate, raspberry and red pepper sorbet makes a refined finisher.

Chef Jason Atherton **Open** All year

Blanchette
PLAN 2, J2

◉ MODERN, TRADITIONAL FRENCH TAPAS

020 7439 8100 | 9 D'Arblay Street, Soho, W1F 8DR
www.blanchettesoho.co.uk
Opened by three brothers from across the Channel, Blanchette delivers imaginative contemporary bistro-style French cuisine served as sharing plates. The setting is oh-so Soho with its counter seats for people watching at the window and hip blend of bare brick walls, mismatched retro tables and chairs and entertaining vintage Francophile bits and bobs.

Bocca di Lupo
PLAN 2, K1

◎ ITALIAN ⚑ NOTABLE WINE LIST

020 7734 2223 | 12 Archer Street, W1D 7BB

www.boccadilupo.com

High-energy, high-octane and fantastic fun, Bocco di Lupo rocks. Grab a stall at the long bar's 'chef's counter' to enjoy the culinary theatre, or head to the restaurant area proper. Leather seating, flower displays and feature lighting catch the eye, while simple regional Italian grazing plates shout flavour; think spaghetti with squid ragù to grilled calves liver, red onion and balsamic.

Cecconi's
PLAN 2, J1

◎◎ TRADITIONAL ITALIAN

020 7434 1500 | 5a Burlington Gardens, W1S 1EP

www.cecconis.co.uk

Cecconi's is a classic, from the glamorous Mayfair crew slurping cocktails and cicchetti at the island bar to the black-and-white humbug-striped marble floors, green leather upholstery and slick Italian staff. Dedication to top-class seasonal produce is clear, and it's simply prepared to deliver full-on flavours.

Charlie's Restaurant at Brown's Hotel *NEW*
PLAN 2, J1

◎◎ MODERN EUROPEAN

020 7493 6020 | Brown's Hotel, Albemarle Street, Mayfair, W1S 4BP

www.roccofortehotels.com

Charlie's Restaurant is a well-established Mayfair eating place, its antique wooden panelling interspersed with large mirrors, complemented by interior designer Olga Polizzi's bright botanical wallpaper. British dishes include modern classics, for example, daily roasts carved on the trolley, and there are French, Italian and Spanish influences too. All is backed up by a comprehensive wine list and an enthusiastic sommelier.

See advertisement on page 221

The Chesterfield Mayfair
PLAN 4, H6

◎◎ TRADITIONAL BRITISH

020 7491 2622 | 35 Charles Street, Mayfair, W1J 5EB

www.chesterfieldmayfair.com

A fine Georgian property jam-packed with antiques and run with a touch of old-school charm. A suckling pig's cheek croquette looks pretty, with a sliver of black pudding and sweetcorn purée. There's a pre-theatre menu, and afternoon tea is served in the conservatory.

China Tang at The Dorchester
PLAN 4, G6

◎◎ CLASSIC CANTONESE

020 7319 7088 | 53 Park Lane, W1K 1QA

www.chinatanglondon.co.uk

This opulent homage to 1930s Shanghai, with smart carpets, upholstery and wallpaper, elevates classic Cantonese cuisine to a higher level; remember, though this is The Dorchester, so don't expect normal high-street prices. Familiar-sounding, nevertheless, are dim sum, vegetarian soups, roast duck mixed platter, and Szechuan peppercorn-braised Dover sole. Vegetarian, halal and gluten free options are all available.

Clipstone
PLAN 2, H3

◎◎ MODERN EUROPEAN

020 7637 0871 | 5 Clipstone Street, W1W 6BB

www.clipstonerestaurant.co.uk

On a compact corner spot with expansive windows for watching Fitzrovia life go by, Clipstone is a casual contemporary bistro with a spartan interior focused on a pocket-sized open kitchen. The menu revolves around creative, lively ideas driven by splendid seasonal ingredients handled with simplicity and precision and delivered in inventive flavour combinations.

The Colony Grill Room
PLAN 2, G1

◎ BRITISH, AMERICAN

020 7499 9499 | The Beaumont, 8 Balderton Street, Mayfair, W1K 6TF

www.colonygrillroom.com

On the south side of Oxford Street, not far from Selfridges, The Beaumont is a burnished slice of Mayfair elegance. The dining room's grill concept sees crustacea, grills and steaks arrive as simply honest, hearty fare, all delivered in a richly decorated room with an art deco theme. A number of dishes are prepared at the table to add further theatre.

Corrigan's Mayfair

PLAN 2, G1

BRITISH, IRISH

020 7499 9943 | 28 Upper Grosvenor Street, W1K 7EH
www.corrigansmayfair.co.uk
Respected Irish chef Richard Corrigan delivers a genuine slice of timeless splendour in his Mayfair flagship. Sumptuous leather seats and an elegant art deco style gives the dining room a clubby feel and service is highly polished. The ingredient-driven Anglo-Irish food is as big-hearted and robust as the owner. To kick off, go for Norfolk quail cooked over hot coals and teamed with Sauternes-soaked Muscat grapes and pickled walnut. A main course John Dory turns up with chickpeas, Morteau sausage and salsa verde, while roasted hazelnut choux bun and caramel is a good way to finish.

Chef Richard Corrigan, Aidan McGee **Seats** 85, Private dining 30 **Closed** 25 December, Bank Holidays
Notes Children welcome

Coya

PLAN 4, H6

MODERN PERUVIAN

020 7042 7118 | 118 Piccadilly, Mayfair, W1J 7NW
www.coyarestaurant.com
With its open kitchen, a céviche counter, a charcoal grill and a glamorous pisco bar, Coya is a hive of Peruvian-inspired activity. Expect classy food full of entertaining South American and Japanese fusion flavours and some spot-on ingredients in the mix.

CUT at 45 Park Lane

PLAN 4, G6

MODERN AMERICAN *V*

020 7493 4554 | 45 Park Lane, W1K 1BJ
www.dorchestercollection.com/en/london/45-park-lane/restaurants-bars/cut-45-park-lane
The Park Lane glitz of a swanky hotel in the Dorchester stable makes a suitably top-end joint for one of US chef and restaurateur Wolfgang Puck's über-glam international steakhouses. With an extravagant decor, no-one could fault the jet-set vibe of this temple to top-grade beef sourced from all over the world. Take your pick: Australian and Japanese Wagyu, South Devon Angus, USDA rib-eye steak with fries, all expertly aged, sold by weight, and precision timed on the grill, with eight sauces to go with it. There's also seared scallops, or steamed sea bass 'Hong Kong' style, plus a delectable baked Alaska to fish finish.

Chef David McIntyre **Seats** 70, Private dining 14
Open All Year **Prices from** S £16, M £26, D £9
Notes Children welcome

Davies and Brook *NEW*

PLAN 2, H1

MODERN

020 7629 8860 | Brook Street, W1K 4HR
www.claridges.co.uk
Davies and Brook is named for the two streets that form the corner location of Claridge's, wherein this rather elegant dining room is ensconced. The look is clean-lined and contemporary, with high ceilings and specially commissioned artworks adding to the chic ambience. The food comes courtesy of chef Daniel Humm, whose high-flying New York reputation translates here as dishes of thrilling flavour clarity and intensity. Dry-aged duck in a fabulous sweet-and-perfumed glaze of honey and lavender with daikon ribbons and rhubarb purée is a dish to write home about, as is a sublime combo of poached lobster with swede and pear.

Chef Daniel Humm **Open** All year

Dehesa

PLAN 2, J1

SPANISH, ITALIAN

020 7494 4170 | 25 Ganton Street, W1F 9BP
www.saltyardgroup.co.uk/dehesa
Dehesa comes from the same stable as Salt Yard and Opera Tavern and, like them, is a charcuterie and tapas bar serving up a lively hybrid of Spanish and Italian dishes. It's a small, buzzy place where you sit elbow-to-elbow at high-level tables.

Dinings

PLAN 2, E3

JAPANESE, EUROPEAN

020 7723 0666 | 22 Harcourt Street, W1H 4HH
www.dinings.co.uk
There's scarcely room to swing a chopstick here, but the exquisitely-crafted array of Japanese tapas is the draw. The creative kitchen fuses Japanese and modern European dishes, so check out the blackboard specials, then tackle the lengthy menu by sharing a selection of small but perfectly-formed dishes.

Ember Yard

PLAN 2, J2

SPANISH, ITALIAN

020 7439 8057 | 60–61 Berwick Street, W1F 8SU
www.emberyard.co.uk
Ember Yard is the latest in the chain of uptempo tapas outfits that have been trending in the capital. The food comes inspired by Spain (the Basque country in particular) and Italy, and is smoked or cooked simply on a Basque-style wood and charcoal grill.

Continued on page 222

CHARLIE'S

Tucked away in London's most fashionable neighbourhood, Charlie's by Adam Byatt is a cheerful blend of much loved tradition and modern excellence. The menu evolves frequently with the seasons, using exceptional, local produce, to offer British dishes including the great classics with a present-day twist. There are Italian, French and Spanish influences too.

Charlie's is a romantic, stylish, warmly-lit, memory-making place with a welcome touch of theatre. Scottish smoked salmon and irresistible, daily roasts are carved on the trolley. Come early evening, cocktails are shaken and stirred at Charlie's Bar.

ALBEMARLE STREET, LONDON, W1S 4BP
020 7518 4004

L'Escargot

PLAN 3, A2

◎◎ FRENCH, MEDITERRANEAN

020 7439 7474 | 48 Greek Street, W1D 4EF

www.lescargotrestaurant.co.uk

This near-century-old Soho institution serves the rich comforts of classic French cuisine. Occupying a fine Georgian townhouse once home to the Duke of Portland, L'Escargot's sumptuous colours and serious art collection set an elegant old-school scene for cooking that reassures, comforts and thrills from the off.

French House

PLAN 2, K1

◎◎

020 7437 2477 | 49 Dean Street, Soho, W1D 5BG

www.frenchhousesoho.com

In the pint-sized dining room above the old French-themed Soho boozer, getting a table is a difficult call. The handwritten menus are pleasingly short, showing daily-changing classic dishes (with confident restraint and pleasingly devoid of cheffy artsy flourishes) come underpinned by precision and bold flavour. Service is defiantly relaxed, while wines are resolutely Francophile with bags available by glass.

Galvin at Windows Restaurant & Bar

PLAN 4, G6

◎◎◎ MODERN FRENCH ⚑NOTABLE WINE LIST

020 7208 4021 | London Hilton on Park Lane, 22 Park Lane, W1K 1BE

www.galvinatwindows.com

High up on the 28th floor, the views of London's iconic skyline are spectacular whether you visit at lunch or dinner. The stylish interior matches the vista with a bold contemporary design and smartly appointed tables. The kitchen here produces a mesmerising take on modern European cuisine with Asian influences. Begin with marinated Iberico pork, house pickles and Korean ssamjang paste, followed by spring lamb rump, breast ragout, offal pastry, anchoïade and olives, or, perhaps, lobster tail, scallop, sea bream and rouille. Things come to a satisfying finale with a perfect banana and chocolate soufflé and peanut butter ice cream.

Chef Joo Won, Chris Galvin **Seats** 130 **Open** All Year **Notes** Children welcome

Gauthier Soho

PLAN 3, A1

◎◎◎ MODERN FRENCH ⚑NOTABLE WINE LIST

020 7494 3111 | 21 Romilly Street, W1D 5AF

www.gauthiersoho.co.uk

With iron railings and glossy black front door, this charming Regency townhouse - with dining spread across three floors - certainly stands out from the regular Soho crowd; you even have to ring the bell to enter. Inside, original fireplaces and striking artworks convey the period charm, while Alex Gauthier's beguiling, fine-dining vegan cooking comes tasting-menu style. And, while white linen, hushed tones and polished service nod toward a more traditional style, the thoroughbred vegan cuisine is at the forefront of change; light, high-gloss modern dishes dressed-to-thrill. Take a classy fondant boulangère with fennel, celery, confit tomato crisps and basil velouté to a 'dashing' dark chocolate praline.

Chef Gerard Virolle, Alexis Gauthier **Seats** 60, Private dining 32 **Closed** Christmas, Bank Holidays **Notes** Children welcome

Le Gavroche Restaurant

PLAN 2, G1

◎◎◎ FRENCH ⚑NOTABLE WINE LIST

020 7408 0881 | 43 Upper Brook Street, W1K 7QR

www.le-gavroche.co.uk

For over half a century Le Gavroche has been synonymous with classic French cuisine. Situated in a smart Mayfair basement, the room sticks to a refined and graceful look that is entirely in keeping with the kind of flawlessly courteous service that has all but disappeared from London's 21st-century dining rooms. Two generations of the Roux family have built a culinary empire on classical French cuisine of the Escoffier era, with discreetly applied modernist notes to tastes and textures. The dishes are virtuoso displays of culinary artistry, while main-course saddle of Herdwick lamb with turnip, beetroot and fennel is the ultimate in meaty comfort food.

Chef Michel Roux Jnr **Seats** 60, Private dining 6 **Closed** Christmas, New Year and Bank Holidays **Notes** Children welcome

Goodman
PLAN 2, J1

◉ BRITISH, CLASSIC AMERICAN ⚑ NOTABLE WINE LIST

020 7499 3776 | 26 Maddox Street, W1S 1QH

www.goodmanrestaurants.com

There's plenty of red meat action going on for die-hard carnivores in this upscale New York-inspired steakhouse serving prime slabs of US and UK beef. Choose your cut, from rib-eye, through bone-in sirloin to porterhouse, and it arrives precision timed and served with béarnaise, pepper or Stilton sauces.

Gridiron by COMO
PLAN 4, H6

◉◉ MODERN BRITISH V

020 7447 1000 | COMO Metropolitan London, Old Park Lane, W1K 1LB

www.gridironlondon.com

One of several dining possibilities at this urbane Park Lane hotel, Gridiron is a quietly luxurious grill restaurant. Sit up close and personal with the fiery action at the marble counter overlooking the open kitchen, or park at a leather seat or banquette to tuck into precision-seared meats and fish of the highest quality.

The Grill at The Dorchester
PLAN 4, G6

◉◉◉ MODERN BRITISH V ⚑ NOTABLE WINE LIST

020 7317 6531 | 53 Park Lane, W1K 1QA

www.dorchestercollection.com/en/london/the-dorchester/restaurants-bars/the-grill-at-the-dorchester

The revamped restaurant at the heart of The Dorchester presents a contemporary reworking of the legendary British grill room first established in 1931. The chandeliers, parquet floor and intricate gilded ceilings provide a glamorous backdrop for a meal here, with some diners seated close to the action in front of the open kitchen. Start with veal sweetbread, potato pancake, bacon and cabbage before a precisely cooked piece of first-rate Cornish turbot with borlotti beans and grelot onion. Yogurt soft serve, apricots, London Honey and almonds is a clean and refreshing finale, although the soufflés are as good as ever.

Chef Tom Booton **Open** All year **Seats** 65 **Parking** 20 **Notes** Vegetarian dishes, children welcome

GYMKHANA
PLAN 4, J6

◉◉ CONTEMPORARY INDIAN

020 3011 5900 | 42 Albermarle Street, W1S 4JH

gymkhanalondon.com

It may look like a colonial-era Indian gentlemen's club with its dark oak panelling, marble tables in rattan-trimmed booths, swishing ceiling fans, and boar's head on the wall, but there's nothing retro about its inventive new-wave Indian cooking.

Hakkasan
PLAN 2, K2

◉◉ MODERN CHINESE

020 7927 7000 | 8 Hanway Place, W1T 1HD

www.hakkasan.com

Escape the Oxford Street crowds in this chic basement and you're immediately seduced by its modern Chinoiserie design, super-cool cocktail bar and uptempo, nightclubby vibe. Innovative new-wave and classic Cantonese dishes cover all bases, and luxury ingredients abound. A heavyweight wine list and an exciting cocktail selection complete the picture.

Hakkasan Mayfair
PLAN 2, H1

◉◉◉ MODERN CANTONESE, CHINESE ⚑ NOTABLE WINE LIST

020 7907 1888 | 17 Bruton Street, W1J 6QB

www.hakkasan.com

The Mayfair branch of the now global Hakkasan chain features a contemporary mix of seductive design and dazzling east-meets-west Cantonese cuisine. A long entrance corridor leads to the ground-floor dining room with its smart bar and low-slung leather seating. A high-gloss high-octane approach abounds; from the slick, informed service to the kitchen's vibrant reimaginings of traditional Cantonese dishes. Divine dim sum encompasses the likes of caviar-dotted abalone and chicken shu mai to royal king crab jade dumplings. House speciality mains might be melt-in-the-mouth stir-fry black pepper rib-eye beef with merlot. Desserts prolong the thrill factor to the very end.

Chef Tong Chee Hwee, Tan Tee Wei **Seats** 220, Private dining 16 **Closed** 25 December **Notes** Children welcome

Heddon Street Kitchen
PLAN 2, J1

◉ MODERN BRITISH

020 7592 1212 | 3–9 Heddon Street, Regent Street
Food Quarter, W1B 4BD
www.heddonstreetkitchen.co.uk

In a pedestrianised oasis just off Regent Street,
Ramsay's contemporary take on the brasserie
theme spreads over two floors, mingling
industrial chic with macho leather and wood
textures that suit the local vibe. The all-day menu
aims to please all comers.

Hide Above NEW
PLAN 4, H6

◉◉◉ CONTEMPORARY ⚑ NOTABLE WINE LIST

020 3146 8666 | 85 Piccadilly, W1J 7NB
www.hide.co.uk

Hide Above is the top-end, first floor restaurant
of chef Ollie Dabbous's glossy drinking and dining
venue. A magnificent oak staircase curves
upwards to the sleek designer space where wall-
to-wall glass gives great views over the snarl of
Piccadilly traffic to the leafy canopy of Green
Park. Five- and eight-course tasting menus bring
on cooking of exceptional precision, taking in
Cornish crab broth spiked with fennel and lime
leaves, then roast scallop with buckwheat dashi,
golden turnips, pear and pine. Roast suckling pig
comes two ways: tenderloin with cauliflower
purée, capers and raisins, followed by shoulder
with mustard sauce, hispi cabbage and black
pudding crumb.

Chef Ollie Dabbous

Hide Ground
PLAN 4, H6

◉◉ MODERN BRITISH

020 3146 8666 | 85 Piccadilly, W1J 7NB
www.hide.co.uk/restaurant/ground

This multi-floor venue on Piccadilly features a
relaxed, if rather swanky, all-day dining operation
on the 'Ground' floor. Floor-to-ceiling windows
look onto the street and Green Park beyond.
Slick, polished service serves up modern British/
European fare with robust flavours. A designer
oak staircase coils up to 'Above', the fine-dining
restaurant upstairs. There's also a basement bar
called 'Below'.

Hélène Darroze at The Connaught
PLAN 2, H1

◉◉◉◉◉ FRENCH 𝑉 ⚑ NOTABLE WINE LIST

020 3147 7200 | 16 Carlos Place, W1K 2AL
**www.the-connaught.co.uk/restaurants-bars/
helene-darroze-at-the-connaught**

Four generations, including Hélène herself,
have worked in the Darroze family restaurant
in Acquitaine. After graduating, she worked for
top chef Alain Ducasse in Monaco, before
opening her own restaurant in Paris, then
joining The Connaught. Darroze's French
culinary craft is showcased amid the splendour
of Iranian designer India Mahdavi's sophisticated
interior, with Damien Hirst artworks on the wall,
and glass cloches displaying the visual appeal
of the ingredients found in her cooking.

With places to sip champagne, tuck into a
magnificent afternoon tea, or dine pretty much
any time of the day, it's a truly high-class
location. Menus reveal the source of each dish's
main element, and are always top quality. Unlike
some places, vegetarians are no mere

afterthought, with dedicated menus. Pre-ordained wine flights may be added at a price, or you can select your own, maybe with the help of one of the team of sommeliers, who will advise on whether to select a Left or Right Bank Bordeaux, or talk you through the whites from the Weingut Keller Collection, one of Germany's truly great estates. Service at every stage strikes a pleasing balance between slick professionalism and relaxed confidence.

Chef Hélène Darroze **Seats** 60, Private dining 100
Open All Year **Notes** No children under 7 years

Inko Nito
PLAN 2, J2
◉ MODERN JAPANESE
020 3959 2650 | 55 Broadwick Street, Soho, W1F 9QS
inkonitorestaurant.com
A smoking robata grill is the engine room at the heart of this buzzy Japanese eatery. For close-up cheffy action, go for one of the seats at the counter, otherwise settle at one of the blond wood tables in the capacious dining room. The food offers a creative take on Japanese classics, and the mood is upbeat.

Jamavar
PLAN 2, H1
◉◉ INDIAN
020 7499 1800 | 8 Mount Street, Mayfair, W1K 3NF
www.jamavarrestaurants.com
A smart Mayfair location suits this stylish restaurant. It's spread over two floors, with dark wood tables and Indian-inspired artwork and brass-framed mirrors. Staff are efficient and friendly, and menus showcase a wide array of flavours from across India.

JW Steakhouse
PLAN 2, G1
◉ AMERICAN
020 7399 8460 | Grosvenor House Hotel, Park Lane, W1K 7TN
www.jwsteakhouse.co.uk
The expansive JW brings American-style steakhouse dining to the Grosvenor House in an ambience of black and white ceramic floor tiles and parquet, dressers and a menu offering variations of cuts and sauces. The beef is either thoroughbred USDA-approved or grass-fed Aberdeen Angus.

Kai Mayfair
PLAN 4, G6
◉◉ MODERN CHINESE
020 7493 8988 | 65 South Audley Street, W1K 2QU
www.kaimayfair.co.uk
This swanky Chinese restaurant is decorated in glossy Mayfair style, with arty photographs on the walls. Judicious use of spicing and seasoning, and subtle combinations of flavours and textures are hallmarks. The menu opens unusually with desserts, showing how seriously they are taken here.

KANISHKA
PLAN 2, J1
◉◉ MODERN INDIAN
020 3978 0978 | 17–19 Maddox Street, W1S 2QH
www.kanishkarestaurant.co.uk
Atul Kochhar's sophisticated restaurant just a short stroll from Bond Street focuses on regional cooking from the north-east of India. A meal might begin with smoked chilli-spiced diver scallops paired with textures of cauliflower. For main course, roasted Gressingham duck breast appears with smoked tomato sauce, potato salad and crispy poha.

The Keeper's House
PLAN 2, J1
◉ MODERN BRITISH
020 7300 5881 | Royal Academy of Arts, Burlington House, Piccadilly, W1J 0BD
www.keepershouse.org.uk
Originally a grace-and-favour residence in the 19th century for the steward of the Royal Academy collections, The Keeper's House has an intimate restaurant tucked away in its basement. Done out with green felt walls, cream leather buttoned banquettes and dramatic casts of classical friezes, it's a stylish space to indulge in a menu of light-touch modern British and European cooking.

Kitchen Table
PLAN 2, J3

◉◉◉ MODERN BRITISH ⚑NOTABLE WINE LIST

020 7637 7770 | 70 Charlotte St, W1T 4QG

kitchentablelondon.co.uk

Advance through the hot dogs and champagne going on out front, and behind a curtain at the back is what feels like a secret gourmands' club, where devotees gather round a counter for an up-close interface with the sizzles and scents of a kitchen in full gear. A multi-course tasting menu chalked up in abbreviations on the board is the drill, delivering small morsels of outstanding, always surprising food. Highlights include a crab bisque with matching custard crowned with Thai basil; rhubarb-wrapped mackerel on seaweed salsa and horseradish cream; and the fascinating contrasts of ribboned squid cooked in chicken fat and topped with preserved gooseberry. Fruit with fish is a confirmed trend as when sea bass appears with elderberry, and there's also a needle-sharp clementine sauce with the pigeon. Desserts then maintain the pace by exploring apples and pears in dazzling variety, the former appearing with sorrel granita, shortbread and chamomile custard.

Chef James Knappett **Seats** 20 **Closed** Christmas and Summer (check website for details) **Notes** No children

Kitty Fisher's
PLAN 4, H6

◉◉ MODERN BRITISH

020 3302 1661 | 10 Shepherd Market, W1J 7QF

www.kittyfishers.com

Closely packed tables and stools at the bar offer diners two options in this low-lit, atmospheric, Bohemian-style restaurant with red velvet banquettes, retro light fittings and candles. The modern British food is driven by what's available at the market on the day.

KOL Restaurant *NEW*
PLAN 2, F2

◉◉◉ MEXICAN

020 3829 6888 | 9 Seymour Street, Marylebone, London W1H 7BA

www.kolrestaurant.com

This hot-spot new Mexican feels unlike dining anywhere else in the capital. Warm tones and textures, beams, leather seating, eye-catching lighting and displays of heritage items create an engaging authentic buzz, reinforced by a centrepiece open kitchen. Uptempo, yet relaxed, Lastra's kitchen turns out labour-intensive, prettily plated super-modern dishes on a repertoire of tasting menus (with a choice at mains) that express Mexican culture and innovation through British ingredients, while also championing wild foods and seasonality. Bright, fresh, colourful flavours dance on the palette with chilli used hyper-skilfully in many forms; witness a 'tostada' course of chalk stream trout with pasilla Oaxaca, courgette, berries and wild garlic.

Chef Santiago Lastra

Levant
PLAN 2, G2

◉ LEBANESE, MIDDLE EASTERN

020 7224 1111 | Jason Court, 76 Wigmore Street, W1U 2SJ

www.levant.co.uk

Levant delivers the authentic flavours of the Middle East, along with an exotic Aladdin's-cave decor of rich fabrics, carved wood, candlelight and lamps. Small plates for grazing and sharing are the way to start, while freshly cooked meat dishes are succulent and full of flavour.

Lima
PLAN 2, K3

◉◉ MODERN PERUVIAN

020 3002 2640 | 31 Rathbone Place, Fitzrovia, W1T 1JH

www.limalondongroup.com/fitzrovia

Named after Peru's capital, this trendy, high-octane restaurant brings a refined take on that country's contemporary cuisine to the West End. Excellent British and Peruvian ingredients are the backbone, all handled confidently and skilfully to produce pretty little plates of knockout flavours.

Locanda Locatelli

PLAN 2, F2

◉◉◉ ITALIAN 👤 NOTABLE WINE LIST

020 7935 9088 | 8 Seymour Street, W1H 7JZ
www.locandalocatelli.com
TV star Giorgio Locatelli's culinary career began
by the shore of Lake Comabbio in the Lombardy
region of northern Italy, a provenance that
attunes him precisely to one of the prevalent
currents of British gastronomy. Italian classical
cooking, gently modernised but staying true to
its principles of honesty and simplicity, will never
lack for devotees. Curving booth seating in
stone-coloured leather, etched glass screens and
mirrors make for an ambience of refined civility,
naturally, but the generously proportioned tables
are designed with convivial family dining in mind.
Traditionally structured menus open with
compendious antipasti salads, before pasta
makes its appearance, perhaps via spaghetti
with octopus. Principal dishes command the
attention with majestic fish – monkfish with
walnut and caper sauce – or pan-fried calves
kidneys with potato purée and stewed lentils.
Finish with tiramisù, naturally, or perhaps bayleaf
pannacotta, orange, basil and grapefruit
compôte with lemon biscuit and green olives.

Chef Giorgio Locatelli **Seats** 85, Private dining 50
Closed 24–26 December, 1 January **Notes** Children
welcome

The Mandeville Hotel

PLAN 2, G2

◉ MODERN BRITISH

020 7935 5599 | Mandeville Place, W1U 2BE
www.mandeville.co.uk
Funky contemporary decor and an upbeat
ambience are the hallmarks of this stylish
boutique hotel, while unclothed tables and
buttoned leather banquettes set the tone in the
restaurant. A Josper Grill puts the heat on the
meat, while uncomplicated comfort-oriented
dishes are the mainstay of the menu.

The Mayfair Chippy

PLAN 2, G1

◉ BRITISH

020 7741 2233 | North Audley Street, W1K 6WE
www.mayfairchippy.com
As a pairing, Mayfair and Chippy breaks new
ground, and so it should. This wealthy quarter of
W1 has as much right to a quintessentially British
fish and chip restaurant as anywhere else. And it
certainly looks the part too.

Mele e Pere

PLAN 2, J1

◉ ITALIAN

020 7096 2096 | 46 Brewer Street, Soho, W1F 9TF
www.meleepere.co.uk
'Apples and Pears' looks a riot of colour and
conviviality on its Soho corner. At ground-floor
level is a café area, but the main dining goes on
downstairs in a dynamic, russet-walled basement
room. Italian sharing plates are the principal
draw to start, with San Daniele ham and gnocchi,
deep-fried squid and smoked aïoli, or beef
carpaccio with pecorino among the offerings.

Mere

PLAN 2, J3

◉◉◉ MODERN EUROPEAN *V* 👤 NOTABLE WINE LIST

020 7268 6565 | 74 Charlotte Street, W1T 4QH
www.mere-restaurant.com
You may know Monica Galetti best from her
appearances as a judge on *MasterChef: The
Professionals*, but she's also a former Michel Roux
Jr/Le Gavroche protégée and Mere, (pronounced
'Mary' – a play on the French for mother and
Monica's mother's name) is her restaurant. It's
classily understated; a sophisticated, grown-up
space, with a smart bar at ground level, while
downstairs the dining room is unexpectedly light,
thanks to its double-height glass frontage. The
cooking is contemporary French-European with
Western Samoan and Kiwi touches, and the
expected consummate skill and attention to
detail comes with a refined approach, backed by
flavour and panache. Service is informed,
professional but relaxed. The wine list is a
corker.

Chef Monica Galetti **Seats** 60, Private dining 10
Closed Bank Holidays **Notes** Children welcome

The Montagu Kitchen
PLAN 2, F2

◎◎ MODERN BRITISH

020 7299 2037 | Hyatt Regency London, The Churchill, 30 Portman Square, W1H 7BH

themontagurestaurant.co.uk

Located within a five-star hotel, this all-day dining destination features a relaxed and welcoming environment and serves up seasonally changing menus of smart, modern British ideas using British produce. There are great views over Portman Square and it's all just a short walk from Oxford Street and Marylebone.

Murano
PLAN 4, H6

◎◎◎◎ MODERN EUROPEAN, ITALIAN INFLUENCE ♨NOTABLE WINE LIST

020 7495 1127 | 20 Queen Street, W1J 5PP

www.muranolondon.com

Simplicity and freshness are the watchwords at Angela Hartnett's upscale Italian, but often those phrases disguise a great deal of preliminary labour, as here where each dish is fine-tuned to a supremely satisfying pitch. Look at the sheer-textured pasta in a starter of pumpkin tortelli in sage butter, its filling silky, the final touch of genius a scattering of smashed amaretti. Fish could be beautifully tender pollock in parsley velouté with charred calçot onion and spicy 'nduja crumble, or there may be a winter warmer of melting venison loin in its own ragù, with smooth celeriac purée, red cabbage and delicate gnocchi. In spring, Herdwick lamb comes into its own, the braised neck and sweetbreads served with the sharpening element of goat curd and a slew of freshly popped peas. For dessert, there's an irresistible Amalfi lemon tart, served slightly warm and sharp enough to produce a pleasurable sucking-in of cheeks, or the signature pistachio soufflé with luxurious hot chocolate sauce.

Chef Angela Hartnett, Emily Brightman **Seats** 46, Private dining 12 **Closed** Christmas **Notes** Children welcome

The Ninth
PLAN 2, K3

◎◎◎ MODERN FRENCH, MEDITERRANEAN

020 3019 0880 | 22 Charlotte Street, W1T 2NB

www.theninthlondon.com

New York-born chef-patron (and TV regular) Jun Tanaka has over two decades of working in starry kitchens. This is simply the ninth place he's worked in, and he delivers a menu of stand-out sharing plates that shout precision, flavour and flair. The light Mediterranean menu is underpinned by Tanaka's classic French background, and bursts with refined simplicity, confidence, flavour and seasonality. Take grilled pink-perfection lamb cutlets teamed with anchovy and charred hispi cabbage, or perhaps wild sea bass (with a basil crust) accompanied by salsify and tardivo (Italian radicchio). The fixed-price lunch menu is a steal.

Chef Jun Tanaka **Seats** 90, Private dining 22 **Closed** 24 December to 4 January, Bank Holidays

Prices from S £9.50, M £25, D £9.50 **Notes** Children welcome

No. 5 Social
PLAN 2, J2

◎◎◎

020 8600 3600 | 5 Pollen Street, Mayfair, W1S 1NE

www.5social.co.uk

In the heart of Mayfair, just across the street from Jason Atherton's flagship Pollen Street Social, this brand-new restaurant offers an elegant, airy dining room – a warm, relaxing environment with an unstuffy vibe, and the ideal place to experience Atherton's trademark modern European dishes. A lovely starter of Orkney scallop, set on top of a light avocado mousse, with a scallop tartare and thinly sliced raw courgette, makes for an impressive starter, while a main course of Josper-grilled Ibérico pork chop is succulent and well-seasoned, garnished with little pieces of black pudding and bacon and served with tender braised hispi cabbage.

Nobu London Old Park Lane
PLAN 4, H6

◎◎ JAPANESE, PERUVIAN 𝑉

020 7447 4747 | COMO Metropolitan London, Old Park Lane, W1K 1LB

www.noburestaurants.com/london-old-park-lane

Since opening 34 years ago, Nobu's brand of Japanese-Peruvian cooking remains highly popular. Classics include hot yellowtail sashimi with jalapeño, and cold baby tiger shrimp with three different sauces. On the seemingly endless menu too are sushi, grilled or stir-fried yakimono dishes, and omakase – tasting dishes that the chef chooses. Anticucho rib-eye steak is a Peruvian representative.

NOPI
PLAN 2, J1

◎ MEDITERRANEAN

020 7494 9584 | 21-22 Warwick Street, W1B 5NE

ottolenghi.co.uk/restaurants#nopi

Inspired by the sun-drenched cuisines of the Middle East, North Africa and the Mediterranean, owner Yotam Ottolenghi's cooking is creative stuff, bursting with punchy flavours and delivered in dishes made for sharing in an all-white brasserie-style space, or in the basement.

Norma London NEW
PLAN 2, K3

◎◎ SICILLIAN/ITALIAN

020 3995 6224 | 8 Charlotte Street, Fitzrovia, W1T 2LS

www.normalondon.com

Housed in a characterful converted townhouse on Charlotte Street, Norma is split across three floors, with dining areas, a cocktail bar and a private dining room. A crudo bar takes centre stage on the ground floor, showcasing a stunning array of seasonal raw seafood. It's busy and crowded, with friendly staff and a Sicilian inspired menu with Moorish influences.

Novikov Asian Restaurant
PLAN 4, H6

◎ CHINESE, PAN-ASIAN

020 7399 4330 | 50a Berkeley Street, W1J 8HA

www.novikovrestaurant.co.uk

Brazenly flashy, contemporary and high energy, Russian restaurateur Arkady Novikov's see-and-be-seen fat-cat Mayfair food palace delivers a palate-tingling cornucopia of pan-Asian grazing dishes. The busy glass-walled kitchen is fronted by a jaw-dropping display of super-fresh produce, while the full-throttle vibe and music are high decibel and prices super-deep wallet.

Ormer NEW
PLAN 4, H6

◎◎◎ MODERN, CLASSIC

0207 016 5601 | Flemings Mayfair, 7-12 Half Moon Street, London W1J 7BH

www.flemings-mayfair.co.uk

Befitting of a hotel restaurant with a swanky Mayfair postcard, Omer ticks all the 'luxury' boxes with its marble tiles, distressed mirrors, linen-clad tables and sumptuous green leather chairs. Chef Sofian Msetfi offers a range of tasting menus at lunch and dinner, each showcasing his precise and technically skilled modern British dishes. Start with warm Ibérico ham jelly, parmesan, Bramley apple and nasturtium before a meltingly tender rump and confit breast of Dorset lamb with cucumber and dill. Kentish strawberries, kefir and extra virgin olive oil is one way to finish, or perhaps the board of seasonal British cheeses.

Chef Sofian Msetfi **Open** All year

Orrery
PLAN 2, G3

◎◎◎ MODERN FRENCH

020 7616 8000 | 55-57 Marylebone High Street, W1U 5RB

www.orrery-restaurant.co.uk

Above the Conran shop, on the first floor of a former stable block, Orrery is something of a veteran of the Marylebone scene. A well groomed venue, the full-length skylight and arched windows provide verdant views across Marylebone church gardens and a roof terrace provides ample alfresco opportunities. The French-inspired dishes are refined and modern but respectful of classic technique. Roasted cauliflower florets, celeriac and truffle makes for a flavour-packed opener and might lead on to duck magret à l'orange and chou farci. Craquelin choux pastry, preserved apple and manjari chocolate is one of the skilful desserts.

Chef Igor Tymchyshyn **Seats** 110, Private dining 16
Closed 26-28 December, 1 January, Easter Monday, Summer Bank Holiday **Notes** Children welcome

The Palomar

PLAN 2, K1

◉◉ MODERN JERUSALEM

020 7439 8777 | 34 Rupert Street, W1D 6DN

www.thepalomar.co.uk

Quick-fire dishes that take inspiration from the Levant, North Africa and southern Spain are the deal in this high-octane operation in Theatreland. It's first come, first served for ringside seats at the open kitchen counter, where the Josper oven works overtime, delivering full-on, sun-drenched flavours to eager diners.

Park Chinois

PLAN 4, H6

◉◉ CHINESE

020 3327 8888 | 17 Berkeley Street, Mayfair, W1J 8EA

parkchinois.com

A green onyx bar and sultry red-velvet French Chinoiserie set the scene in the plush Salon de Chine, or head down to Club Chinois' underground entertainment hideaway for racy cabaret and live jazz in the evening. Whichever you choose, the modern Chinese cooking is certainly not a case of style over substance: expect sharply executed dishes built on top-flight materials.

Pied à Terre

PLAN 2, J3

◉◉◉ MODERN FRENCH ⚑ NOTABLE WINE LIST

020 7636 1178 | 34 Charlotte Street, W1T 2NH

www.pied-a-terre.co.uk

A venerable venue for four decades, Pied à Terre has aged as well as any elder statesman. A redesign provides a sophisticated edge with traditional white linen on the tables and rich autumnal colours on the walls. The cooking is luxurious and creative, with well presented dishes displaying finesse and sound technique. Go for smoked quail, celeriac, winter truffles, Piedmont hazelnuts and confit egg yolk before Gigha halibut, crushed potatoes, mussels, saffron, sea urchin, sea sand wort and Centennial grapes. Milk chocolate namelaka, salted caramel, pretzel, almonds, whisky ice cream is a stand out dessert. The wine list is encyclopaedic.

Chef Asimakis Chaniotis **Seats** 40, Private dining 16
Closed 2 weeks at Christmas and New Year
Notes Children welcome

Plum Valley

PLAN 2, K1

◉ CHINESE

020 7494 4366 | 20 Gerrard Street, W1D 6JQ

chinatown.co.uk/en/restaurant/plum-valley

Plum Valley stands out on Gerrard Street with its sleek black frontage and inside it has a dark, minimalist contemporary gloss. Service is brisk but friendly. The mainstay of the menu is classic Cantonese stuff, with familiar old favourites and some perky modern ideas, too.

Podium

PLAN 4, G6

◉◉ MODERN EUROPEAN

020 7208 4022 | London Hilton on Park Lane, 22 Park Lane, W1K 1BE

www.podiumrestaurant.com

This swish all-day eatery in the Park Lane Hilton fits the bill when you're tootling around Mayfair and fancy a relaxed pit-stop with an eclectic, comfort-oriented menu. The kitchen delivers the goods via unpretentious and well-executed modern European dishes constructed from well-sourced materials, while the service team do their bit with friendly professionalism.

Pollen Street Social

PLAN 2, H2

◉◉◉◉ MODERN BRITISH 𝐕 ⚑ NOTABLE WINE LIST

020 7290 7600 | 8–10 Pollen Street, W1S 1NQ

www.pollenstreetsocial.com

Jason Atherton continues to progress, opening restaurants, collecting awards, always moving forwards. Pollen Street Social is his London flagship, discreetly hidden away down a narrow Mayfair side street. Inside it's all smooth dark wood, white linen and modern British art; soothing, calm, and the perfect setting for Atherton's 'relaxed fine dining' which is as beautiful and uplifting to look at as it is joyful to eat. With a range of menus including vegetarian and vegan tasting menus, which tell you the distance travelled by the main ingredients from, for example, the Orkney waters where they were caught, or the Lake District field in which they once frolicked in, to your plate. A spring meal might begin with Padstow lobster, served with Scottish girolles, followed by roasted Brixham turbot with a warm roe butter sauce, spring peas and leaves before moving on to saddle of Herdwick spring lamb, English spring vegetables and lamb sausage with green olive tapenade. Finish, triumphantly, with zingy Japanese citrus parfait, basil and yogurt sorbet with finger lime. Every dish is unfailingly precise, perfectly balanced, and a wonderful example of the very highest levels of modern British cooking.

Chef Jason Atherton, Dale Bainbridge **Seats** 52, Private dining 12 **Closed** Bank Holidays **Notes** Children welcome

Portland
PLAN 2, H3

◉◉◉ MODERN BRITISH ⚑NOTABLE WINE LIST

020 7436 3261 | 113 Great Portland Street, W1W 6QQ
www.portlandrestaurant.co.uk
The modern clean-lined, upbeat dining room of Portland has an intimate, self-effacing note. The culinary action, headed by Zach Elliot-Crenn, is the big draw with chefs bringing-out dishes to the table. The food is brimming with innovation and seasonality, a classy lightness of touch, balanced and eye-catching presentation, but, above all, flavour. Picking highlights is impossible, but take an opener of hot-smoked Lincolnshire eel topped with golden beetroots, pears and herring roe, or perhaps sparkling-fresh pollock drenched in squid ink with white sprouting broccoli and sea vegetables. Service is spot-on, while the wine list is a labour of love with excellence by the glass too.

Chef Zach Elliot-Crenn, Martin Labron-Johnson **Seats** 36, Private dining 16 **Closed** 23 December to 3 January **Notes** Children welcome

Quo Vadis
PLAN 2, K2

◉◉ MODERN BRITISH

020 7437 9585 | 26-29 Dean Street, W1D 3LL
www.quovadissoho.co.uk
Tan banquettes, modern art and mirrors on the walls and stained-glass windows provide the backdrop for accomplished cooking at this Soho stalwart, with the kitchen favouring the modern British style. Flavour combinations are well considered so dishes maintain interest without over-elaboration.

The Riding House Café
PLAN 2, J3

◉ MODERN EUROPEAN

020 7927 0840 | 43-51 Great Titchfield Street, W1W 7PQ
www.ridinghousecafe.co.uk
This big, high-decibel, all-day operation has an urban brasserie vibe. Head for a swivel seat at the white-tiled island bar overlooking the open kitchen or park at a long refectory table, or if you don't do communal dining, there's a separate space with a more intimate mood. A flexible menu of small plates and modern brasserie dishes is on offer.

The Ritz Restaurant
PLAN 4, J6

◉◉◉◉ BRITISH, FRENCH ⚑NOTABLE WINE LIST

020 7300 2370 | 150 Piccadilly, W1J 9BR
www.theritzlondon.com
At The Ritz Restaurant the experience features tailcoated waiters serving cloche-covered plates of luxurious food. Why not start with a glass of bubbly in the art deco Rivoli Bar to prepare your senses for the extravagant opulence of the dining room – a space to rival Versailles Palace, with its rich Louis XVI-inspired decor of murals, painted ceilings, statues and glittering chandeliers reflecting from mirrored walls. An army of waiting staff pulls off a correctly polite performance with theatrical classic tableside service that avoids any hint of stuffiness. Auguste Escoffier would find no fault with the whole show, although the odd Gallic eyebrow might be raised at distinctively contemporary reworkings of classics – the likes of hay-smoked veal sweetbreads with caramelised shallot and Madeira sauce. Next up, Dover sole is pointed up with new season leeks, cauliflower and caviar at dessert stage, a rather refined take on Yorkshire rhubarb with vanilla custard closes a meal in style.

Chef John T Williams MBE, Spencer Metzger **Seats** 90, Private dining 60 **Open** All Year **Parking** 10 **Notes** Children welcome

Roganic

PLAN 2, G3

ROSETTES SUSPENDED **MODERN BRITISH** ❶ NOTABLE WINE LIST

020 337 06260 | 5-7 Blandford Street, Marylebone, W1U 3DB

www.roganic.uk

The Rosette award for this establishment has been suspended whilst awaiting relocation to a new site and reassessment will take place in due course. The original pop-up Roganic was such a success that Simon Rogan returned to Marylebone in 2018, but word is that he'll be moving again later in 2021 or 2022. You can expect a kitchen tuned to nature and the seasons, with stunning ingredients – some from his own Lake District farm – well to the fore, driving the inspired (and inspiring) cooking of head chef Oli Marlow.

Roka Charlotte Street

PLAN 2, J3

◉◉◉ **JAPANESE**

020 7580 6464 | 37 Charlotte Street, W1T 1RR

www.rokarestaurant.com

A magnet for the fashion and media darlings of Fitzrovia since 2004, this super-cool flagship of the Roka brand shows that London diners still have a big appetite for stylish contemporary Japanese robatayaki cooking. The light-flooded room's plate-glass frontage looks into a lively scene of chunky hardwood furniture around the beating heart of the robata counter, where ringside views of the kitchen action exert a strong pull. The menu's fusion temptations run to black cod, crab and crayfish dumplings, seared yellowtail with sakura leaf and daikon, or Wagyu tempura maki with karashi ponzu and oscietra caviar. As for the robata offerings, heavenly pork belly comes with punchy hoisin sauce and pickled apple, lamb cutlets with Korean spices, or sea bream fillet with ryotei miso and red onion. Desserts pull off an exciting fusion of East and West: witness dark chocolate and green tea pudding with crunchy Jivara and pear ice cream. If choosing for yourself is a trial, there's a tasting menu (with a vegan option), and an enthusiastic service team who are on hand to demystify any alien terminology.

Chef Hamish Brown **Seats** 350, Private dining 20 **Closed** Christmas **Notes** Children welcome

Roka Mayfair

PLAN 2, G1

◉◉◉ **MODERN JAPANESE**

020 7305 5644 | 30 North Audley Street, W1K 6ZF

www.rokarestaurant.com

The Mayfair branch of London's Roka group is just a short stroll from Oxford Street, so it proves a top draw for high-gloss contemporary Japanese food lovers and shoppers in the day, and the trendy, fashionable cocktail set after dusk. The focus is squarely on the large central robata grill, where prized counter seats offer ringside action of the chefs in the engine room that drives the high-energy buzz. The menu offers Roka favourites from the robata, like black cod marinated in yuzu miso, or perhaps salmon fillet teriyaki with sansho salt, while the comfort rice hotpot with Japanese mushrooms, mountain vegetables and shaved truffle offers an equal umami-rich kick. Precision tempura includes an eye-catching array of assorted vegetables served with spicy yuzu sauce, while a galaxy of top-notch sushi and sashimi might include beef tartare with black truffle ponzu. A tasting menu, switched-on service, and an extensive sake list (with tasting notes) means its fans are in for a treat too.

Chef André Camilo **Seats** 113, Private dining 24 **Closed** 25 December **Notes** Children welcome

Roti Chai

PLAN 2, G2

◉ **MODERN INDIAN**

020 7408 0101 | 3 Portman Mews South, W1H 6AY

www.rotichai.com

A restaurant of two halves, Roti Chai takes its inspiration from the lively street food of the Indian sub-continent. The ground-floor, canteen-style Street Kitchen serves small plates, while the basement Dining Room offers more refined nouveau Indian cooking and has a smart contemporary look. Expect a modern take on Indian flavours.

Roux at The Landau

PLAN 2, H3

◉◉ **MODERN EUROPEAN, FRENCH** *V* ❶ NOTABLE WINE LIST

020 7636 1000 | The Langham, London, Portland Place, W1B 1JA

rouxatthelandau.com

Relaunched with a new look in early 2018, there's now more of a brasserie feel to proceedings with leather banquettes and snugs plus a marble-topped oyster and charcuterie island in the middle. The panelled oval restaurant is still a highlight of the hotel with excellent food and wine service.

Sabor
PLAN 2, J1
◎◎ SPANISH
020 3319 8130 | 35–37 Heddon Street, Mayfair, W1B 4BR
www.saborrestaurants.co.uk
Sabor (translating as 'flavour') delivers an authentic regional experience via its trio of dining options; from diminutive tapas bar to dining-counter restaurant facing a high-energy open kitchen. Otherwise, head up the spiral staircase to the asador's communal tables (you'll need to book) for more regional delights.

Salt Yard
PLAN 2, J3
◎◎ ITALIAN, SPANISH
020 7637 0657 | 54 Goodge Street, W1T 4NA
www.saltyard.co.uk
This buzzy restaurant deals in small-but-perfectly formed plates of vibrant food with a Spain-meets-Italy theme. The bar is the place for a glass of fizz with a plate of cured meats, or take a seat and graze, tapas-style, through a mix of the familiar and creative.

Sartoria
PLAN 2, J1
◎◎ ITALIAN
020 7534 7000 | 20 Savile Row, W1S 3PR
www.sartoria-restaurant.co.uk
An immaculately dressed, made-to-measure Savile Row outfit, Sartoria's classy cut and styling is backed by switched-on look-the-part staff and service. Throw in a destination bar and alfresco terrace to the drawcard classic and contemporary Italian cooking of renowned chef-patron Francesco Mazzei's, and you have a bespoke Mayfair top call.

Scott's
PLAN 2, G1
◎◎ SEAFOOD ⚑NOTABLE WINE LIST
020 7495 7309 | 20 Mount Street, W1K 2HE
www.scotts-restaurant.com
Glamour fills Scott's, from its charming service to the eye-catching mountain of seafood on ice in the swanky champagne bar. Apart from celebrities, there are mosaics, mirrors, oak-panelled walls, leather seats, and modern artworks to catch the eye, plus a menu brimming with top-notch seafood.

Continued on page 238

Sketch (The Gallery)

◉◉◉ **MODERN EUROPEAN** 🍷NOTABLE WINE LIST
020 7659 4500 | 9 Conduit Street, W1S 2XG
www.sketch.london/the-gallery

Stunning design-led setting for upmarket brasserie dining

Mayfair is full of elegant Georgian townhouses, but few, if any, of them, are as unexpected within as this Grade II listed example. All the venues at Sketch are unusual in terms of their interior design, and The Gallery is no exception. Designer Indira Mahdavi has conjured a setting for afternoon tea and dinner that is a gift for selfie-takers and Instagrammers, with its astonishing glazed cupola roof and extreme pinkness, it's thrillingly, splendidly camp and effortlessly glamorous. Artist David Shrigley's (he also designed the crockery) cartoonish works line the walls and the barrel chairs and banquettes are reminiscent of big, squishy sponge fingers. It's difficult to do justice to the place in mere words. Pierre Gagnaire's food is as vibrant and entertaining as the setting, exuberantly creative and playful, and although it's been described as 'hilariously expensive' and accompanied by a live DJ,

"...food is as vibrant and entertaining as the setting..."

the modern French/European menus, which change every two months, demonstrate an endless stream of inventive, technically accomplished brasserie dishes. The à la carte offers a choice of hot or cold starter – witness, perhaps, a fruit and summer vegetable tartare, or poached salmon and baby Jersey Royal potato salad (cold) or haddock and scallop soufflé, cabbage fondue and horseradish beurre blanc, or green asparagus tips with pistachio, morels à la crème and pearl onions (hot). You might move on to spatchcocked Caldicott Farm chicken breast, with tagliatelle of

courgette and mint, and diable sauce, or Irish lamb saddle, with crunchy kale and chickpea-flour socca. These are precisely conceived, intelligently constructed dishes, and the dessert menu is a riot of equally precise and beautiful options, from Pavlova, with raspberry jam, vanilla ice cream, strawberry and fudge, to the olive oil dacquoise – creamed rosemary olive oil, black olive confit and sweetened rocket salad. The wine list is a tour de force of thoroughbred bottles perfectly selected to enhance the food.

Chef Pierre Gagnaire, Frederic Don
Seats 126
Closed 25 December
Notes Children welcome

Sketch (Lecture Room & Library)

◎◎◎◎◎ MODERN EUROPEAN *V* ◢NOTABLE WINE LIST

020 7659 4500 | 9 Conduit Street, W1S 2XG

sketch.london/the-lecture-room

Polished service and fabulous setting for complex, innovative cooking

This Grade II listed Georgian townhouse in Mayfair might look sensible and sober from the outside, but once through the door you're in for a treat for all the senses. A jaw-dropping interplay between food and design, the interior's outrageously lavish colour scheme a joyfully theatrical explosion of pink, orange and gold. It's a suitably unforgettable spot for some ground-breaking cuisine. The effortlessly polished service is exemplary, and the cooking is innovative, provocative and skilful, overseen by Pierre Gagnaire and produced by head chef Johannes Nuding. There's a six-course tasting menu, with a vegetarian version also available, or you can go a la carte. The menu descriptions may be lengthy but the complexity they hint at is just that, the merest hint of the thrilling rollercoaster of extravagance and delight you're about to experience. A plethora of small plates will bring you more

"It's breathtaking, a clear demonstration of a chef and brigade at the very top of their game."

ingredients, concepts and techniques than you could dream of. It's breathtaking, a clear demonstration of a chef and brigade at the very top of their game. You might begin with 'Parfums de Terre' – which is duck foie gras terrine marinated with crème de cassis; Sauterne jelly with juniper, caramelised onions and celeriac cream flash-smoked cocotte: stuffed baby artichoke, baby spinach, beetroot syrup, pluma puff pastry, Dorset snails, aubergine cream with Crozes-Hermitage Domaine des Lises 2017, corn ice cream with Madagascan vanilla, and English peas. For your main, choose 'from the sea' or 'from the land' – maybe salt-chamber-aged Creedy duck, marinated with coffee beans, buckwheat grains, angelica and grapefruit, roasted 'en bateau' with braised turnips and radishes coated in a foie gras sauce; with pickled apricots, daikon, and potato knödel filled with smoked duck leg. Chocolate soufflé may sound simple but involves a similar list of techniques and ingredients. The 25 minutes you'll need to wait for it will give you some time to recover from the intensity of your dinner.

Chef Pierre Gagnaire, Johannes Nuding
Seats 50, Private dining 40
Closed 2 weeks August, 2 weeks December, 1 January and Bank Holidays
Notes No children under 6 years

Sexy Fish
PLAN 2, H1

◉◉ ASIAN, SEAFOOD

020 3764 2000 | Berkeley Square House, Berkeley Square, W1J 6BR

www.sexyfish.com

Be prepared for jaw-dropping interiors of marble with aquatic-themed artworks by big names, and a water wall cascading behind the bar. The feel is glittering art deco with bags of bling, but it's not all style over substance: the kitchen sends out a well-executed roster of Asian-inspired fish and seafood, while Japanese whisky, cocktails and champagne add fizz.

Sketch (The Gallery)
PLAN 2, J1

◉◉◉ MODERN EUROPEAN ▮NOTABLE WINE LIST

See pages 234–235

Sketch (Lecture Room & Library)
PLAN 2, J1

◉◉◉◉◉ MODERN EUROPEAN ▮NOTABLE WINE LIST

See pages 236–237

Sketch (The Parlour)
PLAN 2, J1

◉◉ MODERN EUROPEAN

020 7659 4500 | 9 Conduit Street, W1S 2XG

www.sketch.london/the-parlour

Sketch (The Parlour) has a whimsical, Regency-inspired boudoir ambience, with dark gold walls, low lighting, and voile curtains that break up the split-level space. Lots of unusual art and colourful fabrics. The ambience might be a touch frivolous but there's nothing half-hearted about the food. Accurate cooking of good quality materials to produce some impressive flavours and textural combinations.

See advertisement on page 233

Social Eating House
PLAN 2, J2

◉◉◉ MODERN BRITISH ▮NOTABLE WINE LIST

020 7993 3251 | 58-59 Poland Street, W1F 7NS

www.socialeatinghouse.com

The stripped-back bistro-style vibe is vibrant and speakeasy, while service is spot-on; unobtrusive, friendly and informed. Chef-patron Paul Hood's contemporary bistro roster matches the mood and delivers with flair and panache, whether set lunch openers like cured Hampshire chalk stream trout with beetroot, horseradish, crème fraîche and fennel, or carte main offerings like roasted Cornish turbot with cep, pearl barley, chipirones, charred baby leek and mushroom tea. There is flexibility too, with steaks, say 50-day aged native Cumbrian sirloin, while desserts, perhaps hot 70% chocolate moelleux and passionfruit ice cream, hit form too. Downstairs, Paul Hood's kitchen chef's counter offers the ultimate foodie experience, while a corking wine list and upstairs Blind Pig bar rounds-off a class act.

Chef Paul Hood **Seats** 75, Private dining 8 **Closed** 25-26 December and Bank Holidays **Notes** Children welcome

SOLA *NEW*
PLAN 2, K1

◉◉◉ CALIFORNIAN

020 373 07883 | 64 Dean Street, London W1D 4QQ

www.solasoho.com

Victor Garvey brings an authentic piece of California to this intimate Dean Street restaurant, where an abundance of greenery and warm lighting evokes memories of The Golden State. The contemporary cooking of America's Pacific West Coast is served up with a dash of theatre. The cooking of top drawer ingredients is elegant and precise, as in a dish that celebrates Scombridae (the mackerel, tuna, and bonito family) in its raw, cured and smoked forms. It might be followed by a pairing of langoustine, foie gras, mushroom, ginger and dashi. Lemon, vanilla, yuzu, meringue and crème fraîche is a refreshing finale.

Chef Victor Garvey

Tamarind
PLAN 4, H6

◎◎ INDIAN

020 7629 3561 | 20 Queen Street, Mayfair, W1J 5PR

www.tamarindrestaurant.com

Tamarind both features a basement and first-floor restaurant. Downstairs, the open kitchens provide theatre and atmosphere, while upstairs natural light and a central cocktail bar feature while banquettes and booth seating frame the room. Many dishes are designed to be shared and the modern Indian cooking looks to subtle and delicate flavours and cooking methods from across the sub-continent.

Tokii
PLAN 2, F2

◎◎ JAPANESE *V*

020 7724 0486 | The Prince Akatoki London, 50 Great Cumberland Place, W1H 7FD

www.tokii.co.uk/contact

A short stroll from Marble Arch, this luxurious hotel restaurant has a pronounced Japanese influence. Rich in flavours and textures, the dishes are designed to be shared, whether it's delicate sushi, shrimp tempura with ginger dashi or a main course teriyaki-glazed duck breast, orange, toasted coconut and peanut salad.

Trishna
PLAN 2, G3

◎◎ INDIAN ♪NOTABLE WINE LIST

020 7935 5624 | 15-17 Blandford Street, W1U 3DG

www.trishnalondon.com

Trishna takes a minimalist decorative line in two dining rooms done out with oak floors and tables, painted brickwork, mirrored walls, and hues of cream and duck-egg blue. The kitchen celebrates the coastal cuisine of southwest India in fresh, flavour-packed contemporary dishes.

Twist Connubio
PLAN 2, F3

◎◎ MEDITERRANEAN TAPAS

020 7723 3377 | 42 Crawford Street, W1H 1JW

www.twistconnubio.com

Lively, intimate and fun, this Marylebone-hinterland 'kitchen and tapas' is smack on-cue. The in-vogue, pared-back look keeps things relaxed while the Spanish-style tiled open kitchen draws top focus. The chefs bring together Italian roots with Spanish and other Mediterranean influences in small-plate dishes of intelligent simplicity and freshness that allow flavours and textures to shine.

Umu
PLAN 2, H1

◎◎◎ JAPANESE ♪NOTABLE WINE LIST

020 7499 8881 | 14-16 Bruton Place, W1J 6LX

www.umurestaurant.com

With its smart Mayfair address, Umu's fans are prepared to pay handsomely for high-definition food of lightness and bracing freshness, and the stylishness with which the package is achieved. The food is firmly anchored in traditional ways, with Bento-box lunches and various set menus removing the need to agonise over the extensive main menu, the former opening with a precise assemblage of seasonal vegetables and shiitake mushrooms with edamame purée and red miso powder, before going on with a selection of stunning fish and seafood dishes, ringing with resonant freshness and pinpoint seasoning.

Chef Yoshinori Ishii **Seats** 64, Private dining 10
Closed Christmas, New Year and Bank Holidays
Notes Children welcome

Veeraswamy Restaurant
PLAN 2, J1

◎◎ INDIAN

020 7734 1401 | Mezzanine Floor, Victory House, 99 Regent Street, W1B 4RS

www.veeraswamy.com

The granddaddy of the UK's Indian restaurants, this lavishly elegant first-floor venue on Regent Street is a hotspot for tourists keen to try Britain's adopted culinary exotica. The kitchen puts creative spin on subcontinental stalwarts via smoked chicken tikka with garam masala and mace, or delves into the regional repertoire with Keralan seafood moilee.

The Wolseley
PLAN 4, J6

TRADITIONAL EUROPEAN
020 7499 6996 | 160 Piccadilly, W1J 9EB
www.thewolseley.com

Decked out like a European brasserie, with plenty of brass, marble and tiled floors, The Wolseley used to be a car showroom, and is a really grand place to eat. Staff are waistcoated, and there's even a doorman. It's next to the Ritz, after all. Expect an all-day menu of classic European and British food, and a cracking wine list.

Yauatcha
PLAN 2, J2

MODERN CHINESE
020 7494 8888 | 15 Broadwick Street, W1F 0DL
www.yauatcha.com
A colourful array of pâtisserie opens the show in Yauatcha's ground-floor 'tea house', but in the basement dining room things are lively and loud. The menu impresses with its exciting blend of traditional Cantonese favourites and more intriguing contemporary compositions.

Zoilo
PLAN 2, G2

ARGENTINIAN
020 7486 9699 | 9 Duke Street, W1U 3EG
www.zoilo.co.uk

The mayhem of Oxford Street is close by but feels miles away in this racy outpost of South American cuisine. Bare brick walls, crimson banquettes and a midnight-blue palette around a central bar lined with counter seats make a chic backdrop to dynamic food inspired by Argentina's regions, from Patagonia to Mendoza. Sharing is the name of the game.

LONDON W2

Angelus Restaurant
PLAN 2, D1

MODERN FRENCH
020 7402 0083 | 4 Bathurst Street, W2 2SD
www.angelusrestaurant.co.uk
A former pub which was transformed into a classy Parisian-style brasserie by renowned sommelier, Thierry Tomasin, Angelus Restaurant continues to impress with its luxe, art nouveau-inspired finish and ambitious, modern French cooking. The wine list offers some seriously good drinking opportunities.

The Hyde
PLAN 2, D2

MODERN BRITISH
020 7479 6600 | Roseate House London, 3 Westbourne Terrace, Lancaster Gate, Hyde Park, W2 3UL
www.thehydebar.com
The Hyde is located in a swish boutique hotel occupying a row of elegant townhouses a short walk from Paddington railway station. It's just a block away from Hyde Park and ideal for exploring central London's attractions. The hotel's Hyde restaurant and bar is a rather glam spot for appealing contemporary food.

Nipa Thai
PLAN 2, D1

◎◎ TRADITIONAL THAI

020 7551 6039 | Royal Lancaster London, Lancaster Terrace, W2 2TY

www.niparestaurant.co.uk

Opposite Hyde Park, in the Thai-owned Royal Lancaster, an all-female, all-Thai kitchen balances the five main flavours in a comprehensive offering of appetisers, soups, salads, curries, pan-fried dishes, rices and noodles. Examples are crisp-fried prawn dumplings; a mixed seafood curry, beef with onions, mushrooms and oyster sauce; and stir-fried chicken with chillies. Set menus avoid making difficult decisions.

LONDON W4

Restaurant Michael Nadra
PLAN 1, D3

◎◎ MODERN EUROPEAN

020 8742 0766 | 6-8 Elliott Road, Chiswick, W4 1PE

www.restaurant-michaelnadra.co.uk

A stalwart of the Chiswick dining scene, this classy restaurant's pan-European fixed-price repertoire offers bags of interest. Rabbit ballotine and cromesquis are combined with baby turnip, fresh peas and pea purée and fired up with a well-judged glow from spicy Italian 'nduja sauce.

La Trompette
PLAN 1, D3

◎◎ MODERN EUROPEAN ⧫ NOTABLE WINE LIST

020 8747 1836 | 5-7 Devonshire Road, Chiswick, W4 2EU

www.latrompette.co.uk

This neighbourhood restaurant par excellence has been playing to packed houses since 2001. The mood is relaxed, with a broad glass frontage looking in to a classy interior where white linen and a neutral colour palette meet bright abstract artworks. There's a cracking wine list, and the kitchen has a light, creative and pretty modern European outlook.

Le Vacherin
PLAN 1, D3

◎◎ FRENCH

020 8742 2121 | 76-77 South Parade, W4 5LF

www.levacherin.com

Le Vacherin brings a hit of Gallic bonhomie to Chiswick, saving you a trip across the Channel when you're in the mood for some classic French cooking. The place has the look of a smart neighbourhood bistro, simple things are done well by a skilful kitchen, and the prix-fixe menu is particularly good value in any language.

LONDON W6

L'Amorosa
PLAN 1, D3

◎ ITALIAN, BRITISH

020 8563 0300 | 278 King Street, Ravenscourt Park, W6 0SP

www.lamorosa.co.uk

This neighbourhood restaurant on Hammersmith's main drag has a man with pedigree at the stoves in the shape of ex-Zafferano head chef Andy Needham. The setting is smart-casual – darkwood floors, polished wood tables, buttoned brown leather banquettes and cream-painted walls hung with modern art.

Anglesea Arms

PLAN 1, D3

CLASSIC MEDITERRANEAN

020 8749 1291 | 35 Wingate Road, Ravenscourt Park, W6 0UR

www.angleseaarmspub.co.uk

A cosy fire in winter, a suntrap in summer and displays of paintings and photographs on its Long Brick Wall, this is a Hammersmith favourite. Rotating real ales are a big attraction too, but don't expect to find ham, egg and chips on the menu; the dishes here are Mediterranean inspired, with wines favouring European sources more than New World.

The River Café

PLAN 1, D3

ITALIAN

020 7386 4200 | Thames Wharf Studios, Rainville Road, W6 9HA

www.rivercafe.co.uk

The timeless appeal of the River Café's Mediterranean food, constructed from unimpeachable ingredients, to which only the least complicating treatments are given, tells a story all of its own. A quartet of whole young squid emerge from the chargrill with their sea savour intact, the dressing a little rocket and chilli and as much lemon as you feel like squeezing. Similarly, the flawless crisp-skinned sea bass cooked over coals with wood-roasted yellow peppers, olives and spinach is a banner-waving exemplar of the style. Finish with moistly alluring pear and almond tart alongside a slick of crème fraîche.

Chef Ruth Rogers, Sian Wyn Owen, Joseph Trivelli Seats 120, Private dining 18 Closed 24 December to 1 January Parking 29 Notes Children welcome

Sam's Riverside *NEW*

PLAN 1, D3

MODERN EUROPEAN, ANGLO-FRENCH

020 8237 1020 | 1 Crisp Walk, London W6 9DN

www.samsriverside.co.uk

Uptempo, high-profile new brasserie from the much-missed Sam Harrison, back with a bang here complete with trump-card river and Hammersmith Bridge views. Smartly designed, there's huge windows, on-trend seating and a cool marble-topped bar. The open kitchen responds with crowd-pleasing, clean-cut, elegant dishes: witness roasted Cornish hake with Savoy cabbage and pancetta, clams and sweetcorn velouté.

LONDON W8

Clarke's

PLAN 4, A6

MODERN BRITISH, ITALIAN

020 7221 9225 | 124 Kensington Church Street, W8 4BH

www.sallyclarke.com

Sally Clarke's eponymous restaurant is a quietly elegant affair, with walls hung with abstract art. They take the best, freshest produce available in the markets and from Sally's own garden each day to focus on making it all taste resoundingly of itself, with Italian accents.

Kitchen W8

PLAN 4, A4

MODERN BRITISH NOTABLE WINE LIST

020 7937 0120 | 11-13 Abingdon Road, Kensington, W8 6AH

www.kitchenw8.com

Just off fashionable Kensington High Street, Kitchen W8 shrewdly delivers a winning format. Inside follows the theme; a smart, relaxed, light, contemporary decor combined with friendly, efficient service seal that neighbourhood-cum-destination vibe. Appealing menus fit the bill from the off, the kitchen delivering light, clean, well-presented modern dishes with a strong emphasis on flavour and seasonality. Perhaps open with a breast of quail teamed with Scottish girolles, summer truffles, corn and almonds, while main event sea-fresh roasted John Dory, served with coco bean ragù, pancetta and caramelised cauliflower, might rock your boat too. Desserts fly the flag for fruit, perhaps poached greengage plums with stem ginger, yogurt and almond.

Chef Mark Kempson Seats 75, Private dining 14 Closed 25-26 December, Bank Holidays Notes Children welcome

Launceston Place
PLAN 4, C4

◉◉◉◉ MODERN EUROPEAN ⚑NOTABLE WINE LIST

020 7937 6912 | 1a Launceston Place, W8 5RL

www.launcestonplace-restaurant.co.uk

An elegant Georgian townhouse on the corner of a leafy residential Kensington street, Launceston Place has a wonderfully relaxed and contemporary feel. Bespoke artwork from notable artists adorns the French grey walls and the blue-vein dark wood floors and comfortable banquet seating is in keeping with the style of the restaurant's W8 postcode. Head chef Ben Murphy trained under the legendary Pierre Koffmann and it shows in the way he handles raw materials, whether humble or luxury. He uses the finest seasonal ingredients in creative dishes with bold, assertive flavours but it's all delivered with a lightness of touch. A precisely cooked BBQ lamb belly with cucumber and yogurt is a well balanced starter and is followed by a first-rate dish of cod, watermelon, tomato and coriander with serious depth of flavour. To finish, yuzu, dill and white chocolate is a zesty dessert with subtle textural contrasts.

Chef Ben Murphy **Seats** 50, Private dining 12
Closed Christmas **Notes** Children welcome

The Milestone Hotel
PLAN 4, B5

◉◉ MODERN BRITISH ⚑NOTABLE WINE LIST

020 7917 1000 | 1 Kensington Court, W8 5DL

www.milestonehotel.com

Formed from three red-brick Victorian townhouses, this venerable hotel in affluent Kensington offers old-school service in the elegant, wood-panelled dining room, right down to the roast-of-the-day trolley. Start with lobster and Devon crab topped with caviar and move on to Suffolk lamb cooked three ways; or whole piri-piri baby chicken.

Zaika of Kensington
PLAN 4, B5

◉◉ INDIAN *V*

020 7795 6533 | 1 Kensington High Street, W8 5NP

www.zaikaofkensington.com

Comfortably in step with its postcode, this high-end Indian in a former bank has the feel of a Raj-era gentlemen's club, with its high ceilings, oak panels and colonial pictures. Taking classic, Moghul-inspired north Indian dishes as its starting point, the kitchen conjures scintillating, authentic flavours.

LONDON W11

Caractère *NEW*
PLAN 1, E4

◉◉ MEDITERRANEAN

020 8181 3850 | 209 Westbourne Park Road, Notting Hill, W11 1EA

www.caractererestaurant.com

Caractère is an upmarket neighbourhood restaurant on the fringes of Notting Hill. The corner site means windows on two sides, making it bright and welcoming, with dark wood or marble tables and seats upholstered in dark green or burnt orange velour. Staff are relaxed, chatty and well briefed on the very seasonal dishes; classy cooking with an emphasis on Mediterranean French/Italian influences, skilfully executed.

Core by Clare Smyth
PLAN 1, E3

◉◉◉◉◉ BRITISH ⚑NOTABLE WINE LIST

020 3937 5086 | 92 Kensington Park Road, W11 2PN

www.corebyclaresmyth.com

Clare Smyth has become one of the UK's most acclaimed chefs, following a career that took in senior roles with Terence Conran, Alain Ducasse and Gordon Ramsay, who made her chef-patron of his eponymous Chelsea restaurant. The stripped-back setting at Core is as polished as the superlative service and food that are the restaurant's highlights; fine glassware, cutlery and crockery, yes, although tablecloths and carpets have been dispensed with. Smyth, and her kitchen team, work behind a glass partition, from where emerges beautifully crafted, delicious artisanal food, as in the Core Classics, typically roasted monkfish with Morecambe Bay shrimps, Swiss chard and brown butter; and duck and red grapes with thyme, honey and Nepalese timut pepper. She also offers a Core Seasons menu, on which you'll likely find trademark specialities like a starter of morel and asparagus tart with wild garlic and vin jaune; mains of lamb hogget and mutton with celtuce, savory and black cardamom; and Cornish brill with oysters, cucumber and caviar. And to finish, what Smyth calls a 'Core-teser', which on the plate translates as chocolate with malt and hazelnut. A Chef's Table tasting menu dinner for eight to 10 people makes a great gift.

Chef Clare Smyth, Jonny Bone **Seats** 54
Closed Christmas, New Year **Notes** No children

E&O
PLAN 1, D4
@ PAN-ASIAN
020 7229 5454 | 14 Blenheim Crescent, Notting Hill,
W11 1NN
www.rickerrestaurants.com
E&O is trend-central with the Notting Hill
fashionistas. The decor is casually scuffed these
days, but the high-octane vibe (ramped-up by a
lively bar) puts the experience-factor in
overdrive. The young-at-heart pack the place for
the fashionable, well-executed pan-Asian
cuisine, plus great cocktails.

Edera
PLAN 1, D3
@ MODERN ITALIAN
020 7221 6090 | 148 Holland Park Avenue, W11 4UE
www.edera.co.uk
Decked out on tiered levels, with light walls hung
with big mirrors and linen-dressed tables, this
minimally-styled Holland Park eatery pulls in a
well-heeled crowd for its fashionable Sardinian-
accented Italian cooking. The kitchen team
certainly know their stuff, keeping things simple
and straightforward.

Julie's Restaurant *NEW*
PLAN 1, D3
@@ MODERN BRITISH, EUROPEAN
020 7229 8331 | 135 Portland Road, Notting Hill,
W11 4LW
www.juliesrestaurant.com
First opened in 1969, Julie's became one of the
capital's original celebrity hangouts... think Paul
McCartney to Mick Jagger. A major refurb and
relaunch - embracing the idiosyncratic character
and romance of its heyday while going sexy and
upmarket with the decor and comforts - sees the
rebooted kitchen turning-out equally elegant
modern dishes.

LONDON W14,

Cibo
PLAN 1, D3
@@ ITALIAN
020 7371 2085 | 3 Russell Gardens, W14 8EZ
www.ciborestaurant.net
The epitome of the authentic neighbourhood
Italian, long-serving Cibo is a big hit with savvy
Holland Park-ers. Breads and nibbles raise
expectation from the off, and pasta is the real
deal too. This is skilful Italian cooking showing
respect of prime ingredients, flavour and
precision timing.

LONDON WC1

The Montague on the Gardens Hotel
PLAN 3, B3
@ BRITISH V
020 7612 8416 | 15 Montague Street, Bloomsbury,
WC1B 5BJ
www.montaguehotel.com
You'll like the Blue Door Bistro at the Montague
on the Gardens Hotel. It's a Georgian townhouse
full of English charm. The top-hatted doorman
at the entrance is a clue that this is a classy
boutique hotel, on a quiet street next to the
British Museum. The bistro is a welcoming
and informal dining room, decorated with
a frieze depicting London in around 1850
and an uncomplicated repertoire of comfort-
oriented dishes.

Otto's
PLAN 3, C4
@@ CLASSIC FRENCH
020 7713 0107 | 182 Gray's Inn Road, WC1X 8EW
www.ottos-restaurant.com
Small, intimate and owner-run, this old-school
French restaurant feels like it has been around
for decades. As befits a traditional French
restaurant, the wine list is hefty in both range
and price and the food displays confident
cooking skills and high-quality ingredients.
Leave room for classic puds such as tarte Tatin
or Grand Marnier soufflé.

Rosewood London
PLAN 3, C3
@@ MODERN EUROPEAN
020 3747 8620 | 252 High Holborn, WC1V 7EN
www.rosewoodhotels.com/london
This magnificent building on High Holborn is a
fine setting, and the old East Banking Hall with
its soaring marble pillars is an elegant
restaurant. The Mirror Room offers a relaxed and
social dining experience.

LONDON WC2

Balthazar
PLAN 3, B1

⊛ FRENCH, EUROPEAN
020 3301 1155 | 4–6 Russell Street, WC2B 5HZ
balthazarlondon.com

The London offshoot of the legendary New York brasserie has played to packed houses right from the start. It's a real looker, with mosaic floors, art deco lighting, leather banquettes and antique mirrors. The places buzzes from breakfast through to lunch, afternoon tea and dinner, seven days a week.

Barrafina Adelaide Street
PLAN 3, B1

⊛⊛ MODERN SPANISH
10 Adelaide Street, WC2N 4HZ
www.barrafina.co.uk

Tapas is the name of the game here and the place is cool and packed to the rafters. The no booking policy means queues are likely and, once in, you sit at the marble counter and tuck into small plates full of flavour. There are daily specials galore, superb cured meats and lots of things you've maybe not tried before.

Barrafina Drury Lane
PLAN 3, B2

⊛⊛ SPANISH
43 Drury Lane, WC2B 5AJ
www.barrafina.co.uk

A lively repertoire of classic and modern tapas dishes and the perfect spot to grab and graze through a few little plates of big flavours in the pre- and post-theatre slots. There's a no-bookings policy here and it takes groups of up to four people.

Café Murano Covent Garden
PLAN 3, C1

⊛⊛ ITALIAN
020 7240 3654 | 36 Tavistock Street, WC2E 7PB
www.cafemurano.co.uk

A long-raftered room with dark grey banquettes and an adjoining pastificio and coffee shop fits its Covent Garden location like a glove, with pre- and post-theatre menus on offer and a bustling lunchtime trade too. Northern Italian dishes under the aegis of Angela Hartnett are the stock-in-trade here.

Christopher's
PLAN 3, C1

⊛ CONTEMPORARY AMERICAN
020 7240 4222 | 18 Wellington Street, Covent Garden, WC2E 7DD
www.christophersgrill.com

This elegant eatery on the fringes of Covent Garden features a grand staircase, winding up from the uptempo street-level Martini Bar, while corniced high ceilings tower over the airy dining room, where chairs and banquettes in grey and lemon deliver bags of contemporary swagger.

Cigalon
PLAN 3, D2

⊛ MEDITERRANEAN
020 7242 8373 | 115 Chancery Lane, WC2A 1PP
www.cigalon.co.uk

Cigalon's classy dining room certainly evokes memories of sun-drenched South of France dining rather than the dry legal world of Chancery Lane. But it's not all style over substance. The kitchen focuses on the grill to deliver its sunny, seasonal Provençal menu.

Clos Maggiore
PLAN 3, B1

⊛⊛⊛ FRENCH, MEDITERRANEAN 🍷 NOTABLE WINE LIST
See pages 246–247

Cora Pearl
PLAN 3, B1

⊛⊛ MODERN BRITISH
020 7324 7722 | 30 Henrietta Street, Covent Garden, WC2E 8NA
www.corapearl.co.uk

Named after a 19th-century courtesan, this second restaurant from the team behind Mayfair's Kitty Fisher's occupies an elegant Covent Garden townhouse. Modern comfort food is the form here, a meal beginning with cow's curd agnolotti, pea and truffle, continuing with plaice, fennel and brown shrimps. Finish with 'milk and cookies'.

Frenchie Covent Garden
PLAN 3, B1

⊛⊛⊛ FRENCH, EUROPEAN
See page 248

Continued on page 249

Clos Maggiore

◉◉◉ **FRENCH, MEDITERRANEAN** ⚐NOTABLE WINE LIST
020 7379 9696 | 33 King Street, Covent Garden, WC2E 8JD
www.closmaggiore.com

Contemporary take on classic French cuisine in Covent Garden

If you're looking for a romantic spot, then it's hard to beat Clos Maggiore. The garden is brought inside here, with dried foliage adorning the walls and on the ceilings. The decor is plush and upmarket with dark wood, leather banquettes, upholstered seats and pleated floor-length curtains, while the tables are covered with white linen. The conservatory is festooned with boughs of cherry blossom and fairy lights and features a retractable glass roof creating a bright and airy dining space in the summer. It is transformed by candles and a warming fire for the winter months. Staff are immaculate in black, providing seamless service for all those ready to celebrate special occasions or share a romantic meal. The setting may be soft focus but there's nothing whimsical about the cooking. Chef Roxanne Lange serves French dishes inspired by Provençal and Italian cuisine, achieving big, clear flavours

from high-quality British ingredients. These ingredients are well sourced and skilfully handled, with easy-on-the-eye presentations adding to the lustre. These skills are to be found in the starters, with dishes such as Iberico Bellota ham, heirloom tomato with sourdough crisp or Cornish crab served with crispy brioche and a radish and cucumber broth. There's decadence to follow in the main course: Poll Dorset lamb rack is partnered with sweet bread, carrots and a mustard jus, while fish fans could be seduced by lobster with fennel, tarragon and an orange and lobster sauce. Desserts are a beguiling proposition too. They appear to be named after yogurt flavours – peach and raspberry or chocolate, milk and coffee – but deliver

> "…French dishes inspired by Provençal and Italian cuisine, achieving big, clear flavours from high-quality British ingredients."

so much more. Dessert wines are suggested alongside each dish. Being at the heart of Covent Garden makes Clos Maggiore a good choice for a pre-show meal and the restaurant offers a pre-theatre set menu. There's also a prix-fixe menu that changes regularly.

Chef Roxanne Lange
Seats 70, Private dining 23
Closed 24–25 December
Notes No children under 3 years at lunch

Frenchie Covent Garden

◉◉◉ **FRENCH, EUROPEAN**
020 7836 4422 | 16 Henrietta Street, WC2E 8QH
www.frenchiecoventgarden.com

Smack in the heart of Covent Garden, Frenchie is the London outpost of chef-patron Gregory Marchand, who splits his time between his Paris restaurant and WC2. Cool, smart and buzzy, this relaxed modern French brasserie rocks, with spot-on service, innovative cuisine and on-trend good looks. The long street-level room comes with eye-catching lighting and a dining bar, while bare brick, wooden floors and marble or stainless steel tabletops embrace the mood, and downstairs features an open kitchen. Creative, ambitious modern French dishes have equal appeal, as in a well-balanced starter of delicate smoked sea bream carpaccio, chive sabayon, strawberries and jalapeño. These might precede a beautifully cooked piece of steamed Cornish cod teamed with mussels, cauliflower, dill and whey. To finish, there's almond rice pudding, jasmine ice cream and raspberries.

Chef Gregory Marchand **Seats** 72, Private dining 20 **Closed** 25 December, 1 January **Notes** Children welcome

Frog by Adam Handling
PLAN 3, B1

◉◉◉ MODERN BRITISH *V* ♦ NOTABLE WINE LIST

020 7199 8370 | 34-35 Southampton Street, WC2E 7HG
www.frogbyadamhandling.com
Now firmly established as one of Covent Garden's
go-to fine dining restaurants before or after the
theatre, Adam Handling's stylish venue combines
a buzzy downstairs bar with a contemporary
dining room benefiting from floor-to-ceiling
street views. Handling's terse menus offer highly
accomplished dishes displaying a deep skills set
and intelligent use of top drawer raw materials.
Scottish lobster comes with scallop and
lemongrass, while veal sweetbreads are
imaginatively teamed with lemon and truffle.
Main courses include turbot with mussels and
pak choi, and pigeon paired with beetroot and
pink peppercorn. Close with passionfruit, miso
and tarragon.

Chef Adam Handling, Cleverson Cordeiro **Seats** 34,
Private dining 22 **Closed** 24-26 December, 1 January
Notes Children welcome

The Ivy
PLAN 3, A1

◉ BRITISH, INTERNATIONAL
020 7836 4751 | 1-5 West Street, Covent Garden,
WC2H 9NQ
www.the-ivy.co.uk
The curtain opened on this Theatreland dining
institution over a century ago and it's still a
classy act. Looking as elegant as ever, the room's
original harlequin stained-glass windows, green
leather banquettes, mirrors and eye-catching
modern artwork set the scene for a wide-ranging
menu of classic British and international food.

J. Sheekey
PLAN 3, A1

◉ SEAFOOD
020 7240 2565 | 32-34 St Martin's Court, WC2N 4AL
www.j-sheekey.co.uk
This enduring and much-loved seafood
restaurant in the heart of Theatreland began
life as a humble seafood stall in the 1890s.
Today, it's a seafood and oyster bar, offering a
menu dealing in straightforward fish and
shellfish dishes whose impeccable credentials
speak for themselves.

Kerridge's Bar & Grill
PLAN 5, B6

◉◉◉ ♦ NOTABLE WINE LIST

020 7321 3244 | Corinthia Hotel London,
10 Northumberland Avenue, WC2N 5AE
www.kerridgesbarandgrill.co.uk
After thoroughly colonising Marlow with his
big-hearted, refined and yet inherently simple
cooking, Tom Kerridge's first city venture is now
well established in the super-posh Corinthia
Hotel. There's very high, dark-green vaulted
ceilings with contrasting white pillars in a
cavernous room whose decor is more clubby
than pubby. As you'd expect from the jovial TV
chef, the food is a celebration of Britishness via
dishes that are big on flavour and impact.
To start try a beautifully crafted pork and
mushroom terrine with piccalilli followed by a
main course of fillet of seabass with crushed
broad beans, toasted cucumber and lemongrass
and ginger sauce. Finish with a dark chocolate
pudding with crystallised malt biscuit and
buttermilk ice cream.

Chef Tom Kerridge

Lima Floral
PLAN 3, B1

◉◉ MODERN PERUVIAN
020 7240 5778 | 14 Garrick Street, WC2E 9BJ
www.limalondongroup.com/floral
Lima's Covent Garden outpost offers a more
casual setting than its Fitzrovia flagship, but the
blast of South American vivacity is still a big
draw. Peru pretty much invented the potato, and
that fine tuber originally grown at 4,000 metres
turns up in the mains.

Margot

PLAN 3, B2

◉◉ ITALIAN ⚑ NOTABLE WINE LIST

020 3409 4777 | 45 Great Queen Street, Covent Garden, WC2B 5AA

www.margotrestaurant.com

The dining room of this suave Italian looks as sharp as an Armani suit with its black leather banquettes and abstract artworks, and the slick service purrs along like clockwork. The seasonal menu is full of promise, with classic combinations and masterful home-made pasta.

Mon Plaisir Restaurant

PLAN 3, B2

◉ TRADITIONAL FRENCH

020 7836 7243 | 19-21 Monmouth Street, WC2H 9DD

www.monplaisir.co.uk

Impervious to fads and fashion and about as French as they come, the unapologetically 1940s-themed Parisian-bistro look of the original front dining room conjures a suitably retro cross-Channel mood with close-set tables and resolutely French service, while beyond there's a series of lighter, cosy rooms including a mezzanine-style loft. The menu presents safe and respectable traditional Gallic food and timeless classics such as snails or beef tartare.

The Northall

PLAN 5, B6

◉◉◉ BRITISH

020 7321 3100 | Corinthia Hotel London, 10a Northumberland Avenue, WC2N 5AE

www.corinthia.com/london/restaurants-bars/the-northall

This elegant restaurant is housed in the majestic surroundings of one of London's most highly regarded hotels. High ceilings, vast windows and mirrors create a bright and airy space with immaculate service from start to finish. Executive Chef André Garrett's precise cooking makes good use of top drawer raw materials. A classic duck liver parfait is accompanied by mushroom brioche and Madeira jelly. Precisely timed chalk stream trout with confit Charlotte potato, Avruga caviar and chowder sauce is an elegant main and Pavola with toasted coconut cream, pink grapefruit and lemon verbena delivers a perfect balance of flavour and texture.

Chef Andrè Garrett **Seats** , Private dining 30 **Open** All Year **Notes** Children welcome

The Opera Tavern

PLAN 3, C1

◉◉ SPANISH, ITALIAN

020 7836 3680 | 23 Catherine Street, Covent Garden, WC2B 5JS

www.operatavern.co.uk

This classic old London pub, has become a relaxed, two-storeyed tapas joint with the restaurant on the upper level and an intimate bar, with high stools, on the ground floor. You could go three-course if you're an old stickler, but little dishes are the principal bill of fare and they pack quite a punch.

Roka Aldwych
PLAN 3, C2

◎◎ CONTEMPORARY JAPANESE

020 7294 7636 | 71 Aldwych, WC2B 4HN

www.rokarestaurant.com

Roka is characterised by top-drawer ingredients, with the freshest of seafood, to-the-second timings and artful presentation. The speciality is robatayaki: contemporary-style Japanese barbecued food. Puddings include Japanese pancakes with banana, toffee and black sugar syrup, and cherry blossom ice cream accompanying almond crème brûlée.

Savoy Grill – Gordon Ramsay
PLAN 3, C1

◎◎ BRITISH

020 7592 1600 | 1 Savoy Hill, Strand, WC2R 0EU

www.gordonramsayrestaurants.com/savoy-grill

A handsome art deco room with lustrous panelling, antiqued mirrors, chandeliers and velvet banquettes, the Savoy's iconic Grill has always been the place to see and be seen. Built on classic Anglo-French foundations, the cooking aims for comfort.

Spring
PLAN 3, C1

◎◎ EUROPEAN

020 3011 0115 | New Wing, Somerset House, Lancaster Place, WC2R 1LA

www.springrestaurant.co.uk

After winning much acclaim at the rustic glasshouse restaurant of Petersham Nurseries, Skye Gyngell has brought her trademark style to the grander stage of Somerset House. The regularly-changing Mediterranean menu delivers good-looking plates of seasonal fare with flavours that shine. Though prices are high, a fixed-price lunch option eases the bottom line.

■ GREATER LONDON

BROMLEY

Chapter One Restaurant
PLAN 1, H1

◎◎◎ MODERN EUROPEAN V ⫶NOTABLE WINE LIST

See pages 252–253

HOUNSLOW

La Belle Époque
MAP 6, TQ07

◎◎ MODERN FRENCH ⫶NOTABLE WINE LIST

020 8757 5029 | Sofitel London Heathrow, Terminal 5, Wentworth Drive, London Heathrow Airport, TW6 2GD

www.la-belle-epoque.co

There's something a touch counter-intuitive about looking for seriously good cooking in the environs of Heathrow Airport, but put aside your preconceptions and head over the covered walkway from Terminal 5 into the swanky Sofitel hotel. With its lush hues of purple and royal blue, La Belle Époque offers a suave change of mood from the airport mayhem.

Urban Brasserie
MAP 6, TQ07

◎◎ MODERN BRITISH

020 3971 4411 | Crowne Plaza London Heathrow – T4, 1 Swindon Road, Terminal 4, London Heathrow Airport, TW6 3FJ

www.cpheathrowt4.com

Heathrow Airport isn't the most obvious spot to look for accomplished modern British cooking, but that's just what this smart hotel brasserie delivers, and it's easy to reach by foot from Terminal 4. Served in an airy space with grey leather seats, pale wood tables and a soothing ambience, the eclectic menu includes grills and Asian street food.

Continued on page 254

Chapter One Restaurant

◉◉◉ MODERN EUROPEAN *V* ⓘ NOTABLE WINE LIST

01689 854848 | Farnborough Common, Locksbottom, BR6 8NF

www.chapteronerestaurant.co.uk

Intelligent cooking and spot-on service

With its additional options of the relaxed brasserie and popular terrace, Andrew McLeish's upmarket venue has wide appeal. The more formal restaurant sets a refined tone with its crisp linen tablecloths and vibrant gastronomic artwork on the plain white walls. Deceptively spacious with wood floors, dark blue furnishings and pale blue panelling, the decor is contemporary and comfortable. Long established and well supported by the locals, the ambience is chatty and friendly, with well-drilled waiting staff in formal black waistcoats and aprons. Whether you go for the carte, or the wallet-friendly menu du jour, McLeish strikes an inviting balance between assured modern European cooking and the desire to offer value. There is an obvious understanding of classic techniques and the dishes are finely tuned favourites rather than trying to reinvent things for the sake of it. Seasonal

ingredients from a network of high-end suppliers mean that the menus change all the time, depending on what's best at the time and what arrives in the kitchen. Chicken and girolle mushroom ravioli with onion Lyonnaise, chicken and celery jus makes for an arresting starter, as does treacle-cured salmon with soya sesame dressing and chargrilled spring onions. Main courses bring further evidence of intelligent flavour combinations, perhaps tandoori monkfish with curried cauliflower purée, sautéed spinach, roasted cauliflower and cumin sauce or roast guinea fowl, potato gnocchi, hispi cabbage, roasted sweetcorn and smoked guinea fowl jus. Desserts continue the form with an indulgent peanut parfait, double chocolate brownie, Kentish raspberries and raspberry sorbet or a poached blackberry and passionfruit mille-feuille with blackberry

> "...McLeish strikes an inviting balance between assured modern European cooking and the desire to offer value."

sorbet. And if there's still room, the English and French cheeses with fruit toast, Lavroche crackers and spiced apple chutney is hard to resist. Time a visit, perhaps, with one of the restaurant's popular gourmet evenings.

Chef Andrew McLeish
Seats 120, Private dining 50
Closed 2–4 January
Parking 70
Notes No children under 10 years old in the main restaurant; 5 years old in the Brasserie/Terrace

---

Vivre Restaurant
MAP 6, TQ07

◉ INTERNATIONAL

020 8757 5027 | Sofitel London Heathrow, Terminal 5, Wentworth Drive, London Heathrow Airport, TW6 2GD

www.sofitelheathrow.com

The Sofitel at Heathrow Terminal 5 boasts more decent eating than many airport hotels. As an alternative to the fine French goings-on in La Belle Époque, Vivre offers informal dining in an open-plan room of colourful contemporary design. The kitchen team are on view at their wokking and pizza-throwing, and service puts everyone at their ease. The large menu changes seasonally, but is reliably built around a core of firm favourites.

KEW

The Glasshouse
PLAN 1, C3

◉◉◉ MODERN INTERNATIONAL ◢NOTABLE WINE LIST

020 8940 6777 | 14 Station Parade, TW9 3PZ

www.glasshouserestaurant.co.uk

Light and airy as its name implies, and, from the same stable as Chez Bruce in Wandsworth and La Trompette in Chiswick, its pedigree is assured, pulling off neighbourhood fine dining with panache and an unbuttoned gloss. Neutral tones, textured walls, roman blinds, white linen, polished-wood floors and colourful artworks give the space a smart modern sheen, matching the highly polished light, contemporary cooking. Detailed, dressed-to-thrill dishes deliver high on precision, flavour and balance; witness a mains of sea-fresh roasted hake served with standout potted shrimp butter and crisp sarladaise potatoes, romanesco cauliflower and dill. Dessert is equally impressive; malt tart with stout ice cream, cocoa nibs and honeycomb. Corking wine list too.

Chef Gregory Wellman **Seats** 60 **Closed** 24–26 December, 1 January

PINNER

Friends Restaurant
PLAN 1, B5

◉ BRITISH, FRENCH

020 8866 0286 | 11 High Street, HA5 5PJ

www.friendsrestaurant.co.uk

Occupying a 500-year-old timbered building in Betjeman's suburban Metro-Land, Friends' devoted local fan base turns up for top-grade meat and fish handled with skill and sound modern thinking. Perhaps seared scallops with parsnip purée, black pudding crumble, crispy bacon and truffle foam for your opener.

RICHMOND UPON THAMES

144 On The Hill NEW
PLAN 1, C2

◉ MODERN BRITISH

020 8940 2247 | 144–150 Richmond Hill, TW10 6RW

www.richmondhill-hotel.co.uk

Newly renovated and wonderfully redesigned, 144 On The Hill sits on fashionable Richmond Hill next to Royal Richmond Park. There's a central bar between the lounge and the restaurant so you'll always find a bustling atmosphere. Everything is upscale yet friendly, including the cooking. The à la carte offers impressive choices, or you could try a charming takeaway picnic.

Bacco Restaurant & Wine Bar
PLAN 1, C2

◉ ITALIAN

020 8332 0348 | 39–41 Kew Road, TW9 2NQ

www.bacco-restaurant.co.uk

With a loyal local fan base, who come for its lively ambience and straight-talking classic cooking, this smart independent Italian can rock. There's a decked and covered terrace out front, while inside it's all bare floorboards, modern seating and colourful artwork. Expect mains like spinach and ricotta ravioli with butter and sage sauce.

Bingham Riverhouse

PLAN 1, C2

ROSETTES SUSPENDED **MODERN BRITISH** 🍷 NOTABLE WINE LIST

020 8940 0902 | 61–63 Petersham Road, TW10 6UT
www.binghamriverhouse.com

The Rosette award for this establishment has been suspended due to a change of chef and reassessment will take place in due course. Occupying a handsome pair of Georgian townhouses, with gorgeous Thames views making the covered balcony a hot ticket for alfresco dining during the summer, the Bingham sports a boutique look straight out of an interiors magazine. Easy-on-the-eye neutral hues and an ambience of calm set the tone in the elegantly relaxed dining room – it's all very comfortable indeed.

Seats 82, Private dining 110 **Open** All Year **Parking** 20
Notes Vegetarian dishes, Children welcome

The Dysart Petersham

PLAN 1, C2

◉◉◉ **TRADITIONAL EUROPEAN**

020 8940 8005 | 135 Petersham Road, Petersham, TW10 7AA
www.thedysartpetersham.co.uk

The Dysart occupies a 1904 Arts and Crafts building with original leaded windows and wooden window frames facing south over Richmond Park. Sunshine streams in on bright days, and a low-key jazz soundtrack floats around the elegant room. Kenneth Culhane's confident and sure-footed cooking delivers some fascinating, intricately detailed dishes full of subtle interplays of taste and texture. A sublime oxtail risotto made with gold-standard acquerello aged rice and enriched with bone marrow and pickled chilli gets off to a flying start, followed by a beautifully balanced plate of aged Devon duck with orange-braised chicory and prune sauce. Lemon verbena crème brûlée is a masterclass in simplicity.

Chef Kenneth Culhane **Seats** 45, Private dining 40
Closed 25 December, 1 week January, 1 week August
Parking 30

Petersham Nurseries Café

PLAN 1, C2

◉◉ **MODERN BRITISH, ITALIAN** 🍷 NOTABLE WINE LIST

020 8332 8665 | Church Lane, Petersham Road, TW10 7AB
www.petershamnurseries.com

This busy one-off restaurant is a romantically quirky, shabby-chic place, with its dirt floor and mismatched tables and chairs, but that's all part of the fun. The kitchen sends out a weekly-changing menu of modern Italian-accented ideas with fresh produce plucked from the garden.

SURBITON

The French Table

PLAN 1, C1

◉◉ **MODERN FRENCH** 🍷 NOTABLE WINE LIST

020 8399 2365 | 85 Maple Road, KT6 4AW
www.thefrenchtable.co.uk

Tucked away in leafy Maple Road, The French Table is a smart neighbourhood outfit. Dressed-to-impress modern French cooking punches above its weight on a fixed-price repertoire buoyed by a five-course taster. Breads are a triumph, while pastry impresses too – no surprise with its sibling boulangerie/patisserie bang next door.

TWICKENHAM

A Cena

PLAN 1, C2

◉ **MODERN ITALIAN**

020 8288 0108 | 418 Richmond Road, TW1 2EB
www.acena.co.uk

Just the sort of informal neighbourhood bistro-style Italian we'd all like on our patch, A Cena dishes up comforting, authentic cooking made with minimum fuss in a dining room done out with a woody mix of dark floorboards, church pew furniture and white walls hung with mirrors. The kitchen makes a good job of classic dishes.

■ MERSEYSIDE

FRANKBY
MAP 15, SJ28

Riviera at Hillbark
◉◉ FRENCH, MEDITERRANEAN
0151 625 2400 | Hillbark Hotel & Spa, Royden Park,
CH48 1NP
www.hillbarkhotel.co.uk/riviera
This all-mod-cons spa hotel features a light-filled
Riviera dining room, which embraces a sweeping
Mediterranean arc all the way from Nice to
Liguria, presented in the grazing format of little
and large dishes, courtesy of a super-cool
modern brasserie service.

HESWALL
MAP 15, SJ28

Burnt Truffle
◉◉ MODERN BRITISH
0151 342 1111 | 106 Telegraph Road, CH60 0AQ
www.burnttruffle.net

Gary Usher, owner of the six-restaurant Elite
Bistros group, opened his Wirral bridgehead in
2015, following a crowdfunding campaign; its
name was decided by the Twitterati. Walls are
decorated with food and wine pictures, old
London restaurant menus and names of
crowdfunding donors. Monthly changing menus
offer bistro-style takes on modern British and
international dishes. Outside is a heated terrace.

LIVERPOOL
MAP 15, SJ39

60 Hope Street Restaurant
◉ MODERN BRITISH
0151 707 6060 | 60 Hope Street, L1 9BZ
www.60hopestreet.com
A Liverpool dining fixture for two decades, this
popular Georgian townhouse restaurant still pulls
in the crowds. Occupying a convenient spot close
to the Philharmonic Hall, the unfussy decor is
reflected in the simple, seasonal modern food,
which puts an international spin on well-sourced
British ingredients.

The Art School Restaurant, Liverpool
◉◉ MODERN INTERNATIONAL ▲ NOTABLE WINE LIST
0151 230 8600 | 1 Sugnall Street, L7 7EB
www.theartschoolrestaurant.co.uk
Local food hero Paul Askew has brought
thoroughgoing British culinary modernism to
Liverpool, in the stunning Victorian setting of the
light-filled lantern room of what was once the
Home for Destitute Children. Dishes are carefully
composed, full of imaginative juxtapositions, and
confidently rendered.

Chez Mal Brasserie
◉ MODERN BRITISH
0151 229 5000 | Malmaison Liverpool, 7 William Jessop
Way, Princes Dock, L3 1QZ
www.malmaison.com
On the landward side of Princes Dock,
Malmaison's first purpose-built hotel is a
landmark for the maritime city. Echoing the city's
industrial heritage, the exposed bricks, lighting
gantries and air ducts of the double-height
brasserie, are balanced by warm, plush, purple
and black furnishings.

The London Carriage Works
◉◉ MODERN BRITISH ▲ NOTABLE WINE LIST
0151 705 2222 | Hope Street Hotel, 40 Hope Street,
L1 9DA
www.thelondoncarriageworks.co.uk
The stripped-back interior of the old workshop
at The London Carriage Works is a very modern
setting with large windows to give a view of the
street action. The menu makes much of
provenance and there's a satisfying regional
flavour to the food.

Mowgli
@ INDIAN

0151 708 9356 | 69 Bold Street, L1 4EZ

www.mowglistreetfood.com

Restauranteur Nisha Katona brings Indian street and domestic food to Liverpool, in a space with rough-edged Stateside appeal. High-concept recreations of popular subcontinental dishes begin with the likes of chat bombs, crisp potato shells with chickpeas, spices and yogurt garnished with pomegranate.

Panoramic 34
@ MODERN EUROPEAN

0151 236 5534 | 34th Floor, West Tower, Brook Street, L3 9PJ

www.panoramic34.com

From the 34th floor the views from this modern revolving restaurant are spectacular. There's Liverpool and the Mersey estuary of course, but also the Welsh mountains, the Irish Sea and distant Blackpool. Stone, natural wood, glass and underlit tables set the interior scene, while the daily-evolving modern British food includes international flavours such as miso and dukkah.

Röski Restaurant
@ @ MODERN BRITISH

0151 708 8698 | 16 Rodney Street, L1 2TE

www.roskirestaurant.com

MasterChef: The Professionals' 2012 winner Anton Piotrowski's restaurant is a smart venue located in the bustling Georgian quarter of Liverpool. The main kitchen is in the basement, and there are exciting plans to develop a 'chef's table' down there. The tasting menu format has a notable focus on early seasonality and look out for the great value lunch. Reservations and good time-keeping are definitely necessary.

Wreckfish NEW
@ MODERN BRITISH

0151 707 1960 | 60 Seel Street, L1 4BE

www.wreckfish.co

Gary Usher used crowdfunding to get Wreckfish off the ground in this former derelict Georgian building in the cool Ropewalks district. Inside, wooden floors and tables, and exposed brickwork give it a stripped-back industrial feel. Staff know their stuff and make sound recommendations about dishes such as torched sea bream, braised featherblade of beef and pork osso buco.

OXTON   MAP 15, SJ28

Fraiche
@ @ @ @ MODERN FRENCH, EUROPEAN ⚑ NOTABLE WINE LIST

0151 652 2914 | 11 Rose Mount, CH43 5SG

www.restaurantfraiche.com

Oxton is a charming conservation village, and Fraiche's discreet frontage gives little hint of how thrilling things are inside. An intimate space makes impressive use of lighting and projections, and Marc Wilkinson's food is a similarly innovative delight for the senses. Dishes are as stunning to look at as they are satisfying to eat, and a meal here is a truly joyful experience; you'll soon see why it's booked up months in advance. The daily-changing set menu offers refined, sometimes challenging dishes which are complex but perfectly balanced and precise. Descriptions are merely ingredients, witness 'scallop, smoked lime butter, wild rice' or 'Gressingham duck, cocoa crisp, kohlrabi', but rest assured that you can expect creative presentations that will impress and make you smile as you take a celebratory journey of texture and flavour. The wine list leans towards France and has many interesting options for every budget. Wine flights are available.

Chef Marc Wilkinson **Seats** 12, Private dining 12
Closed 25 December, 1 January, 2 weeks August
Notes No children under 8 years

PORT SUNLIGHT
MAP 15, SJ38

Riviera at Leverhulme

⊛⊛ FRENCH, MEDITERRANEAN

0151 644 6655 | Leverhulme Hotel, Central Road, CH62 5EZ

www.leverhulmehotel.co.uk

Lord Leverhulme opened the place in 1907 as a cottage hospital for soap works employees at his Port Sunlight garden village, and who wouldn't find their health restored amid such exquisite art deco surroundings? The comprehensive French-Mediterranean menu is a mix of small and large plates that come to the table 'as and when ready'.

PRESCOT
MAP 15, SJ49

Pinion NEW

⊛ BRITISH

0151 4930660 | 39 Eccleston Street, L34 5QA

www.pinionbistro.com

Pinion is the sixth offering in the Elite Bistros group of neighbourhood restaurants. In a former bookmakers, this charming little bistro sits on the pedestrianised high street in Liverpool's Prescott suburb. Decor is traditionally French in style with chandeliers, mirrors and bare brick walls. The pigs head croquette to start is fast becoming a Pinion favourite – also expect to see the Elite Bistro classic of braised beef with truffle and parmesan chips on there too. The staff are friendly and enthusiastic about the food and will happily recommend their favourite dishes.

SOUTHPORT
MAP 15, SD31

Bistrot Vérité

⊛⊛ FRENCH, INTERNATIONAL

01704 564199 | 7 Liverpool Road, Birkdale, PR8 4AR

www.bistrotverite.co.uk

French roots are very evident in this bustling, frill-free restaurant with a strong local following, thanks in part to its consistency, simplicity and informality. But obviously the food also counts hugely and fish soup and crab thermidor are staples, and crisp-fried frogs' legs and snails (from Dorset) too, while mustard- and herb-crusted lamb, and grilled swordfish also feature.

■ NORFOLK

BAWBURGH
MAP 13, TG10

The Kings Head Bawburgh

⊛⊛ MODERN BRITISH

01603 744977 | Harts Lane, NR9 3LS

www.kingsheadbawburgh.co.uk

The pub itself dates from the early 17th century, but the king in question is Edward VII (born 1841), chosen for his reputation as a bon viveur. There are real ales and the likes of fish and chips up for grabs, plus low oak beams, real fires and plenty of character. Its reputation as a dining pub is confirmed by its well-judged output.

BLAKENEY
MAP 13, TG04

The Blakeney Hotel

⊛ MODERN BRITISH

01263 740797 | The Quay, NR25 7NE

www.blakeneyhotel.co.uk

Those who like to be by the sea need look no further: this is in a perfect spot on the quay, with magnificent views over the estuary to Blakeney Point Area of Outstanding Natural Beauty. Well-sourced raw materials underpin the operation in the sea-facing restaurant.

Morston Hall

◉◉◉◉ MODERN BRITISH ⚜ NOTABLE WINE LIST

01263 741041 | Morston, Holt, NR25 7AA

www.morstonhall.com

Galton and Tracy Blackiston's 17th-century country house is truly an idyllic escape from the daily grind. The old manor is handsome without being overly grand, and your hosts are passionate about the area and its magnificent produce. The conservatory dining room makes a soothing setting, especially when the sun is out and the French doors are open. The seven-course tasting menu presents refined classical technique with contemporary verve and intricate yet seemingly effortless presentation. An opening salvo might be stuffed partridge, wrapped in pancetta to keep it moist, with buttery, silky endive purée providing a welcome mellow sweetness. Timing of Herdwick lamb is spot on, while roasted root vegetables add a lovely earthiness; light, crisply golden haggis complements the dish perfectly. At dessert, a pear and honey tart with delicate, crisp pastry and subtly spiced poached pears is balanced by a quenelle of cream, oats and crushed nuts. The wine list covers the globe and has lots of gems among its pages.

Chef Galton Blackiston, Greg Anderson **Seats** 50
Closed 3 days at Christmas, January **Parking** 50
Notes Children welcome

BRANCASTER STAITHE   MAP 13, TF74

The White Horse

◉◉ MODERN BRITISH, SEAFOOD *V*

01485 210262 | PE31 8BY

www.whitehorsebrancaster.co.uk

Platefuls of fantastic regional produce, including goodies smoked locally by Staithe Smokehouse, are what keep The White Horse firmly on the North Norfolk foodie map. And it's all the more enticing when you add in the big skies and unfettered views over the marshes from a table in the conservatory dining room or, on a balmy day, alfresco on the terrace.

BURNHAM MARKET   MAP 13, TF84

Socius

◉◉ MODERN BRITISH

01328 738307 | 11 Foundry Place, PE31 8LG

www.sociusnorfolk.co.uk

Socius is Latin for joining in/partaking, and that's the essence of this restaurant where the dishes are designed to share and the theme is very much modern British tapas. Well-chosen, locally sourced produce is the order of the day. The open-plan kitchen/restaurant has a contemporary feel and the team are very friendly and demonstrate a high degree of professionalism.

COLTISHALL   MAP 13, TG21

Norfolk Mead Hotel

◉◉ MODERN BRITISH

01603 737531 | Church Lane, NR12 7DN

www.norfolkmead.co.uk

This handsome old house in the heart of the Norfolk Broads is looking dapper with its contemporary, country-chic finish. The smart restaurant follows the theme, seamlessly blending period features with an uncluttered style – white walls, abstract artworks, and simple flower arrangements. On the food front, the kitchen hauls in fine local ingredients and offers a vibrant modern British menu.

CROMER
MAP 13, TG24

Bolton's Bistro NEW
◉ MODERN BRITISH
01263 512543 | The Cliftonville Hotel, Seafront, NR27 9AS
www.cliftonvillehotel.co.uk
Seafood – including the famous Cromer crab and locally-caught lobster – is the draw at Bolton's Bistro, the informal, family-run restaurant that forms part of the Cliftonville Hotel, an Edwardian Grade II listed property overlooking the sea on Cromer's west cliff. Although there are steaks on offer for carnivores, it's the attractively-presented, well-seasoned fish and shellfish dishes that steal the show.

The Grove Cromer
◉◉ BRITISH, SEAFOOD
01263 512412 | 95 Overstrand Road, NR27 0DJ
www.thegrovecromer.co.uk
A private path leads through woodland to the beach from this north Norfolk hotel, a substantial white Georgian house partly covered in creepers. In the restaurant, it's all about clear, fresh flavours. You might try Norfolk cheeses with quince jelly as an alternative to dessert.

FLEGGBURGH
MAP 13, TG41

The Kings Arms
◉◉ MODERN, TRADITIONAL
01493 368333 | Main Road, NR29 3AG
www.kingsarmsfleggburgh.com
This 19th-century red-brick pub in the village of Fleggburgh is split across a few areas with a bar feel to the front and a slightly more formal style dining area to the side with clothed tables. Service is attentive and professional with a gastro pub feel to proceedings.

GREAT YARMOUTH
MAP 13, TG50

Imperial Hotel
◉◉ MODERN BRITISH
01493 842000 | North Drive, NR30 1EQ
www.imperialhotel.co.uk
Generations of the Mobbs family have run the Imperial since the 1930s, when one of its attractions was being seated at separate tables. Today, frosted glass panels demonstrate that separate tables are still the elevated norm. Classic dishes from the brasserie repertoire are the stock-in-trade.

The Prom Hotel
◉ CONTEMPORARY BRITISH
01493 842308 | 77 Marine Parade, NR30 2DH
www.promhotel.co.uk
Overlooking the seafront, the Prom is on Marine Parade. Strollers is its attractively furnished restaurant, with a bar, that's perfectly positioned for pre-meal drinks. Yarmouth's trawler fleet has all but disappeared, but fish and seafood still have their place on the menu.

GRIMSTON
MAP 12, TF72

Congham Hall Country House Hotel
◉◉ MODERN BRITISH, EUROPEAN
01485 600250 | Lynn Road, PE32 1AH
www.conghamhallhotel.co.uk
This Georgian house has gorgeous gardens, a swish spa and a restaurant full of period charm. A herb garden produces an astonishing 400 varieties. French windows look onto the garden, while the cooking that arrives at pristine linen-clad tables is gently modern in outlook.

HEACHAM
MAP 12, TF63

Heacham Manor Hotel
◉ MEDITERRANEAN, EUROPEAN
01485 536030 | Hunstanton Road, PE31 7JX
www.heacham-manor.co.uk
The wide-open skies of Norfolk's fabulous coast make Heacham Manor an attractive prospect, and the place even comes with a coastal golf course. Built as an Elizabethan manor, the hotel has been brought smartly up-to-date and the conservatory-style Mulberry Restaurant has been extended and modernised.

HETHERSETT
MAP 13, TG10

Park Farm Hotel
◉ MODERN BRITISH
01603 810264 | NR9 3DL
www.parkfarm-hotel.co.uk
Park Farm Hotel and its spa and conference facilities are surrounded by 200 acres of beautiful open countryside. The contemporary, open-plan Seasons Restaurant looks out over the gardens while uniformed staff deliver the kitchen's well-presented and well-timed modern British fare.

HEVINGHAM
MAP 13, TG12

Marsham Arms Coaching Inn NEW

◎ MODERN BRITISH

01603 754268 | 40 Holt Road, NR10 5NP

www.marshamarms.co.uk

The Marsham Arms is a former coaching inn with a stylish white and grey exterior and good outdoor space, tables surrounded by flowers. The bar and dining area are homely and welcoming with a central woodburning stove, and dishes are modern British pub classics, from chicken supreme to scampi with beef dripping chips, using homegrown produce where possible. The gin list is great, with a good selection of local varieties.

HOLT
MAP 13, TG03

The Lawns

◎ MODERN EUROPEAN

01263 713390 | 26 Station Road, NR25 6BS

www.lawnshotelholt.co.uk

A small, modern hotel in a Georgian building, The Lawns offers a number of dining options: bar, conservatory, restaurant and south-facing garden. It's a warm and friendly place, reflected in a menu of largely comfortingly reassuring dishes pinned on East Anglian produce.

The Pheasant Hotel & Restaurant

◎ MODERN BRITISH

01263 588382 | Coast Road, Kelling, NR25 7EG

www.pheasanthotelnorfolk.co.uk

With the never ending beaches and marshland of the north Norfolk coast on hand, The Pheasant is plumb in one of the country's most fashionable resort areas. Cooking is modern British, with seafood a strong suit. Afternoon teas are an abiding part of The Pheasant's appeal.

HUNSTANTON
MAP 12, TF64

Caley Hall Hotel

◎ MODERN BRITISH

01485 533486 | Old Hunstanton Road, PE36 6HH

www.caleyhallhotel.co.uk

Built around a manor dating from 1648, Caley Hall is a short walk to the wide beaches on The Wash, a twitcher's paradise. Its restaurant, in a former stable block, is a relaxing-looking room. It's a popular place offering precisely cooked, quality East Anglian produce.

The Neptune Restaurant with Rooms

◎◎◎ MODERN EUROPEAN

01485 532122 | 85 Old Hunstanton Road, Old Hunstanton, PE36 6HZ

www.theneptune.co.uk

Just a short hop from the coast, The Neptune still has the look of an old inn, with its creeper-covered Georgian façade, but it's a top-notch restaurant with rooms these days. Much of the glorious regional bounty around these parts finds its way into Kevin Mangeolles' kitchen and onto a fixed-price carte and full-works tasting menu. The dining room is a smart, intimate space, with a neutral colour scheme and tables dressed in white linen. The cooking has classical roots, loads of good ideas and those local ingredients to the fore; Brancaster mussels, for example, with Serrano ham and apple, or Norfolk quail and truffle terrine. Main course suckling pig is accompanied by cabbage, butternut squash and dauphine potato, while British and French cheeses come with biscuits and grape chutney, or there might be almond iced nougat with strawberry, coconut and lime. The smart wine list has good options by the glass and half bottle.

Chef Kevin Mangeolles Seats 20 Closed 3 weeks January, 1 week May, 1 week November and 26 December Parking 5 Notes No children under 10 years

LODDON
MAP 13, TM39

The Loddon Swan

◎◎ MODERN BRITISH

01508 528039 | 23 Church Plain, NR14 6LX

www.theloddonswan.co.uk

Close to the stunning River Chet, this 18th-century coaching inn retains traditional charm along with 21st-century styling. While much

is made of local sourcing of ingredients, the menu mixes modern British dishes with Mediterranean classics.

NORTH WALSHAM
MAP 13, TG23

Beechwood Hotel

◎◎ MODERN BRITISH

01692 403231 | 20 Cromer Road, NR28 0HD

www.beechwood-hotel.co.uk

Hospitality is top of the agenda at this charming country house hotel, with hands-on owners and plenty of staff ensuring that guests are well looked after. The kitchen sources most ingredients from within 10 miles of the hotel and sends out contemporary British ideas.

Benedicts

◉◉◉ MODERN BRITISH

01603 926080 | 9 St Benedicts Street, NR2 4PE

www.restaurantbenedicts.com

Benedicts is a switched-on operation where pared-back, Scandi-chic looks tick all the boxes of a big-city venue and make a suitably modernist setting for chef-patron Richard Bainbridge's innovative contemporary cooking. Diners can be assured of exciting 21st-century food with stimulating combinations of excellent materials such as Cromer crab with grapefruit and Morston samphire or Cornish wild sea bass with braised baby gem, lemon and lobster bisque. To finish, perhaps a lemon tart with raspberry sorbet or British summer trifle with English rose, Sharrington strawberries and raspberries. There's regularly changing five- or eight-course tasting options or a set lunch menu which offers remarkable value.

Chef Richard Bainbridge **Seats** 40, Private dining 16 **Closed** 29 July to 14 August, 23 December to 8 January **Notes** Children welcome

Brasted's Restaurant

◉◉ MODERN EUROPEAN

01508 491112 | Manor Farm Barns, Fox Road, Framingham Pigot, NR14 7PZ

www.brasteds.co.uk

Brasted's is set in 20 acres of mature, landscaped parkland on the outskirts of Norwich. The restaurant is a bright and elegantly decorated converted barn, with a raftered ceiling, oak floor and exposed brick. The experienced kitchen team offers a menu of traditional British dishes with a modern European twist.

See advertisement opposite

Farmyard

◉◉◉ MODERN BRITISH

01603 733188 | 23 St Benedicts Street, NR2 4PF

www.farmyardrestaurant.com

The philosophy at this modern and minimalist restaurant in the heart of the city is quite simple - find the very best Norfolk produce and serve it in a relaxed bistro setting. From the sourdough to the handmade butter, everything is made from scratch, with meat, fish and vegetables cooked over charcoal for added flavour. From the

daily-changing menu, a tender piece of belly pork with Chinese-style XO sauce and BBQ onions might lead on to roasted rump of lamb with celeriac, mushroom and fenugreek. Finish with a home-made chocolate bar with miso caramel, candied peanuts and milk sorbet.

Chef John Walker **Seats** 52 **Prices** from S£6 M£13 D£6.50 **Notes** Children welcome

Maids Head Hotel

◉◉ MODERN BRITISH

01603 209955 | Tombland, NR3 1LB

www.maidsheadhotel.co.uk

The brick-built hotel in the city centre lays claim to being the UK's oldest, having been feeding and watering East Anglian travellers for 800 years. Dining goes on in a glassed-in courtyard with a quarry-tiled floor and simple wooden tables.

Roger Hickman's Restaurant

◉◉◉ MODERN BRITISH ❚ NOTABLE WINE LIST

01603 633522 | 79 Upper St Giles Street, NR2 1AB

www.rogerhickmansrestaurant.com

Squirrelled away near the cathedral in the Upper St Giles area, Roger Hickman's intimate restaurant is discreetly positioned but draws a crowd nonetheless. Elegant, calm and tastefully appointed with modern artwork and smartly laid tables, it's a comfortable setting for the modern British seasonal cooking. Whether ordering from the fixed-price or tasting menu, you might begin with crispy chicken, glazed wing, spring onion, sesame seed purée and mouli before braised beef short rib, Jerusalem artichoke, shallot and cashew nut. Chocolate fruit and nut, chestnut and pistachio is one way to round things off. The wine list has won awards.

Chef Roger Hickman **Seats** 40, Private dining 18 **Closed** 2 weeks in January **Notes** Children welcome

Stower Grange

◉ MODERN BRITISH

01603 860210 | 40 School Road, Drayton, NR8 6EF

www.stowergrange.co.uk

The ivy-covered country house in its own wooded grounds a few miles out of Norwich is a charming family-run hotel where contemporary cooking based on quality ingredients aims to satisfy rather than startle. Try crisp-skinned sea bass with wild mushrooms, beetroot and puréed onions as a main course.

Continued on page 264

BRASTED'S

MULTI-AWARD WINNING
Fine Dining

Our award winning a la carte menus offer locally sourced ingredients and produce, resulting in traditional British dishes with a modern European twist. As a fine dining restaurant, service and food are paramount, resulting in the ultimate dining experience.

Restaurant Opening Times

Thursday, Friday & Saturday
6.30pm till 10.00pm
Thursday & Friday lunchtime
12.00pm till 2.30pm

Contact Us

01508 491112   brasteds.co.uk   Manor Farm Barns, Framingham Pigot, Norwich NR14 7PZ

NORWICH continued

Thailand Restaurant

◉ THAI

01603 700444 | 9 Ring Road, Thorpe St Andrew, NR7 0XJ

www.thailandnorwich.co.uk

Plants and hanging baskets add dash to the exterior of this well-established restaurant. Inside, the decor is as busy as the bamboo-framed upholstered seats are busy with customers: drapes over the windows, statues in niches, friezes on beams and lots of greenery.

Warwick Street Social

◉ MODERN BRITISH

01603 627687 | 2 Warwick Street, NR2 3LD

www.warwickstsocial.co.uk

In Norwich's Golden Triangle, the WSS has contemporary style. The Norfolk-inspired British cuisine is pretty modern too: sea-salt crackling belly pork with charred tenderloin then a lip-smacking finale of dark chocolate fondant with salted caramel purée and amaretti ice cream.

REEPHAM *MAP 13, TG12*

The Dial House

◉◉ MODERN BRITISH

01603 879900 | Market Place, NR10 4JJ

www.thedialhouse.org.uk

Occupying a splendid Georgian house, The Dial House offers a series of character spaces running from a chandelier-hung main dining room to a garden room with a terrace, and a cellar with bare brick walls. Wherever you choose, expect sparky modern cooking from a kitchen that likes to bang the drum for regional ingredients.

RICKINGHALL *MAP 13, TM07*

The Bell Inn *NEW*

◉ MODERN BRITISH

01379 898445 | The Street, IP22 1BN

www.thebellrickinghall.co.uk

Ideal for families, The Bell Inn is a laid-back 17th-century village pub set in quiet Rickinghall. Dining is available in the cosy bar, formal eating area or on the outdoor terrace. As well as the usual sandwiches and pub classics, there's a reasonably priced à la carte.

STALHAM *MAP 13, TG32*

The Ingham Swan *NEW*

◉◉ MODERN BRITISH/FRENCH *V*

01692 581099 | Sea Palling Road, Ingham, NR12 9AB

www.theinghamswan.co.uk

In the heart of a village close to the north-east Norfolk coastline, this thatched 14th-century former coaching inn retains plenty of original features. Dark wood tables, blue chairs and exposed brick walls set the scene for Cromer crab cakes and wild garlic baked lobster, followed by barbecue fillet of beef and potato terrine.

STOKE HOLY CROSS *MAP 13, TG20*

The Wildebeest

◉◉ MODERN EUROPEAN

01508 492497 | 82-86 Norwich Road, NR14 8QJ

www.thewildebeest.co.uk

Set in a tranquil village, The Wildebeest continues to be a haven of refined eating, now in the skilful hands of chef-patron Daniel Smith. The interior is rich with beams, aged floorboards, wood-topped tables and leather-clad dining chairs. Much produce comes from a nearby farm.

THETFORD *MAP 13, TL88*

The Mulberry

◉ MEDITERRANEAN, ENGLISH

01842 824122 | 11 Raymond Street, IP24 2EA

www.mulberrythetford.co.uk

This intimate restaurant in the heart of Thetford makes good use of local ingredients but looks to the Mediterranean for its inspiration on the plate. Go for the king prawn bruschetta, garlic prawns, tomato, chickpea, tarragon and lobster butter, perhaps followed by aged Norfolk beef sirloin tagliata with rocket, parmesan and red wine jus.

THORNHAM
MAP 12, TF74

The Chequers Inn
◉◉ MODERN BRITISH
01485 512229 | High Street, PE36 6LY
www.chequersinnthornham.com
This pretty village inn dates back to the 16th century and its location on the north Norfolk coast makes it a popular spot for people heading to the beautiful beaches of Brancaster and Holkham. Contemporary but rustic, the restaurant attracts locals as well as visitors.

The Lifeboat Inn
◉ TRADITIONAL BRITISH
01485 512236 | Ship Lane, PE36 6LT
www.lifeboatinnthornham.com
Down a quiet lane behind the church, this charming, white-painted inn has been providing hospitality for more than 500 years. The terrace is a tranquil spot to enjoy a pint in summer, while the coastal location means local seafood gets a strong showing.

TITCHWELL
MAP 13, TF74

Titchwell Manor Hotel
◉◉◉ MODERN EUROPEAN V
01485 210221 | PE31 8BB
www.titchwellmanor.com
Positioned in an idyllic spot on the north Norfolk coast, Titchwell Manor is a boutique hotel, built around a red-brick Victorian farmhouse, with chic interiors of vibrant patterns and colour combinations in fabrics and carpets. The light-flooded Conservatory restaurant looks over the walled garden, where much of the kitchen's veg, fruit and herbs are grown. Chris Mann's cooking is adventurous, modern stuff built on his uncommon culinary ability and exciting dexterity with flavours and textures. A starter might be of Brancaster dressed crab, garden herb mayo and dressed salad. A main course could consist of crispy-skinned, tenderly pink Creedy Carver duck breast accompanied by duck leg sausage, pomme anna, cherry and duck fat leeks. Fish is also imaginatively handled along the likes of grilled seabass, mussel sauce, Jersey Royals, keta caviar and sautéed lettuce. For the grand finale try the Lincolnshire poacher cheddar, malt loaf, fig jam with intriguing textures and flavour contrasts.
Chef Eric Snaith, Chris Mann **Seats** 80 **Open** All Year **Parking** 50 **Notes** Children welcome

WIVETON
MAP 13, TG04

Wiveton Bell
◉◉ MODERN BRITISH
01263 740101 | The Green, Blakeney Road, NR25 7TL
www.wivetonbell.co.uk
An authentic Georgian country pub on the village green, the Bell is near Blakeney and the salt marshes of north Norfolk and is done up in light and airy modern fashion. The cooking has a pleasingly traditional air about it.

WYMONDHAM
MAP 13, TG10

Number Twenty Four Restaurant
◉ MODERN BRITISH
01953 607750 | 24 Middleton Street, NR18 0AD
www.number24.co.uk

Excellent reviews continue to stack up for Jonathan, Isobel and their team's smart, Grade II listed restaurant in this old market town. Modern British in style, every meal is meticulously prepared and presented, backed by good wines from around the world. 'Wind'm' railway station is worth a look, while the cathedral city of Norwich is barely 10 miles away.

■ NORTHAMPTONSHIRE

DAVENTRY
MAP 11, SP56

Fawsley Hall Hotel & Spa
◉◉ MODERN BRITISH
01327 892000 | Fawsley, NN11 3BA
www.handpickedhotels.co.uk/fawsleyhall
Plantagenets, Tudors and Georgians all played a part in the beguiling architectural mishmash seen today, and it screams 'grand' with its oak panels, stone arches and the Cedar Restaurant. However, a feeling of intimacy pervades the place, and the kitchen deals in imaginative 21st-century ideas.

KETTERING
MAP 11, SP87

Kettering Park Hotel & Spa
◉ MODERN BRITISH
01536 416666 | Kettering Parkway, NN15 6XT
www.ketteringparkhotel.co.uk/food-drink
Kettering Park belies its business park location by having plenty of charm with its real fire and sunny terrace. Local Melton Mowbray pies and Leicestershire cheeses make an appearance, but the menu takes a global approach. Wild boar Scotch egg could precede roasted cod with smoked bacon and white wine sauce.

Tresham Restaurant
◉◉◉ MODERN BRITISH
01536 713001 | Rushton Hall Hotel and Spa, Rushton, NN14 1RR
www.rushtonhall.com
The black sheep of the illustrious family who built Rushton Hall in the 15th century was a player in the Gunpowder Plot, and the magnificent pile was the later inspiration for Dickens' Satis House in Great Expectations. These days it earns a crust as a stately leisure retreat with all the trappings of a grand country hotel. The Tresham Restaurant – named after the former owners, including the ill-fated plotter – has relocated to a new spot, and makes a refined and elegant setting for Adrian Coulthard's precise and refined modernist cooking. Smoked ham hock, chicken and foie gras are allied in a carefully composed pressing, with lovage mayonnaise, pickled onion petals and potato crisps. Main course brings pan-fried halibut with brown shrimps, gnocchi, cucumber, tomato and butter sauce, the happy colours reflecting the summer seasonality. The 1593 Brasserie is the more informal dining option.

Chef Adrian Coulthard **Seats** 40, Private dining 60
Open All Year **Parking** 140 **Notes** No children under 12 years

NASSINGTON
MAP 12, TL09

The Queens Head Inn
◉ MODERN BRITISH
01780 784006 | 54 Station Road, PE8 6QB
www.queensheadnassington.co.uk
On the banks of the River Nene, this delightful mellow stone inn does a solid line in muscular modern cooking built on locally sourced ingredients. The 200-year-old hostelry still functions as a pub, but food drives the action with a charcoal-fired Josper grill taking pride of place in the kitchen. If you're up for some serious meat action, the steaks are impeccably sourced.

NORTHAMPTON
MAP 11, SP76

East Wing NEW
◉ MODERN BRITISH
01604 698005 | Castle Ashby, NN7 1LF
www.thefalcon-castleashby.com
The East Wing is a relaxed bar and lounge with an airy feel and a lovely terrace. It's part of The Falcon Hotel, and the whole place has been recently and beautifully renovated. Service is informal bistro style, and the team are smartly uniformed with full-length aprons. A growing menu features Modern British dishes cooked with precision and skill.

Hibiscus Fine Dining NEW
◉ MODERN BRITISH
01604 911073 | Delapre Abbey, London Road, NN4 8AW
www.hibiscusfinedining.co.uk

Tucked away inside the Royal & Derngate theatre, Hibiscus is an intimate space, beautifully decorated in muted greys and silvers. Staff are smartly dressed staff and welcoming, and the menu changes seasonally with regular tweaks according to market availability. Begin with the fresh flavours and pretty pale pinks and greens of marinated Cornish crab with avocado, wasabi and cucumber, followed by roast lamb with lamb fat potato and wild garlic.

The Hopping Hare

@@ MODERN, TRADITIONAL

01604 580090 | 18 Hopping Hill Gardens, Duston, NN5 6PF

www.hoppinghare.com

Spacious, thoughtfully decorated and furnished, with an informal and atmospheric dining room and a popular bar. The modern, and inventive, British culinary output changes with the seasons – Balmoral venison loin bolognese with Szechuan pepper; shepherd's pie; hake fillet roasted in Marmite butter; crispy almond milk polenta, and daily chef's specials.

Nuovo Restaurant NEW

@ CONTEMPORARY ITALIAN V

01604 601100 | 104a Abington Street, NN1 2BP

www.nuovo-restaurant.co.uk

A hidden gem in a unique setting, hidden away down a passageway off the main drag. A long, narrow space, where the feature lighting and bold stripes of the draped ceiling create a great atmosphere. This is casual, relaxed dining, with a Venetian-inspired menu of cicchetti or Italian small plates; really tasty, well-executed, seasonally driven food. You might choose plump and tender scallops with fresh, green flavours of sea vegetables; belly pork topped with a little quince jelly, or perhaps fazzoletto.

OUNDLE MAP 11, TL08

The Talbot

@ BRITISH

01832 273621 | New Street, PE8 4EA

www.thetalbot-oundle.com

If The Talbot looks ancient, that's maybe because its stone façades, mullioned windows and grand timber staircase were recycled from Fotheringhay Castle in the 17th century. Nowadays, it does a brisk trade as a hotel, coffee house and eatery, aka the restaurant.

WHITTLEBURY MAP 11, SP64

Murrays

@@@ MODERN BRITISH, EUROPEAN

01327 850489 | Whittlebury Park, NN12 8QH

www.whittlebury.com

Murrays is the pole-position dining option at Whittlebury Hall, a plush neo-Georgian hotel with a Rolls Royce of a spa and serious golfing just a Ferrari's roar away from Silverstone. While the slick front-of-house team help diners relax in the slow lane, the kitchen hits top gear with modern British cooking. A starter of Devonshire crab with Granny Smith apple and avocado grabs the attention with its layering of flavours and textures, while loin and sweetbreads of lamb with baby leek terrine and celeriac turns up at main course stage. For pudding, a high-octane confection of chocolate, gianduja and praline cream is a winner.

Chef Craig Rose **Seats** 32, Private dining 10
Closed selected dates at Christmas, 31 December
Parking 460 **Notes** No children

◾ NORTHUMBERLAND

BERWICK-UPON-TWEED
MAP 21, NT95

Magna
◉ INDIAN
01289 302736 | 39 Bridge Street, TD15 1ES
www.magnatandooriberwick.co.uk
Close to the bridge over the Tweed at the lower
end of the walled town, Magna has earned a
reputation for top-notch Indian cooking since it
opened in 1982. Occupying a grand Victorian
building, bright red chairs and colourful murals
add a cheery glow to the place. The menu offers
familiar curry-house staples making admirable
use of local produce.

BLANCHLAND
MAP 18, NY95

Lord Crewe Arms Blanchland
◉ TRADITIONAL BRITISH V
01434 675469 | Lord Crewe Arms, The Square,
DH8 9SP
www.lordcrewearmsblanchland.co.uk
Built for the residents of Blanchland Abbey in the
1100s, this wonderfully historic inn has served
everyone from monks to lead miners. It seems
unlikely that the latter would have been
interested in the architecture, not least the
vaulted stone crypt, now an atmospheric bar.

CHATHILL
MAP 21, NU12

Doxford Hall Hotel & Spa
◉◉ MODERN BRITISH
01665 589700 | NE67 5DN
www.doxfordhall.com
Doxford Hall's restaurant has chandeliers in
ornate ceilings, a stone fireplace, deep-red walls
and menus reflecting 21st-century dining
expectations. Seared scallops with two
croquettes of slowly cooked pig's cheek and
celeriac remoulade is just one possible starter
of intense, distinct flavours.

HEXHAM
MAP 21, NY96

The Barrasford Arms
◉ BRITISH
01434 681237 | Barrasford, NE48 4AA
www.barrasfordarms.co.uk
Close to Hadrian's Wall in the tranquil village of
Barrasford, this ivy-clad country inn has three
dining rooms kitted out with rustic furniture. The
kitchen works to a modern British template, the
emphasis firmly placed on produce from local
estates and punchy flavours.

Langley Castle Hotel
◉◉ CONTEMPORARY BRITISH, FRENCH
01434 688888 | Langley, NE47 5LU
www.langleycastle.com
At the Langley Castle restaurant you'll find a
creative and modern output delivered via a table
d'hôte menu; expect dishes based on top quality,
seasonal ingredients sourced from the
Northumberland area. The kitchen's aim is to
produce straightforward flavoursome food
without unnecessary distractions.

LONGFRAMLINGTON
MAP 21, NU10

The Granby Inn NEW
◉ MODERN BRITISH
01665 570228 | Front Street, NE65 8DP
www.thegranbyinn.co.uk
Situated in the heart of the peaceful
Northumberland village of Longframlington, The
Granby is a traditional village inn dating back
over 250 years. Locally sourced produce appears
throughout the appealing modern British menu,
whether it's seared scallops, home-made black
pudding and crushed peas or pork tenderloin
wrapped in dry-cured streaky bacon, pork
croquette, roasted broccoli and jus.

MORPETH
MAP 21, NZ18

Eshott Hall
◉◉ BRITISH, EUROPEAN
01670 787454 | Eshott, NE65 9EN
www.eshotthall.co.uk
Eshott Hall is a compact boutique hotel in a
handsome Georgian property - a perfect base
from which to explore the National Park and end
the day with dinner in the elegant restaurant,
with its soothing gold colour scheme and a fire in
cooler weather.

NEWTON-ON-THE-MOOR
MAP 21, NU10

The Cook and Barker Inn
◉ BRITISH
01665 575234 | NE65 9JY
www.cookandbarkerinn.co.uk
With great views of the Cheviot Hills and the
coast from its elevated location, The Cook and
Barker has turned from a traditional inn to a
stylish place. Exposed brickwork, beams with
fairy lights, upholstered chairs and wooden
tables add up to a sophisticated look.

'Simply... Wow!'

The Duke of Wellington Inn

Newton, Stocksfield, Northumberland NE43 7UL
01661 844 446
info@thedukeofwellingtoninn.co.uk
www.thedukeofwellingtoninn.co.uk

Award winning food

AA Rosette award for culinary excellence 2021

AA ★★★★★ Inn 2021

AA Breakfast Award 2021

STOCKSFIELD
MAP 21 NZ06

The Duke of Wellington Inn
◉◉ MODERN BRITISH

01661 844446 | Newton, NE43 7UL
www.thedukeofwellingtoninn.co.uk
The Duke of Wellington Inn is only minutes from the A69, but it's so peaceful here that you'd never know it. It's reputedly one of Northumberland's oldest pubs, but the food is much more up to date than that. Also, you can be sure of a warm welcome if you're a cyclist, a walker, or want to bring the dog.

See advertisement on page 269

■ NOTTINGHAMSHIRE

BARNBY MOOR
MAP 16, SK68

Restaurant Bar 1650
◉ MODERN BRITISH

01777 705121 | Ye Olde Bell Hotel & Spa, DN22 8QS
www.yeoldebell-hotel.co.uk
This hotel offers beauty therapies aplenty, and lots of room for functions. There's a bistro in the St Leger bar, but the main event is the oak-panelled Restaurant Bar 1650, with its art deco style in the bar area and modern chandeliers to add a touch of glamour.

BLIDWORTH
MAP 16, SK55

The Black Bull
◉◉ MODERN BRITISH

01623 490222 | Main Street, NG21 0QH
www.blackbullblidworth.co.uk
Not far from Sherwood Forest and Byron's Newstead Abbey is this classic Georgian timbered inn. Sand-blasted beams, a brick fireplace and checkered carpeting make for a modernised but still homely atmosphere for showcasing some creatively witty cooking. The inventive pace is sustained to the end.

FARNDON
MAP 17, SK75

Farndon Boathouse
◉◉ MODERN BRITISH

01636 676578 | Off Wyke Road, NG24 3SX
www.farndonboathouse.co.uk
The leafy banks of the River Trent make an interesting contrast to the contemporary exposed ducting, industrial-style lighting, stone floors and glazed frontage of the stylish Boathouse. The kitchen uses modern cooking techniques such as sous-vide, to squeeze every molecule of flavour from the ingredients.

GUNTHORPE
MAP 11, SK64

Tom Browns Brasserie
◉◉ MODERN BRITISH

0115 966 3642 | The Old School House, Trentside, NG14 7FB
www.tombrowns.co.uk

The homage to Thomas Hughes' plucky Victorian schoolboy denotes the fact that this large riverside building was a place of education in the 19th century. No risk of having to face school dinners here now, though, this is a robustly complex, well-considered brasserie cooking in the modern style.

NOTTINGHAM
MAP 11, SK53

Alchemilla
◉◉◉◉ MODERN BRITISH 🍷 NOTABLE WINE LIST

0115 941 3515 | 192 Derby Road, NG7 1NF
alchemillarestaurant.uk
A wall of green foliage is the only real clue in daylight that you've found this almost hidden gem. A former coach house, derelict for a century and a half, with bare brick walls, an arched ceiling and light flooding down from huge skylights onto the simply presented wooden tables and open kitchen. This is modern cookery of the best kind, supported by an understanding of classic techniques, and with an inspired take on the plant-based elements of dishes. Barbecue flavours might feature in a memorable starter of celeriac, finished in goats' butter and topped with fresh herbs, an earthy, tender dish that packs a real punch. Moroccan lamb is served pink, with burnt aubergine, pomegranate and molasses, sticky-sweet and complex, and a colourful apricot and tea purée. A quenelle of shakshuka pulls the dish together brilliantly. Finish with creamy chocolate gelato, salted liquorice custard and a vibrant beetroot sorbet. Petits fours are top notch.

Chef Alex Bond **Seats** 48, Private dining 9 **Closed** 31 July to 13 August **Notes** No children

Byrons

◉ MODERN

0115 950 0566 | Colwick Hall Hotel,
Racecourse Road, NG2 4BH

colwickhallhotel.com

Named for poet Lord Byron, whose ancestral
home this grand Georgian pile once was, the
informal bar and brasserie goes for a more
up-to-date look with its cream leather chairs and
darkwood floors and tables. The kitchen follows
suit, offering an appetising menu of modern,
uncomplicated ideas that aims to please
all comers.

Hart's Kitchen

◉◉ MODERN BRITISH

0115 988 1900 | Hart's Hotel, Standard Hill,
Park Row, NG1 6GN

www.hartsnottingham.co.uk

Set in a red brick building with stylish modern
additions, Hart's Kitchen is a welcoming
restaurant with an approachable, weekly-
changing menu. Crisp linen napkins and cloths
topped with sparkling stemware set the scene
for the modern British food, clean and simple
with fresh ingredients. Look out for the gallery of
signed celebrity photos.

MemSaab Restaurant

◉◉ INDIAN

0115 957 0009 | 12–14 Maid Marian Way, NG1 6HS

www.mem-saab.co.uk

Easily able to cater for 200 covers, MemSaab
is a pretty big operation, but its size doesn't
dilute the quality of the outstanding menu and
its stunning choice of modern and traditional
Indian cooking styles. The decor demonstrates
MemSaab's ethos, a mix of traditional Indian
design and themes, with a modern approach
and execution.

See advertisement on page 272

Park Plaza Nottingham

◉◉ PAN-ASIAN

0115 947 7444 | 41 Maid Marian Way, NG1 6GD

www.chinolatino.eu/nottingham

Latin America meets the Far East in this
Nottingham branch of the Park Plaza. Set across
two levels, this buzzy restaurant and bar fuses
pan-Asian cooking with international cuisine on
the globe-trotting menu. Thai and Korean dishes
appear in the mains.

Restaurant Sat Bains with Rooms

◉◉◉◉◉ MODERN BRITISH 🍷 NOTABLE WINE LIST

0115 986 6566 | Lenton Lane, Trentside, NG7 2SA

www.restaurantsatbains.com

Satwant Singh Bains chose rather an unexpected
location for his restaurant. Not only is it outside
the city centre, it's in a handsomely converted
Victorian farmhouse and outbuildings down a
narrow lane, with the River Trent flowing behind.
Sat's reputation has elevated him to the ranks of
this country's super-chefs. For him, it's all about
research, development and creativity that goes
into his dishes. And, of course, the produce itself
– for example, around 40 per cent of the veg and
herbs that end up on the tables come from the
urban garden outside. There's a small courtyard,
ideal for a pre- or post-prandial drink, as well.
Dining options are several: Chef's Table, with
dishes served by the very chefs you may well
have watched preparing them; Kitchen Bench,
where you sit on high chairs within the main
body of the pastry kitchen while, again, the chefs
themselves look after you; the Conservatory, and
the main restaurant itself. Wine flights ensure
food and drink matches are as perfect as
everything else.

Chef Sat Bains **Seats** 46, Private dining 8 **Closed** 2
weeks in December to January, 1 week in April, 2 weeks
in August **Parking** 16 **Notes** No children under 8 years

NOTTINGHAM continued

World Service
◉◉ MODERN BRITISH ⚑NOTABLE WINE LIST
0115 847 5587 | Newdigate House, Castle Gate, NG1 6AF
www.worldservicerestaurant.com

With a real buzzy atmosphere, World Service is in the 17th-century Newdigate House which has strong connections to the local United Services Club. The other part of the restaurant's name reflects inspiration drawn from around the world, which has created a combination of British cuisine with global influences, using a blend of techniques and flavours.

■ OXFORDSHIRE

BANBURY *MAP 11, SP44*

The White Horse
◉◉ TRADITIONAL BRITISH, FRENCH INFLUENCE
01295 812440 | 2 The Square, Kings Sutton, OX17 3RF
www.whitehorseks.co.uk
This old pub has been given a makeover that, while creating a clean, modern look, still ensures that you are reminded of its past. Clearly popular, it has received regional food accolades for its British and European cooking. Perhaps choose breast and leg of Loomswood duck with carrot, cumin and lentil dhal as a main, and lemon cheesecake with stem-ginger ice cream to finish.

BURFORD *MAP 5, SP21*

The Angel at Burford
◉ CLASSIC BRITISH
01993 822714 | 14 Witney Street, OX18 4SN
www.theangelatburford.co.uk
Just off the main street in pretty Burford, this welcoming Cotswold stone inn oozes character. Perfectly kept pints of Hook Norton lure drinkers to the cosy and bustling bar, with the all-day bar menu offering sandwiches, burgers and a charcuterie board alongside the main carte.

The Bay Tree Hotel
◉ MODERN BRITISH
01993 822791 | Sheep Street, OX18 4LW
www.cotswold-inns-hotels.co.uk/baytree
Built in Cotswold stone, this is a stylishly appointed place and a menu of modern-classic English food. Try perhaps scallops on cauliflower purée, then Ruby White 36-day aged beef with truffle fries.

The Lamb Inn
◉◉ MODERN BRITISH
01993 823155 | Sheep Street, OX18 4LR
www.cotswold-inns-hotels.co.uk/lamb
Beautifully cosy and comfortable, with flagstone floors and open fires, The Lamb is your quintessential Cotswold inn, set in a quaint market town. The dining room, with its grey walls and skylight, makes a very classy setting for their chic food – complex, precise seasonal dishes.

The Maytime Inn NEW
◉ CLASSIC BRITISH V
01993 822068 | Asthall, OX18 4HW
www.themaytime.com
The Maytime Inn is a 17th-century Cotswold countryside pub that once had its own smithy. Inside you'll find a traditional inn with a modern twist to the tasteful decor and seating; expect scrubbed wooden tables, a warming fire and plenty of atmosphere. There's a well-stocked bar which is proud of its gin choices (over 150!). Local ingredients abound. Dogs miss none of the fun – there are treats available for four-legged friends too.

CHECKENDON *MAP 5, SU68*

The Highwayman
◉ MODERN, TRADITIONAL BRITISH
01491 682020 | Exlade Street, RG8 0UA
www.thehighwaymaninn-checkendon.co.uk
Tucked away in a secluded hamlet, this rambling 16th-century inn is all brickwork, beams and wood-burner in a huge inglenook. Fine ales are on tap in the pubby bar, and all bases are covered in the food department by steaks from the grill, and home-made pies.

CHINNOR

MAP 5, SP70

The Sir Charles Napier

◉◉ MODERN BRITISH, EUROPEAN 🏷NOTABLE WINE LIST

01494 483011 | Sprigg's Alley, OX39 4BX

www.sircharlesnapier.co.uk

Hidden down rural Oxfordshire lanes, this sublime flint-and-brick inn is named after the 19th-century British Army general who became commander-in-chief in India. Menus feature hedgerow and field-sourced herbs, mushrooms, berries and game. You can eat inside, on the vine-covered terrace or under the cherry trees.

CHIPPING NORTON

MAP 10, SP32

Wild Thyme Restaurant

◉◉ MODERN BRITISH

01608 645060 | 10 New Street, OX7 5LJ

www.wildthymerestaurant.co.uk

Grade II listed and 400 years old, this smart little restaurant with rooms (35 covers and three bedrooms) has original features on show, but the place feels bright and contemporary just the same. That's down to the easy-going look of exposed stone walls, modern artworks and white-painted woodwork, with the wooden tables left unclothed. Chef-patron Nick Pullen seeks out top-notch seasonal regional produce and cooks smart, contemporary British food that deals in intelligent flavour combinations.

FARINGDON

MAP 5, SU29

Magnolia

◉◉ MODERN BRITISH

01367 241272 | Sudbury House, 56 London Street, SN7 7AA

www.sudburyhouse.co.uk

Close to the M4 between Swindon and Oxford, this smart hotel occupies an enviable spot on the edge of the Cotswolds. The contemporary Magnolia is the more informal of the hotel's two restaurants and the room is dominated by the open kitchen with a wood-burning stove.

FYFIELD

MAP 5, SU49

The White Hart

◉◉ MODERN BRITISH

01865 390585 | Main Road, OX13 5LW

www.whitehart-fyfield.com

There's certainly no lack of character here – Fyfield is a proper picture-book village, and the White Hart, originally a chantry house, has all the flagstones, beams and period features you could hope for. Inside you can dine beneath the impressive vaulted ceilings and choose from a thoughtfully constructed menu of locally sourced, seasonally inspired dishes, maybe grilled mackerel fillet with puffed rice, red pepper relish and coriander, or succulent roasted belly of Kelmscott pork, with apple, celeriac purée and crackling.

GREAT MILTON
MAP 5, SP60

Belmond Le Manoir aux Quat'Saisons

◉◉◉◉◉ MODERN FRENCH ⓵ NOTABLE WINE LIST

01844 278881 | Church Road, OX44 7PD

www.belmond.com/hotels/europe/uk/oxfordshire/
belmond-le-manoir-aux-quat-saisons

Besançon-born Raymond Blanc bought this beautiful 15th-century manor in 1983, opening it a year later as a country house hotel and restaurant. He still runs it today, although it is owned by the Belmond hotel and leisure group. With luxurious bedroom suites, it stands at the heart of glorious grounds with sculptures, an orchard, a Japanese tea garden and a bounteous, organic kitchen garden. It should be no surprise that maître d' Blanc, OBE, remains the life force of the place, with his long-standing executive head chef Gary Jones, chef-pâtissier Benoit Blin, and their amazing teams, loyally alongside him. The dining experience is never less than utterly pleasurable, from the warm greeting and the charming attention to, of course, the delicious, classic French cuisine that has made Le Manoir's five-, six-and seven-course menus, with vegetarian and vegan options, such a gastronomic success. In addition is the three-course carte. And there's a children's menu too. The French led wine list has just a few candidates from the New World. Cookery and gardening schools add to Le Manoir's mix, enabling everyone a chance to take knowledge home, together with wonderful memories.

Chef Raymond Blanc OBE, Gary Jones, Benoit Blin
Seats 80, Private dining 50 **Parking** 60 **Notes** Children welcome

HENLEY-ON-THAMES
MAP 5, SU78

The Baskerville

◉ CLASSIC EUROPEAN

0118 940 3332 | Station Road, Lower Shiplake, RG9 3NY

www.thebaskerville.com

This Baskerville is a handsome beast, a contemporary kind of inn that offers beer and bar snacks, comfortable rooms, and a restaurant that produces serious modern British grub. Pub classics like steak, ale and mushroom pie and Sunday roasts play to the gallery.

Hotel du Vin Henley-on-Thames

◉ EUROPEAN ⓵ NOTABLE WINE LIST

01491 848400 | New Street, RG9 2BP

www.hotelduvin.com

Hotel du Vin always chooses impressive buildings, and the Henley branch is no exception: a Thames-side Georgian property that was the HQ of Brakspears brewery. Bistro classics plus a few less standard dishes are what to expect, all cooked just as they should be.

Orwells

◉◉◉◉ MODERN BRITISH *V*

0118 940 3673 | Shiplake Row, Binfield Heath, RG9 4DP

www.orwellsrestaurant.co.uk

The whitewashed Georgian pub stands on a country road in the unruffled environs of Binfield Heath. Liam Trotman and Ryan Simpson have between them transformed the place into a beacon of modern British gastronomy, to the extent of being around 75% self-sufficient in fresh produce in the summer months, and filling every interior nook and cranny with tables so that the emphasis is very much on dining. There are new-fangled ideas aplenty, but allied to highly burnished classical technical skills, seen in an opener of flavour-drenched, lightly cooked mackerel with pickled cucumber and ozone-fresh sea veg. Acknowledgement of the original pub ethos is evident in a dish that builds a slew of shredded ham hock with a runny egg yolk, bitter endive and dots of fiery mustard on an underlay of crumbled black pudding. For main, there could be seared cod on shredded tromboncino squash with sprouts and chicken jus. A moistly seductive bitter orange marmalade frangipane tart with blood-orange ice cream is a dessert with class.

Chef Ryan Simpson, Liam Trotman **Seats** 35, Private dining 14 **Closed** 2 weeks beginning January and 2 weeks beginning September **Parking** 30 **Notes** Children welcome

HENLEY-ON-THAMES continued

Shaun Dickens at The Boathouse

◉◉◉ MODERN BRITISH ⬆NOTABLE WINE LIST

01491 577937 | Station Road, RG9 1AZ

www.shaundickens.co.uk

As you'd hope from the monicker, the River Thames pursues its unhurried course past the decked terrace and glass frontage of this stylishly converted boathouse. Having honed his skills in some top kitchens, including Le Manoir aux Quat'Saisons and Per Se in New York, Shaun Dickens has his name above the door and his creative, contemporary food on the menu in a smartly neutral modern space, watched over by an engaging service team. Shaun is passionate about the ingredients he uses, building strong links with farmers and producers, which bears fruit in what arrives on the plate. Confit Loch Duart salmon arrives with compressed cucumber, lemon peel purée, pickled shallots and confit potato, while main-course Merrifield Farm duck comes perfectly pink and crisp-skinned alongside a crisp caraway and onion pastilla, mustard leaf, charred onion and rich duck jus. The invention and impressive presentation continues into a finale of rich dark chocolate parfait, chocolate streusel and blood orange.

Chef Shaun Dickens, James Walshaw **Seats** 45 **Open** All Year **Notes** Children welcome

KINGHAM   *MAP 10, SP22*

The Kingham Plough

◉◉ MODERN BRITISH

01608 658327 | The Green, OX7 6YD

www.thekinghamplough.co.uk

An idyllic honey-hued stone inn on the green of a pretty Cotswolds village, the Plough presents a quintessentially English picture. Inside, the place has the sort of stylish rustic-chic decor – all venerable beams and exposed stone walls – that you'd hope for in a foodie pub, but kids and Fido are welcome so there's no standing on ceremony.

The Wild Rabbit

◉◉◉ MODERN BRITISH

01608 658389 | Church Street, OX7 6YA

thewildrabbit.co.uk

A stone-built, wisteria-draped Cotswold country inn on a village corner makes an appealing prospect when its outdoor tables under the sunshades fill up. Allied with the Daylesford Estate, an expansive organic farming business, it makes a virtue of the natural approach, with horsehair mattresses in the guest rooms and a menu informed by nose-to-tail butchery and locally grown produce. Scottish mackerel with heritage beetroot, English wasabi and bittercress is a sound opening move, or you might plunge into a compendious Daylesford market garden salad with creamed curds, pickled walnut dressing and croûtons. The Wild Rabbit might be miles from the sea, but you'll still find Cornish bream, or butter-poached cod with confit leek, sea herbs and potted brown shrimps, or there might be roast cauliflower with Israeli couscous, semi-dried grape and gingerbread. There are temptations galore at the finishing line, including Wye Valley rhubarb with almond frangipane, and rhubarb sorbet.

Chef Nathan Eades **Seats** 50, Private dining 20 **Open** All Year **Parking** 15 **Notes** Children welcome

MILTON COMMON   *MAP 5, SP60*

The Oxfordshire

◉ MODERN BRITISH

01844 278300 | Rycote Lane, OX9 2PU

www.theoxfordshire.com

Whether you're at this new-build hotel in the Chilterns for golf or pampering, the Sakura restaurant has sweeping views of the course and countryside from its picture windows as a backdrop to a broad-ranging menu of modern dishes spiked with global influences.

MINSTER LOVELL *MAP 5, SP31*

Minster Mill *NEW*

◉◉◉ MODERN BRITISH *V*

01993 774441 | OX29 0RN

www.minstermill.co.uk

Minster Mill has plenty going for it: a rather glamorous Cotswold-stone boutique hotel by the River Windrush with a sybaritic spa and an atmospheric restaurant replete with vaulted ceilings and original oak beams. The kitchen, led by Tom Moody along with his team of highly skilled chefs, sends out an appealing fusion of contemporary and classic British ideas built on top-quality ingredients. Thoughtful, sharply executed dishes kick off with a plump scallop, perfectly caramelised, topped with subtle tandoori spicing and balanced by the sharpness of yogurt, cucumber and apple. Main course brings 50 day-aged Belted Galloway beef with duck fat-roasted carrot and oxtail in onion petals. Finish with chocolate délice with peanut and popcorn ice cream. Set in a high gallery overlooking the restaurant, the Mill Bar serves selected fine wines and champagnes, along with perfectly shaken classic cocktails.

Chef Tom Moody **Seats** Private dining 100 **Open** All Year **Prices from** S £11, M £20, D £10 **Parking** 50 **Notes** Children welcome

---

MURCOTT *MAP 11, SP51*

The Nut Tree Inn

◉◉ MODERN EUROPEAN *V* ◢ NOTABLE WINE LIST

01865 331253 | Main Street, OX5 2RE

www.nuttreeinn.co.uk

The Nut Tree has been home to Michael and Imogen North and their family for the last 15 years. In this time, it has become a fine pub with a reputation for great food, beer and wine. Its roots are solidly in classic cooking techniques using the best produce possible and treating the ingredients with integrity to offer balanced dishes full of flavour with a keen eye for presentation.

OXFORD *MAP 5, SP50*

Bear & Ragged Staff

◉ MODERN, CLASSIC BRITISH

01865 862329 | Appleton Road, Cumnor, OX2 9QH

www.bearandraggedstaff.com

The Bear offers an appealing mixture of traditional atmosphere and contemporary design. Masses of artwork on cool green walls in the dining room offset the roughcast stone, and forward-thinking menus offer trend-conscious British food. They create a themed board with ingredients from sea, garden and butchery.

The Cherwell Boathouse

◉ MODERN ENGLISH

01865 552746 | Bardwell Road, OX2 6ST

cherwellboathouse.co.uk

With swans and punts paddling by on the River Cherwell, it's no wonder that this Victorian boathouse restaurant is one of the city's cherished institutions. Waterside tables are at a premium on fine days; inside, the ambience is cosy and humming with the chatter of happy diners tucking into a menu of inventive, modern British ideas.

Chez Mal Brasserie

◉ MODERN BRITISH, FRENCH

01865 268400 | Oxford Castle, 3 New Road, OX1 1AY

www.malmaison.com

Oxford's old slammer is now leading a reformed life as a classy hotel, with seductive bedrooms in the cells and a moodily-lit brasserie in the former basement canteen. The cooking is a little bit French, a little bit British, and a little bit global.

OXFORD continued

Cotswold Lodge Hotel

◎ BRITISH, EUROPEAN

01865 512121 | 66a Banbury Road, OX2 6JP

www.cotswoldlodgehotel.co.uk

This stately Victorian villa is replete with period style, all high ceilings, sweeping staircases and expansive bay windows, but given a modern facelift. The kitchen deals in contemporary food with clear European accents, but you might choose to end with a plate of tempting Oxfordshire cheeses.

Gee's Restaurant

◎ MEDITERRANEAN

01865 553540 | 61 Banbury Road, OX2 6PE

www.gees-restaurant.co.uk

Gee's continues to delight townies and gownies on the northern edge of the city centre. The bright glasshouse setting sees potted olive trees and lightweight café-style furniture in a room flooded with natural light, and the style is very satisfying Mediterranean-influenced modern brasserie cooking.

No. 1 Ship Street

◎ MODERN BRITISH, BRASSERIE 🛡

01865 806637 | Ship Street, OX1 3DA

www.no1shipstreet.co.uk

Tucked away in a side street, this smartly decorated restaurant creates a cosy atmosphere with its polished copper-topped tables, wooden chairs, creative lighting and soft ambient music. The Ground Floor dining space (there's a bar upstairs) offers modern British, brasserie-style food and a good selection of wines.

Two One Five

◎◎◎ MODERN BRITISH

See pages 280–281

SWINBROOK
MAP 10, SP21

The Swan Inn

◎◎ MODERN BRITISH

01993 823339 | OX18 4DY

www.theswanswinbrook.co.uk

The wisteria-clad, 16th-century Swan is the quintessential village pub, with an orchard to the rear and the Windrush River running by. The kitchen sources seasonal ingredients with care (traceability is a big deal here), and knows how to turn it into some skilfully rendered dishes.

TOOT BALDON
MAP 5, SP50

The Mole Inn

◎◎ MODERN EUROPEAN

01865 340001 | OX44 9NG

www.themoleinn.com

Cosy and traditional, The Mole Inn is a classic country pub with a lovely garden and lots of space for outdoor eating. It's only a few miles from central Oxford, and is always very busy, so booking is a must. Most ingredients come from local suppliers, and the steaks are all dry-aged and hung for at least 28 days.

WANTAGE
MAP 5, SU38

The Star Inn
◉◉ MODERN BRITISH

01235 751873 | Watery Lane, Sparsholt, OX12 9PL
www.thestarsparsholt.co.uk
Inside this solid 300-year-old inn in the quintessentially English village of Sparsholt, all is decluttered and open plan with chunky wooden furniture and plain white walls, and the food has a suitably modern accent. So, start perhaps with salt-cured beef brisket and bacon terrine.

WITNEY
MAP 5, SP31

The Harcourt Arms NEW
◉◉ MODERN BRITISH

01865 416516 | Main Road, Stanton Harcourt, OX29 5RJ
www.theharcourtarms.com
A traditional inn with stone walls and roaring fires, The Harcourt Arms is just a short hop from Oxford. There are plenty of places to sit and dine, so you should find somewhere to suit your mood. The menu offers a combination of thoughtfully adapted pub classics, seasonal specials and a well-executed à la carte.

The Hollybush, Witney
◉ BRITISH

01993 708073 | 35 Corn Street, OX28 6BT
www.hollybushwitney.com
The Hollybush is a modern dining pub with a buzzy vibe and a hint of sophistication. Tuck into your favourite pub dishes with an inventive twist. The small frontage to the old property belies the tardis that lies within. It has a cosy feel; tables set with candles and a real charm and a friendly team. Expect great pub classics as well as sharing and grazing plates alongside tasty daily specials; real ales too.

See advertisement on page 282

WOODSTOCK
MAP 11, SP41

The Feathers Hotel
◉◉ MODERN BRITISH *V*

01993 812291 | Market Street, OX20 1SX
www.feathers.co.uk
A brick-built inn in a handsome Cotswold market town, The Feathers has long been a fixture. There can be no doubt about its having been coaxed into the boutique hotel era, including the dining room with its raspberry-red banquettes and bold artworks.

The White House NEW
◉ BRITISH

01993 811288 | 1 Grove Road, Bladon, OX20 1RQ
www.bladonwhitehouse.co.uk
A warm welcome awaits at this friendly pub. Situated close to Blenheim Palace, The White House dates to the 16th century and is full of character, with a garden for warm days and a log fire for cold nights. Simply presented dishes can be found on a menu that changes with availability; pub classics and specials are also available. Start with chicken and tarragon terrine, followed by rump of lamb with crushed new potatoes.

WOOTTON
MAP 11, SP41

The Killingworth Castle
◉◉ CLASSIC BRITISH

01993 811401 | Glympton Road, OX20 1EJ
www.thekillingworthcastle.com
The inn has been an integral part of its community since the 1630s. When the Alexanders (who also run the Ebrington Arms near Chipping Campden) took over in 2012, the old place received the investment it needed, while retaining its earthy charm and period character. Organic beers are brewed on site.

Continued on page 283

Two One Five

◉◉◉ **MODERN BRITISH**

01865 511149 | 215 Banbury Road, Summertown, OX2 7HQ

www.twoonefive.co.uk

Inventive seasonal dishes impeccably presented

Two One Five is set in the heart of the bustling Summertown high street, on the northern edge of Oxford. There are tables with parasols outside, ideal for fair-weather lunches, and the smart frontage gives little away, but the long thin dining room with its clean lines, contemporary styling and well-spaced tables is the perfect setting for Paul Welburn's seasonally changing modern British menus, which include vegetarian and tasting options. Welburn's background includes time cooking with Gary Rhodes and Richard Corrigan, and this restaurant is the successor to his team's equally celebrated Oxford Kitchen. There's a relaxed, friendly atmosphere, making Two One Five a popular spot for every kind of celebration as well as any time you might feel you deserve something a bit special. The cooking style is precise and considered, making great use of both classical and

> "dishes are truly beautiful to look at, but no fear of style over substance, this is the real deal"

modern techniques, and dishes are truly beautiful to look at, but no fear of style over substance, this is the real deal. Begin with confit duck cake with raspberry ketchup, beetroot and black garlic, or mushroom velouté, slow-cooked duck egg and teriyaki hen of the woods. Main course might be roast stonebass with pea pureé, lamb rump and neck with aubergine ketchup and lemon and cumin gravy, or the impressive 48-hour pork with carrot pureé, radish, mustard, pineapple and Szechuan pepper. You can draw things to a close with something intriguing like the caramelised

Ivoire chocolate with coffee, Pedro Ximenez and asparagus ice cream, or play a little safer with Yorkshire rhubarb and custard with salted toffee, or go for the selection of British cheeses, served with fig ketchup and sourdough crackers. The wine list offers a good range by the glass.

Chef Paul Welburn
Seats 80, Private dining 50
Closed 1st 2 weeks January
Notes Children welcome

THE HOLLYBUSH

Our inventive menus are inspired by the best seasonal local ingredients. You'll find clean, pared-back dishes with weekly changing specials. Produce is sourced locally from local farms, butchers, Cotswold cheesemakers and vegetable growers. We make everything from scratch from bread to ice cream.

While you'll find fish and chips, pies and burgers all with the Hollybush twist, we also push out the boat with more sophisticated plates.

Hollybush Sunday roasts are popular - and of course, there are always plenty of options for vegetarians and vegans.

Visit Us

35 Corn Street, Witney, Oxfordshire | info@hollybushwitney.com | 01993 708073

■ RUTLAND

CLIPSHAM
MAP 11, SK91

The Olive Branch
◉◉ BRITISH, EUROPEAN *V*
01780 410355 | Main Street, LE15 7SH
www.theolivebranchpub.com
Home-grown and foraged herbs and berries play
a big part here, alongside local farm meats,
English Channel fish and Norfolk shellfish. Daily-
changing menus offer pan-fried pigeon breast
with braised lentils; hake with mussels and curry
sauce; rump of lamb with sweetbreads; and orzo
pasta with chargrilled shallots. Forced Yorkshire
rhubarb is a popular tailpiece.

OAKHAM
MAP 11, SK80

Barnsdale Lodge Hotel
◉ MODERN BRITISH
01572 724678 | The Avenue, Rutland Water, North
Shore, LE15 8AH
www.barnsdalelodge.co.uk
To one side of the Earl of Gainsborough's Exton
estate, this is a handsome country seat on the
shore of Rutland Water, with a main dining room,
garden room and alfresco courtyard. It's host to
simple modern British menus featuring produce
from the vegetable garden.

Hambleton Hall
◉◉◉◉ MODERN BRITISH ♨ NOTABLE WINE LIST
See pages 284–285

UPPINGHAM
MAP 11, SP89

The Lake Isle
◉◉ BRITISH, FRENCH
01572 822951 | 16 High Street East, LE15 9PZ
www.lakeisle.co.uk
The property may be 350 years old but the
cooking at this restaurant-with-rooms is
thoroughly modern. Global influences are
apparent across the menu, with a starter of
Timothy Taylor ale-cured English Parma ham,
poached duck egg and asparagus soldiers
followed by sea bream, clams, samphire and
lemon sorrel pesto.

KING'S ARMS INN & RESTAURANT

Top Street, Wing, Oakham, Rutland LE15 8SE
info@thekingsarms-wing.co.uk
www.thekingsarms-wing.co.uk

The Kings Arms Inn's laid back, relaxed
ambiance is complemented by award-
winning cuisine created by Head Chef and
Partner James Goss.

Our ethos is dedicated to providing the
finest food in the area, locally sourced and
produced in house. Villagers and visitors
will be found side by side creating that
wonderful country pub community feel.

Our friendly team serves traditional, artisan
and innovative pub fare, surrounded by
beamed ceilings, flagstone floors and open
fires.

The Bar is brimming with a large selection
of homemade snacks from the pub's
Jimmy's Rutland Smokehouse. Awaiting
visitors are a selection of well-kept local real
ales, regional and local ciders, fruit pressés
and traditional soft drinks. A comprehensive
wine list boasts some 30 served by the glass
of which we are especially proud.

The Inn has 8 en-suite rooms, 4 in the old
Bake House and 4 in the slightly newer
Orchard Houses. 2 of the large rooms
can either be triple or twin occupancy.
Excluding the single room, the remaining
spacious accommodation all has either
double or king size beds.

Hambleton Hall

◉◉◉◉ **MODERN BRITISH** 🍷NOTABLE WINE LIST
01572 756991 | Hambleton, LE15 8TH
www.hambletonhall.com

Relaxed formality and refined dishes of deceptive simplicity

Owned by Tim and Stefa Hart since 1979, Hambleton Hall was built as a hunting lodge by a successful Victorian brewer, and enjoys an enviable lakeside setting, with gardens and grounds covering 17 acres and surrounded by Rutland Water. It's a grand and handsome country-house hotel, perfectly designed for pleasure and enjoyment, the stylish public rooms filled with paintings, chandeliers, intricate plaster ceilings and elegant soft furnishings. Staff are engaging and professional and the dining room is reassuringly formal, with linen-clad tables and comfortable seating. Aaron Patterson began his career here nearly 40 years ago, leaving to work with Raymond Blanc and Anton Mosimann before returning to take over as head chef in 1992, and his experience and confidence is apparent in every element of the refined and creative menus. These change to reflect the

seasons, with daily tweaks to reflect the kitchen's focus on the very best local produce, including plenty from the hotel's beautiful kitchen garden. The wine list is extensive and offers a very good choice by the glass. Patterson's cooking is often understated and deceptively simple, with flavours allowed to speak for themselves and the à la carte (there's a vegetarian selection as well) might offer starters like terrine of heritage carrot, spiced carrot ice cream, or lasagne of girolle mushrooms with Iberico ham and grappa sauce, followed by pan-fried fillet of John Dory with English asparagus, sautéed prawns, mousseron mushrooms and vermouth sauce, perhaps, or roast guinea fowl, pea and mint risotto, morels and Madeira sauce. Apricot soufflé with caramelised

> "Patterson's cooking is often understated and deceptively simple, with flavours allowed to speak for themselves..."

almond ice cream is a fine way to end the meal, or perhaps Hambleton's tiramisù will appeal. The great value 'lunch for less' might offer ham hock ravioli with lovage sauce followed by pan-fried fillet of sea bass Niçoise and bouillabaisse sauce.

Chef Aaron Patterson
Seats 60, Private dining 40
Open All Year
Parking 40
Notes No children under 5 years

WING

MAP 11, SK80

Kings Arms Inn & Restaurant

◉◉ TRADITIONAL BRITISH

01572 737634 | 13 Top Street, LE15 8SE

www.thekingsarms-wing.co.uk

The Kings Arms is a traditional, rustic inn; all exposed stone walls, open fires and quarry tile flooring, with decor to match. It's full of charming little nooks and crannies, but mind your head on some of those beams. The menu is classic British with a modern twist, and be sure to look out for the products of Jimmy's Rutland Smokehouse.

See advertisement on page 283

■ SHROPSHIRE

IRONBRIDGE

MAP 10, SJ60

Number Ten

◉ MODERN BRITISH V

01952 432901 | White Hart, The Wharfage, TF8 7AW

www.whitehartironbridge.com

Set just beyond Abraham Darby's famous bridge, the White Hart is located deep in the Severn Gorge and surrounded by reminders of the industrial revolution. Their Number Ten restaurant is a fine dining option with large windows that look out to the river.

Restaurant Severn

◉ MODERN BRITISH V

01952 432233 | 33 High Street, TF8 7AG

www.restaurantsevern.co.uk

This small restaurant blends in with the terrace of souvenir and tea shops facing Abraham Darby's Iron Bridge World Heritage Site. Inside, however, the bare wooden floors, unclothed tables and high-backed, toffee-brown leather chairs make for an intimate brasserie look.

LUDLOW

MAP 10, SO57

The Charlton Arms

◉ MODERN BRITISH

01584 872813 | Ludford Bridge, SY8 1PJ

www.thecharltonarms.co.uk

You can eat and drink not only by, but above, the River Teme here, because the lower of two outdoor decks projects over it; the views are delightful. On the modern British menu, a good selection of dishes includes ham hock Scotch egg with piccalilli coulis; and pan-fried hake fillet with crab and chorizo croquettes.

See advertisement opposite

The Cliffe at Dinham

◉◉ MODERN BRITISH

01584 872063 | Halton Lane, Dinham, SY8 2JE

www.thecliffeatdinham.co.uk

A handsome red-brick Victorian mansion beside the River Teme with views across to Ludlow Castle, The Cliffe has morphed into a stylish restaurant with rooms with a breezily modern approach to its interior decor. Sporting sage-green walls, bare floorboards and unclothed tables, the restaurant is a suitably contemporary spot for the kitchen's modern bistro dishes.

The Clive Arms

◉ MODERN BRITISH

01584 856565 | Bromfield, SY8 2JR

www.theclive.co.uk

Once the home of Clive of India, then a pub, this brick-built Georgian house has been imaginatively appointed. Seasonality dictates the modern British menu, which may feature pickled wild mushrooms with chicken liver parfait with toasted sourdough bread.

Fishmore Hall

◉◉◉ MODERN BRITISH

01584 875148 | Fishmore Road, SY8 3DP

www.fishmorehall.co.uk

It's hard to believe that the handsome Fishmore Hall – a Georgian country pile just outside the foodie hub of Ludlow – was falling apart until its current owners restored it to the porticoed, pristine white boutique bolt-hole (with a spa tucked away in the garden) that we see today. Housed in an orangery extension, Forelles restaurant enjoys views of the rolling Shropshire hills as a backdrop to the classic country-house cuisine. As you'd hope, it's all built on pedigree materials sourced from within a 30-mile radius (apart from seafood, of course, which comes from Brixham and Skye). Begin with an imaginative frogs leg Kiev delivered in a crispy parsley croquette with ratatouille and a faultlessly executed plump scallop before moving on to butter-soft Wagyu beef with silky-smooth truffled mash, velvety swede purée, cep mushrooms and horseradish sauce. An innovative take on baked Alaska has a filling of pistachio, peach and cardamom.

Chef Joe Gould **Seats** 60, Private dining 20 **Closed** 2-13 January **Parking** 30 **Notes** Children welcome

Old Downton Lodge

◉◉◉ MODERN BRITISH

01568 771826 | Downton on the Rock, SY8 2HU

www.olddowntonlodge.com

A short drive from foodie Ludlow, Old Downton Lodge is a rural idyll overlooking the hills of the Welsh Marches. Originally a farmhouse and cider mill, the country-chic restaurant with rooms comprises a fascinating cluster of buildings – medieval, half-timbered, Georgian – around a courtyard filled with herbs and flowers. Dating from Norman times, the restaurant has the feel of a medieval great hall with its stone walls, tapestry and chandelier. Dinner takes the form of daily-changing six- and nine-course menus or a three-course market menu, all built on local, home-grown and foraged produce.

Chef Nick Bennett **Seats** 25, Private dining 60
Closed Christmas **Parking** 20 **Notes** No children

MARKET DRAYTON
MAP 15, SJ63

Goldstone Hall

◉◉ MODERN BRITISH ⚜ NOTABLE WINE LIST

01630 661202 | Goldstone Road, TF9 2NA

www.goldstonehall.com

The two stand-out elements to Goldstone Hall are its magnificent gardens and ambitious restaurant. The kitchen garden is a major part of the operation, providing seasonal produce, and dishes are bright and modern while avoiding jumping on the bandwagon of every contemporary fashion.

MUCH WENLOCK
MAP 10, SO69

Raven Hotel

◉◉ MODERN BRITISH

01952 727251 | 30 Barrow Street, TF13 6EN

www.ravenhotel.com

Raven Hotel is a former coaching inn dating from the 17th century with plenty of period charm, with venerable beams, log fires and hand-pulled ales available in the bar. On the dining front, though, things are positively 21st century, for the kitchen turns out smart, modern dishes.

Located in the beautiful town of Ludlow in Shropshire overlooking the river Teme. The Charlton Arms has 12 ensuite bedrooms with a focus on fresh, seasonal & local ingredients.

Opening times
Monday/ Tuesday: 3pm – 11pm
Wednesday to Saturday: 12pm – 11pm
Sunday: 12pm-10pm

Lunch served Wednesday to Sunday
12pm-2:30pm
Dinner served everyday
6pm-8:30pm

THE CHARLTON ARMS
LUDLOW

AA

MUNSLOW

Crown Country Inn

◎◎ MODERN BRITISH

01584 841205 | SY7 9ET

www.crowncountryinn.co.uk

In an Area of Outstanding Natural Beauty, the Crown dates from Tudor times and was first licensed in 1790. The kitchen has a 'Local to Ludlow' policy that might include a reworking of breakfast for black pudding croquettes with Boston beans, bacon and 'fried bread'.

NORTON

The Hundred House

◎ BRITISH, FRENCH

01952 580240 | Bridgnorth Road, TF11 9EE

www.hundredhouse.co.uk

Run by the Phillips family since the mid-1980s, The Hundred House is brimful of character and personality. The handsome Georgian coaching inn has stylish bedrooms, a bar serving pretty nifty pub grub, and a brasserie and restaurant producing classy dishes based on tip-top regional ingredients, many from the house's own bountiful gardens.

OSWESTRY

Pen-y-Dyffryn Country Hotel

◎◎ MODERN BRITISH

01691 653700 | Rhydycroesau, SY10 7JD

www.peny.co.uk

A construction company built the rectory, church and village school here in 1840. Nowadays, the church is on the Welsh side of the border and the rectory is in England. With sweeping views over the valley, it is traditionally furnished in country-house style.

Sebastians

◎◎ FRENCH

01691 655444 | 45 Willow Street, SY11 1AQ

www.sebastians-hotel.com

Sebastian's is located in a 17th-century inn, full of cossetting beamed character, but not stuck in the past. Monthly-changing menus (with complimentary appetiser and sorbet before mains) take you through three courses of well-crafted, Gallic-influenced ideas, with an appetiser to set the ball rolling, and a refreshing sorbet before mains.

SHREWSBURY

Henry Tudor House

◎ MODERN BRITISH 𝑉

01743 361666 | Henry Tudor House, Barracks Passage, SY1 1XA

www.henrytudorhouse.com

Among the town's oldest half-timbered buildings, HTH's whimsical interior boasts a Parisian-style zinc bar bathed in ever-changing coloured light, while elegant chandeliers in the conservatory shine through delicate iron birdcages. The all-day menu offers a range of classics, while things are more elaborate in the evenings.

House of the Rising Sun

◎ MODERN INTERNATIONAL

01743 588040 | 18 Butcher Row, SY1 1UW

www.hotrs.co.uk

This restaurant is tucked away down a narrow lane, where in medieval times butchers plied their trade. The two dining areas vary greatly – upstairs is very clubby with dark walls and geisha-inspired artwork, while the ground floor is more open plan with long tables. The staff are well informed and clearly passionate about the food on offer – imagine Asian street food meets Spanish tapas.

La Dolce Vita

◉ MODERN ITALIAN 𝑉
01743 249126 | 35A Hill's Lane, SY1 1QU
www.ladolcevitashrewsbury.co.uk

Tucked away but handy for the centre of town, this is a traditional, family-run (dad out front, mum and son in the kitchen) Italian restaurant, brought bang up to date with modern cooking techniques and presentation. Low key, simple decor puts the emphasis firmly on the food and the quality of ingredients is second to none.

Lion & Pheasant Hotel

◉◉ BRITISH
01743 770345 | 49–50 Wyle Cop, SY1 1XJ
www.lionandpheasant.co.uk
This coaching inn has stood since the 16th century and before the street called Wyle Cop became a bridge over the River Severn. Its period façade gives way to a contemporary New England-style interior, with neutral tones and tongue-and-groove-panelling combining harmoniously with the brickwork and beams.

The Mytton and Mermaid

◉ MODERN BRITISH
01743 761220 | Atcham, SY5 6QG
www.myttonandmermaid.co.uk
Alongside the River Severn, this handsome Grade II listed building has a dining room that's partially separated from the large open-plan bar but the atmosphere flows well across both areas. The modern British menu is split between pub favourites and specials which often lean towards the Far East as in the Vietnamese bahn mi salad.

The Peach Tree Restaurant

◉ MODERN BRITISH, ASIAN FUSION
01743 355055 | 18–21 Abbey Foregate, SY2 6AE
www.thepeachtree.co.uk
Modern flavours with influences from the East share the menu with more traditional dishes at this 15th-century building opposite Shrewsbury Abbey. Kick off with chicken liver pâté, onion jam and artisan toast, then onto mains like wild salmon with miso butter crust, and a Korean barbecue rice noodle salad.

The Royalist Restaurant

◉ MODERN, CLASSIC
01743 499955 | Prince Rupert Hotel, Butcher Row, SY1 1UQ
www.princeruperthotel.co.uk
As befits a former home of the grandson of King James I, the Grade II listed Prince Rupert Hotel is a regal affair surrounded by cobbled streets and Tudor buildings. With tapestries and suits of armour, the oak-panelled Royalist Restaurant provides a medieval ambience.

TELFORD *MAP 10, SJ60*

Chez Maw Restaurant

◉◉ MODERN BRITISH
01952 432247 | The Valley Hotel, Ironbridge, TF8 7DW
www.chezmawrestaurant.co.uk
On the bank of the Severn in Ironbridge, and barely a rivet's throw from the bridge, The Valley Hotel was owned by Arthur Maw and his family, suppliers of ceramic tiles, hence the name of its smart restaurant; there's an outside terrace for a pre-dinner drink.

UPTON MAGNA *MAP 10, SJ51*

The Haughmond

◉◉◉ MODERN BRITISH

01743 709918 | Pelham Road, SY4 4TZ

www.thehaughmond.co.uk

The Haughmond had a smart makeover a few years back and there's now a fresh and light contemporary country feel to this smart coaching inn. Family-run, it retains a nicely relaxed and pubby atmosphere, while drawing diners from afar. Classics are served in the bar, while the restaurant ramps things up a notch or two with bold, unpretentious cooking highlighting seasonal, Shropshire ingredients. Pan-seared scallops alongside turnip, curried squash purée and lentils is a good way to start, then follow with a 'nose-to-tail' serving of pork taking in ribs, faggot, belly, loin and cheek, all that piggy richness lifted with celeriac remoulade and pear.

Chef Martin Board **Seats** 48, Private dining 20 **Open** All Year **Prices from** S £7, M £14, D £8 **Parking** 30 **Notes** Children welcome

■ SOMERSET

BATH *MAP 4, ST76*

Bailbrook House Hotel

◉◉ MODERN BRITISH

01225 855100 | Eveleigh Avenue, London Road West, BA1 7JD

www.bailbrookhouse.co.uk

Bailbrook is a handsome Georgian country mansion done out in classy contemporary boutique style. Its Cloisters Restaurant is the fine-dining option, an intimate split-level space. Flavours counterpoint well in fish dishes such as halibut fillet with pea and bacon fricassée, Jersey Royals and girolles.

The Bath Priory Hotel, Restaurant & Spa

◉◉◉ MODERN EUROPEAN, FRENCH 🍷NOTABLE WINE LIST

01225 331922 | Weston Road, BA1 2XT

www.thebathpriory.co.uk

What is now Bath Priory Hotel was built in 1835 on land owned by the priory of Bath Abbey. These days it's a family-owned hotel and spa in a tranquil area on the western side of this Georgian city, dedicated to the full range of creature comforts, from massages to classic country house dining cuisine with modern Asian

influences. An elegant dish of squab pigeon with confit leg tart, cherry and braised kohlrabi in a superb Madeira jus starts the meal, followed by Cornish wild turbot with scallop mousse, sliced morels and caviar. For a light finish try the apricot soufflé with yogurt ice cream.

Chef Jauca Catalin **Seats** 50, Private dining 72 **Open** All Year **Parking** 40 **Notes** No children under 12 years

The Circus Restaurant

◉ MODERN EUROPEAN

01225 466020 | 34 Brock Street, BA1 2LN

www.thecircusrestaurant.co.uk

In a prime location between two of Bath's most iconic locations, The Circus and the Royal Crescent, this is an upmarket all-day eatery, with high-ceilinged dining rooms offering a bold, modern setting for the monthly-changing, seasonally-inspired menu, based on fine West Country produce.

The Dower House Restaurant

◉◉◉ MODERN BRITISH 𝑽 🍷NOTABLE WINE LIST

See pages 292–293

Gainsborough Brasserie

ROSETTES SUSPENDED MODERN BRITISH

01225 358888 | The Gainsborough Bath Spa, Beau Street, BA1 1QY

www.thegainsboroughbathspa.co.uk

The Rosette award for this establishment has been suspended due to a change of chef and reassessment will take place in due course.

If it's a blowout stay in Bath you're after, its hotels don't come with a more blue-blooded pedigree than The Gainsborough Bath Spa. Named after the eponymous artist, an erstwhile Bath resident, the place spreads across a handsome Grade II listed building dating from the 18th century. Looking elegantly understated with its unclothed tables, blue-and-white walls and caramel leather seats, the dining room is a suitably contemporary setting for the Gainsborough Brasserie.

Seats 70 **Open** All Year **Notes** Children welcome

The Hare & Hounds
⊕ MODERN BRITISH
01225 482682 | Lansdown Road, BA1 5TJ
www.hareandhoundsbath.com
Standing nearly 750 feet above sea level on
Bath's northern fringes, this pub is blessed with
wide-ranging views from its terrace and gardens.
Seasonal menus featuring dishes such as
roasted chicken, wild mushroom and parmesan
risotto, and plenty of classics, are bolstered by
daily specials. Several lovely walks start and
finish at the pub.

The Marlborough Tavern
⊕⊕ MODERN BRITISH
01225 423731 | 35 Marlborough Buildings, BA1 2LY
www.marlborough-tavern.com
This Bath-stone corner local bills itself as
offering 'great British food' — indeed it does.
Perhaps, though, 'modern British' better
describes the likes of sweet potato, coconut and
chilli soup, or spiced venison burger with kimchi.
Service is friendly and attentive, and outside is a
walled courtyard that the Georgians must surely
have built for today's drinkers and diners in mind.

Menu Gordon Jones
⊕⊕ MODERN BRITISH
01225 480871 | 2 Wellsway, BA2 3AQ
www.menugordonjones.co.uk
Gordon Jones has form in Bath, having run the
Royal Crescent Hotel kitchen, but here he's doing
his own thing in an unassuming little spot with
foodies beating down the door to enjoy what's
put before them. The main concepts here are
surprise and anticipation.

Olio NEW
⊕⊕ MEDITERRANEAN, BRITISH
01225 723731 | Abbey Lane, Freshford, BA2 7TB
www.homewoodbath.co.uk
A meal at Olio should not be missed. Expect a
Mediterranean style mix of plancha and skillet
dishes, lighter fresh salads, bites and sharing
board tapas style along with more traditional
classics. The fish is superb and very fresh, while
for dessert the chocolate fondant, mint ganache
and white chocolate ice cream is excellent.

The Olive Tree at the Queensberry Hotel
⊕⊕⊕ MODERN BRITISH *V* ⫶ NOTABLE WINE LIST
See pages 294–295

The Scallop Shell
⊕ BRITISH
01225 420928 | 22 Monmouth Place, BA1 2AY
www.thescallopshell.co.uk

Behind a sky-blue frontage not far from Queen
Square, this popular venue offers a versatile
range of fish and seafood dishes in a relaxed
café-style format where food is ordered at the
counter. Freshness is everything at The Scallop
Shell. There is no separate dessert menu, just
one sweet thing per day.

Woods Restaurant
⊕ MODERN BRITISH, FRENCH
01225 314812 | 9-13 Alfred Street, BA1 2QX
www.woodsrestaurant.com
Woods stands in a very 'Bath' setting, occupying
the ground floor of five Georgian townhouses,
and its comfortable bistro look is pretty much
timeless. The cooking is broadly European, with
French and Italy to the fore, and a British flavour
here and there.

CHEDDAR MAP 4, ST45

The Bath Arms
⊕⊕ MODERN BRITISH
01934 742425 | Bath Street, BS27 3AA
www.batharms.com
Smack in the centre of Cheddar village and
within footslogging distance of the eponymous
gorge and caves, The Bath Arms has kept faith
with those essential pubby virtues - real ales, a
genuine welcome and great food. The kitchen
turns out some impressive culinary action.

Continued on page 296

The Dower House Restaurant

◉◉◉ **MODERN BRITISH** *V* 🍷 NOTABLE WINE LIST

01225 823333 | The Royal Crescent Hotel & Spa, 16 Royal Crescent, BA1 2LS
www.royalcrescent.co.uk

Modern takes on classic themes in Georgian splendour

The Dower House Restaurant can be found at Bath's most elegant address. Sitting at the heart of the sweeping Georgian landmark that is the Royal Crescent, the restaurant overlooks the acre of immaculate landscaped gardens behind the namesake luxury hotel. As you'd expect in a hotel of this calibre, it's refined, stylish and comfortable. Bedrooms have individual style and many have views across the city. Public rooms make the most of the character of the building and are styled in keeping with the elegance of the period, with flowers on well-spaced tables, thickly carpeted floors, soft furnishings of blue and gold, silk wallpapers, and French windows opening on to the garden – perfect for pre-dinner drinks on balmy days. Service is on the formal side, with staff knowledgeable and willing, while a sommelier is on hand to help with choosing wines from an international list. Head chef

David Campbell's culinary style might be described as a modern take on classic themes, but that fails to do full justice to the creativity and imagination – as well as labour intensiveness – of his cooking. Things are sharp and precise from the off, featuring big flavours and the all-important inventive touch. However, dishes aren't pushed so far that they are become unrecognisable. Both the seven-course and five-course tasting menus offer you a chance to explore Campbell's style. You might start with good-quality, freshly baked Bath Ale bread with smoked salmon or cep espuma, wild garlic flowers, crispy chicken skin and shimeji mushrooms. Next, a Dingwall scallop, spiced pea and mussel broth and lobster emulsion. Following

"Things are sharp and precise from the off, featuring big flavours and the all-important inventive touch."

courses continue to showcase big flavours such as roast lamb, braised shoulder tart, peas, barbecue lettuce and black garlic and desserts offer a touch of indulgence, with strawberry cheesecake, caramelised white chocolate and crème fraîche ice cream.

Chef David Campbell
Seats 60, Private dining 30
Open All Year
Parking 17
Notes Children welcome

BATH

The Olive Tree at the Queensberry Hotel

◎◎◎ **MODERN BRITISH** *V* ♦ NOTABLE WINE LIST

01225 447928 | 4-7 Russell Street, BA1 2QF
www.olivetreebath.co.uk

Classic Bath elegance and sophisticated modern cuisine

Built for the 8th Marquess of Queensbury in 1771, this truly magnificent and uniquely stylish Georgian townhouse is everything you could ask for in a boutique hotel. Bedrooms are boldly and individually decorated and it's clear that owners Laurence and Helen Beere are driven by a passion for hospitality and a keen eye for interior aesthetics, while chef Chris Cleghorn's cooking is sharply contemporary. The Olive Tree restaurant is down in the basement and revels in a sophisticated, minimalist look, with fresh flowers, unclothed tables and understated appointments. Two tasting menus are offered, of six or nine courses, or you can choose à la carte from these, a thoughtful and flexible approach that allows even those with a less robust appetite to experience his delightfully conceived and constructed dishes. (Vegetarian, vegan, and dairy-free menus in the same format

"Cleghorn has worked with plenty of top-flight chefs and his spot-on technical skill and creative abilities are amply demonstrated throughout."

are also available.) Cleghorn has worked with plenty of top-flight chefs and his spot-on technical skill and creative abilities are amply demonstrated throughout. A winter meal might begin with raw Orkney scallops with horseradish mayonnaise, pink grapefruit and a good hit of aniseed from dill oil, the whole dish a perfect combination of clean, individual flavours. Salted lemon gel proves a successful counterbalance of acidity and saltiness to soft and creamy veal sweetbreads; nasturtiums bringing a good peppery kick. The main course might bring poached Cornish turbot with Roscoff onion, Exmoor caviar and a spicy citrus zing from yuzu kosho, while pink and tender Woolley Park Farm duck breast gets a kick from a punchy kumquat gel, with more big flavours from the accompanying duck bolognaise. End on a high note with a beautifully indulgent warm Tulakalum chocolate mousse with crisp chocolate 'brittle' and refreshing yogurt sorbet. The wine list offers an eclectic international selection that bears the owners' hands-on stamp.

Chef Chris Cleghorn
Seats 55, Private dining 25
Closed 20 to 27 April, 3 to 10 August, 2 to 9 November
Prices from S £16.50, M £29, D £10.50
Notes Children welcome

CONGRESBURY
MAP 4, ST64

Congresbury Arms *NEW*
◉◉ BRITISH

01934 782283 | High Street, BS49 5JA

www.congresburyarms.co.uk

Painted creamy-white, with a fine tiled roof, The Congresbury Arms is welcoming roadside inn that's been stylishly refurbished. Dine in the bar, with its enormous flagstones, or the bright and airy dining room, where pale green button banquettes give a contemporary feel. The seasonal menus are supplemented by regularly changing daily specials. Choose from classics like fish and chips, or complex dishes with top quality produce and flavour combinations. There's a suggested wine pairing for each dish.

DULVERTON
MAP 3, SS92

Woods Bar & Restaurant
◉◉ MODERN BRITISH, FRENCH

01398 324007 | 4 Banks Square, TA22 9BU

www.woodsdulverton.co.uk

On the edge of Exmoor, Woods is a pub cunningly disguised on the outside to look like a café. The interior scene is cheered with a log fire in winter, and wooden partitions roughly divide the place between the drinking of local ales and the eating of locally-sourced food. The kitchen offers intricately worked modern British cooking.

DUNSTER
MAP 3, SS94

The Luttrell Arms Hotel
◉◉ BRITISH

01643 821555 | Exmoor National Park, TA24 6SG

www.luttrellarms.co.uk

Located within the delightful setting of this 15th-century hotel, the restaurant offers relaxed and comfortable dining and a pleasing combination of traditional style with a more modern country-house feel. Hearty portions from an inspiring menu might include beef Wellington with truffle mash or poached fillet of turbot.

HOLCOMBE
MAP 4, ST64

The Holcombe
◉◉ BRITISH, INTERNATIONAL, FRENCH

01761 232478 | Stratton Road, BA3 5EB

theholcombe.com

The Holcombe is a textbook country inn with fires, local ales and amicable staff. Regional ingredients, including the produce of its own garden, supply the menus of mostly traditional fare. Desserts get creative with a raspberry and nougat parfait choc ice to accompany a Valrhona brownie.

See advertisement opposite

HUNSTRETE
MAP 4, ST66

THE PIG near Bath
◉◉ MODERN BRITISH ♨ NOTABLE WINE LIST

01761 490490 | Hunstrete House, Pensford, BS39 4NS

www.thepighotel.com

Well positioned between Bristol and Bath, this chilled shabby-chic country-house hotel is proud of its walled garden, which supplies much of the produce on the menu. Elephant garlic, chive crumpet and bacon jam might be followed by chargrilled pork tomahawk, garden greens, Somerset cider brandy and mustard sauce and triple-cooked chips.

LITTON
MAP 4, ST55

The Litton
◉ BRITISH, EUROPEAN

01761 241554 | BA3 4PW

www.thelitton.co.uk

The Litton's stylish interior is light and airy with bare stone walls, wood-burning stove, chesterfields, mix and match furniture and, definitely worth admiring, a long bar that's made from one solid piece of elm. There's also a whisky bar, terrace and gardens. The up-to-the-minute cooking is firmly rooted in the changing seasons.

THE HOLCOMBE

A Contemporary British Inn, set in the heart of Somerset.
A place to Eat, Drink & Sleep.

www.theholcombe.com
01761 232478
info@theholcombe.com

MILVERTON
MAP 3, ST12

The Globe
◉ MODERN BRITISH

01823 400534 | Fore Street, TA4 1JX

www.theglobemilverton.co.uk

The Globe is still very much a pub, but it's a strong food destination too. The food is up-to-date country-pub fare and Sundays bring on traditionally garnished roasts – beef topside, lamb leg, pork – with roasties and Yorkshire puddings.

MONKSILVER
MAP 3, ST03

The Notley Arms Inn
◉ CLASSIC BRITISH

01984 656095 | Front Street, TA4 4JB

www.notleyarmsinn.co.uk

Chesterfields at an open fire, a mix of dining chairs and pew-style seating, and attentive staff add to the enjoyable experience of a visit to this whitewashed village inn. The kitchen turns out eloquently flavoured, well-executed dishes as well as some pub classics.

NORTH WOOTTON
MAP 4, ST54

Crossways Inn
◉ MODERN BRITISH

01749 899000 | Stocks Lane, BA4 4EU

www.thecrossways.co.uk

A thoroughly contemporary kind of inn these days, the 18th-century Crossways looks much the same as it always has from the outside, but a 21st-century makeover has opened-up the place. It's the kind of inn where you can eat what you want where you want.

OAKHILL
MAP 4, ST64

The Oakhill Inn
◉ MODERN BRITISH

01749 840442 | Fosse Road, BA3 5HU

www.theoakhillinn.com

An ancient stone-built inn with hanging baskets is many people's idea of old England, and The Oakhill looks the part. The food itself edges more firmly into modern British territory than hitherto, although devotees of pub classics such as bubble-and-squeak have not been abandoned.

SHEPTON MALLET
MAP 4, ST64

Charlton House Hotel & Spa
◉◉ MODERN BRITISH

01749 342008 | Charlton Road, BA4 4PR

www.bannatyne.co.uk/hotel/charlton-house

On the fringes of the town centre, this grand, stone manor combines period charm and contemporary style. A menu of modern dishes includes global flavours. Start with pan-fried octopus, cauliflower purée, smoked chorizo and pickled pear before confit leg and roasted breast of duck with dauphinoise potatoes, shallot purée and spinach.

TAUNTON
MAP 4, ST22

Augustus
◉◉ BRITISH, FRENCH

01823 324354 | 3 The Courtyard, St James Street, TA1 1JR

www.augustustaunton.co.uk

The repeated shrilling of the phone serves notice of the popularity of Richard Guest's stylish, friendly courtyard restaurant in the town centre. There's a pared-down, contemporary look, with white-painted brick walls and unclothed, dark wood tables complementing the equally modern brasserie-style food.

The Rock Inn *NEW*
◉ MODERN BRITISH

01984 623293 | Waterrow, TA4 2AX

www.rockinnwaterrow.co.uk

Dating back 450 years, and popular with local shoots, The Rock Inn is a sprawling black-and-white timbered gastro pub in a beautiful part of Somerset. Food is served in the cosy dining room, and if you're a big steak fan, try the featherblade of Aberdeen Angus beef marinated in black garlic and black treacle, and cooked slowly for 14 hours.

TINTINHULL
MAP 4, ST41

Crown & Victoria
◉ BRITISH

01935 823341 | Farm Street, BA22 8PZ

www.thecrownandvictoria.co.uk

This is the kind of country pub that spurs urbanites to up sticks and move to a rural idyll. It's a proper pub, with a changing rota of ales and a serious approach to food. The kitchen keeps things local, seeking out organic, free-range ingredients for the tempting dishes.

WELLS
MAP 4, ST54

Goodfellows
◉◉ MEDITERRANEAN, EUROPEAN
01749 673866 | 5 Sadler Street, BA5 2RR
www.goodfellowswells.co.uk
Look for the plum-coloured façade in the town centre. If it's first thing, breakfast is on hand in the café, or you might have a Danish and cappuccino for elevenses. Otherwise, sign up for some distinguished seafood-led cookery in the adjoining restaurant.

■ STAFFORDSHIRE

ELLASTONE
MAP 10, SK14

The Duncombe Arms
◉◉ MODERN BRITISH
01335 324275 | Main Road, DE6 2GZ
www.duncombearms.co.uk
In the picturesque village of Ellastone, this attractive whitewashed country inn close to Alton Towers makes for an enjoyable pitstop for a pint but the modern food ensures visitors stay for much longer. Polished wooden tables, linen napkins and fresh flowers provide an informal setting and the cooking is creative, with intelligent flavour combinations.

HOAR CROSS
MAP 10, SK12

The Ballroom Restaurant
◉ MODERN BRITISH
01283 575671 | Hoar Cross Hall, Maker Lane, DE13 8QS
www.hoarcross.co.uk
The Ballroom Restaurant is a grand space within Hoar Cross Hall, a stately home built in 1871. Huge chandeliers hang from its ornate ceilings, the wallpaper is William Morris-style and mullioned windows provide views across the beautiful gardens. Modern British menus appeal, not least with spiced monkfish, duo of pork, and satay sweet potato and spinach curry.

See advertisement on page 300

LEEK
MAP 16, SJ95

Three Horseshoes Country Inn & Spa
◉ CLASSIC BRITISH
01538 300296 | Buxton Road, Blackshaw Moor, ST13 8TW
www.threeshoesinn.co.uk
The stone-built inn overlooked by lowering gritstone outcrops in the southern stretches of the Peak District covers many bases. Original oak beams, exposed brick walls and dark slate tiles are matched to create contemporary styling, with an open-to-view kitchen augmenting the dynamic atmosphere.

LICHFIELD
MAP 10, SK10

The Boat Inn *NEW*
◉◉◉ MODERN BRITISH *V*
01543 361692 | Walsall Road, Summerhill, WS14 0BU
www.theboatinnlichfield.com
The Boat occupies a rather unassuming location just off the busy A461 but once inside it's clear that this is a restaurant of substance with serious foodie crudentials. An open kitchen with a chef's table takes pole position in a light, airy space that maintains a relaxed charm. And the menu? It has a sharp eye for the seasons and a love of big-hearted, well-matched flavours, as in Dorset crab with ribbons of kohlrabi, seaweed and wild cranberry, or pig's cheek with squash and sumac. Elsewhere, there's rose veal served with crisp sweetbreads and chanterelles and, for pudding, a lush chocolate gâteau with caramel ice cream.

Chef Liam Dillon **Seats** 60 **Closed** 1 - 8 September
Parking 45 **Notes** Children welcome

Continued on page 301

LICHFIELD continued

The Larder NEW

◎◎ MODERN BRITISH

01543 471342 | Bore Street, WS13 6LZ

larderlichfield.com

Teal blue velvet chairs and gold banquettes glow against the otherwise muted colours in this smart urban dining room with its exposed brick and feature lighting. You can see the attention to detail in the cutlery and crockery as well as in the very precisely constructed dishes. There's a chef's table upstairs if you want to be part of the action, watching the preparation of the accomplished, seasonally focused cooking.

Swinfen Hall Hotel

ROSETTES SUSPENDED MODERN BRITISH

01543 481494 | Swinfen, WS14 9RE

www.swinfenhallhotel.co.uk

The Rosette award for this establishment has been suspended due to a change of chef and reassessment will take place in due course. Dating from 1757, this splendid mansion, complete with columns and pediment, is set in 100 acres of parkland, including a walled kitchen garden, deer park and formal gardens – hard to believe it's just half an hour from Birmingham's city centre. A careful restoration has created a stylish hotel, with elegant bedrooms and fine public areas with many period features. The oak-panelled dining room, with its ornate ceiling and heavily-swagged drapes, enjoys views across the terrace and gardens to the deer park.

Seats 45 Private dining 22 **Closed** 26 December and 1 January **Prices** from S £11 M £24 D £10 **Parking** 80 **Notes** Children welcome

STAFFORD   MAP 10, SJ92

The Moat House

◎◎ MODERN BRITISH

01785 712217 | Lower Penkridge Road, Acton Trussell, ST17 0RJ

www.moathouse.co.uk

The Moat House is indeed moated, a part-timbered manor dating from the 14th century. Main courses on the seasonally-changing carte can be complex too but equally satisfying. For dessert try Turkish delight cheesecake with rose water gel and chocolate sorbet.

The Shropshire Inn

◎ TRADITIONAL BRITISH

01785 780904 | Newport Road, Haughton, ST18 9HB

www.theshropshireinnhaughton.co.uk

The family-run Shropshire hasn't decamped to Staffordshire, but has stood firm while county boundaries have flowed around it. Its physiognomy is a little different these days, with full-length windows looking on to the garden, and gathered curtains in the dining area creating an upscale ambience.

■ SUFFOLK

ALDEBURGH
MAP 13, TM45

Regatta Restaurant
◉ MODERN BRITISH

01728 452011 | 171 High Street, IP15 5AN

www.regattaaldeburgh.com

In a fine building in the town centre, this long-running restaurant specialises in fresh fish and seafood, often locally landed. Daily specials support the carte, opening with Mediterranean fish soup and rouille, then continues with home-smoked whole prawns in garlic mayo; bradan rost (roasted salmon) with chilli chutney; and roast chicken breast in Parma ham.

BILDESTON
MAP 13, TL94

The Bildeston Crown
◉◉◉ MODERN AND CLASSIC BRITISH

01449 740510 | 104–106 High Street, IP7 7EB

www.thebildestoncrown.com

The Bildeston Crown has all the chocolate-box charm you'd hope for in a 15th-century former coaching inn, although there's a very 21st-century take on things these days, which means boutique bedrooms, an atmospheric beamed bar, a smart restaurant and classy food ranging from pub classics to more modern ideas from a kitchen that's firing on all cylinders. Chef Chris Lee's understanding of how flavours work together results in outstanding dishes, whether you go for something pubby from the Classics menu – a Red Poll cheese burger poshed up with foie gras and truffle mayo, say – or look to the Select menu and open with cumin-roasted scallop with cauliflower and apple. Main courses such as loin of local rabbit with duck liver, beetroot, fennel and endive, or hake fillet with curried mussels and coriander demonstrate mastery of both texture and taste. Flavours punch above their weight in deserts too, particularly when warm chocolate mousse is matched with ginger ice cream.

Chef Chris Lee **Seats** 100, Private dining 34 **Open** All Year **Parking** 20 **Notes** Children welcome

BURY ST EDMUNDS
MAP 13, TL86

1921 Angel Hill
◉◉ MODERN BRITISH

01284 704870 | IP33 1UZ

www.nineteen-twentyone.co.uk

It may occupy a timbered period building in the historic heart of Bury St Edmunds, but there's nothing old-fashioned about the modern British food here. Seasonal and local ingredients are at the fore in dishes like hay-smoked duck breast, rhubarb and celeriac, and fillet of coley, parsley root, snails and garlic velouté.

The Angel Hotel
◉◉ MODERN BRITISH

01284 714000 | Angel Hill, IP33 1LT

www.theangel.co.uk

Overlooking the cathedral and abbey walls, The Angel is a quintessential Georgian coaching inn with a creeper-curtained façade. Inside, the generous spaces have been overlaid with a contemporary boutique mood. The Eaterie's kitchen shows equally 21st-century sensibilities in its repertoire of upbeat brasserie food.

Best Western Priory Hotel
◉ MODERN BRITISH, INTERNATIONAL

01284 766181 | Mildenhall Road, IP32 6EH

www.prioryhotel.co.uk

A peaceful atmosphere reigns throughout the Priory, including in the Garden Room restaurant, which offers soft lighting and a comforting feeling of being looked after by endlessly helpful staff. The kitchen produces dishes that pull in inspiration from all over the known world.

The Leaping Hare Restaurant & Country Store
◉◉ CLASSIC, TRADITIONAL

01359 250287 | Wyken Vineyards, Stanton, IP31 2DW

www.wykenvineyards.co.uk

Set on a 1,200-acre farm complete with Shetland sheep and Red Poll cattle, plus a vineyard, The Leaping Hare occupies a splendid 400-year-old barn with a high raftered ceiling. What the farm doesn't provide is locally sourced, with fish landed at Lowestoft.

Maison Bleue

◉◉ MODERN FRENCH

01284 760623 | 30–31 Churchgate Street, IP33 1RG

www.maisonbleue.co.uk

The Maison Bleue flies the tricolour for proudly French seafood cuisine in the bustling heart of the town. The place is teemingly popular, indicating that the taste for unreconstructed Gallic cooking never went away. Meat dishes include beef featherblade which is a cut above.

Pea Porridge

◉◉ MODERN BISTRO

01284 700200 | 28–29 Cannon Street, IP33 1JR

www.peaporridge.co.uk

Two cottages dating from 1820 have been converted into this unpretentious restaurant where 'simplicity' is key, although plenty of expertise goes into the cooking. Snails with bone marrow, bacon, parsley, capers and garlic is a great way to kick things off.

The View Restaurant *NEW*

◉◉ MODERN BRITISH

01284 706777 | All Saints Hotel, Fornham St Genevieve, IP28 6JQ

www.allsaintshotel.com

Whether it's observing the chefs in action in the open kitchen or watching the sun set overlooking the adjacent golf course, The View certainly lives up to its name. Modern British with an Asian twist is the style: barbecue octopus, satay sauce, cucumber and mint followed by lamb rump, courgette stew, barbecue aubergine purée, potato terrine and broad beans.

The White Horse

◉ MODERN BRITISH

01284 735760 | Rede Road, Whepstead, IP29 4SS

www.whitehorsewhepstead.co.uk

This stylishly made over, mustard-yellow village inn sits comfortably at the gastro pub end of the spectrum, but without losing any of the features one hopes for – smart and cosy rooms with a copper-sheathed bar serving Suffolk ales, a huge inglenook and country-style tables.

FRESSINGFIELD   MAP 13, TM27

Fox & Goose Inn

◉◉ MODERN BRITISH

01379 586247 | Church Road, IP21 5PB

www.foxandgoose.net

The Fox & Goose is a Grade II* listed former Guildhall, dating back to 1509, full of period details and tons of atmosphere. It's the perfect setting for some really spot-on modern British cooking, where beef fillet might come with mustard gel, a pickled shallot, green bean and carrot salad, garlic mayonnaise and wild mushroom croquette potatoes.

HINTLESHAM *MAP 13, TM04*

Hintlesham Hall Hotel

◉◉ MODERN BRITISH

01473 652334 | George Street, IP8 3NS

hintleshamhall.co.uk/

Hintlesham Hall is a beautifully proportioned Grade I listed building of three wings, the façade a 1720 addition to the 16th-century core. The kitchen displays originality not commonly seen in such surroundings, producing thoughtfully-constructed and elegant dishes eminently suited to the stylish dining room.

IPSWICH *MAP 13, TM14*

Mariners

◉◉ FRENCH, MEDITERRANEAN

01473 289748 | Neptune Quay, IP4 1AX

www.marinersipswich.co.uk

Built as a gunboat in Bruges in 1899, it was sunk in 1940, became a hospital ship in the 1950s and was an Italian restaurant in Ipswich before becoming a French brasserie. Mains might be pan-fried fillet of Scottish salmon with creamy wild mushroom Carnaroli risotto.

Milsoms Kesgrave Hall

◉◉ MODERN INTERNATIONAL

01473 333741 | Hall Road, Kesgrave, IP5 2PU

www.milsomhotels.com

Still deep in woodland after more than 200 years, this hotel restaurant's open kitchen is the source of modern international dishes, typically smoked haddock fishcake with a soft-boiled egg centre; and pan-fried Creedy Carver duck breast with beetroot and sour cherries. Lastly, maybe yogurt pannacotta, raspberries and basil. No dress code, and no booking necessary.

Salthouse Harbour Hotel

◉◉ MODERN BRITISH

01473 226789 | No 1 Neptune Quay, IP4 1AX

www.salthouseharbour.co.uk

A harbourside warehouse makeover with eye-popping interior collisions of lime-green and violet, the Salthouse deals in brasserie food with look-at-me flavours. A gin and tonic arrives later than is conventional perhaps, in a dessert of apple and Hendrick's jelly, with cucumber sorbet and lime granita.

IXWORTH *MAP 13, TL97*

Theobald's Restaurant

◉◉ MODERN BRITISH

01359 231707 | 68 High Street, IP31 2HJ

www.theobaldsrestaurant.co.uk

Theobald's Restaurant was converted from a Tudor inn in the early 1980s, but much of the historic atmosphere and many original features have been kept intact. It's an intimate venue, with only around 30 covers, and offers very nicely presented traditional British cooking. Menus focus on locally reared meats and East Anglian fish.

LAVENHAM
MAP 13, TL94

The Great House
◉◉ MODERN FRENCH

01787 247431 | Market Place, CO10 9QZ

www.greathouse.co.uk

In a 14th-century former house on Market Place, this elegant restaurant with rooms brings a genuine flavour of France to historic Lavenham. Local raw materials are transformed into creative Gallic dishes like rack of lamb, buttered golden turnips, local asparagus, mange tout, garlic and rosemary jus. Service is efficient and attentive.

See advertisement below

LAYHAM
MAP 13, TM04

The Marquis NEW
◉◉ MODERN BRITISH

01473 377977 | Upper Street, IP7 5JZ

www.themarquissuffolk.co.uk

The Marquis is an old coaching inn that has undergone an extremely stylish transformation. The floor to ceiling window that spans the length of the airy dining room offers spectacular panoramic views across the Brett Valley, making this a wonderful setting for the seasonal British dishes created in the open kitchen. Cornish crab tacos might start things off, followed by Josper grilled lamb with triple cooked chips.

NEWMARKET
MAP 12, TL66

Bedford Lodge Hotel & Spa
◉ BRITISH, MEDITERRANEAN
01638 663175 | Bury Road, CB8 7BX
www.bedfordlodgehotel.co.uk
This one-time Georgian hunting lodge offers
plenty of top-end facilities to satisfy the modern
epicure. The red-hued dining room sticks to a
modern British mantra, starting perhaps with
chicken liver parfait and moving on to seared
fillet of Denham venison, smoked game sausage,
celeriac dauphinoise and roasted baby turnips.

The King's Head NEW
◉◉ MODERN BRITISH
01638 507702 | 1 Stetchworth Road, Dullingham,
CB8 9UJ
www.kingsheaddullingham.com

The King's Head is a stylishly reinvented public
house for the 21st century, featuring a warm and
inviting dining room with open fires, oak floors,
contemporary furnishings and art from a local
artist. A well-presented main course of duo of
lamb might be followed by elderflower
pannacotta with pistachio meringue.

Tuddenham Mill
◉◉◉◉ MODERN BRITISH ⚑NOTABLE WINE LIST
See pages 308-309

SIBTON
MAP 13, TM36

Sibton White Horse Inn
◉◉ MODERN BRITISH
01728 660337 | Halesworth Road, IP17 2JJ
www.sibtonwhitehorseinn.co.uk
This fascinating pub's Tudor origins – low
ceilings, mighty ships' timbers, quarry tiles –
are impossible to miss. The bar has a raised
gallery, an elegant dining room and a secluded
courtyard. The kitchen produces globally
influenced modern cooking that's won a heap
of awards.

SOUTHWOLD
MAP 13, TM57

The Crown
◉ MODERN BRITISH
01502 722275 | 90 High Street, IP18 6DP
www.thecrownsouthwold.co.uk
The grand Georgian portico on Southwold's high
street looks imposing, but once inside, bare
floorboards and mismatched tables and chairs
give The Crown a relaxed and pubby ambience.
The kitchen draws on the local larder for a
crowd-pleasing menu of uncomplicated modern
British food, backed by a great roll-call of
Adnams' beers and wines.

The Still Room Restaurant

◉◉ MODERN BRITISH

01502 722186 | The Swan, Market Place, IP18 6EG
theswansouthwold.co.uk/food-drink/still-room-restaurant

The 17th-century Swan is the jewel in the Adnams empire's crown. Blending contemporary panache with its Georgian features, The Still Room's light and airy, modern and funky design references the house brewery and small-batch distillery as a backdrop to some inventive contemporary cooking.

Sutherland House

◉◉ MODERN BRITISH, SEAFOOD

01502 724544 | 56 High Street, IP18 6DN
www.sutherlandhouse.co.uk

A period property of genuine charm, Sutherland House has wooden beams, ornate ceilings, coving and real fireplaces, with fixtures and fittings creating a chic finish. Likewise, the cooking impresses with its modern ambitions, passion for top-quality seafood and loyalty to locally-sourced ingredients.

WOODBRIDGE MAP 13, TM24

Seckford Hall Hotel

◉◉ MODERN EUROPEAN, BRITISH

01394 385678 | IP13 6NU
www.seckford.co.uk

Approached by a sweeping drive through well-preened grounds, this blue-blooded Tudor pile impresses with its creeper-curtained brick façade, soaring chimneys and carved-oak front door. Culinary style is classical country house with a contemporary sensibility and the dessert menu offers old-school comforts.

The Unruly Pig

◉◉ BRITISH, ITALIAN *V*

01394 460310 | Orford Road, Bromeswell, IP12 2PU
www.theunrulypig.co.uk

Just five minutes from the market town of Woodbridge, this 16th-century pub is a lovely spot to enjoy a pint beneath original oak beams. Despite its age, The Unruly Pig has a contemporary look and feel with shabby-chic decor, a modern European menu, and relaxed, friendly service.

YAXLEY MAP 13, TM17

The Auberge

◉◉ MODERN EUROPEAN

01379 783604 | Ipswich Road, IP23 8BZ
www.the-auberge.co.uk

Ancient beams, panelling and exposed brickwork dating back to medieval times are clear evidence that this was an inn for many centuries, but the name describes today's modern restaurant with rooms. The dining room is darkly intimate and French influences underpin modern, skilfully rendered food.

Tuddenham Mill

◎◎◎◎ **MODERN BRITISH** 🍷 NOTABLE WINE LIST

01638 713552 | High Street, Tuddenham St Mary, IP28 6SQ

www.tuddenhammill.co.uk

Pin-sharp, modern British cuisine in a renovated mill

From the outside, the weatherboarded 18th-century Tuddenham Mill looks solid enough to carry on its grinding career today, but a peek inside the doors reveals a seductive modern boutique hotel. Meticulous renovation means its heritage remains intact – the fast-flowing stream that turned its waterwheel is now a thriving wildlife habitat, while the impressive cast-iron wheel that was once its beating heart is atmospherically lit within glass walls to form a centrepiece to the first-floor restaurant. With its framework of exposed beams, bare black tables, gauzy curtain partitions and views over the millpond, it's a classy setting for chef-patron Lee Bye's confident cooking. As a local lad, he's in touch with his East Anglian roots and has an instinctive feel for combining ingredients from the surrounding region to good effect, thus a typical opener strikes a balance between no-nonsense and

contemporary refinement via langoustines with caviar, beurre blanc and Japanese cresses, a simple yet stunning dish in terms of texture and flavours. Another clever construction might be Aberdeen Angus rib-eye steak partnered with seared marrow bone, triple cooked chips and a smooth peppercorn sauce; the beautiful piece of rib-eye takes on lovely flavours from its marinade and the wood-fired oven. Fish dishes such as Gigha halibut with wild nettles, smoked eel and cobnuts are equally well handled. Desserts are executed with memorable dexterity, bringing entertaining plays of flavour and texture in ideas such bitter chocolate marquise served with tiramisù cream and honeycomb. Again, it sounds straightforward in terms of the simplicity

'...strikes a balance between no-nonsense and contemporary refinement...'

of the dish, but a beautifully smooth, rich chocolate flavoured marquise and the well-balanced subtle flavour of the tiramisù cream is a great combination. For an alternative way to experience Bye's cooking, try Tipi on the Stream. It's set on the water's edge and offers a more casual menu and relaxed atmosphere.

Chef Lee Bye
Seats 54, Private dining 36
Open All Year
Parking 40
Notes Children welcome

■ SURREY

BAGSHOT
MAP 6, SU96

Steve Smith at Latymer
◎◎◎◎ MODERN EUROPEAN ▲ NOTABLE WINE LIST

01276 471774 | Pennyhill Park, London Road, GU19 5EU
www.exclusive.co.uk/pennyhill-park/food/latymer

The Latymer is one of the top restaurants in the
country, set in the creeper-covered Victorian
manor at the heart of the 123-acre Pennyhill
estate whose grounds encompass a high-
powered hotel with elegant gardens, wild
woodland, a less wild golf course and a swish
spa. It's a genteel and luxurious space with
panelled walls and rich floral fabrics all
contributing to a formal and elegant setting
for food of thrilling modernity, with
contemporary cooking techniques showcased
on six-course tasting menus. The menu is highly
seasonal and constantly evolving. You might
start with crown prince pumpkin, cep and quail's
egg – the perfectly timed egg dusted in cep
powder, a highly flavoured cep ice cream
and variants of pumpkin. The main course might
see you choosing an outstanding dish such as
the single, huge plump Orkney Scallop, perfectly
timed and topped with grated truffle and
including stunning celeriac elements (both purée
and pickled). At dessert, the rhubarb and nitro
basil salad refreshes the palate perfectly and is
presented excellently.

Chef Steve Smith **Seats** 46, Private dining 8 **Closed** 1st
2 weeks January **Parking** 500 **Notes** No children
under 12 years

CHOBHAM
MAP 6, SU96

Stovell's
◎◎◎ MODERN EUROPEAN ▲ NOTABLE WINE LIST

01276 858000 | 125 Windsor Road, GU24 8QS
www.stovells.com

This old inn wears its age on its sleeve, with a
timbered façade under red slate roof and a
beamed interior with open fireplaces and mind-
your-head ceilings. It makes a diverting setting
for high-end creative cooking, sourced locally
and presented with confident artistry. A domed
terrine of pig trotter, ham hock and apple is
garnished with pickled red onion and carrot for a
robust opener to poached cod with brown
shrimps and samphire from the set lunch menu.
Elsewhere, it might be venison carpaccio with
ash-baked beetroot as a prelude to properly
hung, seasonal roast grouse in blackberry jus

with the sharpening flavours of endive, fennel
and pomegranate. Side dishes are hard to avoid
adding, when they might include charred broccoli
dressed in anchovy and chilli. Two-tone Valrhona
chocolate mousse, caramelised banana and
seductive milk ice cream is a classy finale or go
for artisanal English and French cheeses.

Chef Fernando Stovell **Seats** 60, Private dining 16
Closed 19–25 August **Parking** 20 **Notes** Children
welcome

DORKING
MAP 6, TQ14

Sorrel
◎◎◎◎ MODERN BRITISH **V** ▲ NOTABLE WINE LIST

01306 889414 | 77 South Street, RH4 2JU
sorrelrestaurant.co.uk

Menus change seasonally at Sorrel, a
300-year-old Grade II listed brick building with a
unique glass walled kitchen. Steve Drake's
cooking is stylish and contemporary and his
seasonal, ingredients-led compositions are full
of creativity, with the kitchen delivering
inspirational dishes via a great value set lunch
plus seven-and nine-course tasting menus. You
might begin with a beautiful fillet of vibrant red
mullet, served with smoked cauliflower purée, a
wonderfully light dish full of precise flavour. A
main of tender, full flavoured venison
demonstrates kitchen's skills, while a dessert of
'chocolate breakfast' is visually elegant and
satisfyingly delicious. There's a lovely cosy feel to
the restaurant, rooms are divided by delightful
exposed wooden beams which add both
character and warmth. Immaculately set tables
add to the luxury feel which is mirrored by the
excellent and attentive service by the friendly,
professional, well drilled front of house team
complete with knowledgeable sommelier.

Chef Steve Drake **Seats** 40 **Closed** 24 - 28 December
Parking 10 **Notes** Children welcome

EGHAM
MAP 6, TQ07

The Estate Grill at Great Fosters
◎◎ MODERN BRITISH

01784 433822 | Stroude Road, TW20 9UR
www.greatfosters.co.uk

The Estate Grill chefs use Old Spots pigs reared
in the grounds and honey from the apiary, as well
as Cumbrian fell-bred lamb. Sharing platters are
a possibility – charcuterie to start and a selection
of the estate-reared pork for main.

The Lock Bar and Kitchen at The Runnymede on Thames

@ MODERN

01784 220999 | Windsor Road, TW20 0AG
www.runnymedehotel.com/food-drink

The scene could hardly be more 'Wind in the Willows' with the Thames burbling by, and outdoor tables and parasols set out by Bell Weir lock that lends its name to the kitchen and bar. The parquet-floored brasserie room has a light, breezy ambience.

Tony Parkin at the Tudor Room

@@@ MODERN EUROPEAN ⏻ NOTABLE WINE LIST

01784 433822 | Great Fosters, Stroude Road, TW20 9UR
www.alexanderhotels.co.uk/great-fosters

Great Fosters is a splendid, many-gabled, red-brick Tudor house with 50 acres of gardens and parkland. The main dining room, with its ornately carved fireplace and dramatic 17th-century Flemish tapestry, is an intimate space of just seven tables. Here you'll find restrained, sophisticated dishes, and fantastic ingredients handled with skill and precision. A starter of Jerusalem artichoke with chestnut and lemon sorrel offers a silky-smooth chestnut purée and great depth of flavour from salt-baked artichoke, while a main of tender venison comes with deliciously creamy celeriac and earthy flavours from baked beetroot. Apple crumble with cinnamon ice cream is pitch perfect.

Chef Tony Parkin **Seats** 24 **Closed** 2 weeks in January, 1 week at Easter, 2 weeks in August **Parking** 200 **Notes** Children welcome

EPSOM

MAP 6, TQ26

Dastaan

@@ INDIAN

020 8786 8999 | 447 Kingston Road, Ewell, KT19 0DB
www.dastaan.co.uk

Forget the low-key location off a traffic-mobbed dual carriageway in Epsom's hinterland, Dastaan is a neighbourhood gem and anything but your regular curry house. There's an open kitchen and the heady whiff of spices, and the atmosphere's much more Mumbai café than Surrey Indian. Even better, the intelligently compact menu delivers a succession of authentic flavours bursting with freshness, finesse and attitude.

GUILDFORD

MAP 6, SU94

The Jetty

@ CLASSIC BRITISH

01483 792300 | Guildford Harbour Hotel, 3 Alexandra Terrace, High Street, GU1 3DA
www.guildford-harbour-hotel.co.uk

Located within the Harbour Hotel, The Jetty has a separate entrance leading into a jolly ambience of sand- and sea-coloured seating. These signifiers announce a seafood bar and grill, the appealing menus built around main courses such as herby crab-crusted cod with creamy mash and peas.

HORLEY

MAP 6, TQ24

Langshott Manor

@@@ MODERN EUROPEAN

01293 786680 | Langshott Lane, RH6 9LN
www.langshottmanor.com

Not every hotel within striking distance of Gatwick bears the marks of corporate anonymity. A Tudor mansion faced in exquisitely laid red brickwork with original beams and mullioned windows is a sight for travel-weary eyes if ever there was, not least for its garden tables under the trees, and Langshott's Elizabethan interiors – all low ceilings and blazing fireplaces – have been discreetly augmented with the accoutrements of the modern hotel. In the Mulberry Restaurant, views over the grounds are a welcome complement to Phil Dixon's assured and stylish country-house cooking. A gentle richness characterises many of his dishes, meats are out of the top drawer and desserts aim to seduce with lashings of chocolate, caramel and coffee in the enveloping forms of mousses and soufflés, or there might be roasted peanut parfait, with 'textures of banana' – that's caramelised, dried and in the form of banana cake.

Chef Phil Dixon **Seats** 55, Private dining 60 **Open** All Year **Parking** 30 **Notes** Children welcome

OTTERSHAW
MAP 6, TQ06

Foxhills Club & Resort

◉◉ MODERN, CLASSIC BRITISH

01932 704471 | Stonehill Road, KT16 0EL

www.foxhills.co.uk

A short hop from Heathrow, this Victorian manor comes with a championship golf course, a spa and multifarious sporting pursuits spread around its 400-acre estate to help work up an appetite for contemporary, ingredient-led cooking in the Manor Restaurant. A starter of pressed pigeon might precede a main course of venison.

REDHILL
MAP 6, TQ25

Nutfield Priory Hotel & Spa

◉◉ MODERN BRITISH

01737 824400 | Nutfield, RH1 4EL

www.handpickedhotels.co.uk/nutfieldpriory

The Priory is a classic Victorian Gothic extravaganza dating from the 1870s. Set in 12 acres on Nutfield Ridge, The Cloisters Restaurant has mullioned windows offering expansive views over the grounds towards the spine of the South Downs and makes an atmospheric backdrop for a creative, modern take on country-house cooking.

RIPLEY
MAP 6, TQ05

The Anchor

◉◉ MODERN BRITISH *V*

01483 211866 | High Street, GU23 6AE

www.ripleyanchor.co.uk

Dating back to the 16th century, the old brick-and-timber building's interior sympathetically blends old and new – think beams and exposed brick meets pastel tones and trendy leatherette seating, while a cosy snug, bar and alfresco courtyard add kudos. Light, adept, pretty, modern dishes fit the bill.

The Clock House

◉◉◉ MODERN BRITISH ♦ NOTABLE WINE LIST

01483 224777 | High Street, GU23 6AQ

www.theclockhouserestaurant.co.uk

The namesake signature clock above the front door of this imposing Georgian building certainly draws the eye on well-healed Ripley's pretty High Street. Inside is equally elegant, with on-trend pastel shades and clean lines set against stripped-back old wall timbers and tall street-side windows. A relaxed vibe extends to the informed, sunny-natured service, while chef Paul Nicholson's thoroughbred modern cooking delivers via a roster of fixed-price menus, including tasting options. Simplicity, lightness of touch and flavour rein supreme in dressed-to-thrill dishes of panache; take 'sparkling-fresh' line-caught plaice with coco beans, pork and fennel to a Bakewell dessert with cherry and almond, while formal-code amuse bouche and in-house bread are equally classy.

Chef Paul Nicholson **Seats** 40 **Closed** 1 week in January, 1 week after Easter, 2 weeks in August, 1 week at Christmas **Parking** 2 **Notes** Children welcome

STOKE D'ABERNON
MAP 6, TQ15

Oak Room

◉◉ MODERN BRITISH

01372 843933 | Woodlands Park Hotel, Woodlands Lane, KT11 3QB

www.handpickedhotels.co.uk/woodlandspark

Built in 1885 by William Bryant of the safety match dynasty, this magnificent pile is set in landscaped gardens and the grandeur extends to the oak-panelled restaurant. Provenance drives the menu, a typical meal starting with duck and goose liver terrine before sea bream, baby squid, samphire and red pepper marmalade.

WARLINGHAM
MAP 6, TQ35

India Dining

◉ MODERN INDIAN

01883 625905 | 6 The Green, CR6 9NA

www.indiadining.co.uk

India Dining features a stylish cocktail bar, black leatherette banquettes, polished-wood tables and highly contemporary artworks. The authentic pan-Indian cooking takes an equally creative, modern and upmarket approach. Maybe start with monkfish tikka, cooked in the tandoor, its peppy spicing not overwhelming the sparkling-fresh fish.

WEYBRIDGE
MAP 6, TQ06

Brooklands Hotel
◉◉ BRITISH, EUROPEAN

01932 335700 | Brooklands Drive, KT13 0SL

www.brooklandshotelsurrey.com

This thrillingly modern structure overlooks the first purpose-built car-racing circuit in the world, opening back in 1907. There's a creative modern brasserie feel to the food, with the kitchen team keenly producing dishes that arrive on the plate dressed to thrill.

WONERSH
MAP 6, TQ04

Oak Room Restaurant
◉◉ MODERN BRITISH

01483 893361 | Barnett Hill Hotel, Blackheath Lane, GU5 0RF

www.alexanderhotels.co.uk/barnett-hill

A striking Queen Anne-style building set within 26 tranquil acres of woodlands and lovely gardens, the Barnett Hill Hotel is conveniently located just a 10-minute drive from Guildford. The wood-panelled Oak Room Restaurant overlooks a terrace and well-manicured lawns and it's an elegant setting for the contemporary British food.

■ EAST SUSSEX

ALFRISTON
MAP 6, TQ50

Deans Place
◉◉ MODERN BRITISH

01323 870248 | Seaford Road, BN26 5TW

www.deansplacehotel.co.uk

Dating back to the 14th-century, but much extended, Deans Place is set in a lovely village on the South Downs. The restaurant has a contemporary, welcoming feel; all clean lines, window screens and wall lights. The menu is modern British and comfort-oriented, offering burgers, and fish and chips, as well as more ambitious dishes.

BATTLE
MAP 7, TQ71

The Powder Mills Hotel
◉◉ MODERN BRITISH

01424 775511 | Powdermill Lane, TN33 0SP

www.powdermillshotel.com

Powder Mills was once the site of a major gunpowder-making operation that helped defeat Napoleon. It stands in 150 acres of lush parkland with a seven-acre fishing lake. The owner's springer spaniels sometimes welcome arrivals and dining takes place in the Orangery Restaurant. The kitchen offers high quality produce executed with accuracy and attention to detail.

BRIGHTON
MAP 6, TQ30

64 Degrees
◉◉ MODERN BRITISH

01273 770115 | 53 Meeting House Lane, BN1 1HB

www.64degrees.co.uk

In the heart of Brighton's famous Lanes, this bijou restaurant is big on small plates, the idea being convivial tapas-style sharing in a buzzy ambience focused on the counter at the open kitchen. The menu's economically worded fish, veg and meat options – four of each – reveal nothing of the creativity within each sharply crafted dish.

Chard *NEW*
◉ MODERN BRITISH

01273 027147 | 31A Western Road, BN3 1AF

www.chardbrighton.co.uk

Bleached wooden tables and pine floors help create a pleasing neutral feel in this bright, first-floor restaurant — a bit like a friend's modern kitchen diner, perhaps. Dinner may be chosen from a monthly changing five- or seven-course tasting menu, with an optional wine flight; the lunchtime carte revisits some of Chard's dinner highlights of the previous year.

BRIGHTON continued

The Chilli Pickle

◉ REGIONAL INDIAN

01273 900383 | 17 Jubilee Street, BN1 1GE

www.thechillipickle.com

The Chilli Pickle's open-plan interior works a casual, rustic look, with chunky wooden tables, blond-wood floors and vivid splashes of colour while full-length glass walls create the impression of dining alfresco. The vibe is breezy and buzzy, and the menu gives subcontinental clichés a swerve.

etch. by Steven Edwards

◉◉◉ MODERN BRITISH ⚑NOTABLE WINE LIST

01273 227485 | 216 Church Road, Hove, BN3 2DJ

www.etchfood.co.uk

The man leading the young team in this exciting new-generation Brit eatery is a former BBC *MasterChef: The Professionals* winner, and since he set up shop at the western end of Hove's main drag in 2017, the cooking has really gathered momentum. The space is cool with its midnight-blue walls, brass-edged tables and open kitchen adding to a buzzy air of all-round vitality. Monthly-changing set menus of five, seven or nine courses have their heart in Sussex produce, and, the palate primed with an umami hit from Marmite brioche with seaweed butter, creative and intricately detailed combos score hit after hit. Among them sea bass with cauliflower in various incarnations, apple, capers and shrimps, then outstanding South Downs smoked venison loin, with a crisp samosa of haunch, plus pickled, roasted and puréed squash. As for sweet ideas, cranberry Bakewell tart is matched with cinnamon ice cream, cranberry gel and poached and puréed pear.

Chef Steven Edwards, George Boarer **Seats** 32, Private dining 8 **Closed** Christmas and New Year **Notes** No children under 8 years

The Ginger Dog

◉ MODERN BRITISH

01273 620990 | 12–13 College Place, BN2 1HN

www.thegingerdog.com

This Kemp Town boozer took on a new lease of life when it joined the stable of local Ginger venues. The bar is a convivial hangout, while the simple setting of pine floors, buttoned grey banquettes and whimsical animal themed wallpaper in the dining room sets a perfect tone for the kitchen's flavour-driven modern British menus.

The Gingerman Restaurant

◉◉ MODERN BRITISH

01273 326688 | 21a Norfolk Square, BN1 2PD

www.gingermanrestaurants.com

A stalwart of the Brighton dining scene, the original mothership of chef Ben McKellar's Ginger-themed stable of restaurants is tucked away on a side-street near the seafront. It's a cosy, bistro-style venue done out with bare brickwork, darkwood tables and buttoned leather banquettes. Uncomplicated modern dishes are constructed from local materials handled with skill and imagination.

Hotel du Vin Brighton

◉ TRADITIONAL BRITISH, FRENCH ⚑NOTABLE WINE LIST

01273 718588 | 2–6 Ship Street, BN1 1AD

www.hotelduvin.com

The Brighton branch of the chain has all the expected Francophile touches, its walls adorned with posters and risqué pictures, leather-look banquettes running back to back down the centre and small wooden tables. A glance at the menu reveals more than your average bistro fare.

Isaac At

◉◉ MODERN BRITISH

07765 934740 | 2 Gloucester Street, BN1 4EW

www.isaac-at.com

'Local' and 'seasonal' is the mantra in this ambitious, pocket-sized outfit in the trendy North Laine quarter – even the wines are from Sussex vineyards. Serving just 20 or so diners from an open kitchen in a stripped-back space, the venue fits the youthful Brighton mood, and the food keeps step with modern trends.

The Little Fish Market

◉◉◉ MODERN, FISH

01273 722213 | 10 Upper Market Street, Hove, BN3 1AS

www.thelittlefishmarket.co.uk

Tucked away in a little side street off Hove's Western Road, chef-patron Duncan Ray's modest little operation certainly punches above its weight. After stints at The Fat Duck and Pennyhill Park, here he works with meticulous attention to detail in the kitchen, and the results speak for themselves: stunning local and sustainable seafood cooked with exemplary accuracy and an intelligent creative edge. The setting is a light-filled space done out with a pared-back contemporary look – neutral colours, bright, seafood-themed local art, wooden tables and quarry-tiled floors – it's comfortable and atmospheric in the evening, with charming, well informed service. The tersely-worded fixed-price menu offers five no-choice courses and delivers dishes of pure seafood-driven flavour, witness a powerful trio of 18-hour cooked featherblade with oysters done three ways and pointed up with dashi and a vibrant watercress sauce. The bright, clean flavours continue in stunning Dover sole with cep foam and purée, Roscoff onion with Comté cheese and the intense Marmitey jolt of yeast.

Chef Duncan Ray **Seats** 22 **Closed** 1 week in March, 2 weeks in September, Christmas **Notes** No children under 12 years

The Salt Room
◉ MODERN, SEAFOOD
01273 929488 | 106 Kings Road, BN1 2FU
www.saltroom-restaurant.co.uk
The Salt Room overlooks the seafront and with a terrace for alfresco dining, this is a smart, contemporary space with a buzzy atmosphere presided over by friendly, young, black-clad staff. The expansive split-level dining room looks the part for modern British cooking - specials are chalked up on blackboards, and unfussy treatments allow prime cuts of fish and meat to speak for themselves.

Terre à Terre
◉ MODERN VEGETARIAN
01273 729051 | 71 East Street, BN1 1HQ
terreaterre.co.uk

This trendsetting restaurant serves creative, classy veggie-vegan food. It's just back from the seafront, and the pared-back dining area stretches back to a small terrace. The service team can help with the eccentric menu's sometimes baffling descriptions. Inspiration comes from around the globe.

CAMBER
`MAP 7, TQ91`

The Gallivant
◉◉ MODERN BRITISH ⭐NOTABLE WINE LIST
01797 225057 | New Lydd Road, TN31 7RB
www.thegallivant.co.uk
Overlooking the Camber shoreline near Rye and right on the beach, The Gallivant has its heart in New England, where that laid-back eastern seaboard style translates as oceans of space, light wood, and café furniture. Sourcing from within a 10-mile radius is an especially good idea when the radius takes in such impeccable meals.

DITCHLING
`MAP 6, TQ31`

The Bull Ditchling
◉ MODERN BRITISH
01273 843147 | 2 High Street, BN6 8TA
www.thebullditchling.com
In the heart of Ditchling, The Bull has been a community hub for centuries, as the inglenook fire, half-timbered walls and old beams testify. The restaurant has a buzzing brasserie feel and the modern British cooking uses some produce so local that's its grown in their kitchen garden.

EASTBOURNE
`MAP 6, TV69`

The Mirabelle Restaurant
◉ MODERN, CLASSIC EUROPEAN ⭐NOTABLE WINE LIST
01323 412345 | The Grand Hotel, King Edwards Parade, BN21 4EQ
www.grandeastbourne.com
The Grand Hotel embodies glorious Victorian grandeur. The Mirabelle Restaurant makes an appropriately ritzy showing, with cloches, trolleys and attentive service. But there's nothing passé about the kitchen's contemporary take on flavour combinations and textures, with dishes revealing modern European thinking and fine-tuned techniques.

EAST CHILTINGTON
`MAP 6, TQ31`

Jolly Sportsman
◉ MODERN, CLASSIC
01273 890400 | Chapel Lane, BN7 3BA
www.thejollysportsman.com
Located deep in the South Downs hinterland, a GPS comes in handy for hunting down this weatherboarded country inn. There's a cosy bar area with casks on trestles and a rustic-chic restaurant. The kitchen delivers full-flavoured, contemporary cooking.

FOREST ROW
MAP 6, TQ43

The Anderida Restaurant

◉◉ MODERN BRITISH *V*

01342 824988 | Ashdown Park Hotel & Country Club, Wych Cross, RH18 5JR

www.ashdownpark.com

Ashdown Park is a magnificent Victorian pile in acres of grounds, and The Anderida Restaurant, with its elegant drapes, sparkling glassware, double-clothed tables and grand piano, is a fine setting for cooking that is a sophisticated take on both classical and contemporary.

HOVE
MAP 6, TQ20

Cin Cin NEW

◉ MODERN ITALIAN

01273 726047 | 60 Western Road, BN3 1JD

www.cincin.co.uk

Visit Cin Cin and take a seat at the counter by the open charcoal grill in this vibrant little eatery on the Western Road strip. Choose wines from a blackboard while the passionate young team send out some seriously intense flavours on a regularly changing modern Italian roster.

RYE
MAP 7, TQ92

Mermaid Inn

◉◉ BRITISH, TRADITIONAL FRENCH *V*

01797 223065 | Mermaid Street, TN31 7EY

www.mermaidinn.com

Near the top of a cobbled side street, the Mermaid Inn dates back to 1450, with 12th-century cellars, and was once well-known for its clientele of smugglers, including the notorious 17th-century Hawkhurst Gang. British and French-style food is on the table under the black-and-white timbers of the atmospheric dining room.

Webbe's at The Fish Café

◉ MODERN, SEAFOOD

01797 222226 | 17 Tower Street, TN31 7AT

www.webbesrestaurants.co.uk

A brick-built former warehouse dating from 1907 is home to this modern seafood restaurant. Exposed brickwork, high ceilings and fish-related artwork all feel in to the buzz of the smart dining room where the chefs work their magic in the open kitchen. Fish is king here, but meat eaters and veggies won't feel left out judging by the wide-ranging menu.

TICEHURST
MAP 6, TQ63

Dale Hill Hotel & Golf Club

◉ MODERN EUROPEAN

01580 200112 | TN5 7DQ

www.dalehill.co.uk

At Dale Hill Hotel & Golf Club, with its pair of 18-hole courses, golf may be top of the agenda, but hill views and a pair of restaurants are reason enough for non-players to visit. The fine-dining Wealden View restaurant is the star attraction; modern European cooking is par for this particular course.

UCKFIELD
MAP 6, TQ42
Buxted Park Hotel
◉◉ MODERN EUROPEAN
01825 733333 | Buxted, TN22 4AY
www.handpickedhotels.co.uk/buxtedpark
Offering the full country-house package, the hotel has hosted eminent guests, including William Wordsworth and Marlon Brando, and indeed many others. Celebrity or not, diners will enjoy good, honest modern European dishes, including textures of Cornish crab, pickled rhubarb and avocado purée; pork fillet and belly with tomato and olive croquettes; and chocolate and banana fondant.

Horsted Place
◉◉ MODERN BRITISH
01825 750581 | Little Horsted, TN22 5TS
www.horstedplace.co.uk
Gothic Revivalist architect Augustus Pugin certainly worked his wonders here at Horsted Place, hard on the heels of his design for the interior of the new Palace of Westminster. Done in elegant Victorian mode, the rich green dining room is a calming space for well-executed modern British dishes built from top-class seasonal materials.

WESTFIELD
MAP 7, TQ81
The Wild Mushroom Restaurant
◉◉ MODERN BRITISH
01424 751137 | Woodgate House, Westfield Lane, TN35 4SB
www.wildmushroom.co.uk

Paul and Rebecca Webbe opened their restaurant in this former private house in 1998. They were inspired by their love of the natural ingredients on their doorstep, such as the sustainable fish and shellfish landed daily at Hastings, and the bounty from wild food foraging. Thus their 'Sussex by the Season' philosophy, which Paul teaches in his Fish Café in Rye.

■ WEST SUSSEX

ALBOURNE
MAP 6, TQ21
The Ginger Fox
◉ MODERN BRITISH, EUROPEAN
01273 857888 | Muddleswood Road, BN6 9EA
thegingerfox.com
The Brighton-based Ginger group of restaurants and refashioned pubs has given its country bolt-hole a stripped-down look with parquet and slate floors, chunky tables and brown leather banquettes, plus a beer-garden and raised beds where the Fox's own vegetables are grown. The menu mixes English staples with modern European thinking.

AMBERLEY
MAP 6, TQ01
Amberley Castle
◉◉◉ CLASSIC EUROPEAN 🍷 NOTABLE WINE LIST
01798 831992 | BN18 9LT
www.amberleycastle.co.uk
Looking like the kind of place you'd happily pay the National Trust for the chance to look around, the Castle is a nearly millennium-old fortification at the foot of the South Downs that did time as a Royalist stronghold in the Civil War. Anywhere that is entered via a portcullis has more than a touch of class, an impression reinforced by the dining rooms with their armoury, tapestries, barrel-vault ceilings and lancet windows. Paul Peters produces assertive modern dishes with plenty to say for themselves, from amuse-bouche of mushroom arancini and cheese gougère onwards. You might begin with a nicely-constructed scallop dish with caramelised cauliflower, hazelnut, golden raisin, caper, apple and Amberley ver jus. Main courses of wild sea bass, or veal (loin, cheek and sweetbread) are thoughtfully conceived and full of flavour. Bring things to a close with a beautiful pistachio bavarois with grapefruit and banana.

Chef Paul Peters **Seats** 56, Private dining 12 **Open** All Year **Parking** 40 **Notes** No children under 8 years

ARUNDEL
MAP 6, T000

The Parsons Table
◎◎ BRITISH, EUROPEAN

01903 883477 | 2 & 8 Castle Mews, Tarrant Street, BN18 9DG

theparsonstable.co.uk

Picture-perfect Arundel, laid out prettily beneath its majestic castle, is home to this bright, airy venue named not after a local cleric but the chef-patron. White walls and unclothed light wood tables furnish a neutral backdrop to thoroughgoing modern British culinary wizardry.

BOSHAM
MAP 5, SU80

Sea School Restaurant
◎◎ MODERN BRITISH

01243 573234 | Bosham Lane, PO18 8HL

www.millstreamhotel.com

The Sea School Restaurant is a quiet and charming place to enjoy a meal, and is part of The Millstream Hotel, created from a row of beautiful 17th-century red brick and flint cottages. The kitchen offers a happy blend of modern trends alongside traditional favourites. Seafood and Asian themed cooking are both particularly well served.

CHICHESTER
MAP 5, SU80

Earl of March
◎ MODERN BRITISH

01243 533993 | Lavant Road, PO18 0BQ

www.theearlofmarch.com

Just a short drive out of Chichester, this 18th-century coaching inn looks out over the South Downs. There's a small patio garden, but most of the action takes place inside, in the large dining area or the snug bar area with a fire and sofas.

Halliday's
◎◎ MODERN BRITISH

01243 575331 | Watery Lane, Funtington, PO18 9LF

www.hallidaysrestaurant.co.uk

At the foot of the South Downs in the peaceful village of Funtington, Halliday's occupies three flint-fronted thatched cottages dating from the 13th century. Chef and owner Andy Stephenson sources first-rate produce from the local area, shown off to advantage in his seasonally-changing menus.

Horse and Groom NEW
◎◎ MODERN BRITISH V

01243 575339 | East Ashling, PO18 9AX

thehorseandgroom.pub

Once a blacksmith's shop, the Horse and Groom has been the village pub for over 200 years, and retains many traditional features such as flagstone floors, wooden paneling, and exposed stone walls. The restaurant is full of art and interesting features, as well as fine seasonal modern British cooking. The chicken Wellington should make it well worth the visit.

Potager Restaurant
◎◎ MODERN BRITISH

01243 784995 | Crouchers Hotel, Birdham Road, PO20 7EH

www.crouchershotel.co.uk

Over the past two decades as a stalwart of the Chichester dining scene, Crouchers has traded upwards from a simple B&B to a smart modern hotel near Dell Quay and the marina. Desserts maintain the high standards, as shown by the well-balanced flavours and textures.

Richmond Arms
◎◎ ECLECTIC

01243 572046 | Mill Road, West Ashling, PO18 8EA

www.therichmondarms.co.uk

The whitewashed Richmond is one of the glories of West Ashling, a peaceful village at the foot of the South Downs, only five minutes from Chichester. Daily specials are written up on the blackboard, and there's a wood-fired oven for traditional pizzas. Indeed, the extensive menus look far and wide for inspiration.

The Ship Restaurant
◎ BRITISH, SEAFOOD

01243 778000 | 57 North Street, PO19 1NH

www.chichester-harbour-hotel.co.uk

In the heart of Chichester, this hotel presents a sober, red-brick Georgian exterior, but inside the designers have unleashed a riot of boutique style. Murray's Restaurant is a split-level dining room that works a classy colonial look with palm trees, touchy-feely fabrics, exposed floorboards and unclothed dark wood tables. Brasserie-style menus tick the right boxes.

MAP 6, TQ24

Sofitel London Gatwick

◉◉ FRENCH

01293 567070 | North Terminal, RH6 0PH
all.accor.com/hotel/6204/index.en.shtml
An impressive central atrium makes a massive impact at this smart hotel close to Gatwick's North Terminal. The menu at La Brasserie, with its neatly laid tables and its contemporary artworks, takes a modern British path, with a French accent.

MAP 6, SU80

The Goodwood Hotel

◉◉ MODERN BRITISH

01243 775537 | PO18 0QB
www.goodwood.com
Part of the 12,000-acre Goodwood Estate, the Farmer, Butcher, Chef restaurant at this luxurious hotel uses pork, lamb and beef from the estate's organic home farm. Although there are plenty of fish and vegetarian options on the menu, home-reared meat dominates.

MAP 6, TQ21

The Glass House Restaurant & Terrace

◉ MODERN BRITISH

01273 857567 | Wickwoods Country Club Hotel & Spa, Shaveswood Lane, Albourne, BN6 9DY
www.wickwoods.co.uk
The contemporary Glass House Restaurant at Wickwoods Country Club Hotel & Spa occupies an orangery overlooking the landscaped grounds. The crowd-pleasing modern British menu includes local steaks cooked on the chargrill, burgers and ribs, although there's plenty of other options to choose from.

MAP 6, TQ13

Restaurant Tristan

◉◉◉ MODERN BRITISH, FRENCH *V* ♦ NOTABLE WINE LIST

01403 255688 | 3 Stan's Way, East Street, RH12 1HU
www.restauranttristan.co.uk
The building, in the heart of old Horsham, may be 16th century, but chef-patron Tristan Mason's food is bang up-to-date. The first-floor dining room blends ancient and modern with panache, its striking beamed vaulted ceiling, wall timbers and oak floorboards sitting alongside sleek contemporary decor. As is often the way with this kind of innovative, creative, technically skilful cooking, menus make a virtue of conciseness, listing the components of each composition, but whether you go for three, four, six or eight courses, you can be sure that the full gamut of taste categories, textural contrasts and temperatures will be deployed. Clever stuff, then, but this isn't just about techno flim-flam; having trained with Marco Pierre White, Mason's ideas are solidly grounded in classic French technique. Fish and meat combinations are favoured, as in the crisp chicken wings and turbot that arrive beautifully cooked alongside trompette mushroom foam and jelly, and parsley root purée and crisps.

Chef Tristan Mason **Seats** 34 **Closed** 25–26 December, 1–2 January **Notes** No children under 10 years

MAP 6, TQ02

The Half Moon Inn

◉◉ MODERN BRITISH

01403 820223 | Glasshouse Lane, RH14 0LT
www.halfmoonkirdford.co.uk
Owned by TV presenter and international model Jodie Kidd, it ticks all the 'quintessential village pub' boxes – oak beams, red-brick floors, an inglenook fireplace and friendly staff. A tasty, indeed attractively presented, opener is salmon and langoustine ravioli with rich shellfish cream, peas and broad beans and decorated with pub garden flowers.

LICKFOLD
MAP 6, SU92

The Lickfold Inn
BRITISH
01789 532535 | GU28 9EY
www.thelickfoldinn.co.uk

This Tudor inn with its eye-catching facing in herringboned red brick is an upstairs-downstairs operation. On the ground floor, village drinkers are regaled with hand-pumped ales, while the first floor, with its exposed brickwork and dark beams, is consecrated to modern dining. Aspirational the food may be, but not at the expense of remembering its surroundings, by offering a slice of venison and game pie with a fruity jelly lining, garnished with puréed and roasted quince, as a loin-girding starter. Balance that with a fish main course such as expertly timed cod with brown shrimps and spinach in brown butter, with delightful sharp notes coming from pickled and barbecued fennel, or perhaps truffled gnocchi with wild mushrooms and hazelnuts. The must-have dessert is lemon curd sponge cake with stunning milk ice-cream and a milk cracker, to which honey from the Lickfold's own beehive is added at the table.

Chef Tom Sellers, Graham Squire **Seats** 40 **Closed** 25 December **Parking** 20 **Notes** Children welcome

LODSWORTH
MAP 6, SU92

The Halfway Bridge Inn
MODERN BRITISH
01798 861281 | Halfway Bridge, GU28 9BP
www.halfwaybridge.co.uk

This classy 18th-century roadside inn makes an inviting pitstop after a hike on the South Downs Way or a leisurely perusal of Petworth's antique emporia. The ambience is friendly and unbuttoned, while the kitchen deals in pub classics given a contemporary tweak.

LOWER BEEDING
MAP 6, TQ22

The Camellia Restaurant at South Lodge
BRITISH
01403 891711 | Brighton Road, RH13 6PS
www.exclusive.co.uk

A handsome Victorian mansion hotel where starters range from slow-braised octopus to feta pannacotta by way of duck terrine, and main courses wander merrily from Sussex beef fillet to pistachio falafel via pan-fried halibut with mussels. Navigating from berries, vanilla and cream to cheese and fruit could easily mean passing over the sticky toffee pudding.

Restaurant Interlude NEW
MODERN BRITISH
0871 873 3363 | Leonardslee Gardens, Brighton Road, RH13 6PP
www.restaurant-interlude.co.uk

Interlude occupies a glorious setting in the woodland gardens of Leonardslee Estate. The grand old house doesn't lack for character with its high ceilings, ornate fireplaces, oil paintings and chandeliers, while the kitchen takes its cue from the seasons and makes full use of pickings from its own gardens, as well as foraging and tapping into the local food network for top-notch Sussex produce. Expect bright, lively flavours in epic-length tasting format, from beef tartare smoked with gorse flowers, to poached plaice with parsley purée and knotweed vinegar, or 28 day-aged Middlewhite pork with wild garlic and capers.

Chef Jean Delport

ROWHOOK
MAP 6, TQ13

The Chequers Inn
BRITISH
01403 790480 | RH12 3PY
thechequersrowhook.com

In business since the 15th century, The Chequers is a proper village local with flagstones, oak beams, chunky wooden tables, open fires and well-kept real ales on hand pump. A skilful kitchen keeps the food department in tune with modern tastes, with no pretensions, just bang-on-the-money pub classics and more modern ideas with a clear French influence.

SIDLESHAM
MAP 5, SZ89

The Crab & Lobster
◉◉ MODERN BRITISH
01243 641233 | Mill Lane, PO20 7NB
www.crab-lobster.co.uk
The whitewashed 17th-century pub is an upscale restaurant with rooms, and looks spruce from top to bottom. On the edge of the Pagham Harbour nature reserve, it offers a stylish restaurant that aims to impress with ambitious, top-notch modern British food.

TANGMERE
MAP 6, SU90

Cassons Restaurant
◉◉ MODERN BRITISH
01243 773294 | Arundel Road, PO18 0DU
www.cassonsrestaurant.co.uk
Chef-patronne Viv Casson ran a successful restaurant in France, so you can expect Gallic culinary influences to her work. Inside, the place gains character from the huge inglenook and low-beamed ceilings, while the modern menu takes in classically influenced ideas. Super-fresh crab from nearby Selsey often appears on the menus.

TILLINGTON
MAP 6, SU92

The Horse Guards Inn
◉◉ TRADITIONAL BRITISH
01798 342332 | Upperton Road, GU28 9AF
www.thehorseguardsinn.co.uk
The Horse Guards is a relaxed and friendly pub dating back 350 years, with open fires, wooden tables, beams and a boarded floor. It's a foodie destination with a daily-changing menu showcasing what's been bought or foraged locally or dug up from the garden.

TURNERS HILL
MAP 6, TQ33

AG's Restaurant at Alexander House Hotel
◉◉◉ BRITISH, FRENCH
01342 714914 | East Street, RH10 4QD
www.alexanderhouse.co.uk
With 120 acres of Sussex countryside all to itself, Alexander House is in a Goldilocks spot, close enough to Gatwick Airport for those jetting in and out, but tranquil enough as a getaway in its own right. The handsome red-brick hotel has glam bedrooms, a spa to pamper you into submission, and two smart dining options. Royal-blue upholstery and white linen reinforce the fine dining mood in AG's, the principal dining room.

The kitchen has all dietary bases covered with vegetarian, vegan and dairy-free versions of set-price and tasting menus, and the cooking is contemporary, with striking combinations of ingredients and heaps of visual artistry. First off, scallops are teamed with miso, kimchi, sesame dressing, radishes and a seaweed cracker. Next up, herb-crusted lamb cannon with moist and tender braised belly wrapped in crisp potato, with confit garlic, hispi cabbage and mint jellies. Look out for the excellent Marmite bread.

Chef Darrel Wilde **Seats** 30, Private dining 12
Open All Year **Parking** 100

Reflections at Alexander House
◉◉ MODERN BRITISH
01342 714914 | Alexander House Hotel & Utopia Spa, East Street, RH10 4QD
www.alexanderhouse.co.uk
The handsome 17th-century mansion has moved into boutique territory after a thoroughly modern makeover, with pampering facilities to delight spa enthusiasts and a buzzy brasserie – Reflections – to lift the spirits still further (the fine-dining option is AG's Restaurant).

WEST HOATHLY
MAP 6, TQ33

Gravetye Manor Hotel
◉◉◉◉ MODERN BRITISH ⬧NOTABLE WINE LIST
See pages 322–323

WORTHING
MAP 6, TQ10

Indigo Seafood & Grill
◉ MODERN BRITISH, EUROPEAN
01903 230451 | Ardington Hotel, Steyne Gardens, BN11 3DZ
www.indigorestaurant.info
Just outside the town centre, and a few minutes' walk from the seafront, Indigo is a contemporary seafood and grill restaurant. Red leather banquettes and lavish chandeliers add a luxurious touch to the proceedings, although the vibrant, globally-influenced food is simple and well-defined.

Continued on page 324

WEST HOATHLY

Gravetye Manor Hotel

◎◎◎◎ **MODERN BRITISH** ⚑ NOTABLE WINE LIST
01342 810567 | Vowels Lane, RH19 4LJ
www.gravetyemanor.co.uk

Historic setting for a dazzling dining room and cooking to match

If you want the full-on Tudor mansion experience, you could do worse than spend a day or so at this sumptuous country house hotel with its acres of panelling, intricate plasterwork ceilings, stone mullioned windows and delightful gardens. From the mellow stone walls to the complicated chimneys, it's everything an Elizabethan bride could have desired – which is lucky, since it was built for one. You can see her initials, and those of her husband, above the garden entrance. In the kitchens, however, things have come on a bit since the 16th century. There are no scullions to turn the spit now, instead head chef George Blogg has all the shiny stainless steel he could desire from which to work his magic. The stylish dining room – an effortlessly stunning space with jaw-dropping floor-to-ceiling windows overlooking the gardens and beautiful grassy-green banquettes to add to the

> "...one of the most atmospheric places to eat in the country."

sensation that room and garden are one – is the perfect backdrop for the dynamic, contemporary British cooking. Light and airy during the day and subtly lit at night it must surely be one of the most atmospheric places to eat in the country. The daily-changing set menus (three course lunch, four course dinner) are seasonal, and dishes are pretty as a picture. Midsummer might see you start things off with cured Dorset char, or perhaps Shropshire rose veal tartare with lovage, caper and smoked potato. An intermediate course of native lobster with scallop, chamomile and carrot will lead nicely into a main of Cumbrian lamb; loin and belly, with spinach, mint and baby turnip, or the freshest turbot, with fresh peas, wilted lettuce and black truffle. Then a choice – cheese or dessert? There are six Sussex artisan cheeses, so that's tempting, but who wants to miss out on the blackcurrant soufflé and cassis ice cream or strawberries, meringue, yogurt and verbena? Luckily you can pay a supplement and have both.

Chef George Blogg
Seats 60, Private dining 30
Open All Year
Parking 40
Notes No children under 7 years

WORTHING continued

PITCH Restaurant *NEW*

◎◎ MODERN BRITSH *V*

01903 952460 | 16 Warwick Street, BN11 3DJ

www.pitchrestaurant.co.uk

Local lad and *MasterChef* 2018 winner Kenny Tutt's aim is 'to cook food that makes people smile', and he's certainly ticking that box here judging by the burble of happy diners in his bright and breezy contemporary brasserie-style venue. Expect plenty of top-class local produce in skilfully cooked modern dishes.

■ TYNE & WEAR

GATESHEAD   *MAP 21, NZ26*

Eslington Villa Hotel

◎ MODERN

0191 487 6017 | 8 Station Road, Low Fell, NE9 6DR

www.eslingtonvilla.co.uk

Originally built for a Victorian industrialist, today's hotel retains bags of period features, allied with contemporary verve and character. Dining goes on mainly in a light and airy conservatory extension with tiled floor and commanding views over the lawns, as well as in the interior room behind it.

NEWCASTLE UPON TYNE   *MAP 21, NZ26*

21

◎ MODERN BRITISH

0191 222 0755 | Trinity Gardens, Quayside, NE1 2HH

www.21newcastle.co.uk

Located just off the Quayside, the spacious, glass-fronted brasserie is popular with the area's office folk but also with the people who 'do lunch'. Bright and welcoming, it remains as buzzy as ever, with slick and smooth service. The appealing modern brasserie-style dishes playing a big part in the attraction.

The Broad Chare

◎ MODERN BRITISH

0191 211 2144 | 25 Broad Chare, NE1 3DQ

www.thebroadchare.co.uk

Located just off the Quayside, this new kind of 'old' pub features stripped back rustic wood and exposed stone. Nothing fancy, nothing fussy, but great beer with quality produce simply put together to maximise flavour. The specials board changes on a regular basis. Local produce is used to good effect.

Cal's Own

◎ ITALIAN, MEDITERRANEAN

0191 281 5522 | 1–2 Holly Avenue West, Jesmond, NE2 2AR

www.calsown.co.uk

When you're up for a slice of pizza nirvana, this family-run joint delivers the authentic goods, courtesy of a hand-built wood-fired pizza oven imported from Naples sitting centre stage amid a no-nonsense setting of unclothed tables and bare brick walls. Pukka regional salami, hams and cheeses are sourced meticulously from Italy. Tapas-style starters change daily.

Hotel du Vin Newcastle
◎ BRITISH, FRENCH ♨NOTABLE WINE LIST

0191 229 2200 | Allan House, City Road, NE1 2BE
www.hotelduvin.com

The converted red-brick Edwardian warehouse of the Tyne Tees Steam Shipping Company enjoys commanding views of the city's many bridges, while, as might be expected from this well-established chain, the restaurant has the look of a French bistro, with dark wood floors and wooden-topped tables.

House of Tides
◎◎◎◎ MODERN BRITISH *V* ♨NOTABLE WINE LIST

See pages 326–327

Jesmond Dene House
◎◎ MODERN BRITISH, EUROPEAN

0191 212 3000 | Jesmond Dene Road, NE2 2EY
jesmonddenehouse.co.uk

Part of the allure of Jesmond Dene House is that it has the feel of a grand country house sitting in a tranquil wooded valley, yet is actually within the city limits of Newcastle. There is refinement, creativity and skill in the execution of dishes.

Leila Lily's *NEW*
◎ MODERN, ASIAN

0191 230 6777 | Grey Street Hotel, 2–12 Grey Street, NE1 6EE
www.greystreethotel.co.uk

Leila Lily's is located in Grey Street Hotel in the heart of Newcastle. The bar and restaurant flow into each other and are equally as popular for non-residents as it is for house guests. The marble centre table is a real feature, off set with neon lights and flower displays. Food-wise, expect a modern grill with Asian influences.

Peace and Loaf
◎◎ MODERN BRITISH

0191 281 5222 | 217 Jesmond Road, Jesmond, NE2 1LA
www.peaceandloaf.co.uk

In the fashionable Jesmond district of Newcastle, this is a thoroughly 21st-century place, with wood floors and brick walls offset by quirky decorative touches. Bag a table on the mezzanine floor for views of the kitchen pass and the folks below. The menus deal in avant-garde brasserie food with an imaginative edge.

Ury Restaurant
◎ INDIAN

0191 232 7799 | 27 Queen Street, NE1 3UG
www.uryrestaurants.com

An ury is a clay pot used for storing preserved food, a traditional feature of Keralan homes in south India, which is where the regional specialities hail from in this large, exuberantly decorated restaurant just off the quayside. Mains run from turmeric-spiked lamb cooked with coconut and curry leaves to chemmeen masala.

NORTH SHIELDS   MAP 21, NZ36
The Staith House
◎ MODERN BRITISH

0191 270 8441 | NE30 1JA
www.thestaithhouse.co.uk

Since it was taken over by former *MasterChef: The Professionals* finalist John Calton, this venerable pub on the regenerated North Shields fish quay has established itself as a foodie hotspot. Rubbing shoulders with the fish merchants, the quality of the piscine produce is beyond question.

TYNEMOUTH   MAP 21, NZ36
Buddha Lounge
◎ PAN-ASIAN

0191 270 8990 | 76 Front Street, NE30 4BP
www.buddhaloungetynemouth.co.uk

The setting is memorable: a converted church where a huge Buddha statue surveys a galleried upper floor beneath the soaring timber roof. Local ingredients and seafood from day boats shine through, appearing in vibrant ideas that take their cue from Indian, Japanese, Thai and Chinese cuisines.

Continued on page 328

House of Tides

◉◉◉◉ MODERN BRITISH *V* ⏶ NOTABLE WINE LIST

0191 230 3720 | 28–30 The Close, Quayside, NE1 3RF
www.houseoftides.co.uk

Assured cooking in characterful dockside building

An elegant Grade 1 listed 16th-century merchant's townhouse in the shadow of the iconic Tyne Bridge, House of Tides is the flagship of local culinary hero Kenny Atkinson. This contemporary restaurant set across two floors has brought top-flight modern cooking to Newcastle's bustling quayside. Expertly crafted cocktails in the downstairs bar are a curtain-raiser to the main event, which is delivered via a tasting menu in the refined beamed dining room with its sloping floors and lopsided ceilings. Although produce from the North East is the cornerstone of the modern British menus, the kitchen isn't afraid to look globally for inspiration, as in a fragrant canapé of tomato and cumin gougère. Everything that appears from the kitchen is top-drawer, starting with the warm malted sourdough and creamy cultured butter. Seafood is exceptional, whether it's king crab with cucumber, ginger and dill or

a piece of super-fresh halibut teamed with a Mediterranean-style courgette, basil, tomato and sea herbs. Meat is a strong point, too, with a precisely cooked veal sweetbread turning up with apple, lovage and truffle, and Yorkshire lamb accompanied by baby gem lettuce, smoky barbecued aubergine and mint. A separate tasting menu for vegetarians is certainly no afterthought and includes such intelligent dishes as the silky kohlrabi ravioli with pine nuts, pak choi and chive, and carrot, baby gem, sea buckthorn, black garlic. Texture and temperature tends to be the template for the inventive desserts which might include coconut parfait, white chocolate, mango, sesame and mango praline choux. The attention to detail continues with the intricate petits fours.

"...has brought top-flight modern cooking to Newcastle's bustling quayside."

Although the carefully chosen wine pairings by the glass with the tasting menu are spot on, there is also an excellent list which showcases Atkinson's favourite bottles from around the world.

Chef Kenny Atkinson
Seats 50
Closed See website for dates
Parking 70
Notes No children under 9 years

■ WARWICKSHIRE

ALDERMINSTER
MAP 10, SP24

Ettington Park Hotel
◎◎ MODERN, TRADITIONAL BRITISH
01789 450123 | CV37 8BU
www.handpickedhotels.co.uk/ettingtonpark
A magnificent example of mid-Victorian Gothic architecture, Ettington Park stands in 40 acres of grounds in the Stour Valley. The interior bursts with antiques and walls hung with paintings, plus several friezes. Staff are friendly as they serve up some modern contemporary cooking.

ARMSCOTE
MAP 10, SP24

The Fuzzy Duck
◎◎ SEASONAL, MODERN BRITISH
01608 682635 | Ilmington Road, CV37 8DD
www.fuzzyduckarmscote.com
This upmarket gastro pub is looking pretty swanky these days after a makeover that made the most of the original character of the place (it's been doing the business as a coaching inn since the 18th century) and injected a bit of contemporary style.

HENLEY-IN-ARDEN
MAP 10, SP16

Cheal's of Henley
◎◎ MODERN EUROPEAN V
01564 793856 | 64 High Street, B95 5BX
www.chealsofhenley.co.uk
The black-and-white timbered façade of Cheal's slots in unobtrusively among the wonky beamed buildings of the affluent 'Henley Mile' high street. Inside, the dining room is as you'd hope, all gnarly beams and tables dressed up smartly with white linen. The kitchen sends out confidently executed, well conceived dishes bursting with sharply defined flavours and contemporary verve.

ILMINGTON
MAP 10, SP24

The Howard Arms Ilmington
◎ BRITISH V
01608 682226 | Lower Green, CV36 4LT
www.howardarms.com
History seeps from every stone of the Howard, a 400-year-old inn on a Warwickshire village green to the south of Stratford. A big old stone fireplace, weathered armchairs and unclothed tables make for a relaxing ambience, and the cooking is in the modern country-pub mould.

KENILWORTH
MAP 10, SP27

The Cross at Kenilworth
◎◎◎ MODERN BRITISH ⚫NOTABLE WINE LIST
01926 853840 | 16 New Steet, CV8 2EZ
www.thecrosskenilworth.co.uk
This whitewashed 19th-century inn has flourished under the auspices of Andreas Antona. Tasteful modern design makes the most of its beams and exposed brickwork, with warm tones, dark wood and polished tables entirely in tune with the pubby mood. The cooking has its roots in classic European ideas and delivers a touch of modern refinement whilst not turning its nose up at steak and chips with onion rings on the same menu. A big-hitting opener partners crispy duck egg with beer-cured ham, caramelised celeriac, intense cep purée and a rich and glossy chicken jus. Next up, a piggy plateful of pork belly, tender cheek and a croquette of head meat is helped along by crackling, smoked onion, salted apple purée, sage jus and braised barley, while caramelised white chocolate sauce poured into hazelnut praline soufflé alongside blood orange ice cream provides a final flourish.

Chef Adam Bennett Seats 74, Private dining 12
Closed 25-26 December, 1 January Parking 25
Notes Children welcome

LONG COMPTON
MAP 10, SP23

The Red Lion
◎ TRADITIONAL BRITISH
01608 684221 | Main Street, CV36 5JS
www.redlion-longcompton.co.uk
Built as a coaching stop in 1748, The Red Lion is a textbook country inn, right down to its inglenook fireplace, settles and eclectic furniture and local artwork. The cooking takes traditional pub food to a higher level, both in terms of preparation and presentation.

ROYAL LEAMINGTON SPA   *MAP 10, SP36*

The Brasserie at Mallory Court Hotel

@@ MODERN BRITISH

01926 453939 | Harbury Lane, Bishop's Tachbrook, CV33 9QB

www.mallory.co.uk

As well as the main dining room, Mallory Court boasts a more contemporary-looking brasserie just a short stroll from the main house, serving modern European and traditional British classic food. No mere adjunct to the main action, this is a fine venue in its own right, with art deco-style lines and glass-topped wicker tables.

The Dining Room at Mallory Court Hotel

@@@ MODERN BRITISH ⚑ NOTABLE WINE LIST

See pages 330-331

See advertisement below

Queans Restaurant

@ MODERN EUROPEAN

01926 315522 | 15 Dormer Place, CV32 5AA

www.queans-restaurant.co.uk

This is a delightful establishment with a good deal of genteel charm, where a smartly neutral decor meets an appealing menu of unpretentious dishes based on high-quality regional produce. Save room for a dessert of strawberry and pink champagne cheesecake.

STRATFORD-UPON-AVON   *MAP 10, SP25*

Hotel du Vin Stratford upon Avon

@ BISTRO ⚑ NOTABLE WINE LIST

01789 613685 | 7-8 Rother Street, CV37 6LU

www.hotelduvin.com/locations/stratford-upon-avon

Set in a building dating from Georgian times, this branch of the HdV chain combines blond wood tables and midnight-blue banquettes to stylish effect in its sleek contemporary bistro. Expect classic French favourites such as snails in garlic butter, then sea bass en papillote, and tarte au citron for pudding.

Continued on page 332

The Dining Room at Mallory Court Hotel

◉◉◉ **MODERN BRITISH** 🍷NOTABLE WINE LIST

01926 330214 | Harbury Lane, Bishop's Tachbrook, CV33 9QB
www.mallory.co.uk

Grown-up dining in a romantic setting

Set in 10 acres of grounds not far from Leamington Spa, including a kitchen garden where they grow some of the produce for the restaurant, Mallory Court dates from the early 20th-century and has a comfortably authentic country-house feel. It's an elegantly Arts and Crafts style building with fabulous detailing and a romantic atmosphere. There are lovely garden and countryside views from the restaurant, which has beautiful panelling and an air of calm serenity. Tables are smartly dressed, staff are attentive without being intrusive, and everything feels relaxed and grown-up – rather like the cooking. The seven-course tasting menu changes daily and seasonally to make best use of what's available from the garden and locally. The wine list is comprehensive and well presented, and staff are happy to suggest and discuss wines. A summer meal might offer 'a taste' of Cornish crab with

"...staff are attentive without being intrusive, and everything feels relaxed and grown-up – rather like the cooking."

heirloom tomatoes and basil emulsion, followed by a confit chicken starter with little gem lettuce, marinated anchovies, parmesan and garlic. A choice of mains – perhaps a light seafood broth with garden herbs and vegetables or Cotswold lamb with Mallory garden vegetables, English peas and mint. A fruit bun topped with Beauvale cheese and port wine syrup makes a good savoury, while a sweet of English strawberries macerated in balsamic vinegar and black pepper, strawberry sorbet with a hint of basil, topped with shortcake, is refreshingly summery. At Sunday lunch they offer 'a nod to tradition' in the form of a preliminary offering of Yorkshire pudding with a Madeira and bone marrow sauce. The tradition being to fill you up a bit before your main course – so don't indulge too heavily or you might miss out on pan-roasted stone bass with Evesham asparagus, samphire and caviar cream sauce, or a hearty dish of roast and braised sirloin of beef with roast potatoes and garden veg.

Chef Paul Evans
Seats 56, Private dining 14
Open All Year
Parking 100
Notes Children welcome

See advertisement on page 329

STRATFORD-UPON-AVON *continued*

No 44 Brasserie on The Waterside
◉◉ MODERN BRITISH
01789 298682 | The Arden Hotel, Waterside, CV37 6BA
www.theardenhotelstratford.com
Just across the river from the theatres of the
Royal Shakespeare Company, this contemporary
brasserie offers a champagne bar and
enterprising modern cooking. Expect fashionable
twists on the classics – for example a dessert of
dark chocolate pavé with a deconstructed
garnish of griottine cherries, cherry sorbet and
Chantilly cream.

Salt
◉◉◉ MODERN BRITISH
01789 263566 | 8 Church Street, CV37 6HB
www.salt-restaurant.co.uk
Three cheers for crowdfunding, without which
the lucky residents of Stratford-upon-Avon would
be without this high-flying addition to the local
gastronomic scene. The bijou dining room is
shoehorned into a snug space, all low beams,
bare brick and wood and a tiny open kitchen.
Chef-patron Paul Foster brings a sound pedigree
from world-class kitchens, conveying a clear
passion for the very best ingredients and a sound
grasp of contemporary cooking techniques in his
captivating à la carte and tasting menus. His
clear vision of how flavours and textures work
together is amply demonstrated in a vibrant dish
of cured halibut with pickled cucumber, grapes,
almonds and sea purslane, all deftly offset with
suave dill emulsion. Meat is also handled with
impressive dexterity, as in a pairing of deeply
flavoured Herdwick hogget shoulder and tender
lamb rump served with minted goats' curd,
charred hispi cabbage and pickled onion.
Chef Paul Foster **Seats** 35 **Closed** Christmas
Notes Children welcome

WARWICK
MAP 10, SP26
Tailors Restaurant
◉◉ MODERN BRITISH
01926 410590 | 22 Market Place, CV34 4SL
www.tailorsrestaurant.co.uk
In a pint-sized room centred on an old brick
fireplace, the cooking is complex, with much
technical skill. The seafood cocktail consists of
prawns and brown shrimps, Marie Rose dressing
deep-fried in breadcrumbs, red pepper purée
and a gel of preserved lemon; all in all a
conceptual triumph.

WISHAW
MAP 10, SP19
The Belfry
◉ MODERN BRITISH, EUROPEAN
01675 238600 | B76 9PR
www.thebelfry.com
The Belfry has more than 300 bedrooms, a
nightclub and four eating places, including the
lively Ryder Grill. Enjoy views across the famous
Brabazon golf course, and in summer relax on its
outdoor terrace. Steaks, chargrills and spit-
roasts, fish and lobster are the stock in trade.

■ WEST MIDLANDS

BALSALL COMMON
MAP 10, SP27
Nailcote Hall
◉ TRADITIONAL EUROPEAN
024 7646 6174 | Nailcote Lane, Berkswell, CV7 7DE
www.nailcotehall.co.uk
Built on the eve of the Civil War, Nailcote is a
stately home on a modest scale, with 15 acres of
grounds containing what are reputedly some of
England's oldest yew trees. Old-school service
extends to tableside steak-flambéing, but
otherwise the mood is modern.

BIRMINGHAM
MAP 10, SP08
Adam's
◉◉◉ MODERN BRITISH *V* NOTABLE WINE LIST
See pages 334–335

Carters of Moseley

    MODERN BRITISH *V*

0121 449 8885 | 2c Wake Green Road, Moseley, B13 9EZ

cartersofmoseley.co.uk

Away from the crowds in one of Birmingham's more peaceful suburbs, Brad Carter's understated venue doesn't quite prepare diners for the culinary magic that awaits them. This is a restaurant that works as closely as possible with the best producers around the UK, but also local allotment growers. This farm-to-table approach is evident at every stage of the tasting menus. A meal might kick off with Evesham tomatoes, chilled shrimp broth and Exmoor caviar before Gigha halibut with drawn butter and seaweeds. A palate-cleanser of Cornish saffron yogurt could be followed by chocolate, Cotswold sherry and cobnuts.

Chef Brad Carter **Seats** 27 **Closed** 1-17 January, 24 April to 3 May and 11-21 August **Parking** 4 **Notes** No children under 8 years

Chez Mal Brasserie

    MODERN, TRADITIONAL

0121 246 5000 | Malmaison Birmingham, 1 Wharfside Street, The Mailbox, B1 1RD

www.malmaison.com

The Malmaison team bring their brand of boutique swagger to this place in The Mailbox, a swanky shopping and eating venue. The Brasserie, with its floor-to-ceiling windows and contemporary finish, is a relaxed and lively spot offering a menu of globally inspired contemporary dishes.

Circle Restaurant Birmingham Hippodrome

    MODERN BRITISH

0844 338 9000 | B5 4TB

www.birminghamhippodrome.com/circle-restaurant

Pre-theatre dining doesn't get much closer to curtain-up than at this large, open-plan restaurant on the second floor of the Hippodrome. You can even save your dessert for the interval; a uniquely quirky and thoughtful touch. Service is friendly and the modern British cooking is confident.

Harborne Kitchen

    MODERN BRITISH *V*

0121 439 9150 | 175 High Street, Harborne, B17 9QE

www.harbornekitchen.com

A neighbourhood restaurant with an already very excellent local reputation, this former butcher's shop has been transformed into a modern and bright dining venue with a bar area at the front. The kitchen is open plan and a tiled wall is also used as a white board to run the service. The restaurant team of three are welcoming and knowledgeable. A small garden to the rear provides seasonal fruit and vegetables.

Hotel du Vin & Bistro Birmingham

    BRITISH, FRENCH ⬤NOTABLE WINE LIST

0121 200 0600 | 25 Church Street, B3 2NR

www.hotelduvin.com

Light floods through the tall windows of this hotel dining room in Birmingham's financial area. The Gallic-inspired decor is backed up by a menu of bistro classics. A typical meal could begin with steak tartare, followed by roast cod with braised Puy lentils, button onions and pancetta, and finish with crème brûlée.

Lasan Restaurant

    INDIAN

0121 212 3664 | 3-4 Dakota Buildings, James Street, St Paul's Square, B3 1SD

lasan.co.uk

Set in the Jewellery Quarter, Lasan is a stylish contemporary Indian restaurant. A vibrant atmosphere pervades the light and spacious split-level dining room, where the menu takes a broad sweep across the Indian subcontinent to deliver regional authenticity alongside modern fusion touches. A quixotic fever dream of exquisite food and drink enveloped in a rich dining culture that is unmistakably true to India.

Continued on page 336

BIRMINGHAM

Adam's

◎◎◎ **MODERN BRITISH** *V* 🍷
0121 643 3745 | 16 Waterloo Street, B2 5UG
www.adamsrestaurant.co.uk

Contemporary dishes full of surprise and innovation

Not far from New Street Station and the city Museum and Art Gallery, Adam Stokes' classy contemporary set-up looks the part, with its neutral hues of grey and mushroom and unclothed darkwood tables combining in an image of city-slicker coolness. And there's no need to whisper, either – this is not one of those hushed temples to fine dining, but a buzzy, convivial space tended by a relaxed and knowledgeable team. Ably interpreted by head chef Keiron Stevens,

Stokes' mission has always been to "excite and enthuse guests with the accurate cooking of quality ingredients" and that's just what he delivers, whether you opt for the three-course lunch and dinner format, or go for broke with the seven-course taster and wine flight. The cooking sits on a solid bedrock of finely honed, classic haute cuisine technique, then takes off into a realm of imagination that layers dishes with contrasts of flavour and

texture that are never less than thrilling. Asian accents are never far off, perhaps prime Cornish mackerel ramped up with the umami depth of nori and dashi and the crisp crunch of radish, or lightly salted cod matched with lobster, Thai green curry, choi and the balancing citrus note of calamansi. You can expect foraged ingredients to pop up here and there, too, as when hen of the woods mushrooms are used in support of Label Anglais chicken presented in various forms, including stuffed wings with choy sum cabbage. Some ideas sound almost stubbornly classical, such as the perfectly timed aged beef sirloin that comes with asparagus, truffle and potato, although you can rest assured that the presentation will remain intelligent and innovative. Desserts rework

> "...takes off into a realm of imagination that layers dishes with contrasts of flavour and texture that are never less than thrilling."

intuitive combinations of flavour and remain in touch with the seasons to the very end, perhaps teaming wild strawberries with elderflower and pistachio, or raspberries with yogurt, white chocolate and lemon verbena.

Chef Adam Stokes, Keiron Stevens
Seats 34, Private dining 16
Closed 2 weeks in summer, 2 weeks in January, 1 week Easter
Notes Children welcome

BIRMINGHAM continued

Opheem NEW

◎◎ MODERN INDIAN

0121 201 3377 | Summer Row, B3 1JJ

www.opheem.com

Opheem is on Summer Row close to UCB, and offers modern Indian cuisine. A real talking point is the large artificial pink blossom tree that provides a contrast to austere grey polished walls and gold detailing. Food from a number of different Indian regions and ethnicities are well represented, not least on the impressive 10-course tasting menu.

Purnell's

◎◎◎ MODERN BRITISH

0121 212 9799 | 55 Cornwall Street, B3 2DH

purnellsrestaurant.com

Glynn Purnell's personality shines through on his menus, where playful puns and little details give insight into his development as a chef. The building in the financial district has been on a journey as well, and it's looking fine and dandy right now; the old red-brick warehouse has surely never looked so dapper within – a fashionably muted colour palette with the occasional splash of something more daring, and stylish artworks. In this smart and confident setting, Glynn's menus include a fixed-price carte and tasting menus: '10 Years in the Making', 'Brummie Tapas', and 'A Purnell's journey...', the latter featuring the BBC *Great British Menu* -winning monkfish masala (which is also a regular on the carte). Main courses extend to Wiltshire pork belly, paired with burnt apple purée and confit turnip, while desserts might be burnt English surprise (a rhubarb and custard number also seen on *Great British Menu*). The impressive wine list features staff favourites.

Chef Glynn Purnell **Seats** 45, Private dining 12
Closed 1 week Easter, Christmas and New Year
Notes No children under 10 years

Simpsons

◎◎◎ MODERN BRITISH 𝓥 ♨

0121 454 3434 | 20 Highfield Road, Edgbaston, B15 3DU

www.simpsonsrestaurant.co.uk

Tucked away in leafy Edgbaston, Simpsons may occupy a converted mansion but the airy interior has a strikingly contemporary Scandi-style. The focal point of this modern dining space is a central chef's table where the brigade of chefs are in full sight of diners. The intuitive cooking is as vibrant and highly crafted as the room. Carrot broth, smoked cheese dumpling, black garlic, hen of the woods, chickweed and fennel pollen might lead on to venison loin, parsnip purée, wilted kales, barley and elderberry vinegar sauce. Banoffee pie soufflé, banana ice cream and caramel sauce is a must-order.

Chef Luke Tipping **Seats** 70, Private dining 14
Closed Bank holidays **Parking** 12 **Notes** Children welcome

The Wilderness

ROSETTES SUSPENDED BRITISH

0121 233 9425 | 27 Warstone Lane, Jewellery Quarter, B18 6JQ

www.wearethewilderness.co.uk

The Rosette award for this establishment has been suspended and reassessment will take place in due course. Tucked down an alleyway in the jewellery quarter, The Wilderness is an atmospheric venue with skylight panels and an open kitchen, decked with foliage to bring a sense of sylvan repose to city eating.

Closed Christmas and New Year **Seats** 20
Notes No children under 12 years

ROYAL SUTTON COLDFIELD
MAP 10, SP19

The Bridge at New Hall

◎◎ MODERN BRITISH

0121 378 2442 | Walmley Road, B76 1QX

www.handpickedhotels.co.uk/newhall

Before Birmingham's suburban sprawl engulfed the village of Sutton Coldfield, this 800-year-old moat house stood in empty countryside. Nowadays, it's cushioned from the hurly-burly by 26 acres of grounds. The Bridge Restaurant is the top-end dining option, where mullioned stained-glass windows blend with modern decor.

The Oak Room Restaurant

◉ MODERN BRITISH

0121 308 3751 | Moor Hall Hotel & Spa, Moor Hall Drive, Four Oaks, B75 6LN

www.moorhallhotel.co.uk

A family-run country-house hotel set in parkland, Moor Hall's panelled Oak Room restaurant has a real sense of grandeur and lovely views over the grounds, including the golf course. The contemporary British cooking from a young kitchen team emphasises quality ingredients.

SOLIHULL   *MAP 10, SP17*

Hampton Manor

◉◉◉◉ MODERN BRITISH ⚑ NOTABLE WINE LIST

01675 446080 | Swadowbrook Lane, Hampton-in-Arden, B92 0EN

www.hamptonmanor.com

Towers and turrets mark the spot within the 45 acres of land surrounding this impressive stately manor, built by a son of Sir Robert Peel. These days it's a divertingly stylish restaurant with rooms, with a kitchen garden providing its bounty and the dynamic contemporary cooking of Rob Palmer in the offing. The design of the place is timelessly tasteful; the part-panelled dining room is a mix of traditional comfort and contemporary sophistication, while the staff are just as engaging as the setting. The format sees three tasting menus vying for your attention - two four-course options, the more expensive of which features Wagyu beef - and a full-throttle seven-course menu that includes all the bells and all the whistles. Flavour combinations are not designed to shock, and what arrives on the plate is creative, pretty as a picture, and never less than delicious.

Chef Rob Palmer **Seats** 28, Private dining 14 **Closed** 21 December to 6 January **Parking** 30 **Notes** No children under 12 years

The Regency Hotel

◉ MODERN, CLASSIC

0121 745 6119 | Stratford Road, Shirley, B90 4EB

www.theregencysolihull.com/

Less than 20 minutes from Birmingham Airport and the NEC, The Regency is a well-positioned base for visitors, but the hotel's stylish restaurant appeals equally to Solihull locals. A contemporary space with its own courtyard, the restaurant offers inventive British dishes inspired by international flavour combinations.

WOLVERHAMPTON   *MAP 10, SO99*

Bilash

◉ INDIAN, BANGLADESHI

01902 427762 | 2 Cheapside, Civic Centre, WV1 1TU

www.thebilash.co.uk

After 40 years, the family-run Bilash is something of a Wolverhampton institution, popular with the pre-theatre crowd as well as football fans heading to or from Molineux Stadium. The stylish interior uses neutral colours with cream chairs, booths, banquette seating and walls hung with sparkling mirrors. The menu is a thrilling mix of modern Indian and Bangladeshi food.

WILTSHIRE

BEANACRE
MAP 4, ST96

Beechfield House Restaurant
◉◉ MODERN BRITISH
01225 703700 | BEANACRE, SN12 7PU
www.beechfieldhouse.co.uk
A charming, privately-owned hotel in eight beautiful acres with its own arboretum. At dinner there's a good selection of carefully prepared dishes, including, as a starter, Scottish smoked salmon with caperberries; to be followed by Cornish cod with dressed linguine and brown shrimp; braised duck leg and smoked sausage; or roasted gnocchi with sun-dried tomatoes.

BOX
MAP 4, ST86

The Northey Arms
◉ BRITISH, EUROPEAN
01225 742333 | Bath Road, SN13 8AE
www.ohhpubs.co.uk/the-northey-arms/
Looking rather swish these days, this old stone-built inn has been brought up to full 21st-century spec with seagrass chairs and boldly-patterned wallpaper in the split-level dining area. Locally-reared 32-day-aged steaks get star billing; perhaps a 14oz T-bone if you're feeling peckish.

BRADFORD-ON-AVON
MAP 4, ST86

The Bunch of Grapes
◉◉ MODERN BRITISH
01225 938088 | 14 Silver Street, BA15 1JY
www.thebunchofgrapes.com
Very much a food-oriented hostelry in the contemporary vein, The Bunch of Grapes has a dapper pared-back decor with a rich blue finish, bare wood tables and floors – a look that's more bistro than boozer. The kitchen draws on high quality ingredients to deliver a modern British menu full of up-to-date ideas and big flavours.

The George
◉◉ MODERN BRITISH
01225 865650 | 67 Woolley Street, BA15 1AQ
www.thegeorgebradfordonavon.co.uk
On the outskirts of historic Bradford-on-Avon stands the comfortably spacious George at Woolley, where seasonally changing modern British food awaits diners. The management's long-standing, high-end experience is evident throughout. In the dining room, typical dishes include rack of lamb with mini shepherd's pie, grilled fillet of black bream, cheese and potato gnocchi, and traditional pub favourites.

See advertisement opposite

CALNE
MAP 4, ST97

The Shelburne Restaurant NEW
◉◉ MODERN BRITISH
01249 822228 | Bowood Hotel, Spa and Golf Resort, Derry Hill, SN11 9PQ
www.bowood.org
Part of Bowood Hotel, an elegant boutique country house set on the Bowood Estate, the Shelburne Restaurant is an impressive space. An elegant, curved room with window-shaped mirrors, French windows with wonderful views and a mural. There's also a terrace for summer dining. Seasonal menus make the modern British most of produce from the estate.

Strand Room
◉◉ MODERN BRITISH
01249 812488 | The Lansdowne, The Strand, SN11 0EH
www.lansdownestrand.co.uk
Dating from the 16th century, The Lansdowne pub is owned by Arkell's Brewery and the Strand Room restaurant is at the very heart of the place. The modern cooking keeps things simple on the plate, allowing local produce to shine.

The White Horse Inn
◉◉ MODERN BRITISH
01249 813118 | Compon Bassett, SN11 8RG
www.whitehorse-comptonbassett.co.uk
Taking its name from the giant chalk carving at nearby Cherhill, which features on the pub sign, The White Horse is a charming 18th-century inn. Meals can be taken in the bar, the dining room, or weather permitting, out in the garden. The approach is modern British and the home-made pie of the day is a best seller.

See advertisement on page 341

The George

are three unique dining spaces to choose from at this Wiltshire inn, so whether
ant to cosy up by the inglenook fire on a chesterfield, or watch the team of chefs
theatre kitchen or catch up with friends in the pantry dining room, there's a spot
ery occasion. Supper is best started with a G&T, the bar boasts a healthy selection,
browsing the à la carte menu of modern British and European influenced
. Experienced head chef and owner Alex Venables oversees the classically trained
. Expect favorites such as beef Wellington, executed with skill and style. The whole
ence can be topped off with a night in one of the charming bedrooms.

67 Woolley Street, Bradford on Avon, Wiltshire BA15 1AQ

25 865650 **W**: thegeorgebradfordonavon.co.uk **E**: info@thegeorgebradfordonavon.co.uk

CASTLE COMBE
MAP 4, ST87

Bybrook at The Manor House Hotel
◉◉◉ MODERN BRITISH V NOTABLE WINE LIST
01249 782206 | SN14 7HR
www.exclusive.co.uk

Quality underpins everything at the Bybrook, named after the river that runs through the hotel grounds. There's a formal air, as you'd expect at a luxury hotel, yet service is from an approachable and knowledgeable team. Robert Potter's cooking is elegant and light, with the kitchen garden making a meaningful contribution, as can be seen in the duck starter – a beautiful terrine using ethical foie gras and preserved plum, which adds sweetness and acidity. The main courses keep up the standard with a beautiful piece of super-fresh turbot, and the beef with white asparagus, maitake mushrooms and red wine sauce delivers lots of rich flavour. Desserts are kept light, with a clever play on the theme of strawberries and cream or a very good burrata ice cream with apricot and citrus fruits.

Chef Robert Potter **Seats** 60, Private dining 100 **Open** All Year **Parking** 100 **Notes** No children under 11 years

The Castle Inn NEW
◉◉ BRITISH
01249 783030 | SN14 7HN
www.thecastleinn.co.uk

Exposed stone walls, wooden floorboards and antique furnishings are all signs that you're in a proper old English inn. The Castle Inn is just such a place, in a picturesque village with views of the church. On offer is excellent and comforting pub food that has reached an impressively high standard.

COLERNE
MAP 4, ST87

The Brasserie
◉◉ MODERN BRITISH
01225 742777 | Lucknam Park Hotel & Spa, SN14 8AZ
www.lucknampark.co.uk

The Brasserie is the less formal dining option at Lucknam Park. Located within the walled garden, with a wall of glass of its own, it has a classy finish and serves up high-end food from its open kitchen and a wood-burning oven.

Restaurant Hywel Jones by Lucknam Park
◉◉◉ MODERN BRITISH V NOTABLE WINE LIST
01225 742777 | Lucknam Park Hotel & Spa, SN14 8AZ
www.lucknampark.co.uk

Lucknam Park is a beautiful, symmetrical Palladian mansion, set in 500 acres of unspoilt parkland. For the last 30 years it has been a splendidly luxurious hotel and spa, offering an indulgent escape from the daily grind into a world of elegant country-house living. From the mile-long drive lined with beech trees to the delightful public spaces, it's all effortlessly sumptuous. The dining room, with its curved walls, cloud-painted ceiling and pristine double-clothed tables, is the perfect setting for Hywel Jones' sophisticated, focused cooking. This is not fanciful stuff at the whim of fashion, but mature and well directed, where great produce is treated with respect. To begin, heritage beetroot comes with buffalo ricotta tart and Wiltshire truffle, and a main course of roast Bwlch Farm venison is supported by miso and ginger roast hispi cabbage and plum chutney. Butter roast pear with buttermilk sorbet and walnut wafers is a fine way to finish.

Chef Hywel Jones **Seats** 64, Private dining 28 **Open** All Year **Parking** 80 **Notes** No children under 5 years

CORSHAM
MAP 4, ST87

Guyers House Hotel
◉ MODERN EUROPEAN, BRITISH
01249 713399 | Pickwick, SN13 0PS
www.guyershouse.com

An elegant country house in handsome grounds with a relaxing dining room patrolled by friendly staff, and menus with a real sense of creative elan. Save room for an up-to-the-minute Earl Grey and lavender crème brûlée with pistachio brittle and mullet wine sorbet.

DEVIZES
MAP 4, SU06

The Peppermill
◉◉ BRITISH
01380 710407 | 40 St John's Street, SN10 1BL
www.peppermilldevizes.co.uk

This family-run restaurant with rooms impresses with its contemporary, feel-good menu. In the evening you might start with BBQ-infused, slow-roasted pork belly with carrot 'slaw', or potted shrimps with home-made brioche. It is a popular place so it's worth booking ahead.

THE WHITE HORSE INN

COMPTON BASSETT

Nestled in the beautiful Wiltshire countryside, we are a traditional Free House with good homemade food and welcoming accommodation.

Nr Calne SN11 8RG 01249 813118
www.whitehorse-comptonbassett.co.uk

EDINGTON
MAP 4, ST95

Three Daggers
◎◎ BRITISH *V*

01380 830940 | 47 Westbury Road, BA13 4PG
www.threedaggers.co.uk

A pub with its own microbrewery, farm and farm shop, The Three Daggers has plenty to offer locals and destination diners. Bare tables, mismatched wooden chairs, exposed brick and heritage colours add to the informal country pub feel, as does the seasonal modern cooking.

GREAT BEDWYN
MAP 5, SU26

Three Tuns Freehouse
◎ BRITISH

01672 870280 | 1 High Street, SN8 3NU
www.tunsfreehouse.com

A welcoming and dog-friendly pub on the edge of the Savernake Forest, the Three Tuns combines the traditional charms of a local village inn with an excellent selection of carefully prepared tempting dishes. Everything from bread to ice cream is made on the premises.

LACOCK
MAP 4, ST96

Sign of the Angel
◎◎ BRITISH

01249 730230 | 6 Church Street, SN15 2LB
www.signoftheangel.co.uk

This 500-year-old, timbered inn is the very personification of classy Cotswold charm. Low-beamed ceilings, walk-in fireplaces and cosy nooks and crannies are all present and correct, and candlelit tables add to the cossetting mood. On the food side, the kitchen takes local sourcing very seriously.

MALMESBURY
MAP 4, ST98

The Dining Room
◎◎◎◎ MODERN BRITISH, ASIAN INFLUENCES *V* **★** NOTABLE WINE LIST

01666 822888 | Whatley Manor Hotel and Spa, Easton Grey, SN16 0RB
www.whatleymanor.com

Sustainability is close to the heart of everyone at Whatley Manor. For example the kitchen runs entirely on renewable electricity - lighting and equipment was upgraded to reduce consumption by 75%. Chef Niall Keating is CPD certified waste management trained and food waste is either composted and used in the gardens or sent to an anaerobic digestion plant to produce biogas and liquid fertiliser for the farming industry. Hyper local is key, the neighbour's farm is organic and supplies the beef and a local beekeeper looks after four hives located in the garden. There is also a kitchen garden, where as much produce as feasible is harvested for the menus. The restaurant itself is an understated modern space, with cream walls, bare floors and a generously spaced tables. Niall leads the kitchen team here and his refined contemporary cooking draws inspiration from Asia and his travels - this is serious food, realised with ambition, confidence and panache. Delivered via a Chef's Menu, including a vegetarian and vegan version, guests can expect phenomenal precision and flavours.

Chef Niall Keating **Seats** 46, Private dining 30 **Open** All Year **Parking** 120 **Notes** No children

Grey's Brasserie *NEW*
◎◎ BRITISH *V*

01666 822888 | Whatley Manor Hotel and Spa, Easton Grey, SN16 0RB
www.whatleymanor.com/eat-drink

Grey's Brasserie's location within Whatley Manor is undeniably a major draw. Another is the food, served in a stylish dining room furnished in muted tones of grey, appropriately enough, and pink. Start maybe with pan-fried mackerel, pickled beetroot, horseradish and chervil, followed by chorizo and scallop risotto, or slow-cooked pork belly, perhaps while listening to live jazz (on selected dates).

PEWSEY
MAP 5, SU16

Red Lion Freehouse
◎◎◎ MODERN BRITISH 𝒱

01980 671124 | East Chisenbury, SN9 6AQ

www.redlionfreehouse.com

Along a narrow lane in a tiny Wiltshire village, the thatched Red Lion Freehouse is the epitome of a country inn. A big brick fireplace and bare-boards, with menus chalked up on blackboards and service from cheerful staff, set the tone. There is also an option to sit outside and for extra special occasions, a private dining room on the second floor. The regionally based menus of well-defined country cooking are extremely appealing. Ceviche of Orkney scallops with Chisenbury gooseberries, ginger, hazelnuts and marigold might raise the curtain for roast halibut with baby artichokes, wild mushrooms and confit lemon in a parsley and barigoule sauce. At the end, there could be classic crème brûlée, or raspberry and dark chocolate gâteau with roast almond ice cream.

Chef Guy Manning, Daniel Barker and Brittany Manning **Seats** 45, Private dining 23 **Closed** 1st 2 weeks January **Prices from** S £10, M £22, D £8.50 **Parking** 14 **Notes** Children welcome

RAMSBURY
MAP 5, SU27

The Bell at Ramsbury
◎◎ MODERN BRITISH, EUROPEAN

01672 520230 | The Square, SN8 2PE

www.thebellramsbury.com

A whitewashed coaching inn dating back 300 years, The Bell is a popular pitstop for walkers and visitors to nearby Marlborough. It has its own brewery, distillery and smokehouse, with much of the produce used in the kitchen coming from the estate and walled garden.

ROWDE
MAP 4, ST96

The George & Dragon
◎◎ SEAFOOD

01380 723053 | High Street, SN10 2PN

www.thegeorge-and-dragon.co.uk

This Tudor coaching inn in the unassuming village of Rowde has a reputation as a destination dining venue. The rustic country finish is part of its charm, while the menu makes a speciality of seafood hauled in from the boats at St Mawes in Cornwall.

SOUTH WRAXALL
MAP 4, ST86

The Longs Arms
◎◎ SEASONAL MODERN BRITISH

01225 864450 | BA15 2SB

www.thelongsarms.com

Across the road from the church in the picturesque village of South Wraxall, The Longs Arms is a welcoming stone-built pub with traditional flagstone floors and a wood-burning stove in the fireplace. Everything here is made on the premises including the delicious bread.

SWINDON
MAP 5, SU18

The Angel
◎ MODERN BRITISH

01793 851161 | 47 High Street, Royal Wootton Bassett, SN4 7AQ

www.theangelhotelwoottonbassett.co.uk

Ancient oak panelling and flagstone floors confirm the pedigree of this veteran coaching inn, which continues life as a high-street hub of local goings-on into the 21st century. The kitchen keeps up with the times, sending out starters such as seared pigeon breast accompanied by a Merlot-poached pear.

Chiseldon House Hotel
◎ MODERN EUROPEAN, BRITISH

01793 741010 | New Road, Chiseldon, SN4 0NE

www.chiseldonhouse.com

The grand Regency manor house is a popular wedding venue, with the Marlborough Downs and attractive gardens providing a stunning backdrop, and the M4 nearby. The restaurant is a bright space with crisp white linen on the tables and a cheerful service team.

WHITEPARISH
MAP 5, SU22

Betony by Matt Tomkinson NEW
◎◎ MODERN BRITISH

01794 884004 | The Kings Head, The Street, SP5 2SG

www.thekingshead.co.uk

You'll find Matt Tompkinson's latest venture, Betony, in The Kings Head, a lovely old village pub. The stylish, intimate dining room, with its mix of old and new, is the perfect setting for an evolving menu that centres local produce. It's small, so book ahead for the chance to try things like confit duck croquette with smoked Morteau sausage and pickled pear; and fish of the day with braised artichokes and fresh borlotti beans.

■ WORCESTERSHIRE

ABBERLEY
MAP 10, SO76

The Herb Garden
◉◉ MODERN BRITISH
01299 896666 | Stockton Road, WR6 6AT
www.theelmshotel.co.uk
Dating from 1710, this grand Queen Anne manor house has been a country house hotel since 1946, with 10 acres of grounds including tennis courts and croquet lawns. Produce from the hotel's kitchen garden forms the basis of seasonal menus in The Herb Garden, one of three eating options here.

The Manor Arms
◉ MODERN BRITISH
01299 890300 | The Village, WR6 6BN
www.themanorarms.co.uk
Originally dating from the 17th century, today's pub is a valuable part of the community, appreciated by locals and visitors alike (note the six classy bedrooms). The traditional decor inside is entirely in keeping and the finish is smart but informal.

BEWDLEY
MAP 10, SO77

Royal Forester Country Inn
◉ MODERN EUROPEAN
01299 266286 | Callow Hill, DY14 9XW
www.royalforesterinn.co.uk
This historic inn has plenty of exposed brickwork and beams to boost the feelgood factor in its cosy nooks and crannies. With a convivial mood in its quirky bar, it's an inviting spot. The kitchen deals in no-nonsense dishes featuring diligently sourced local materials handled with skill to deliver clear and hearty flavours.

BROADWAY
MAP 10, SP03

The Back Garden
◉◉◉ MODERN *V* 1 NOTABLE WINE LIST
01386 852711 | Dormy House Hotel, Willersey Hill, WR12 7LF
www.dormyhouse.co.uk
The Back Garden is one of the eating options at Dormy House, a 17th-century former farmhouse built of honey-coloured stone, perched on a hill above Broadway. Its elegant, contemporary design scheme is worthy of an interiors magazine, with its use of calming greys, blues and honey yellows. Big windows allow views out of the walled garden that supplies a lot of the veg used in the kitchen. Start dinner with smoked salmon lasagne, nasturtium oil and vermouth sauce, continue with braised veal cheek, Swiss chard, polenta and Madeira sauce, and finish off with passionfruit baked Alaska with coconut and lime.

Chef Martin Burge **Seats** 90, Private dining 14 **Open** All Year **Parking** 70 **Notes** Children welcome

Foxhill Manor
◉◉ MODERN CLASSIC
01386 852711 | Farncombe Estate, WR12 7LJ
www.foxhillmanor.com
Foxhill Manor is a relaxed and home-away-from-home where the residents-only dining can be taken anywhere in the property, be it an intimate table for two or while catching a movie in the cinema room – even discussions with the chef are encouraged. The brasserie-style, modern, yet classic cooking has a focus on high quality ingredients and there's a compact well-chosen wine list too.

Hook by Martin Burge
◉◉ BRITISH *V*
01386 858000 | The Fish Hotel, Farncombe Estate, WR12 7LJ
www.thefishhotel.co.uk
The sea is miles away, no river flows past, for The Fish is named after the hill on which it stands, because monks once cured fish in caves on the hillside. Forming part of a 400-acre estate, today's boutique hotel has an informal Scandi-chic style restaurant.

The Lygon Grill NEW
◉ BRITISH, GRILL
01386 852255 | High Street, WR12 7DU
www.lygonarmshotel.co.uk
The Lygon Grill is at the heart of the village of
Broadway, and has been for some 600 years.
When you step into this amazing space you can
see how unspoilt the place is, with its beautiful
barrelled ceiling, large windows, minstrels'
gallery and well-kept wood panelling. The popular
grill-based menu is well executed and there's a
decent vegan offering too.

MO
◉◉◉ MODERN BRITISH
01386 852711 | Dormy House Hotel, Willersey Hill,
WR12 7LF
www.dormyhouse.co.uk
Up on the hill above Broadway, that
quintessential Cotswolds honeypot, Dormy House
started life as a humble farmhouse in the 17th
century but has morphed into a slinky designer
retreat with a glossy spa. The place is also a
beacon of culinary pleasures, the latest addition
being MO, an intimate and interactive dining
experience that takes place around a marble-
topped counter in a cosy space with a pineapple-
themed decor. With just a dozen guests to serve,
the chefs can deliver a remarkable level of
precision in the seven-course exploration of
tastes and textures. Expect technical
showmanship and plenty of theatre and fun,
starting with scrambled duck egg served in the
shell with Jerusalem artichoke foam and grated
truffle. Along the way, charcoal-grilled prawns
turn up with a rich bisque and lemon curd, while
tender monkfish comes with black curry sauce
and mung beans, and smoked rose veal fillet is
matched with maple-glazed salsify and sprouting
broccoli. The virtuoso performance ends with a
confection of orange, rhubarb and cheesecake.

Chef Sam Bowser Seats 12 Parking Notes No children

Tattersall's Brasserie
◉◉ TRADITIONAL BRITISH
01386 852401 | The Green, High Street, WR12 7AA
www.cotswold-inns-hotels.co.uk/broadway
The Broadway Hotel, overlooking the green, has
its roots in the 16th century, so Tattersall's
Brasserie, in a contemporary light-filled atrium,
is in sharp contrast to its traditional
surroundings. The kitchen focuses on quality
seasonal produce and has an assured sense of
what will work.

CALLOW END   MAP 10, SO84
The Refectory NEW
◉ MODERN BRITISH
01905 409300 | Stanbrook Abbey, Jennet Tree Lane,
WR2 4TY
www.stanbrookabbey.com
Unsurprisingly, the impressive Stanbrook Abbey
hotel was converted from an old abbey, and The
Refectory was originally the nuns' dining room.
It's clear from the architecture; wood panelling,
vaulted ceilings, large high windows, and
pictures that reflect the place's history, but this
has also given way to an elegant contemporary
design, reflected in a modern British menu.

CHADDESLEY CORBETT   MAP 10, SO87
Brockencote Hall Country House Hotel
◉◉◉ MODERN BRITISH
01562 777876 | DY10 4PY
www.brockencotehall.com
Victorian Brockencote stands in 70 acres of
landscaped gardens and parkland overlooking
the waters of its ornamental lake. The place has
been made over with a light touch that blends
original features with a sprinkle of contemporary
pizzazz. Sweeping pastoral views are best
appreciated from either a seat in the Le Colonial
lounge-bar or a table in the linen-swathed
elegance of the Chaddesley Restaurant, or if you
are going about things in the right spirit, one
after the other. Tim Jenkins is in charge of the
gastronomic show, setting high standards with
precisely executed modern dishes – an opener of
pan-fried scallops with pickled quince and
chestnut velouté being a case in point. Main
courses might see roasted venison loin next to
Jerusalem artichoke, Oxford Blue cheese and
elderberry jus, and technical dexterity is once
again in abundance at dessert, when iced
muscovado parfait with pear textures is a
beautifully presented dish.

Chef Tim Jenkins Seats 40, Private dining 16 Open All
Year Parking 50 Notes Children welcome

MALVERN
MAP 10, SO74

L'Amuse Bouche Restaurant

◉◉ MODERN FRENCH

01684 572427 | The Cotford Hotel, 51 Graham Road, WR14 2HU

www.cotfordhotel.co.uk

Set in a Victorian building with a faux Tudor style, L'Amuse Bouche Restaurant is a taste of French-style cuisine in a quaint English setting. It was built as a summer home for the Bishop of Worcester, and the restaurant is in the converted chapel, and enjoys lovely views over the garden.

The Cottage in the Wood

◉◉ MODERN BRITISH

01684 588860 | Holywell Road, Malvern Wells, WR14 4LG

www.cottageinthewood.co.uk

This delightful Georgian property has a panoramic view across the Severn Valley from its position high up on a wooded hillside. The aptly named Outlook Restaurant makes the best of its situation while the kitchen's rather refined, classically inspired yet modern output is a distraction in itself.

The Inn at Welland

◉◉ MODERN CLASSIC

01684 592317 | Hook Bank, WR13 6LN

www.theinnatwelland.co.uk

The proprietors at this pub have a long history with the AA, having previously held Rosettes elsewhere. In its modern farmhouse-style interior, a friendly, mostly young team serves seasonally driven, modern British dishes and specials such as stone bass fillet with pickled seaweed, and char-griddled woodland pork cutlet. Wines are listed by style rather than region.

OMBERSLEY
MAP 10, SO86

The Venture In Restaurant

◉◉ BRITISH, FRENCH

01905 620552 | Main Road, WR9 0EW

www.theventurein.co.uk

Behind the half-timbered façade of this 15th-century property is a bar with a open fire, comfortable sofas and low tables and a restaurant with bags of ancient character from its ceiling beams and standing timbers. Chef-patron Toby Fletcher stamps his style on the Anglo-French repertoire.

TENBURY WELLS
MAP 10, SO56

Pensons

ROSETTES SUSPENDED MODERN BRITISH *V*

01885 410333 | Pensons Yard, WR15 8RT

www.pensons.co.uk

The Rosette award for this establishment has been suspended due to a change of chef and reassessment will take place in due course.

A labour-of-love project has transformed derelict farm buildings into this high-flying newcomer. Located on the Netherwood Estate on the Herefordshire/Worcestershire border, Pensons occupies a stripped-back, barn-like space with sturdy rafters soaring to the vaulted roof, bare brickwork and a stylishly minimalist decor.

Seats 30, Private dining 18 **Parking** 40
Notes Vegetarian dishes

■ EAST RIDING OF YORKSHIRE

BEVERLEY   *MAP 17, TA03*
The Westwood Restaurant
⊛⊛ MODERN BRITISH
01482 881999 | New Walk, HU17 7AE
www.thewestwood.co.uk

Owned by twins Matt and Michelle Barker, the Westwood began life as a courthouse and the building is full of character. Decorated in dark colours with copper and gold highlights, it has a contemporary feel, with an open kitchen and a terrace for outdoor dining. The kitchen produces confident modern British cooking, with simple, effective flavour combinations.

■ NORTH YORKSHIRE

ARKENGARTHDALE   *MAP 18, NY90*
Charles Bathurst Inn
⊛ BRITISH
01748 884567 | DL11 6EN
www.cbinn.co.uk
The CB – to its friends – is named after a Georgian parliamentarian, and the beamed dining room is done out with pale wood and generously spaced tables. Local farmers and fishermen supply its seasonally-changing menus of modern Yorkshire cooking.

AUSTWICK   *MAP 18, SD76*
The Traddock
⊛⊛ MODERN BRITISH *V*
01524 251224 | The Traddock, AUSTWICK, LA2 8BY
www.thetraddock.co.uk
The Yorkshire Dales extend gloriously all around the character stone house, where a vigorous rendition of British modernism is the stock-in-trade, with overlays of various Mediterranean traditions. A white-truffled pumpkin and chestnut risotto is one way to start a meal.

BAINBRIDGE   *MAP 18, SD99*
Yorebridge House
⊛⊛⊛ MODERN BRITISH ▲NOTABLE WINE LIST
See page 349

BIRSTWITH   *MAP 19, SE25*
The Station Hotel
⊛ MODERN BRITISH *V*
01423 770254 | Station Road, Birstwith, HG3 3AG
www.station-hotel.net
The Station is a venerable building in a village on the edge of Nidderdale, near Harrogate. The pick of the eating areas is the smart room that looks over the garden, but the main menu is served throughout. Classical cooking is given a high shine by Tim Bradley and his team.

BOLTON ABBEY   *MAP 19, SE05*
The Burlington Restaurant
⊛⊛⊛ MODERN BRITISH *V* ▲NOTABLE WINE LIST
01756 718100 | The Devonshire Arms Hotel & Spa, BD23 6AJ
devonshirehotels.co.uk/devonshire-arms-hotel-spa
The Devonshire Arms may sound like a cosy village pub, but is actually a country house hotel set in 30,000 acres of the Duke of Devonshire's estate, and The Burlington Restaurant is the star of the show, where chef Peter Howarth delivers food of craft and creativity, making good use of the estate's excellent produce and the kitchen garden for herbs, vegetables and fruits. For main you might try the John Dory – fresh, firm in texture and very well timed; the tempura batter is super crisp and has a lovely brittleness. Perhaps finish with the delicious blood orange salsa, chocolate tart, crème fraîche sorbet with mint. Table d'hôte dining or the multi-course tasting option are recommended and of course, there are wine pairings from the extensive list available.

Seats 60, Private dining 90 **Closed** Christmas and New Year (open residents only) **Parking** 100 **Notes** Children welcome

BOLTON ABBEY continued

The Devonshire Brasserie & Bar
⊛ TRADITIONAL BRITISH V
01756 710710 | The Devonshire Arms Hotel & Spa,
BD23 6AJ
www.thedevonshirearms.co.uk
The Devonshire Arms has a lot going for it, from
its fabulous position on the 30,000-acre estate,
the luxe bedrooms and the high-end restaurant,
but don't forget about the Brasserie & Bar. The
menu deals in upscale brasserie food, with a
Yorkshire flavour.

BURNSALL   *MAP 19, SE06*

The Devonshire Fell
⊛⊛ MODERN BRITISH V
01756 729000 | BD23 6BT
www.devonshirefell.co.uk
The informal, friendly service here feeds into the
easy-going vibe of The Devonshire Fell. The
please-all menus are driven by quality
ingredients, with simple pubby classics such as
fish and chips or steaks thrown into the mix.
There's a very good use of quality, local produce
and the dishes are honest and well balanced.

ESCRICK   *MAP 16, SE64*

Lascelles NEW
⊛⊛ MODERN BRITISH
01904 728111 | The Parsonage Country House Hotel,
York Road, YO19 6LF
www.parsonagehotel.co.uk
A 19th-century, former parsonage set within six
acres of gardens, a meal in the light-filled
Lascelles restaurant makes for an elegant dining
experience. Much of the menu showcases
produce grown within a 20-mile radius. Navarin
of Seaton Ross lamb with Puy lentils, carrots and
peas might be followed by Yorkshire curd tart,
local honey, grapes and mascarpone.

GILLING EAST   *MAP 19, SE67*

The Fairfax Arms
⊛⊛ CLASSIC BRITISH
01439 788212 | Main Street, YO62 4JH
www.thefairfaxarms.co.uk
Popular with the local farming community, The
Fairfax guards the village crossroads, one of
which leads to Gilling Castle, prep school for the
well-known Ampleforth College. The pub's black-
beamed, open-plan bar and dining area leads out
to a beer garden bordered by a stream.

GOATHLAND   *MAP 19, NZ80*

Mallyan Spout Hotel
⊛ MODERN BRITISH
01947 896486 | YO22 5AN
www.mallyanspout.co.uk
Named after the tumbling 70-ft waterfall behind
the hotel, the Mallyan Spout clings comfortingly
to a traditional style of furnishing and decor –
textured wallpaper, mirrors, high-backed
upholstered chairs, that sort of thing. Old
and New World wines are well balanced on the
50-bin list.

GOLDSBOROUGH   *MAP 19, SE35*

Goldsborough Hall
⊛⊛⊛ BRITISH
01423 867321 | Church Street, HG5 8NR
www.goldsboroughhall.com
Goldsborough Hall is a Jacobean stately home
with blue-blooded pedigree: Princess Mary, one
of the Queen's aunts, lived in this 1620s mansion
until 1929. Canapés are served in the lounge
before guests are shown through to an intimate
dining space of linen-swathed tables, a baby
grand, and a splendid marble fireplace for
complex, distinctly modern dishes. A delightfully
poised starter matches whipped goats' cheese
with spicy parkin and pear and artichoke in
various textures. Main-course Yorkshire dry-aged
duck comes alongside smoked cauliflower, black
garlic, hen of the woods mushrooms and onion,
while salted caramel custard tart and stem
ginger ice cream make for a simple, deeply
satisfying finish.

Seats 60, Private dining 110 **Closed** 24–26 December
Parking 50 **Notes** Children welcome

GRASSINGTON   *MAP 19, SE06*

Grassington House
⊛⊛ MODERN BRITISH
01756 752406 | 5 The Square, BD23 5AQ
www.grassingtonhouse.co.uk
The parquet-floored restaurant in this stone-
built Georgian house in the market square is
known for its traditional dishes prepared the
modern way. Proof is found throughout the
menu, so try starting with seared scallop and
glazed pork belly, then Thirsk lamb rump with
aubergine and roast red pepper, or pure and
simple beer-battered sustainable fish of the day.

BAINBRIDGE   *MAP 18, SD99*

Yorebridge House

◎◎◎ MODERN BRITISH 🍷 NOTABLE WINE LIST
01969 652060 | DL8 3EE
www.yorebridgehouse.co.uk

Yorebridge House is set in the former headmaster's house of the 17th-century grammar school and surrounded by the Yorkshire Dales. Today, the buildings make a fine country hotel, with the interior decorated to perfection and an understated neutral contemporary style in the dining room. Dan Shotton and his brigade champion the region's produce in menus that reflect ambition and a desire to impress via modern British ideas executed with skill and creativity, but without undue complication. The kitchen's flair for comforting, intuitive flavour combinations is clear in dishes such as beef carpaccio, teamed with celeriac and shimeji mushrooms and in well-balanced combinations of, say, Wensleydale lamb with turnips, or Nidderdale chicken with girolles and broccoli. If you're an aficionado of rhubarb, you're in the right county, and could find it teaming up with wood pigeon. The finale might be based on luxuriant 72% chocolate accessorised with honeycomb and cherry sorbet.

Chef Daniel Shotton **Seats** 35, Private dining 18 **Open** All Year **Parking** 30 **Notes** Children welcome

GUISBOROUGH
MAP 19, NZ61

Gisborough Hall
◉ MODERN BRITISH
01287 611500 | Whitby Lane, TS14 6PT
www.gisborough-hall.com
The hall is an imposing creeper-covered country-house hotel situated in well-kept grounds, and Chaloner's restaurant occupies a large space with pillars and a fireplace in what was once the billiard room. The kitchen team turns out some rather interesting dishes.

HAROME
MAP 19, SE68

The Star Inn
◉◉ MODERN BRITISH ▮NOTABLE WINE LIST
01439 770397 | YO62 5JE
www.thestaratharome.co.uk
This thatched pub in a moorland village boasts a rustic bar, a dining room with chunky tables, a real fire and knick-knacks galore, and a more modern restaurant. The country cooking places a high premium on big, rugged flavours, seen in a main of grilled fillet of John Dory with Jerusalem artichoke purée, salsify, a lobster fritter, a poached egg yolk and celeriac ash.

HARROGATE
MAP 19, SE35

Clocktower
◉◉ MODERN BRITISH
01423 871350 | Rudding Park, Follifoot, HG3 1JH
www.ruddingpark.co.uk/dine/clocktower
Rudding Park's Clocktower boasts food that's worth a detour. It's all vibrant, colourful spaces, from the long limestone bar to the grand conservatory with its Catalonian olive tree, and a dining room complete with an eye-catching pink glass chandelier.

Horto Restaurant
◉◉◉ MODERN BRITISH
01423 871350 | Rudding Park, Follifoot, HG3 1JH
www.ruddingpark.co.uk/dine/horto-restaurant
Latin for 'kitchen garden', Horto is set in the 300 acres of landscaped gardens and woodland at Rudding Park, a classy spa and golfing hotel. Restaurants where the gardener gets equal billing with the chef are rare, but that's the case in Horto, located within the modern spa area (there's also a separate informal café). There's a very trendy feel to the place, staff casually/smartly dressed and service is from the restaurant team and chefs combined. There are some very modern skills and techniques at play here and no division between starters, mains or

desserts - dishes are simply served when they are ready. The flavour combinations are quite simple and clean, but there's fantastic clarity, depth of flavour and execution. Ample ingredients are used from the local area, but also truly from the kitchen garden. Try confit chalk stream trout with radish, cucumber and buttermilk or lamb saddle with turnip and black garlic. At the sweet end of the menu, there's the 'tropical rhapsody' of avocado, chilli and mango.

Chef Callum Bowmer **Seats** 45 **Open** All Year **Parking** 350 **Notes** Children welcome

Hotel du Vin & Bistro Harrogate
◉ BRITISH, FRENCH, EUROPEAN ▮NOTABLE WINE LIST
01423 856800 | Prospect Place, HG1 1LB
www.hotelduvin.com/locations/harrogate
The Harrogate outpost of the HdV chain occupies a luxuriously converted terrace of eight Georgian townhouses opposite the 200-acre Stray Common. With hops around the windows and mustard-coloured walls, the place bears the group's corporate stamp, and the kitchen makes a virtue of simplicity.

Studley Hotel
◉ PACIFIC RIM, THAI
01423 560425 | 28 Swan Road, HG1 2SE
www.orchidrestaurant.co.uk
In the Studley Hotel's Orchid restaurant, a multinational brigade of chefs delivers authentic regional flavours in an eclectic pan-Asian melting pot of cuisines. Mango and darkwood interiors divided by Japanese lattice-style screens make for a classy, contemporary setting.

West Park Hotel
◉ TRADITIONAL BRITISH
01423 524471 | West Park, HG1 1BJ
www.thewestparkhotel.com
This contemporary boutique hotel occupies a lovely spot overlooking the Harrogate Stray, an open area of 200 acres of grassland in the centre of the historic spa town. In the comfortable modern dining room or in the alfresco courtyard, everything looks good on the plate.

White Hart Hotel
◉ CLASSIC BRITISH
01423 505681 | 2 Cold Bath Road, HG2 0NF
www.whiteharthotelharrogate.com
The White Hart is a Harrogate landmark, having provided bed and sustenance to travellers since the Georgian era. The Fat Badger Grill is its main eating space, serving up classic British food with a bit of a contemporary twist.

HEBDEN
MAP 19, SEO6

The Clarendon Country Pub With Rooms NEW
@ FRENCH/BRITISH MODERN V
01756 752446 | BD23 5DE
clarendoninn.co.uk
With most ingredients on the menu sourced from farmers and growers within the village, The Clarendon is rightly proud of the fresh, local produce it showcases. In the main, dishes based on Yorkshire Dales venison, and nearby Grimwith Estate wood pigeon are skilled, balanced and modern, and delivered by knowledgeable waiting staff in an unpretentious pub-style environment.

HELMSLEY
MAP 19, SE68

The Black Swan
@@ CLASSIC BRITISH, FRENCH V
01439 770466 | Market Place, YO62 5BJ
www.inncollectiongroup.com/the-black-swan
The Black Swan has been providing travellers with a warm welcome and famous hospitality for centuries, with parts of the building dating back to the 15th-century. Expect inviting open fires, cosy armchairs and a warm welcome. After your meal, explore nearby Rievaulx Abbey, Helmsley Castle and Helmsley Walled Garden.

Feversham Arms Hotel & Verbena Spa
@@ MODERN BRITISH
01439 770766 | 1-8 High Street, YO62 5AG
www.fevershamarmshotel.com
Sophisticated cooking built on fine regional ingredients is the order of the day here in The Weathervane Restaurant. The seared scallop with warm apple jelly, black pudding and smoked roe emulsion seems appropriate for a hotel in an affluent market town.

The Pheasant Hotel
@@@ MODERN BRITISH 🍷NOTABLE WINE LIST
See page 352

HETTON
MAP 18, SD95

The Angel at Hetton
@@@@ MODERN EUROPEAN
01756 730263 | BD23 6LT
angelhetton.co.uk
Since Michael Wignall (formerly of Gidleigh Park) took over this 500-year-old inn, a makeover has injected a brighter style to the warren-like interior to chime with the classy new culinary regime; like the food, it's certainly not pubby in the traditional sense of the word. Wignall crafts complex dishes, layering crystal-clear flavours and textures into finely balanced creations, as seen in a starter of 72-hour-cooked suckling pig with puréed and roasted parsnip, wafer-thin crackling and sublime cider-enriched jus. Main course powers ahead with fillet of aged Yorkshire beef alongside caramelised onion, wild garlic and forest mushrooms, and carrots boosted by cumin and coriander, or there might be turbot in the robust company of charred leeks and purée, cep velouté and Madeira sauce. A splendid dessert of über-rich treacle tart with crunchy caramelised walnuts and Dark Horse Brewery beer-flavoured ice cream is cut by the deftly managed sharpness of lemon curd.

Chef Michael Wignall **Seats** 65, Private dining 24 **Closed** 25 December, 2 weeks January **Parking** 40 **Notes** Children welcome

HOVINGHAM
MAP 19, SE67

The Worsley Arms Hotel
@@ BRITISH
01653 628234 | High Street, YO62 4LA
www.worsleyarms.co.uk
This Victorian hotel is well positioned in a pretty village set against a backdrop of the spectacular Howardian Hills. With its red walls, white linen and floral drapes, the restaurant is an elegant and traditional setting for fine-tuned dishes.

KETTLEWELL
MAP 18, SD97

King's Head Restaurant
@ MODERN BRITISH
01756 761600 | The Green, BD23 5RD
www.thekingsheadkettlewell.co.uk
This owner-run inn is a great base for leisure guests and keen walkers alike. Meals can be enjoyed in the cosy bar area beside an open roaring fire. It's all very seasonal and the blackboard-style menu allows for frequent changes and the best of local produce – expect a lot of game. Honest food, very well done.

KIRKBY FLEETHAM
MAP 19, SE29

Black Horse Inn
@ MODERN BRITISH V
01609 749010 | 7 Lumley Lane, DL7 0SH
www.blackhorseinnkirkbyfleetham.com
A short spin from the whirling traffic at Scotch Corner, this stone-built traditional inn pushes all the right buttons for a northern country hostelry. The main dining room overlooks the back garden and delivers classic and modern British dishes.

HELMSLEY

The Pheasant Hotel

◉◉◉ MODERN BRITISH ▲ NOTABLE WINE LIST

01439 771241 | Mill Street, Harome, YO62 5JG

www.thepheasanthotel.com

Although The Pheasant might sound like a simple pub – it was once the blacksmith's and village shop overlooking the duckpond in the charming village of Harome – its current incarnation is a rather refined hotel with bags of smart country style. Head chef Peter Neville takes a classical approach to his menu but with a contemporary cooking style that produces technically adept, imaginative dishes with wonderful depth and clarity of flavours. You'll find these elements in a main course of steamed Gigha halibut partnered with courgette and basil, lobster fritter, warm potato salad and tomato butter sauce. Finish with a luxuriant chocolate fondant served with blackcurrant leaf ice cream, salted caramel sauce and a cocoa nib tuile. There are different menus to choose from, including tasting and à la carte menus and one for children too.

Chef Peter Neville **Seats** 60, Private dining 30
Open All Year **Parking** 15
Notes Children welcome

MALHAM
MAP 18, SD96

The Lister Arms NEW
◉ MODERN BRITISH
01729 830444 | BD23 4DB
www.listerarms.co.uk
The Lister Arms is a country pub with pride of place in the village. It's a superb location, popular with walkers and a very busy operation throughout the year. The Yorkshire stone frontage, faces onto a small green. Inside, open fires, low ceilings snug areas in the bar with lots of blackboards and a superbly stocked bar always with at least eight hand pulls on including the core Thwaites five ales. The specials are what drives this place, although all of the other food offerings look really sharp – regardless of whether it's a simple burger or fish and chips. The pies here are excellent.

MASHAM
MAP 19, SE28

Samuel's at Swinton Park
◉◉ MODERN BRITISH
01765 680900 | Swinton, HG4 4JH
www.swintonestate.com
With its baronial tower and castellated walls hung with creeper, Swinton Park makes quite an impression. Samuel's restaurant is a suitably grand space, with its high gilded ceilings, carved fireplace and views onto the 20,000-acre estate. The kitchen celebrates the produce from Swinton's four acres of walled kitchen garden and the local area.

The Terrace
◉ MODERN, INTERNATIONAL
01765 680900 | Swinton Park, HG4 4JH
www.swintonestate.com
The Swinton Park estate is well known for the impressive Samuel's in the main hotel, but if you're looking for casual dining with a relaxed atmosphere then The Terrace restaurant serves a globally inspired menu throughout the day and there's a cosy bar area with a range of cocktails. The seasonally changing menus are focused around small grazing plates.

MIDDLEHAM
MAP 19, SE18

The Tack Room Restaurant NEW
◉◉ PAN-EUROPEAN, CLASSIC
01969 622093 | Market Place, DL8 4PE
www.thewensleydalehotel.com
In the charming hill town of Middleham, The Tack Room has a horse racing theme that reflects the local industry of breeding thoroughbreds, and comes with wooden floors and plenty of natural light. The menu has an old-school French brasserie feel, but also serves up a decent collection of English classics for Sunday lunch.

MIDDLESBROUGH
MAP 19, NZ41

Chadwicks Inn Maltby
◉◉ MODERN BRITISH
01642 590300 | High Lane, Maltby, TS8 0BG
www.chadwicksinnmaltby.co.uk
In a quiet village on the edge of the North Yorks Moors, you can dine either in the bar, with its wood-burner and sofas, or in the comfortable restaurant. Wherever, the dinner menu guarantees your full attention by listing Whitby crab and curry; pan-roasted Neasham beef with oxtail dumpling; and Hartlepool-landed halibut with lobster ravioli.

MIDDLETON TYAS
MAP 19, NZ20

The Coach House
◉◉ ENGLISH, MEDITERRANEAN
01325 377977 | Middleton Lodge, DL10 6NJ
www.middletonlodge.co.uk
The Coach House restaurant with its smart, rustic finish, soothing natural colours and a ceiling opened to the rafters, is a stylish spot to tuck into fine Yorkshire produce treated with respect. The hard-working kitchen has a sure touch, with main courses such as soy-glazed duck with sweet potatoes and toasted seeds.

MIDDLETON TYAS continued

Forge

◉◉◉ CONTEMPORARY BRITISH

01325 377977 | Middleton Lodge, DL10 6NJ

www.middletonlodge.co.uk/forge-restaurant

Forge has been created from a long-neglected barn at Middleton Lodge, a classic example of a Palladian country house in 200 acres of beautiful English countryside, with views across North Yorkshire. Forge makes extensive use of produce from the estate's two-acre kitchen garden and from the team's local foraging expeditions, and much of the food is cooked on open fires. Among the nine courses on a seasonal tasting menu expect heritage carrot with whipped cheese and pickled carrot; Skrei cod with cauliflower leaves and vin jaune; Yorkshire chicken, hen of the woods mushroom, asparagus and black garlic; and rhubarb with vanilla cream. Local merchants and wineries are behind the curated wine list.

Chef Gareth Rayner **Seats** 50 **Open** All Year **Parking** 100 **Notes** Children welcome

---

OLDSTEAD
MAP 19, SE58

The Black Swan at Oldstead

◉◉◉◉ MODERN BRITISH *V* 𝟑 NOTABLE WINE LIST

01347 868387 | Main Street, YO61 4BL

www.blackswanoldstead.co.uk

Down on the farm on the edge of the North York Moors, is where the Banks family calls home. With foraging forays to supplement the growing of fresh produce, it's a very modern enterprise, which is to say it has taken on many of the attributes of the rural life of 200 years ago. James Banks runs a tight ship out front, while his brother Tommy works wonders in the kitchen. It's worth a wander around the kitchen gardens to get a handle on how your dinner will eventually come together. The tasting menu, which is the standard bill of fare, opens with the customary nibbles, and posts notice of the intent straight away: mussel and wood sorrel; Jerusalem artichoke; a langoustine with caramelised whey. You're offered sour butter to spread on your sourdough bread, then it's on to raw Oldstead deer, followed by scallop with razor clam and rhubarb wild ferment. There's aged sirloin with onion and lovage, and then cheese, which is optional, before rhubarb and clotted cream, hay and Topaz apples, and a final savoury of root vegetable toast.

Chef Tommy Banks **Seats** 50, Private dining 13 **Open** All Year **Parking** 20 **Notes** No children under 10 years

---

OSMOTHERLEY
MAP 19, SE49

The Cleveland Tontine

◉◉ MODERN BRITISH, FRENCH

01609 882671 | Staddlebridge, DL6 3JB

www.theclevelandtontine.com

Once an overnight stop for travellers using the London to Sunderland mail coach, this has been an iconic restaurant for the past four decades. Now modernised for contemporary diners, the candlelit dining room oozes atmosphere with its stone fireplace and rustic carvings.

RIPON
MAP 19, SE37

Fletchers NEW

◉◉ MODERN BRITISH

01765 620070 | HG4 3ET

www.grantleyhall.co.uk/dining/fletchers-restaurant

Fletchers is the more relaxed of the two dining options - both are located in the original part of Grantley Hall. Offering all-day dining, the wood-panelled restaurant has banquette-style seating around the room's edges. It's far more than your usual brasserie operation and the main course offers great flavours and appearance. The hotel features a state-of-the-art spa, gym and private wine tasting areas.

Shaun Rankin at Grantley Hall NEW

◉◉◉ MODERN BRITISH 𝟑 NOTABLE WINE LIST

01765 620070 | HG4 3ET

www.grantleyhall.co.uk

Shaun Rankin's set-up in the Palladian splendour of Grantley Hall is unlikely to disappoint when you're up for the full Five-Star Monty. When you're done exploring the vast swathes of grounds, spa and elegant public rooms, Shaun and his team deliver cooking of serious quality and distinction in opulent surroundings. There's much to applaud, from chicken terrine with truffle-topped brioche and artichoke textures to an exquisitely constructed dish of venison loin with barbecued celeriac and blackcurrant gel. After that, terrine of quince and elderflower is matched with yogurt ice cream.

Chef Shaun Rankin **Seats** 16 **Open** All year

SALTBURN-BY-THE-SEA
MAP 19, NZ62

Brockley Hall Boutique Hotel & Fine Dining Restaurant
◉◉ MODERN BRITISH
01287 622179 | Glenside, TS12 1JS
www.brockleyhallhotel.com
Located close to the seafront in the heart of Saltburn, this hotel has been lovingly restored, and the restaurant has a dark and opulent theme that works really well. For dessert how about a wickedly sweet apple tart Tatin, apple textures and ginger?

SCARBOROUGH
MAP 17, TA08

Clark's Restaurant
◉ BRITISH, SEAFOOD *V*
01723 447373 | 40 Queen Street, YO11 1HQ
www.clarksrestaurant.co.uk

A very tempting frontage is your gateway into this neighbourhood restaurant where the tables are made from Singer sewing machine bases. The room is dominated by the bar/servery and a big display of gins, including products from Scarborough and Yorkshire. Locally-caught lobsters are a feature of the menus, which are seasonal and dependent on the catch of the day.

Lanterna Ristorante
◉ ITALIAN, SEAFOOD
01723 363616 | 33 Queen Street, YO11 1HQ
www.lanterna-ristorante.co.uk
It has been honoured by Italian newspaper La Stampa as 'the English temple of Italian cuisine', which seems an extraordinary accolade for an unassuming, albeit heartily convivial restaurant. Chef-patron, tireless Giorgio Alessio, oversees a venue done out in reds, oranges, sunny yellow and sky-blue.

SCAWTON
MAP 19, SE58

The Hare
◉◉◉ MODERN BRITISH
01845 597769 | YO7 2HG
www.thehare-inn.com
There's a wire sculpture of two fighting hares outside the Hare Inn, and it's possible that they're arguing about who gets to sit down at one of the restaurant's 12 covers. It's a luxurious venue with minimalist design, exposed stonework, and a rich colour palate of dark blues. The approach is a little bit different too; tasting menus all the way. Choose from six or eight courses, which the chef suggests may take around three or four hours respectively. Dishes come with a suggested wine, and may include tomato and goats' cheese; rump steak with beetroot and elderberry; or bass, razor clam and courgette.

Chef Paul Jackson Seats 16 Closed See website for details Parking 12 Notes No children

TIMBLE
MAP 19, SE15

The Timble Inn
◉◉ MODERN BRITISH *V*
01943 880530 | LS21 2NN
www.thetimbleinn.co.uk
Retaining all that makes a village pub such an asset, this Grade II listed, 18th-century coaching inn is squirrelled away in the beautiful Washburn Valley inside the Nidderdale Area of Outstanding Natural Beauty. Five miles from the Yorkshire Dales National Park, it's a popular pit stop for walkers in search of a pint of local ale. Warmed by a real fire, the comfortable restaurant showcases prime regional ingredients.

WEST WITTON
MAP 19, SE08

The Wensleydale Heifer
◉◉ MODERN BRITISH, SEAFOOD *V*
01969 622322 | Main Street, DL8 4LS
www.wensleydaleheifer.co.uk
Dining on super-fresh fish and seafood isn't the first thing that comes to mind when you're in the heart of the beautiful Yorkshire Dales National Park, but this chic 17th-century inn with boutique rooms draws foodies from far and wide for its piscine pleasures.

WHITBY
MAP 19, NZ81

Estbek House

◎◎ MODERN BRITISH

01947 893424 | East Row, Sandsend, YO21 3SU

www.estbekhouse.co.uk

Overlooking the North Sea just north of Whitby, Estbek House is perfectly positioned to source its materials from the chilly waters out front and the rolling moors behind. It all takes place in a handsome Regency house that operates as a restaurant with charming rooms.

The Star Inn The Harbour

◎ BRITISH, SEAFOOD

01947 821900 | Langborne Road, YO21 1YN

www.starinntheharbour.co.uk

An ideal harbourside location is the setting for this spacious restaurant with its delightfully styled fishing/natutical-themed interior. Catch-of-the-day fish and meat specials, sometimes from local game, feature. A separate ice cream parlour provides the desserts, but is also open to non-restaurant clientele. All in all, it's very tempting indeed.

YARM
MAP 19, NZ41

The Conservatory

◎◎ MODERN BRITISH ⚑ NOTABLE WINE LIST

01642 789000 | Judges Country House Hotel, Kirklevington Hall, TS15 9LW

www.judgeshotel.co.uk

Dating from 1881, the Judges Country House Hotel occupies a magnificent edifice within 22 acres of well-maintained grounds that include a walled kitchen garden. The dining room is appointed in keeping with the age and the style of the property, with double-clothed tables set with silver cutlery and fresh flowers, and large windows in the conservatory. Service is formal, but staff are friendly and keen to engage. First-class ingredients underpin the kitchen's output.

Crathorne Hall Hotel

◎ MODERN BRITISH

01642 700398 | Crathorne, TS15 0AR

www.handpickedhotels.co.uk/crathorne-hall

While the decor and furnishings of The Leven Restaurant are all early 20th century – oak half-panelled walls, heavy drapes at the tall sash windows, oil paintings, and a gilt-edged coffered ceiling – the cuisine tends towards modern British sensibilities, with sound, classical technique on display throughout the seasons.

YORK
MAP 16, SE65

The Bow Room Restaurant at Grays Court

◎◎◎ MODERN BRITISH

01904 612613 | Chapter House Street, YO1 7JH

www.grayscourtyork.com

The Bow Room Restaurant is part of the historic Grays Court, the oldest continuously inhabited house with links back to the 11th century. The 90ft-long gallery is delightful and features a bay window with views out to the city walls and the hotel grounds. The impressive kitchen garden supplies the all-day food options, which features exciting contemporary British dishes. Menu descriptions may be terse but they disguise the huge amount of skill involved. Wild sea trout paired with cucumber, pea and mint is one of the successful flavour combinations, as is a dessert of lemon, gooseberry and elderflower.

Chef Adam Jackson Closed 24–27 December Seats 24

Dean Court Hotel
◉ MODERN BRITISH

01904 625082 | Duncombe Place, YO1 7EF
www.deancourt-york.co.uk
The buildings that now make up Dean Court Hotel
were built to house clergy, so it's no surprise that
it's directly opposite stunning York Minster. The
restaurant decor is calming and neutral, which
means diners aren't distracted from the view, or
the food. The modern British menu is well-
balanced and seasonal.

Guy Fawkes Inn
◉ BRITISH

01904 466674 | 25 High Petergate, YO1 7HP
www.guyfawkesinnyork.com
The gunpowder plotter was born here in 1570, in
the shadow of York Minster. It is a darkly
atmospheric den with an interior akin to
stepping into an 'old master' painting, with log
fires, wooden floors, gas lighting, and lots of
cosy nooks and crannies.

Hotel du Vin & Bistro York
◉ EUROPEAN, FRENCH ⬩ NOTABLE WINE LIST

01904 557350 | 89 The Mount, YO24 1AX
www.hotelduvin.com
The York billet of the HdV group is a late
Georgian townhouse in the vicinity of the
Minster's Gothic splendour and the city
racecourse. Bare tables and wooden floor fit
in with the unbuttoned ethos, and the menu
offers sturdy French domestic fare with
minimal flounce.

The Judge's Lodging
◉ MODERN BRITISH

01904 638733 | 9 Lendal, YO1 8AQ
www.judgeslodgingyork.co.uk/food-drink
The Georgian townhouse hard by the Minster
has been reinvented as a modern inn of much
character with a plethora of eating and drinking
options. Dining can be elegantly panelled or
domestic-cosy, and the all-day menus offer a
wide range of international favourites.

Middlethorpe Hall & Spa
◉◉ MODERN BRITISH ⬩ NOTABLE WINE LIST

01904 641241 | Bishopthorpe Road, Middlethorpe,
YO23 2GB
www.middlethorpe.com
This majestic old building stands in 20 acres of
gardens and parkland. The kitchen offers a
fashionable surf 'n' turf combination of diver-
caught roasted scallop with sticky pork belly,
kohlrabi and apple purée. The cracking wine list
offers good advice on food and wine matching.

Roots York Restaurant *NEW*
◉◉◉ MODERN BRITISH

68 Marygate, York, North Yorkshire, YO30 7BH
www.rootsyork.com
Sister restaurant to Tommy Banks's celebrated
Black Swan at Oldstead, this relaxed restaurant
in the heart of York occupies a characterful
19th-century building. Light wood panelling,
coloured glass windows and an open kitchen
combine to create a relaxed and informal setting
overseen by a well-drilled team. A seasonal
tasting menu is the only option on offer, many of
the dishes showcasing produce from the chef's
family farm. Menu descriptions are concise but
hide the amount of work and skill involved.
Inventive flavour pairings are evident in dishes
such as 'trout, carrot, whey' and 'monkfish,
smoked butter, pickled mussel'.

Chef Tommy Banks, Sean Wrest

YORK continued

Skosh

◉◉ MODERN, INTERNATIONAL
01904 634849 | 98 Micklegate, YO1 6JX
www.skoshyork.co.uk

Skosh has made a big splash on the local and national food radar. Occupying a former shop in central York, a slate grey and vivid yellow colour scheme adds a bright and cheery vibe, as does the jeans and T-shirt attire of the relaxed staff.

The Star Inn The City

◉ MODERN BRITISH
01904 619208 | Lendal Engine House, Museum Street, YO1 7DR
www.starinnthecity.co.uk
This former pump engine house in a stunning riverside setting in the centre of York has been redeveloped into a modern bustling restaurant. There are various dining spaces, including a terrace and a cellar, but overall the decor has a pub-like feel.

■ SOUTH YORKSHIRE

SHEFFIELD
MAP 16, SK38

JÖRO Restaurant

◉◉◉ BRITISH, SCANDINAVIAN, JAPANESE *V*
0114 299 1539 | Krynkl, 294 Shalesmoor, S3 8UL
www.jororestaurant.co.uk
A converted shipping container off a roundabout on the outskirts of Steel City doesn't sound too inviting a prospect, but Jöro's urban edginess is bang in tune with the contemporary trend for neo-Nordic-influenced eating. Inside, the space has a minimalist feel with bare wood floors and tables decorated with flowers and baby vegetables, the buzz of an open kitchen adding to the convivial vibe. Despite the urban surrounds, the kitchen team maintains a close bond to nature, working with local farms and foragers to provide a steady flow of seasonal materials, and the small plate concept encourages diners to try a salvo of different dishes. Expect pin-sharp techniques and combinations that pack a punch, starting with a perfect piece of mackerel in miso-boosted broth alongside kohlrabi pickled in buttermilk whey, intensely sweet and smoky wood-fired onions, and roasted yeast purée, followed by mallard with red cabbage ketchup and blackcurrant jam.

Chef Luke French (owner executive chef) & Joe Bains (head chef) **Seats** 32, Private dining 10
Closed 5 - 11 July, 20 - 26 September, 20 - 27 December, 1 - 15 January **Notes** Children welcome

Juke and Loe

◉ MODERN BRITISH
01142 680271 | 617 Ecclesall Road, S11 8PT
www.jukeandloe.com
This small shop-fronted restaurant is situated in a trendy area of Sheffield and serves up modern British fare in a relaxed and informal atmosphere. Expect rustic-style wooden tables and contemporary, seasonal dishes which are good on flavour and natural presentation.

Nonnas

◉ MODERN ITALIAN

0114 268 6166 | 535–541 Ecclesall Road, S11 8PR

www.nonnas.co.uk

Nonnas is a bustling, good-natured Italian restaurant with friendly staff, café-style marble-topped tables and green walls. This is an imaginative kitchen turning out properly cooked, highly original dishes. Among accomplished dishes there might be the vivid combinations of Merlot-braised oxtail with beetroot mash and horseradish canederli (bread dumplings) and grilled sea bass fillet with borlotti bean and tomato stew and rosemary aïoli.

Rafters Restaurant

◉◉ MODERN BRITISH *V*

0114 230 4819 | 220 Oakbrook Road, Nethergreen, S11 7ED

www.raftersrestaurant.co.uk

A well-established venue away from the bustle of the city centre, Rafters Restaurant is in an unusual corner building, and sits at the top of the stairs, as the name implies. Only around 30 covers, it has undergone a refurb that includes an open kitchen and chef's table. It's quite formal but friendly, and offers very modern British cooking.

WORTLEY *MAP 16, SK39*

The Wortley Arms

◉ MODERN BRITISH

0114 288 8749 | Halifax Road, S35 7DB

www.wortley-arms.co.uk

The Wortley Arms is an appealing spot for a pint of local ale and some modern gastro-pub cooking. Timeless staples (beer-battered fish and chips with home-made tartare sauce, or gammon steak with griddled pineapple) rub shoulders with more up-to-date ideas.

■ WEST YORKSHIRE

BRADFORD *MAP 19, SE13*

Prashad

◉◉ INDIAN VEGETARIAN

0113 285 2037 | 137 Whitehall Road, Drighlington, BD11 1AT

www.prashad.co.uk

There is strong competition in Bradford when it comes to authentic Indian cooking, but Prashad's meat-free repertoire ensures a loyal local following. A mural depicting an Indian street scene provides a vibrant look, and food has its roots in the vegetarian cuisine of the Gujarat.

HALIFAX
MAP 19, SE02

Shibden Mill Inn

◉◉ MODERN BRITISH

01422 365840 | Shibden Mill Fold, Shibden, HX3 7UL
www.shibdenmillinn.com

With milling abandoned long ago, it's left to the beams and exposed stone to remind us of its history. An inviting menu covers a lot of ground, ranging from a starter such as cured chalk stream trout, to mains like 65-day salt-aged pavé of beef with ox-cheek crumble; and vegetarian cauliflower arancini.

HUDDERSFIELD
MAP 16, SE11

315 Bar and Restaurant

◉ MODERN

01484 602613 | 315 Wakefield Road, Lepton, HD8 0LX
www.315barandrestaurant.co.uk

This place brings a touch of metropolitan chic to Huddersfield. The menu bursts with bright, modern ideas such as crab and lobster mousse wrapped in nori with ginger, lime and coriander dressing to start. Main courses are no less original and puddings are attractively presented.

ILKLEY
MAP 19, SE14

Box Tree

◉◉◉ MODERN, CLASSIC INTERNATIONAL ⚑ NOTABLE WINE LIST

01943 608484 | 35-37 Church Street, LS29 9DR
www.theboxtree.co.uk

An iconic restaurant for six decades, The Box Tree continues to thrive under current custodians Simon and Rena Gueller. A stone-built property on the road through Ilkley, the abundant hanging baskets and pretty garden enhance the cottage-like feel. Linen tablecloths and impeccable service add a touch of luxury and the modern food is underpinned by classical techniques. Dinner might begin with glazed veal sweetbreads, crispy chicken, local corn, pickled shallot, burnt cauliflower purée, followed by Anjou squab pigeon, foie gras parfait, cherries, salsify and port. Finish with strawberry soufflé, clotted cream, oat crumble, pickled pine berries and basil.

Chef Simon Gueller, Samira Effa **Seats** 50, Private dining 20 **Closed** 27–31 December, 1–8 January **Notes** No children under 5 years at lunch, 10 years at dinner

LEEDS
MAP 19, SE23

Chez Mal Brasserie

◉ MODERN BRITISH ⚑ NOTABLE WINE LIST

0113 398 1000 | Malmaison Leeds, 1 Swinegate, LS1 4AG
www.malmaison.com

The Malmaison group's Leeds branch is decorated and furnished to a high standard and the brasserie is no exception, with plush leather booths and fireplaces under its elegant ceiling. The cooking is built on quality ingredients, and talented chefs are clearly at work.

Fourth Floor Café

◉ CLASSIC

0113 204 8888 | 107–111 Briggate, LS1 6AZ
www.harveynichols.com/restaurant/leeds-dining

As the name suggests, the restaurant is located on the fourth floor and it has a similarly chic, minimalist style as other in-store restaurants in the Harvey Nichols collection. The dining area is flanked by the bar and an open kitchen.

HOME *NEW*

◉◉ MODERN BRITISH

0113 430 0161 | 16/17 Kirkgate, LS1 6BY
www.homeleeds.co.uk

Home's loft-style location is accessed through a very discrete entrance from a pedestrian shopping area of Leeds city centre. Up two flights of darkened stairs, you'll reach the bar first, which is laid out with sofas and quite minimal decor in dark colours. The brighter restaurant is well-spaced and clothed tables are set only with candle, flowers and napkins. The team from the open kitchen are very knowledgeable, clearly professional and helpfully explain most courses and their reimagined British flavours.

The Man Behind The Curtain

◉◉◉◉ MODERN EUROPEAN

0113 243 2376 | 68–78 Vicar Lane, Lower Ground Floor Flannels, LS1 7JH

www.themanbehindthecurtain.co.uk

The determinedly monochrome basement room of Michael O'Hare's contemporary restaurant is in stark contrast to the culinary approach. While black marble tables and floor tiles offset the grey-veined walls, which are lightened with vertical displays of skateboards, marble surfboards and scrawls of incoherent graffiti, the black-shaded lamps illuminate plates – and many another receptacles – of cutting-edge experimental food that manages to avoid a lot of what have become the modern clichés. The standard offering is a taster of 10 to 14 'sequences', with a shorter version at lunchtime, built around a repertoire of dazzlingly imaginative dishes. A single octopus tentacle in butter emulsion has a strong hit of paprika, while a pâté of perfect crab is balanced on a crisp cracker and topped with a quail egg. Coarsely sliced, eloquently fatted Wagyu beef in olive juice with a sheet of potato paper is extraordinary in its impact. Creativity is unflagging to the end.

Chef Michael O'Hare **Seats** 44 **Closed** 21 December to 13 January **Notes** No children under 8 years at dinner

Salvo's Restaurant & Salumeria

◉ ITALIAN

0113 275 5017 | 115 Otley Road, Headingley, LS6 3PX

salvos.co.uk

Forty-five years ago, Salvatore Dammone opened this Headingley restaurant, not far from the famous cricket ground. Today, it's the second and third generations of the family who maintain Salvo's simple approach to providing contemporary Italian food, including interesting pastas and pizzas. Great items are brought in from the motherland, especially for tasting menu dishes from different Italian regions.

Thorpe Park Hotel & Spa

◉ BRITISH, FRENCH

01132 641000 | Century Way, Thorpe Park, LS15 8ZB

www.thorpeparkhotel.co.uk/food-drink

With quick access into Leeds or the countryside, the modern Thorpe Park Hotel is a handy base for exploring the area. The split-level dining room has a contemporary finish with artwork on the walls, and black leather-type chairs. The populist menu offers feel-good stuff.

Wentbridge House Hotel

◉◉ MODERN BRITISH ⬧ NOTABLE WINE LIST

01977 620444 | The Great North Road, Wentbridge, WF8 3JJ

www.wentbridgehouse.co.uk

Set in 20 acres of landscaped grounds in a conservation village, Wentbridge is a stone-built grand manor house. There's a degree of glossy formality, where candy-coloured upholstery creates a light, bright effect, and the cooking reaches out in all directions for its references.

The Moorcock Inn

◉◉ BRITISH SEASONAL

01422 832103 | Moorbottom Lane, HX6 3RP

www.themoorcock.co.uk

The Moorcock Inn is a substantial stone building with fine views, a traditional Yorkshire inn with flagstones and a carved wooden bar. Chairs and bare wooden tables fill the cosy dining room, where you'll see snacks and desserts called up on boards. The chef makes the organic-looking dishes and plates as well as the food – his very seasonal cooking is very contemporary style, informed by the seasons and local produce.

Wood Hall Hotel & Spa

◉◉ MODERN BRITISH

01937 587271 | Trip Lane, Linton, LS22 4JA

www.handpickedhotels.co.uk/woodhall

High on a hill with fine views, the Georgian Wood Hall retains much of its original detailing. Its dining room is an elegant, relaxing space where a rigorous dedication to Yorkshire produce is observed, and the cooking is marked by clear, distinct flavours.

CHANNEL ISLANDS

■ GUERNSEY

ST MARTIN   MAP 24

La Barbarie Hotel
◉ TRADITIONAL BRITISH
01481 235217 | Saints Road, Saints Bay, GY4 6ES
www.labarbariehotel.com
This former priory is now a comfortable hotel
with a soothing vibe and a restaurant using the
peerless fresh produce of Guernsey's coasts and
meadows. The kitchen looks to the French
mainland for inspiration in their repertoire of
simply cooked and presented dishes.

Bella Luce Hotel, Restaurant & Spa
◉◉ FRENCH, MEDITERRANEAN
01481 238764 | La Fosse, GY4 6EB
www.bellalucehotel.com
With its 12th-century granite walls, period charm
and luxe boutique finish, Bella Luce is a class
act. The culinary action takes place in the
romantic restaurant, where there's some sharp,
contemporary European cooking built on a good
showing of local produce.

ST PETER PORT   MAP 24

The Duke of Richmond Hotel
◉ MODERN, BRITISH, FRENCH
01481 726221 | Cambridge Park, GY1 1UY
www.dukeofrichmond.com
The Leopard Bar and Restaurant, with its
distinctive style and excellent quality
ingredients, has developed a unique identity.
Guests might choose to dine alfresco on the
large terrace, but those who dine inside will have
a view through to the open kitchen.

The Old Government House Hotel & Spa
◉ MODERN EUROPEAN
01481 724921 | St Ann's Place, GY1 2NU
www.theoghhotel.com
The beautiful white Georgian building was once
the island governor's harbourside residence,
converted into a hotel in 1858. Among several
dining options at the hotel, The Brasserie is the
place to be, offering fresh Guernsey fish as part
of the menu at lunch and dinner.

St Pierre Park Hotel, Spa and Golf Resort
◉ BRITISH
01481 736676 | Rohais, GY1 1FD
www.handpickedhotels.co.uk/stpierrepark
One mile from St Peter Port, this peaceful
hotel is surrounded by 35 acres of grounds
and a golf course. Overlooking the garden and
with its own terrace and water feature, the
bright and contemporary Pavilion Restaurant
offers a crowd-pleasing menu with something
for everybody.

■ JERSEY

GOREY   MAP 24

Sumas
◉◉ MODERN BRITISH V
01534 853291 | Gorey Hill, JE3 6ET
www.sumasrestaurant.com

The seasonal menus in this family-run restaurant
are mainly modern British, featuring abundant
fish and seafood, maybe hand-dived scallops and
John Dory, although hints of French and Asian
cooking appear too. Dining on the terrace
overlooking Gorey harbour and Mont Orgueil
Castle is rather enjoyable, especially when it's
sunny. An affordable wine list ranges worldwide.

ROZEL — MAP 24

Château la Chaire

�� CLASSIC TRADITIONAL

01534 863354 | Rozel Bay, JE3 6AJ

www.chateau-la-chaire.co.uk

Snuggled into a wooded valley, and yet only moments from the seashore, La Chaire is an early Victorian edifice with grounds laid out by the Kew Gardens luminary Samuel Curtis, and interiors full of oak panelling and intricate plaster scrollwork. The conservatory dining room capitalises fully on the majestic green views.

ST AUBIN — MAP 24

The Boat House

� BRITISH

01534 744226 | 1 North Quay, JE3 8BS

www.randalls-jersey.co.uk/the-boat-house

With its full-drop glass walls overlooking the harbour and town, The Boat House has staked its claim to the best spot in St Aubin. Light and airy with an open kitchen, the first-floor restaurant deals in fresh, modern and traditional food, mixing fine ingredients and confident technique.

ST BRELADE — MAP 24

L'Horizon Beach Hotel and Spa

�� MODERN BRITISH

01534 743101 | St Brelade's Bay, JE3 8EF

www.handpickedhotels.co.uk/lhorizon

The view over the bay is a big draw here but the Grill restaurant really puts the place on the map. It's a smart room with neutral colours, and the menu makes excellent use of the island's bounty, in bright, modern dishes.

Ocean Restaurant at The Atlantic Hotel

��� MODERN BRITISH ♦ NOTABLE WINE LIST

01534 744101 | Le Mont de la Pulente, JE3 8HE

www.theatlantichotel.com

The Ocean Restaurant is the jewel in the crown of The Atlantic Hotel, a boutique retreat amid exotic palm trees in a conservation area overlooking the wild dunes of St Ouen's Bay. The timeless sea views are best savoured from the louvred windows of the dining room, a gloriously light and airy setting with a soft-focus palette of blue, white and beige, and modern artwork on the walls. Chef Will Holland's stellar cooking is the real draw. You might open with accurately seared scallops with salt cod brandade, carrot remoulade and sweet-and-sour carrot purée, a sensational marriage of sweet and salty savour. That could be followed by juniper-roasted venison loin with a breaded bonbon of the meat, smoked bacon choucroute, salsify and pickled blueberries, in a glossy, deeply resonant bitter chocolate jus. The showstopping finale is chocoholic heaven of cacao streusel coated with Guanaja, with 70% chocolate gelée and coffee ice cream.

Chef Will Holland **Seats** 60, Private dining 60
Closed January **Parking** 60 **Notes** Children welcome

Oyster Box

�� MODERN BRITISH

01534 850888 | St Brelade's Bay, JE3 8EF

www.oysterbox.co.uk

The views of St Brelade's Bay are unbeatable from the Oyster Box, whether you're dining on the terrace or in the cool, contemporary dining room. A starter of Jersey rock oysters is hard to beat, to be followed by brill 'chop' served on the bone with spinach, Jersey Royals and brown shrimp béarnaise.

ST CLEMENT
MAP 24

Green Island Restaurant
🏵 MEDITERRANEAN, SEAFOOD
01534 857787 | Green Island, JE2 6LS
www.greenisland.je
This laid-back beach café and restaurant claims to the most southerly eatery in the British Isles, so kick back and bask in sun-kissed views over the sandy bay. The emphasis is on fish and shellfish, and the kitchen has the nous to treat them with a light touch to let the freshness and quality do the talking.

ST HELIER
MAP 24

Best Western Royal Hotel
🏵 MODERN EUROPEAN
01534 726521 | David Place, JE2 4TD
www.morvanhotels.com
In the hotel's Seasons restaurant, a predominantly white colour scheme, with lightwood flooring, flowers on the tables and comfortable leather chairs, creates a coolly elegant atmosphere, appropriate surroundings for some polished cooking. A decent choice of bread, all made on the premises, is offered.

Bohemia Restaurant
ROSETTES SUSPENDED MODERN FRENCH, BRITISH 🍷 NOTABLE WINE LIST
01534 880588 | The Club Hotel & Spa, Green Street, JE2 4UH
www.bohemiajersey.com
The Rosette award for this establishment has been suspended due to a change of chef and reassessment will take place in due course.
When a road sign in southern England points to The North it could mean a journey of perhaps a couple of hundred miles; not so in Green Street, St Helier, where an identically worded sign means an easy four- or five-mile trip to Jersey's north coast. The road soon passes The Club Hotel & Spa, in the shadow of Fort Regent, the island capital's 19th-century fortifications, and from the hotel's rooftop terrace there's a good view across this essentially low-rise town. A separate entrance leads from the street to the Bohemia Bar & Restaurant, the bar area itself providing an informal setting for lunch, dinner, drinks and afternoon tea.

Seats 60, Private dining 24 **Closed** 24-30 December
Notes Children welcome

Doran's Courtyard Bistro
🏵 BRITISH, FRENCH, STEAKS, SEAFOOD
01534 734866 | The Hotel Revere, Kensington Place, JE2 3PA
www.reverehoteljersey.com
It's easy to see why Doran's is popular with the locals as well as with guests staying at The Hotel Revere. Service is relaxed in the cosy restaurant with stone-flagged floors and exposed oak beams, and the menu is simple but well done.

Sirocco@The Royal Yacht
ROSETTES SUSPENDED AUSTRALASIAN INSPIRED 𝑉
01534 720511 | The Weighbridge, JE2 3NF
www.theroyalyacht.com
The Rosette award for this establishment has been suspended due to a change of chef and reassessment will take place in due course.
Curvaceous, wave-shaped balconies echo the maritime location at this contemporary harbourfront bolt-hole. It's a slick, upmarket affair, with a glossy spa centre, plus ample dining and drinking opportunities to keep you refuelled and refreshed, the pick of the bunch being the snazzy Sirocco with its huge terrace opening up sweeping views over the marina through full-drop windows.

Seats 65, Private dining 20 **Open** All year
Prices from S £11.65, M £21.50, D £12 **Notes** Vegetarian dishes, Children welcome

Samphire

ROSETTES SUSPENDED **MODERN EUROPEAN** 🍷NOTABLE WINE LIST

01534 725100 | 7-11 Don Street, JE2 4TQ

www.samphire.je

The Rosette award for this establishment has been suspended due to a change of chef and reassessment will take place in due course. Gorgeously done out with clean art deco-style lines worthy of a 1920s ocean liner, Samphire looks stunning with its wooden floors, plush blue velvet banquettes and mustard yellow leather seating. The place will sort you out all day from breakfast, through brunch and onwards to killer evening cocktails in a lively ground-floor bar, a see-and-be-seen terrace on the street out front and, up on the roof, a garden terrace for those balmy Jersey days.

Seats 50, Private dining 14 **Closed** 25 December
Prices from S £10, M £18, D £9.50
Notes Children welcome

Tassili

◉◉◉◉ **BRITISH, FRENCH**

01534 722301 | Grand Jersey Hotel & Spa, The Esplanade, JE2 3QA

www.handpickedhotels.co.uk/grandjersey

The Grand Jersey is a rather glamorous late-Victorian hotel – there are wonderful views from the terrace, just a stone's throw from the waters of St Aubin's Bay. The restaurant, Tassili, is a darkly luxurious space that comes into its own in the evenings. Service is excellent, with a great eye for detail, and you can expect high-level French technique from Nicolas Valmagna and his team, taking inspiration from the island's produce and ideas from further afield. An early spring menu offers a delightfully presented starter of Nantes duck liver terrine, full of flavour and richness, with charred sweetcorn providing sweetness and balance. For main course, you might choose Anjou pigeon, with cromesquis leg and a vibrant candied heritage beetroot sorbet is a great dish, the pigeon perfectly timed and very tender. A beautifully constructed dessert of Valrhona chocolate with orange cremeux, sweetly peppery piment d'espelette ganache and Jivara chocolate sorbet proves an unexpected yet brilliant combination of flavours.

Chef Nicolas Valmagna **Seats** 24 **Closed** 25 December, 1–30 January **Parking** 32 **Notes** No children under 12 years

Greenhills Country Hotel

◉ **MODERN, MEDITERRANEAN, BRITISH, FRENCH**

01534 481042 | Mont de L'Ecole, JE3 7EL

www.greenhillshotel.com

There is much to like about this relaxed country hotel with its riotously colourful gardens, heated outdoor pool and bags of traditional charm. The kitchen team turns out a wide-ranging menu taking in everything from a classic straight-up fillet steak to more ambitious ideas.

Mark Jordan at the Beach

◉◉ **ANGLO-FRENCH**

01534 780180 | La Plage, La Route de la Haule, JE3 7YD

www.markjordanatthebeach.com

Get yourself a table with a sea view – or out on the terrace if the weather is kind – for skilful cooking with a relaxed approach. You'll see plenty of local produce, especially fish, on the menu, and there's a great choice of wines by the glass. A signature starter is the Jersey squid 'riceless risotto', made from teeny tiny cubes of squid in a creamy sauce, providing a bed for scallop carpaccio and pickled cauliflower, all delightfully fresh and delicious. Next up, local brill with asparagus, a nicely plump home-made crab tortellini and a wonderful lobster bisque.

ST SAVIOUR
MAP 24

Longueville Manor Hotel

◉◉◉ MODERN ANGLO-FRENCH ⚑ NOTABLE WINE LIST

01534 725501 | JE2 7WF

www.longuevillemanor.com

Set on a lovely 18-acre estate, with woodland walks, restored Victorian kitchen garden, and a lake, Longueville Manor has been the grande dame of the Jersey hotel scene since the 1940s. Andrew Baird's kitchen focuses on local produce – plenty of which comes from that beautiful kitchen garden – and the cooking is a refined, innovative Anglo-French take on classic techniques. The Oak Room is a wonderfully atmospheric panelled dining room, a delightful setting for compelling dishes inspired by wonderful produce. Start with impeccable, perfectly-timed scallops served with caramelised apple, cider butter sauce, crisp pancetta and potato rösti, perhaps, followed by a beautifully cooked piece of turbot with a vibrant Beaufort crust, fricassée of woodland mushrooms and salsify. Bring things to a close with a superbly fresh-tasting garden lemon mousse, accompanied by a ginger sablé and gin and tonic sorbet. The state-of-the-art wine cellar, home to some 4,500 bottles, needs to be seen to be believed.

Chef Andrew Baird **Seats** 65, Private dining 40 **Open** All Year **Parking** 45 **Notes** Children welcome

■ SARK

SARK
MAP 24

Stocks Hotel

ROSETTES SUSPENDED MODERN BRITISH

01481 832001 | GY10 1SD

www.stockshotel.com

The Rosette award for this establishment has been suspended due to a change of chef and reassessment will take place in due course.

Tucked away in a tranquil and picturesque valley – but then again just about everywhere on Sark is quiet and picturesque – Stocks is a smart hotel built around a Georgian farmhouse. It's done out in a traditional manner, and that goes for the fine-dining restaurant, too. With its opulent drapes and white tablecloths, the panelled dining room provides a traditional and formal setting.

SCOTLAND

■ ABERDEEN

ABERDEEN
MAP 23, NJ90

Chez Mal Brasserie
⊛ MODERN FRENCH
01224 327370 | Malmaison Aberdeen,
49-53 Queens Road, AB15 4YP
www.malmaisonaberdeen.com
Built from the solid granite that gives the city its
moniker, the Aberdeen Mal is suitably dashing,
with boutique allure and a cool industrial-chic
finish. The brasserie is at the heart of the
operation, with an open-to-view kitchen
revealing the Josper grill.

IX Restaurant
⊛⊛ MODERN SCOTTISH
01244 327777 | The Chester Hotel, 59-63 Queens Road,
AB15 4YP
www.chester-hotel.com
The kitchen team behind this glossy
contemporary grill are on a mission to be one
of Aberdeen's top restaurants, and their
switched-on menu is heading straight for that
target. Happily, the food here is about great
flavours rather than ego.

Moonfish Café
⊛ MODERN BRITISH
01224 644166 | 9 Correction Wynd, AB10 1HP
www.moonfishcafe.co.uk
Tucked away in a medieval wynd, or narrow lane,
Moonfish Café has that fit-for-purpose, ready-
to-go look about it. And go it does, with
innovative modern British cooking, perhaps
opening with crispy potato, cheese custard and
Madras curry, then hake with onion, rice and
brown butter, ending with rhubarb millefeuille,
mascarpone and vanilla.

The Silver Darling
⊛ SEAFOOD
01224 576229 | Pocra Quay, North Pier, AB11 5DQ
www.thesilverdarling.co.uk
A harbour-mouth restaurant specialising in fish
and seafood in the old customs house, whose
huge windows provide a ringside view of trawlers
off to catch it. Indubitably Scottish are Loch Fyne
oysters and Cullen skink starters; although they
sound more cosmopolitan, mains such as pan-
seared monkfish, sole goujons, chargrilled steak
and seasonal game are just as patriotic.

■ ABERDEENSHIRE

BALMEDIE
MAP 23, NJ91

The Cock and Bull
⊛ MODERN SCOTTISH, BRITISH
01358 743249 | Ellon Road, Blairton, AB23 8XY
www.thecockandbull.co.uk
Open fires and modern artworks bring cossetting
warmth to this creeper-clad, stone-built
coaching inn standing in open farmland north of
Aberdeen. You can be sure of a well-kept pint
and no-nonsense food ranging from pub classics
to more accomplished dishes based on
Peterhead-landed fish and shellfish, or regionally
sourced meats.

BANCHORY
MAP 23, NO69

The Falls of Feugh Restaurant
⊛ MODERN BRITISH
01330 822123 | Bridge of Feugh, AB31 6NL
www.thefallsoffeugh.com
In a bucolic spot by the river, surrounded by
trees, the sound of running water is particularly
evocative if you're sitting on the small terrace.
There's a charming café, but the main draw is the
modern French- and Scottish-inflected food on
offer in the restaurant.

ELLON
MAP 23, NJ93

Eat on the Green
⊛⊛ BRITISH, SCOTTISH, EUROPEAN
01651 842337 | Udny Green, AB41 7RS
www.eatonthegreen.co.uk

In a picture-perfect Scottish stone house with a
gloriously inviting interior of rich colours, Eat on
the Green is going from strength to strength.
Attention to detail is everything from the 'kilted
chef' here, with vegetables and herbs picked
from their own gardens and meat and game
arriving from local farms. They have a 'Gin
Garden' too.

INVERURIE

Green Lady NEW
◉ MODERN SCOTTISH
01467 621643 | AB51 5NT
www.crerarhotels.com/thainstone-house-hotel
Thainstone House is a grand family home and hotel in Inverurie, near Aberdeen. The house dates back to the 18th century and has a rich history as both a grand private home and as a much loved Aberdeenshire landmark. Now lovingly restored, this elegant hotel welcomes its guests with traditional Scottish hospitality.

KILDRUMMY

Kildrummy Inn
◉◉ MODERN SCOTTISH
01975 571227 | AB33 8QS
www.kildrummyinn.co.uk
Kildrummy Inn has an authenticity that appeals to tourists and locals, while the output from its dynamic kitchen has put it on the foodie map. Menus reveal classical sensibilities and a contemporary touch and flavours hit the mark when it comes to desserts, too.

PETERHEAD

Buchan Braes Hotel
◉ MODERN SCOTTISH, EUROPEAN
01779 871471 | Boddam, AB42 3AR
www.buchanbraes.co.uk
The low-slung Buchan Braes won't win any architectural prizes, but it's a splendid contemporary hotel with a rural aspect and up-to-date wedding and conference facilities to boot. There's also the Grill Room restaurant, with its open kitchen and warmly colourful decor.

STONEHAVEN

The Tolbooth Seafood Restaurant
◉ MODERN BRITISH, SEAFOOD
01569 762287 | Old Pier, Stonehaven Harbour, AB39 2JU
www.tolbooth-restaurant.co.uk
There can't be many better spots than this for tucking into seafood: it's right on the harbour wall, with a museum on the ground floor and the upstairs restaurant giving sea views. What you eat depends on what's been landed that day.

TARLAND

Douneside House
◉◉◉ CLASSIC
013398 81230 | Tarland, AB34 4UL
www.dounesidehouse.co.uk
Initially bought as a holiday home by the MacRobert family in the 1880s, Douneside was creatively enhanced with a crenellated tower and extra rooms, and presents a pleasingly asymmetrical façade to the world. The family trust still oversees the running of the place, from its excellent gardens to the fully equipped spa hotel. Completing the picture is a dynamic kitchen supplied by an industrious kitchen garden, fish from the Peterhead boats, and meat from a local butcher with a royal warrant. Matt Price combines forward-looking culinary thinking with plenty of old-school opulence on menus that might open with new season asparagus and truffle mousse, with a salad of raw and pickled vegetables and aged parmesan. Move on to loin and belly of Fife pork, or seared fillet of halibut, before finishing triumphantly with rhubarb bavarois with vanilla custard, ginger ale and rhubarb sorbet. There's a five-course tasting menu too, available Thursday to Saturday.

Chef Matt Price Seats 40, Private dining 12 Open All Year Parking 40 Notes Children welcome

◼ ANGUS

CARNOUSTIE

Carnoustie Golf Hotel & Spa
◉ BISTRO, SCOTTISH, EUROPEAN
01241 411999 | The Links, DD7 7JE
www.bespokehotels.com/carnoustiegolfhotel
Calder's Bistro enjoys a stunning location overlooking the 1st tee and 18th green of the world-famous Carnoustie Links golf course. With floor-to-ceiling windows providing impressive views of the golf course, this makes a pleasant place to sample an eclectic range of dishes.

FORFAR

Drovers
◉ MODERN SCOTTISH
01307 860322 | Memus By Forfar, DD8 3TY
www.the-drovers.com
Surrounded by beautiful glens, Drovers is the kind of wild place you want to be stranded when the weather closes in. Although a modern pub in many ways, the walls of antlers remind you this rustic bolt-hole has been around for many years.

INVERKEILOR
MAP 23, NO64

Gordon's
◉◉◉ MODERN SCOTTISH

01241 830364 | Main Street, DD11 5RN

www.gordonsrestaurant.co.uk

Blink, and you'd miss the tiny coastal hamlet of Inverkeilor, were it not for for the discreet restaurant with rooms along the high street that's put the village on the map of gastronomic destinations. Thanks to the Watson family's efforts over 30-odd years, the place ticks all the boxes for a food-and-sea-themed getaway, with boutique rooms and a beamed and stone-walled dining room. These days, Gordon's son Garry heads up the kitchen side of things, keeping all-comers on side with his precise modern Scottish cooking. The drill is a fixed-price menu of five courses at dinner, opening with roe deer tartare, perhaps, enriched with quail's egg yolk and served with pickled shimeji, hazelnut aïoli and apple salad. A fish main might be a beautiful piece of turbot, served with brown shrimps, couscous, squash, and curry dressing; a very thoughtfully-constructed, well-balanced dish with precise flavours. Finish with pistachio crème brûlée, raspberries and chocolate.

Chef Garry Watson **Seats** 24, Private dining 8
Closed January **Parking** 6 **Notes** No children under 12 years

■ ARGYLL & BUTE

COVE
MAP 20, NS28

Knockderry House
◉◉ MODERN SCOTTISH

01436 842283 | Shore Road, G84 0NX

www.knockderryhouse.co.uk

Standing on the shore of Loch Long, this much-altered Victorian house is a period treat inside, with a billiard room, intricate wood panelling and magnificent stained windows in the dining room. Gloved staff serve Scottish food that embraces modern techniques.

ERISKA
MAP 20, NM94

Restaurant at Isle of Eriska
◉◉◉ CLASSIC

01631 720371 | PA37 1SD

www.eriska-hotel.co.uk

It may be just a short drive north of Oban, but this Victorian, baronial-style country house on its own 300-acre private island exudes an exclusivity factor that makes you feel you should arrive by helicopter. Add in a nine-hole golf course, a serious spa and leisure package, and the undeniable magic of the gorgeous views overlooking Loch Linnhe and the dramatic Morvern Mountains beyond, and you're in for a truly unique and memorable experience. Seriously good food is, of course, a major part of the deal with refined, classically based cooking grounded firmly in the abundant regional larder. A well-balanced starter brings superb scallops offset by grapefruit-glazed sea kale and citrus butter sauce, while main-course saddle of roe deer is supported by baked celeriac, morels, spelt and green pepper sauce. Presentation, right through to a dessert of poached Yorkshire rhubarb with white chocolate mousse and rhubarb and ginger sorbet, is impeccable.

Chef Andrew Turnbull **Notes** No children

HELENSBURGH
MAP 20, NS28

Sugar Boat
◉◉ MODERN SCOTTISH
01436 647522 | 30 Colquhoun Square, G84 8AQ
www.sugarboat.co.uk

On a square in the heart of town, with tables out front and back, Sugar Boat is an all-day bistro with real foodie credentials. The design is done out in natural colours of earth and sea, with a marble-topped bar and viewable kitchen. The hearty modern bistro cooking features big flavours and an essentially simple approach to treating Scottish produce with care and attention and not a little European flare.

INVERARAY
MAP 20, NN00

Loch Fyne Hotel & Spa
◉ CLASSIC TRADITIONAL V
01499 302980 | Shore Street, PA32 8XT
www.crerarhotels.com/loch-fyne-hotel-spa
The Cladach Mòr Bistro, from the Gaelic for 'great shore', takes its inspiration from both land and sea. Open fires, rich tones and stone walls set the scene from breakfast to dinner. Expect seafood, meats and produce, locally whenever possible, to reflect and celebrate each season. From West Coast langoustines in the bar to champagne afternoon tea in the lounge or a Josper-grilled steak dinner – you can enjoy beautiful loch views as you indulge in the carefully crafted dishes.

KILCHRENAN
MAP 20, NN02

The Dining Room NEW
◉ MODERN SCOTTISH
01866 833337 | Ardanaiseig Hotel, PA35 1HE
www.ardanaiseig.com
The elegant Dining Room at Ardanaiseig Hotel offers a daily rolling menu of dishes on a classical basis with some modern touches to bring it all up to date. There's a strong emphasis on local larder and very commendable wine choice. Expect a balanced blend of old and new world wines with a few options to tempt the connoisseur.

Faodail at Taychreggan Hotel
◉◉ CLASSIC SCOTTISH V
01866 833211 | PA35 1HQ
www.taychregganhotel.co.uk
Faodail means 'lucky find' and your dining experience may be just that when you discover this 17th-century former coaching inn nestled in its own private bay on the shores of Loch Awe. The kitchen delivers set dinner menus and there's always a friendly team waiting to welcome you. Plus there are 14 individual bedrooms so you can retire in comfort after a good meal.

LOCHGOILHEAD
MAP 20, NN10

The Lodge on Loch Goil
◉◉ MODERN SCOTTISH
01301 703193 | Loch Goil, PA24 8AE
www.thelodge-scotland.com
At the head of a sea loch, the beautifully restored Lodge offers three dining spaces: the Orangery, the Treehouse and the lochside Arts and Crafts restaurant. Scottish produce leads the menu; indeed, many ingredients are grown in the Lodge's gardens or at least locally foraged. With the sea so close, expect seafood too.

LUSS
MAP 20, NS39

The Lodge on Loch Lomond
◉◉ MODERN INTERNATIONAL
01436 860201 | G83 8PA
www.loch-lomond.co.uk
Situated on the edge of Loch Lomond, The Lodge occupies a peaceful woodland setting. The unbeatable loch views and sense of tranquillity in the balcony restaurant give the impression that you are floating on water. The modern food is underpinned by classic technique.

OBAN
MAP 20, NM82

Coast

MODERN BRITISH

01631 569900 | 104 George Street, PA34 5NT

www.coastoban.co.uk

Next door to the art gallery, Coast is the very image of a modern brasserie, with a seasonally changing menu of vivacious dishes. Start with home-made chicken liver parfait with apple chutney, and move on to haunch of Argyll venison with spiced red cabbage, pickled walnuts and a mash fired up with truffle and chives.

Etive Restaurant NEW

MODERN SCOTTISH V

01631 564899 | 43 Stevenson Street, PA34 5NA

etiverestaurant.co.uk

A small and intimate restaurant in Oban, Etive offers modern, fresh menus which clearly reflect the unbridled passion of its owners John McNulty and David Lapsley. So, expect quality Scottish ingredients, and high-calibre cooking of a classical nature with some added novel concepts, all culminating in a fun dining experience with attentive friendly service.

Grill Room NEW

MODERN SCOTTISH

01631 564395 | Corran Esplanade, PA34 5AE

www.crerarhotels.com/oban-bay-hotel/grill-room/

You'll like the Grill Room. The port of Oban provides the backdrop and much of the produce on seasonal menus which try to capture the essence of the Scottish larder in an accessible grill room format. Focused cooking here might include scallops simply paired with Stornoway black pudding, rich linguine with lobster, cray fish and prawns (a seafood lovers' delight) or Crerar's own red deer and, rounding things off with a perfectly oozing chocolate fondant.

Tigh an Truish NEW

MODERN SCOTTISH

01852 300242 | Clachan Seil, PA34 4QZ

www.tighantruish.com

An inn, restaurant and bar, the 250-year-old Tigh an Truish stands on Seil Island hard by Clachan Sound, with the Atlantic Ocean at both ends. Given a new lease of life following major refurbishment, the inn's modern Scottish menu features locally landed fish, such as seafood stew, and Auchnasaul braised beef pie. Beer gardens are to the front and rear.

PORT APPIN
MAP 20, NM94

Airds Hotel and Restaurant

MODERN SCOTTISH NOTABLE WINE LIST

01631 730236 | PA38 4DF

www.airds-hotel.com

The short drive from Fort William to Port Appin is a tonic in itself, but the location of the Airds Hotel, on the shore of Loch Linnhe, looking over to the Isle of Lismore, is guaranteed to unwind the troubled mind. In a long, low-ceilinged dining room, an atmosphere of considerate civility reigns, and the cooking is characterised by classical techniques delivered with polish and the kind of simplicity that allows quality to shine through. Roulade of Mull crab presents you with sweetly flavoured fresh meat, watercress gel and a grain mustard sabayon, a satisfying introduction before moving on to roast breast of Gressingham duck with pommes Anna, creamed cabbage, and carrot and anise purée. Rhubarb soufflé comes with walnut crumble ice cream and a vanilla doughnut. Breads are excellent - look out for the pumpkin seed loaf and the sourdough in particular.

Chef Chris Stanley **Seats** 30 **Parking** **Notes** No children under 8 years

The Pierhouse Seafood Restaurant

SCOTTISH SEAFOOD V

01631 730302 | The Pierhouse Hotel, PA38 4DE

www.pierhousehotel.co.uk

Tucked away on a quiet arm of Loch Linnhe, this waterside restaurant is a simple, magnolia-painted space - there's no point fretting over interior design when all eyes are turned towards the mountains stretching across the skyline above the loch.

PORTAVADIE
MAP 20, NR96

Portavadie Marina Restaurant
◉◉ SCOTTISH
01700 811075 | PA21 2DA
www.portavadie.com
Floor-to-ceiling glass awaits you here, with a view of the marina and beyond from every table. There's local produce in abundance, of course, to wit hand-dived Tarbert-landed scallops with crispy pork belly; Isle of Gigha halibut with dulse (seaweed) butter sauce; and lavender crème brûlée with Scottish strawberries and shortbread.

STRACHUR
MAP 20, NN00

Inver Restaurant
◉◉◉ MODERN SCOTTISH
01369 860537 | Strathlachlan, PA27 8BU
www.inverrestaurant.co.uk
An isolated and wild location on the shores of Loch Fyne is the perfect setting for the cooking of chef Pam Brunton, who previously worked at Noma in Copenhagen. A whitewashed cottage with unfussy Scandi designs, it's a minimalist backdrop for the sharp-edged cooking and bold flavours. Wild and foraged ingredients, plus shellfish from nearby lochs, dominate the menu, which might kick off with grilled squid, yellow tomatoes and a spicy red sausage. A signature main of Gigha halibut, mussels and coastal greens could lead on to raspberry and burnt honey meringue pie with raspberry sorbet and lemon curd.

Chef Pamela Brunton Seats 40 Closed Christmas, January to February Parking 20 Notes Children welcome

■ SOUTH AYRSHIRE

AYR
MAP 20, NS32

Fairfield House Hotel
◉ MODERN, TRADITIONAL
01292 267461 | 12 Fairfield Road, KA7 2AS
www.fairfieldhotel.co.uk
With its views across to the Isle of Arran, this seafront hotel puts contemporary cooking at the forefront of menus in Martin's Bar & Grill with its walls displaying modern Scottish artwork. Pedigree local produce is the cornerstone of big-flavoured dishes like breast of duck, black cabbage, plum, potatoes and redcurrant jus.

BALLANTRAE
MAP 20, NX08

Glenapp Castle
◉◉◉ MODERN BRITISH NOTABLE WINE LIST
01465 831212 | KA26 0NZ
www.glenappcastle.com
Glenapp Castle is a Victorian creation in the Scottish baronial style, and the oak-panelled dining room has views of Ailsa Craig. Menus come in two types, three courses at lunch, or six courses at dinner. Breaded John Dory with tartar sauce, then pea risotto with mint, feta and parmesan, followed by West Coast cod in parsley sauce. Now choose between roast Goosnargh duck breast with butternut squash purée and a haggis bonbon, or fillet of salmon with Jersey Royals, asparagus and chive hollandaise. Dessert brings buttermilk and rosewater pannacotta, with strawberries, raspberry coulis and pink peppercorn honeycomb, or a super cheese platter.

Chef David Alexander Seats 34, Private dining 20 Open All Year Parking 20 Notes Children welcome

TROON
MAP 20, NS33

MacCallums of Troon
◉ INTERNATIONAL, SEAFOOD
01292 319339 | The Harbour, KA10 6DH
www.maccallumsoftroon.co.uk
There should really only be one thing on your mind when dining at the Oyster Bar. It's all about the bass, the turbot, the sole... for this is a seafood restaurant in a glorious harbourside setting within a converted pump house.

Walkers Lounge NEW
◉ TRADITIONAL SCOTTISH
01292 314747 | 15 Craigend Road, KA10 6HD
www.piersland.co.uk
Piersland House is a delightful, historic hotel in the heart of Troon, once home to the Johnnie Walker whisky family. Walkers Lounge, with its carved fireplaces and dramatic beamed ceiling, is a comfortable, elegant setting for classic, traditional dining. Dishes such as a warming vegetable soup and poached fillet of sole with a cheese and leek glaze are well executed and a white chocolate and raspberry tart makes for an indulgent finale.

■ DUMFRIES & GALLOWAY

AUCHENCAIRN
MAP 21, NX75

Balcary Bay Hotel
◉◉ MODERN EUROPEAN
01556 640217 | Shore Road, DG7 1QZ
www.balcary-bay-hotel.co.uk
The solid-looking white hotel stands on the shore of the Solway Firth with views across the water to Heston Isle and the Lake District beyond. The hotel might be in a secluded spot, but the kitchen team proves to be a forward-looking lot.

DUMFRIES
MAP 21, NX97

The Auldgirth Inn
◉◉ MODERN SCOTTISH
01387 740250 | Auldgirth, DG2 0XG
auldgirthinn.co.uk
Discover a relaxing dining experience at this 500-year-old inn where the locally sourced produce is transformed into contemporary cuisine with a classical basis, finished with more modern techniques and innovative touches. The menu features a collection of bold and ambitious dishes, all with good balance of flavour and clarity, which is evident in the taste.

GRETNA
MAP 21, NY36

Smiths at Gretna Green
◉◉ MODERN BRITISH, INTERNATIONAL
01461 337007 | Gretna Green, DG16 5EA
www.smithsgretnagreen.com
Smiths certainly extends the options for those fleeing here with marriage on their minds, and makes a stylish stay to celebrate a landmark anniversary. The imaginative menus are especially good at game. Don't miss the excellent bread, which comes in a plant-pot.

MOFFAT
MAP 21, NT00

Brodies
◉ MODERN BRITISH
01683 222870 | Holm Street, DG10 9EB
www.brodiesofmoffat.co.uk

The first thing you notice about Brodies is the decor, a display of colour, eclectic and eccentric wallpapers, and mixed fabrics that's all been updated since lockdown. A lovely place for dining or a very popular afternoon tea. The gin bar is incredible, while the menu has a classic base with some novel touches.

PORTPATRICK
MAP 20, NW95

Knockinaam Lodge
◉◉◉ MODERN SCOTTISH ▮NOTABLE WINE LIST
01776 810471 | DG9 9AD
www.knockinaamlodge.com
For a small country hotel, Knockinaam is something of a knockout. About three miles out of Portpatrick, it stands in 30 acres, with access to a private shingle beach. It's decorated in elegant but homely style, with panoramic views of the Irish Sea from the dining room. Tony Pierce, with his star-studded CV, has brought distinction to the kitchens here. The evening agenda is a fixed-price, four-course affair, beginning on summer's night with a perfectly balanced dish of pan-seared Skye scallops, simply paired with caviar and a chive beurre blanc. Main course is a vibrantly presented roast breast of St Brides chicken, served with a chicken and truffle ravioli, courgette, charred baby leek and a Madeira emulsion. The final course requires a choice between British and French cheeses with walnut bread, or a Knockinaam marmalade soufflé with double vanilla bean ice cream.

Chef Anthony Pierce **Seats** 32, Private dining 18
Open All Year **Parking** 20 **Notes** No children

SANQUHAR

MAP 21, NS70

Blackaddie House

@ @ MODERN BRITISH
01659 50270 | Blackaddie Road, DG4 6JJ
www.blackaddiehotel.co.uk
This stone-built house on the east bank of the
River Nith is in the perfect location for sourcing
top-drawer produce. Firm classical
underpinnings produce a Scotch beef study that
combines sautéed fillet, a sticky ragoût and beef
terrine with accompanying greens.

■ WEST DUNBARTONSHIRE

BALLOCH

MAP 20, NS38

The Cameron Grill

@ @ MODERN BRITISH
01389 310 777 | Cameron House on Loch Lomond,
G83 8QZ
www.cameronhouse.co.uk
After a catastrophic fire in 2017, Cameron
House fully re-opened in September 2021
following a spectacular renovation. Bedrooms
and public areas all look wonderful, the perfect
combination of Scottish country-house comfort
and pin-sharp contemporary style. The Cameron
Grill enjoys stunning views across Loch Lomond
and you
can expect precise modern cooking in an
intimate setting.

CLYDEBANK

MAP 20, NS47

Golden Jubilee Conference Hotel

@ MODERN BRITISH
0141 951 6015 | Beardmore Street, G81 4SA
www.goldenjubileehotel.com
A hotel and conference centre next to the
Jubilee hospital, the Golden Jubilee Conference
Hotel is a multi-purpose hub for business
meetings, fitness workouts and aspirational
dining with a new spin on some classics.
Ecclefechan tart with toffee ice cream is a fine
regional speciality.

■ DUNDEE

DUNDEE

MAP 21, NO43

Chez Mal Brasserie

@ BRITISH, FRENCH
01382 339715 | Malmaison Dundee, 44 Whitehall
Crescent, DD1 4AY
www.malmaison.com/locations/dundee
The Dundee branch of the Malmaison chain
is a majestic old hotel with a domed ceiling
above a central wrought-iron staircase, with
the trademark sexy looks, which run through
to the candlelit brasserie's darkly atmospheric
colour scheme. The menu plays the modern
brasserie game.

The Tayberry

@ @ SCOTTISH
01382 698280 | 594 Brook Street, Broughty Ferry,
DD5 2EA
www.tayberryrestaurant.com
This relaxed, contemporary operation has made
quite a splash on the local culinary scene. Spread
over two floors, its purple-toned decor is a nod
to the namesake berry, and views across the
River Tay from the first-floor tables are a real
bonus. Focused, modern dishes allow local
produce to shine.

■ EDINBURGH

EDINBURGH
MAP 21, NT27

21212
◎◎◎◎ MODERN FRENCH 𝑉 🍷
0131 523 1030 | 3 Royal Terrace, EH7 5AB
www.21212restaurant.co.uk
Paul Kitching and Katie O'Brien's sumptuous restaurant with rooms is not one to follow the herd. The sandstone Georgian townhouse on Royal Terrace seems par for the course for a high-end joint, while inside there's contemporary design and classic elegance combining in a true one-off operation. The four bedrooms have a glossy finish, and the swish restaurant works a dramatic look, mingling ornate plasterwork, curvaceous banquettes and quirky design; a glass partition lets you eyeball the open-to-view kitchen where Paul gives full rein to his off-the-wall culinary artistry. The place's name derives from the weekly-changing five-course menu format: a choice of two starters, two mains and two desserts, punctuated by one soup course and a cheese course – that's if you're doing lunch. Cryptic menu descriptions will need some elucidation from Katie, who orchestrates front-of-house with charm and efficiency, but you can expect creative and dynamic modern cooking in dishes that are unconventional and thought provoking.

Chef Paul Kitching Seats 36, Private dining 10 Closed 2 weeks in January, 2 weeks in September Notes No children under 5 years

Bia Bistrot
◎ BRITISH, FRENCH
0131 452 8453 | 19 Colinton Road, EH10 5DP
www.biabistrot.co.uk
The 'Bia' element of the name is the Gaelic for food, the 'Bistrot' part more self-evident, and it's the winning setting for the cooking of husband-and-wife team Roisin and Matthias Llorente. Their Irish/Scottish and French/Spanish backgrounds are apparent in well-crafted and satisfying food in a charming and easy-going environment with wooden tables and smart leather seats.

The Brasserie - Norton House Hotel & Spa
◎ MODERN BRITISH
0131 333 1275 | Ingliston, EH28 8LX
www.handpickedhotels.co.uk/nortonhouse
Buffered by 50-odd acres of well-tended grounds, you'd hardly know that this Victorian country house is handy for motorways and the airport. After you've worked up an appetite in the spa's swimming pool, the brasserie offers an unbuttoned, contemporary setting and modern Scottish food to match.

Chaophraya
◎ THAI
0131 226 7614 | 4th Floor, 33 Castle Street, EH2 3DN
www.chaophraya.co.uk/edinburgh
Located on the 4th floor, this panoramic restaurant offers magnificent rooftop views of Edinburgh all the way to the Forth. Helpful, courteous staff offer a traditional welcome and explain the lengthy menu, which combines traditional Thai dishes with more modern interpretations. Great cocktails, too.

Chez Mal Brasserie
◎ BRITISH, FRENCH
0131 468 5000 | Malmaison Edinburgh, One Tower Place, Leith, EH6 7BZ
www.malmaison.com/locations/edinburgh
This was the first opening for the Malmaison chain, housed in a renovated seamen's mission on the waterfront in the old part of Leith, and is nowadays the grande dame of the boutique chain. The restaurant overlooks the docks with a terrace for alfresco dining.

Divino Enoteca
◎ MODERN ITALIAN, INTERNATIONAL 🍷
0131 225 1770 | 5 Merchant Street, EH1 2QD
www.vittoriagroup.co.uk/divinoenoteca
A hip venue with contemporary artworks on the walls, exposed brickwork and displays of wine bottles wherever you look: it's dark, moody, and a lot of fun. The kitchen's Italian output includes an excellent range of antipasti plus some more modern interpretations of the classics.

The Dungeon Restaurant at Dalhousie Castle

⊚⊚ TRADITIONAL EUROPEAN

01875 820153 | Bonnyrigg, EH19 3JB

www.dalhousiecastle.co.uk

Dalhousie Castle is a 13th-century fortress in wooded parkland on the banks of the River Esk, so you know you're in for something special at The Dungeon Restaurant. The cooking here has its roots in French classicism and a bedrock of top-class Scottish ingredients.

l'escargot blanc

⊚ FRENCH

0131 226 1890 | 17 Queensferry Street, EH2 4QW

www.lescargotblanc.co.uk

A West End fixture for more than 20 years, the first floor l'escargot blanc is accessed via the restaurant's own standalone wine bar. The intimate restaurant is classic bistro through and through, from the stripped wooden floors and distressed furniture to the Gallic objets d'art.

l'escargot bleu

⊚ FRENCH, SCOTTISH

0131 557 1600 | 56 Broughton Street, EH1 3SA

www.lescargotbleu.co.uk

L'escargot bleu is indeed blue – on the outside at least, and snails are present and correct among les entrées. The bilingual menu deals in classic bistro dishes such as those snails, which come from Barra in the Outer Hebrides, and there's a Scottish flavour.

La Favorita

⊚ MODERN ITALIAN, MEDITERRANEAN

0131 554 2430 | 325-331 Leith Walk, EH6 8SA

www.vittoriagroup.co.uk/lafavorita

Well-sourced Italian ingredients supply the wherewithal for the Vittoria group's Leith pizzeria. From its wood-fired ovens comes a compendious list of pizzas, as well as cured meat platters and an imaginative diversity of pasta dishes and risottos. The ambience is upbeat and casual, and there's a bargain weekday set-price lunch worth considering.

The Gardener's Cottage

⊚ BRITISH

0131 677 0244 | 1 Royal Terrace Gardens, London Road, EH7 5DX

www.thegardenerscottage.co

With its blackboard menu in the gravel outside, this restaurant with full-on royal connections is an oasis of pastoral calm in the bustling city. Cosy up in wicker chairs at big communal tables for Scottish cooking that takes pride in its carefully sourced prime materials. That's clear from a starter of mutton and roe-deer meatballs in maltagliati pasta.

La Garrigue

⊚ FRENCH, MEDITERRANEAN 🍷 NOTABLE WINE LIST

0131 557 3032 | 31 Jeffrey Street, EH1 1DH

www.lagarrigue.co.uk

Named for the wild, herb-scented scrubland in Provence and Languedoc in the south of France. Chef-patron Jean-Michel Gauffre has brought the region's honest rustic cooking to his smart neighbourhood restaurant in Edinburgh's old town. Born in the heartlands of cassoulet, his take on the hearty stew of belly pork, duck confit, Toulouse sausage and white beans is the real deal.

EDINBURGH continued

Grazing by Mark Greenaway *NEW*

◎◎ MODERN BRITISH

0131 222 8888 | Waldorf Astoria Edinburgh -
The Caledonian, Princes Street, EH1 2AB

markgreenaway.com/grazing-restaurant

Grazing by Mark Greenaway is the buzzy,
informal dining room of the Waldorf Astoria
Edinburgh - The Caledonian, and the high
ceilings, leather and wood reflect the building's
Victorian railway station heritage. The
eponymous Scottish chef presents a wide-
ranging menu of solid bistro cooking – from
small sharing plates to traditional starters and
mains, with everything from comfort classics to
dishes that display greater technical prowess.

Harajuku Kitchen

◎ JAPANESE *V*

0131 281 0526 | 10 Gillespie Place, EH10 4HS

harajukukitchen.co.uk

Named after an area of Tokyo, this bistro offers
authentic Japanese dishes with a touch of
panache in an informal café-like atmosphere
of exposed stone, vibrant artworks and chunky
wood tables and low-back chairs. Family run,
the kitchen sends out exciting and authentic
cooking, with some dishes passed down through
three generations.

Harvey Nichols Forth Floor Restaurant

◎ MODERN EUROPEAN ⚑NOTABLE WINE LIST

0131 524 8350 | 30–34 St Andrew Square, EH2 2AD

www.harveynichols.com/restaurants

No, it's not a typo. It is on the fourth floor, but
also enjoys great views of the city and the Forth
Bridge. Clever stuff. The restaurant is a slick
contemporary space with white linen on the
tables, burgundy-coloured leather seats and a
smart line in seasonal dishes combining
contemporary finesse with Scottish ingredients.

Hotel du Vin Edinburgh

◎ CLASSIC FRENCH ⚑NOTABLE WINE LIST

0131 247 4900 | 11 Bristo Place, EH1 1EZ

www.hotelduvin.com

The former city asylum is the setting for HdV's
Edinburgh outpost. The setting is considerably
more cheerful thanks to the group's trademark
gentleman's-club look of well-worn leather seats
and woody textures. There's a splendid tartan-
clad whisky snug, plus a buzzy mezzanine bar
overlooking the bistro.

Kanpai Sushi

@ JAPANESE *V*

0131 228 1602 | 8–10 Grindlay Street, EH3 9AS
www.kanpaisushiedinburgh.co.uk

Near Waverley station, wood-filled Kanpai is one of the city's longest standing Japanese restaurants. It calls its cooking 'a simple art', but judge for yourself at the intimate sushi bar by observing it being made. Firm favourites remain on the restaurant menu, although new dishes appear from time to time. Kanpai, the Japanese way of toasting, means 'bottoms up'.

The Kitchin

@@@@@ MODERN SCOTTISH WITH FRENCH INFLUENCES *V* ⭐ NOTABLE WINE LIST

0131 555 1755 | 78 Commercial Quay, Leith, EH6 6LX
www.thekitchin.com

A former whisky warehouse in the regenerated Leith docklands has been Tom Kitchin's address since 2006, and immediately shot into the premier league of the top foodie destinations in the country. The interior looks sharp in hues of teal blue and grey, with exposed stone walls, painted brick pillars and industrial girders, while Kitchin's 'From Nature to Plate' mantra is articulated through cooking that applies top-level refinement and technical skills to Scotland's finest materials. The three-course set lunch menu offers remarkable value, delivering a starter of crispy veal sweetbreads atop Jerusalem artichoke risotto, hen of the woods mushrooms and hazelnuts. Next comes sea-fresh Scrabster monkfish wrapped in salty pancetta, alongside fondant new potatoes, sea vegetables, plump mussels, chanterelles, confit garlic and an outstanding chicken gravy with lemon and thyme. Desserts are also handled with awe-inspiring dexterity, as in the masterclass blueberry crumble soufflé served with the balancing sharpness of yogurt ice cream.

Chef Tom Kitchin **Seats** 75, Private dining 20 **Closed** 23 December to 12 January inclusive **Parking** 30 **Notes** Children welcome

The Little Chartroom *NEW*

@@ MODERN SCOTTISH

0131 556 6600 | 30–31 Albert Place, EH7 5HN
www.thelittlechartroom.com

A tiny restaurant on Leith Walk, The Little Chartroom is a tightly packed and lively place with open brickwork and plain tables. The food is ultra-seasonal, with menus changing daily and focused on the delights of the Scottish larder. Stripped back dishes are full of flavour and perfectly timed.

Locanda De Gusti

@@ ITALIAN, MEDITERRANEAN, SEAFOOD

0131 346 8800 | 102 Dalry Road, EH11 2DW
www.locandadegusti.com

With its painted brickwork and all-round rustic appeal, this inviting restaurant has more than a hint of an Italian domestic kitchen about it. Translating loosely as 'inn of taste', you'll certainly find heaps of flavour in the kitchen's big-hearted cooking; top-drawer local produce is boosted by ingredients shipped in from Italy to keep it all authentic.

EDINBURGH continued

Mother India's Cafe

◉ INDIAN TAPAS

0131 524 9801 | 3-5 Infirmary Street, EH1 1LT

www.motherindia.co.uk

Open since 2008 and a boisterous Edinburgh sibling to the Glasgow mothership, this bustling Indian café is tucked away behind the university buildings but it's well worth going off the beaten track for. With its mismatched furniture, unclothed tables and disposable napkins, it's chaotic and unpretentious.

Mumbai Diners' Club

◉◉ MODERN INDIAN

0131 229 8291 | 3 Atholl Place, EH3 8HP

www.mumbaidinersclub.co.uk

An Indian restaurant where both the interior design and menu take a glamorous and contemporary approach. A statement chandelier, plum-coloured columns and chairs, and chunky wooden designer tables make for an appealing space, watched over by a smartly turned-out service team.

NAVADHANYA

◉◉ MODERN INDIAN

0131 269 7868 | 32-34 Grindlay Street, EH3 9AP

www.navadhanya-scotland.co.uk

Navadhanya's Haymarket venue was always a popular spot and this continues in their newer, larger and more central premises on Grindlay Street. The modern Indian food steers clear of the usual high street curry and offers an inventive menu of regional dishes. Sunhari Jhingha (chargrilled king prawns, mustard, cumin and coriander chutney) is a strong way to start, perhaps followed by slow-cooked Hyderabadi lamb shank.

New Chapter

◉ SCOTTISH, EUROPEAN

0131 556 0006 | 18 Eyre Place, EH3 5EP

www.newchapterrestaurant.co.uk

A godsend for the neighbourhood, this cheery venue combines a laid-back demeanour with clean-cut, contemporary looks, breezy service, and a kitchen that produces unfussy, full-flavoured dishes with European leanings. If you're after top value, the lunch menu is a steal.

Number One, The Balmoral

◉◉◉◉ MODERN SCOTTISH ⚑ NOTABLE WINE LIST

0131 557 6727 | 1 Princes Street, EH2 2EQ

www.roccofortehotels.com

Named after its address on Princes Street, Number One was once the British Transport Hotel for guests arriving at nearby Waverley Station. This magnificent Edinburgh landmark still exudes luxury, from the elegant public areas with their marble and ornate plasterwork to the classy Number One dining room with its oak flooring offset, dove-grey banquettes and striking artworks. Spacious with immaculately presented tables, it's a fitting backdrop for the high quality cooking and exemplary service. The food is exciting and makes good use of high-end raw materials, as in an opulent starter of cured duck foie gras, pineapple and Périgord truffle. Fish is taken as seriously as thoroughbred Scottish meats, with a main course of North Sea cod, mushroom dashi and crispy chicken skin vying for attention alongside rare-breed Gaindykehead beef, watercress and alliums. Lemon sherbet soufflé, galangal and lemon slice makes for a light and refreshing finale.

Chef Mark Donald, Gary Robinson **Seats** 50 **Closed** 2 weeks in January **Notes** No children under 5 years

Ondine Restaurant

◉◉ SEAFOOD ⚑ NOTABLE WINE LIST

0131 226 1888 | 2 George IV Bridge, EH1 1AD

www.ondinerestaurant.co.uk

Ondine has earned a loyal following on the city's culinary scene, and it's not hard to see why: just off the Royal Mile, on George IV Bridge, it's a contemporary space with an upbeat bustle and great views out over the old town. Sustainable seafood, prepared simply and with an eye on exciting global flavours, is the main draw.

One Square

◉ MODERN SCOTTISH

0131 221 6422 | Sheraton Grand Hotel & Spa, 1 Festival Square, EH3 9SR

www.onesquareedinburgh.co.uk

The views of Edinburgh Castle give a sense of place to this slick, modern dining option. The floor-to-ceiling windows add a cool, classy finish. The lunch and dinner menus have a sharp focus on Scotland's fine produce in their crowd-pleasing medley of modern ideas.

The Pompadour

◉◉◉ MODERN BRITISH

0131 222 8945 | Waldorf Astoria Edinburgh,
The Caledonian, Princes Street, EH1 2AB
www.thepompadour.com

Surely one of Edinburgh's most splendid places to eat, in one of the most impressive hotels in Britain, the iconic Waldorf Astoria Edinburgh – The Caledonian. The best tables enjoy views over Lothian Road and up to the castle, and the intricate plasterwork and stunning blue velvet chairs really do make this the perfect setting for Dean Banks' seasonally evolving tasting menus. Expect fantastic local produce and an intensely sensory experience from dishes featuring king scallops, Loch Etive trout, or smoked lobster from St Andrews Bay. There's a Scottish cheese selection, and wine pairings are available.

Chef Dean Banks **Seats** 60, Private dining 20 **Closed** 2 weeks in January **Parking** 48 **Notes** Children welcome

Restaurant Martin Wishart

◉◉◉◉ MODERN FRENCH *V* ♨ NOTABLE WINE LIST

0131 553 3557 | 54 The Shore, Leith, EH6 6RA
www.restaurantmartinwishart.co.uk

Martin Wishart's recognition of Leith as an opportunity and a destination made him a bit of a trailblazer, and it's hard to imagine, as you look round this buzzy hive of restaurants and bars, that it hasn't always been like this. Understated on the outside, discreetly located on the cobbled quayside, the restaurant is cool and elegant within. Pale wood and muted colours make sure your focus is where is should be - on the food. Menus change seasonally and include a vegetarian tasting option, and the style is classic French with clear Scottish influences. Dishes are thoroughly fresh and vibrant, with precise attention to detail in every option, from the haggis bonbon that kicks things off to starters like céviche of Gigha halibut with mango and passionfruit, while mains like roast loin of Borders roe deer, with braised gem lettuce, goats' cheese gnocchi, morels and Grand Veneur sauce are equally inspiring.

Chef Martin Wishart, Joe Taggart **Seats** 45 **Closed** 25–26 December, 1 January, 3 weeks in January **Notes** No children under 7 years

Rhubarb at Prestonfield

◉◉ TRADITIONAL BRITISH ♨ NOTABLE WINE LIST

0131 225 1333 | Priestfield Road, EH16 5UT
www.rhubarb-edinburgh.com

One of the city's most visually impressive dining rooms, Rhubarb at Prestonfield is a real stunner. Classical preparations mix with contemporary ideas in a menu with broad appeal. Have a classic Scottish steak followed by tarte Tatin for two.

The Scran & Scallie

◉ MODERN SCOTTISH *V* ♨ NOTABLE WINE LIST

0131 332 6281 | 1 Comely Bank Road, Stockbridge, EH4 1DR
www.scranandscallie.com

Readers from south of the Scottish border might like to know that 'scran' is food and 'scallie' is a scallywag. Occupying two narrowly separated buildings, its many original features blend harmoniously with trendy Scandinavian influences, reclaimed furniture, Isle of Bute fabrics and wallpapers from Scottish designers. Now for the scran: on 'Oor menu' appear modern twists on pub classics. The focus is firmly on food in top chefs Tom Kitchin and Dominic Jack's pub, all chiming with the 'From Nature to Plate' house ethos. Seasonal dishes and regional classics feature.

Southside Scran

◉ FRENCH, SCOTTISH

0131 342 3333 | 14–17 Bruntsfield Place, EH10 4HN
southsidescran.com/

In the Bruntsfield area of Edinburgh, this latest addition to the Tom Kitchin empire is styled as a French bistro and it's all very informal with many dishes cooked on the rotisserie grill in the open kitchen. Try Borders roe deer pithiver and rhubarb followed by North Sea plaice, pancetta, gnocchi, mussels and wild garlic.

Continued on page 386

Timberyard

ROSETTES SUSPENDED **MODERN BRITISH** 🍷 NOTABLE WINE LIST

0131 221 1222 | 10 Lady Lawson Street, EH3 9DS

www.timberyard.co

Contemporary Scottish cooking in unique setting

The Rosette award for this establishment has been suspended due to a change of chef and reassessment will take place in due course. First time visitors to Timberyard would be forgiven for thinking they'd arrived at the wrong place as they approach this modest venue. Concealed behind large red garage doors, this former warehouse just to the south of Edinburgh Castle, still gives the impression of a space used for commercial manufacturing purposes rather than high-level gastronomy. Inside, beyond the south-facing, sun-trap yard, original brick walls, stripped wood floors and rusty panels keep things the industrial side of shabby chic but pots of edible flowers and herbs soon give the game away that this is a serious food operation. The menu confirms this with a namecheck for the local foragers and Scottish artisan breeders that keep the kitchen supplied with hyper-seasonal

raw materials. The food is modern, bold and exciting, with intelligent flavour combinations, sound technique and precise presentation, all of which belies the tersely written menu descriptions. A typical meal from the daily menu might start with snacks of fried globe artichoke, sunflower, lemon and sumac or lamb tartare, ramson, cured yolk and black garlic mustard. Follow these with 'small' plates of glazed duck, apricot, golden beetroot and honey or confit trout, gooseberry and fennel. Making an appearance at the main course stage might be BBQ venison, celeriac, cherry and kale or quail with wild mushroom, salsify and ale. Sides such as smoked aubergine, toasted nigella and sesame, and purple sprouting, charred greens, black garlic and chilli are worth a detour in their own right. Finish with an

> "..pots of edible flowers and herbs soon give the game away that this is a serious food operation."

inventive honey, almond and brown butter cake with woodruff ice cream or peach, crème fraîche and white chocolate. The drinks list is notable whether it's softs such as apple and Douglas fir or organic beers brewed in the Highlands. The wine list is full of interesting bottles from lesser-known territories.

Chef James Murray
Seats 65, Private dining 10
Closed 24–26 December, 1st week in January, 1 week in April, October
Notes No children under 12 years at dinner

EDINBURGH continued

The Stockbridge Restaurant

◉◉ MODERN, CLASSIC BRITISH

0131 226 6766 | 54 St Stephen Street, EH3 5AL

www.thestockbridgerestaurant.com

Affluent Stockbridge has quite a concentration of restaurants and bars, this being one of the longer established. Access is down stone steps into, in their words, a 'decadent grotto'. Modern Scottish cooking reigns on the weekly changing fixed-price menu and on the rolling carte, typified by Gressingham duck breast with crisp duck confit, and grilled halibut with Scotch quail egg.

Timberyard

ROSETTES SUSPENDED MODERN BRITISH ▲ NOTABLE WINE LIST

See pages 384–385

The Witchery by the Castle

◉◉ TRADITIONAL SCOTTISH ▲ NOTABLE WINE LIST

0131 225 5613 | Castlehill, The Royal Mile, EH1 2NF

www.thewitchery.com

One of several historic buildings at the gates of Edinburgh Castle, the baroque, oak-panelled restaurant within this 16th-century merchant's house makes for an atmospheric dining experience. Built around traditional dishes and native produce, the assured cooking follows a contemporary and seasonal route with Scottish seafood getting a strong showing.

RATHO
MAP 21, NT17

The Bridge Inn at Ratho

◉ MODERN BRITISH

0131 333 1320 | 27 Baird Road, EH28 8RA

www.bridgeinn.com

Right by the Union Canal, with views over the water from both garden and restaurant, The Bridge Inn is the perfect spot for watching the passing boats. If the canal-side action doesn't float your boat, there are cask ales, regional whiskies, and an appealing menu.

■ FALKIRK

BANKNOCK
MAP 21, NS77

Glenskirlie House & Castle

◉◉ MODERN BRITISH

01324 840201 | Kilsyth Road, FK4 1UF

www.glenskirliehouse.com/dining

A castle for the 21st century, Glenskirlie is a bright white pile, kitted out with a conical-roofed turret here, a little step-gabling there. The restaurant has a good ambience and a friendly and brisk service from staff.

■ FIFE

ANSTRUTHER
MAP 21, NO50

The Cellar

◉◉◉ MODERN BRITISH

01333 310378 | 24 East Green, KY10 3AA

www.thecellaranstruther.co.uk

The fishing harbour of Anstruther is a fitting location for chef Billy Boyter's restaurant housed in a 17th-century former smokehouse and cooperage just off the quayside. With beamed ceilings, stone walls and wood-burning stoves, the ambience is rustic and Boyter's inventive modern Scottish cooking sticks faithfully to the seasons on the nine-course tasting menu at dinner (six at lunch). Superb technique is evident in a pairing of smoked mussel, seaweed and lemon, which might lead on to heritage potato, Arbroath smokie and lovage. Well defined flavours continue with a dessert of set hay cream, apple and marigold.

Chef Billy Boyter **Seats** 28 **Closed** 25-26 December, 1 January, 3 weeks January, 1 week May, 10 days September **Notes** No children under 5 years at lunch, 12 years at dinner

CAIRNEYHILL
The Restaurant and Acanthus
◉◉ MODERN BRITISH

01383 880505 | Forrester Park, Pitdinnie Road, KY12 8RF

www.forresterparkresort.com

Forrester Park is a chic, contemporary take on a traditional Scottish mansion. There are two dining rooms, The Restaurant is smaller and more modern in style, while the much larger Acanthus is all starched white linen and chandeliers. The same set-price dinner menu is served in both.

CUPAR
Ostlers Close Restaurant
◉◉ MODERN SCOTTISH

01334 655574 | Bonnygate, KY15 4BU

www.ostlersclose.co.uk

This one-time scullery of a 17th-century temperance hotel has been a popular destination since 1981. With red-painted walls and linen-clad tables, it's an intimate space run with charm and enthusiasm. Concise handwritten menus showcase produce from the garden and wild mushrooms from local woods.

ELIE
The Ship Inn
◉ MODERN, SEAFOOD

01333 330246 | The Toft, KY9 1DT

www.shipinn.scot

Not many pubs can boast a beachside beer garden and cricket matches played on the sand, but The Ship Inn is no ordinary tavern. Overlooking the briny, the first-floor restaurant sports a jaunty modern look involving bare tables and duck-egg-blue panelling and serves an unfussy roll-call of eclectic modern dishes, including splendid local seafood.

NEWPORT-ON-TAY
The Newport Restaurant
◉◉ MODERN SCOTTISH

01382 541449 | 1 High Street, DD6 8AB

www.thenewportrestaurant.co.uk

There's not much better publicity than winning *MasterChef: The Professionals*, so 2014 winner Jamie Scott got off to a flyer when he opened his own restaurant. Cheerful and enthusiastic service and a breezy contemporary decor make for a relaxed dining experience, while pin-sharp contemporary cooking from Scott and his team make it a hot ticket.

PEAT INN
The Peat Inn
◉◉◉ MODERN BRITISH

01334 840206 | KY15 5LH

www.thepeatinn.co.uk

This inn has been enough of a local landmark since the mid-18th century that the village in which it stands was named after it, rather than the other way round. It's a handsomely white-fronted, stone-built former coach-stop, the dining room decorated in sleek contemporary fashion with light woods, thick cloths and smart tableware. Geoffrey Smeddle has maintained the place in the upper ranks of Scottish gastronomy over an impressive stretch, and the modernist flourishes and precise presentations confer real character on the cooking. Begin with warm St Andrews Bay lobster with romesco sauce, cauliflower pannacotta (with perfect 'wobble') and sea herbs. For main, roast crown and smoked legs of Scottish partridge come with young parsnips, spiced Puy lentils and thyme and cider velouté. A mille feuille of lemon posset and blackberries with an intense lemongrass, chilli and ginger sorbet is beautifully made, with delicate pastry and great flavour.

Chef Geoffrey Smeddle **Seats** 50, Private dining 12 **Closed** 25-26 December, 1-10 January **Parking** 24 **Notes** No children under 7 years at dinner

The Adamson

◉◉ MODERN BRITISH

01334 479191 | 127 South Street, KY16 9UH

theadamson.com

Once home to photographer and physician Dr John Adamson (hence the name), the handsome building now houses a cool restaurant with exposed bricks, darkwood tables, an open kitchen, and a bar serving up creative cocktails. The menu brings up-to-date oomph to the brasserie format with oodles of contemporary style and high-quality ingredients.

The Grange Inn

◉◉ MODERN SCOTTISH

01334 472670 | Grange Road, KY16 8LJ

thegrangeinn.com

A lovely 17th-century converted farmhouse is the setting for this delightful restaurant with panoramic views looking out over St Andrews and St Andrews Bay. Chef-proprietor John Kelly has created a superb menu finished with modern techniques and innovative touches using the freshest of local produce available. There's a warm and welcoming ambience throughout.

Playfair's Restaurant and Steakhouse

◉ STEAKHOUSE, SCOTTISH

01334 472970 | Ardgowan Hotel, 2 Playfair Terrace, North Street, KY16 9HX

www.playfairsrestaurant.co.uk

Not far from the 18th green of St Andrew's Old Course, Playfair's restaurant is a bustling and welcoming eatery, with attentive service and a modern Scottish approach. The restaurant is located under the reception, and the configuration means that diners can often find themselves eating close to drinkers using the bar.

See advertisement below

Road Hole Restaurant
◉◉◉ MODERN STEAK, SEAFOOD
See pages 390-391

See advertisement on page 392

Rufflets St Andrews
◉◉ MODERN BRITISH, EUROPEAN ⚑NOTABLE WINE LIST
01334 460890 | Strathkinness Low Road, KY16 9TX
www.rufflets.co.uk/wine-dine
The creeper-covered turreted mansion has been in the same family since 1952, sitting in 10 acres of exquisite gardens. Its name refers to the 'rough flat lands' that once comprised the local landscape. The cooking is as modern as can be.

St Andrews Bar & Grill
◉◉ SCOTTISH, SEAFOOD
01334 837000 | Fairmont St Andrews, Scotland, KY16 8PN
www.fairmont.com/standrews
A free shuttle bus takes you from the Fairmont to this dining option in the clubhouse, but it is a lovely walk. Spectacularly situated on a promontory overlooking St Andrews Bay, the evening sees the seafood bar and grill come into their own.

Sands Grill
◉ MODERN SCOTTISH
01334 474371 | Old Course Hotel, Golf Resort & Spa, KY16 9SP
www.oldcoursehotel.co.uk
Overlooking the world-famous golf course and the coast beyond, the Old Course Hotel occupies a desirable position and offers a wide range of dining options. The Sands Grill is the more informal option, a contemporary brasserie run by slick, unstuffy staff.

ST MONANS *MAP 21, NO50*

Craig Millar@16 West End
◉◉ MODERN SCOTTISH ⚑NOTABLE WINE LIST
01333 730327 | 16 West End, KY10 2BX
www.16westend.com

Craig Millar@16 West End is an elegant, innovative restaurant and bar that enjoys sweeping views of the Firth of Forth and harbour at St Monans. The sea can get dramatic but then so can the cooking, especially the seafood, which was always going to be a big focus. Don't forget to check out the outstanding top quality wine list.

Continued on page 393

Road Hole Restaurant

◎◎◎ **MODERN STEAK, SEAFOOD**
01334 474371 | Old Course Hotel, Golf Resort & Spa, KY16 9SP
www.oldcoursehotel.co.uk

Famous golf hotel with reliably traditional cuisine

St Andrews has a ruined cathedral and castle and lots of delightful ancient buildings. It has a university and coastal views and is altogether charming. It's probably best known for something else, though – the oldest and surely one of the most famous golf links in the world. The suitably named Old Course Hotel overlooks both the beach and the 17th hole, aka the 'Road Hole', hence the name of the dining room. Staff are genuinely engaged and highly professional, and the open kitchen gives you an insight into what's happening before your food arrives at your table. Dishes suit the clientele, with a solid basis in classical technique, and the very best luxury Scottish ingredients. Don't expect to find anything outrageously cutting edge or overtly modern here, that's not the style. Choose something appropriate to begin – the mini chieftain haggis, perhaps, served with bashed neeps, champit tatties

"Staff are genuinely engaged and highly professional, and the open kitchen gives you an insight into what's happening before your food arrives..."

and whisky sauce, or the equally suitable Cullen skink and wholemeal soda bread. There's salmon, too, of course, caught in Loch Duart and cured with whisky and treacle. Main course offerings might include braised pork belly with langoustine, apple, baby spinach, and pancetta, or rump of Scotch lamb with confit thyme potatoes. There are steaks of excellent quality, sirloin, perhaps, served with dauphinoise potatoes and braised red cabbage, or rib eye or fillet, with pont neuf potatoes. Roasted hake comes with crushed new potatoes, kale, mussels and mariniere sauce. Draw things to a satisfying conclusion with a refreshing passionfruit cheesecake with compressed mango, kaffir lime and mango sorbet, or fig and frangipane tart with whipped pannacotta, honey baked figs and pistachio ice cream. There are some superb Scottish cheeses, too – perhaps Smoked Anster, Lochnagar, Ailsa Craig and Arran Blue. The wine list is very good, with plenty by the glass – and don't forget to check out the extremely impressive whisky selection.

Chef Martin Hollis
Seats 70, Private dining 16
Open All Year
Parking 150
Notes Children welcome

See advertisement on page 392

■ GLASGOW

GLASGOW
MAP 20, NS56

Bo & Birdy NEW
◉ SCOTTISH/BRITISH
0141 248 8888 | Kimpton Blythswood Square Hotel,
11 Blythswood Square, G2 4AD
www.boandbirdy.com
Once the HQ of the Royal Scottish Automobile
Club, Kimpton Blythswood Square Hotel's Bo &
Birdy restaurant has a bright brasserie feel to it
with polished brass and light streaming through
tall windows. Scottish produce is handled with
respect in a rolled spring lamb breast with salt
baked beetroot and goats' cheese, and cod, burnt
leek, oyster leaf and chicken wing.

La Bonne Auberge
◉ FRENCH, MEDITERRANEAN
0141 352 8310 | Holiday Inn Glasgow City Centre -
Theatreland, 161 West Nile Street, G1 2RL
www.labonneauberge.co.uk
This ever-popular venue is kitted out in
contemporary style with exposed brickwork, tiled
and wooden flooring and lamps on wooden
tables, and has attentive and friendly staff.
Meats, including BBQ pork loin and rib-eye
steaks, are cooked on the grill.

Brasserie NEW
◉ BRITISH
0141 221 6789 | ABode Glasgow, 129 Bath Street, G2 2SZ
www.abodeglasgow.co.uk
The Brasserie at ABode Glasgow offers a stylishly
designed brassiere with white brick-tiled wall
that goes back to the Victorian and Edwardian
origins of the building. Bold feature walls break
up the starkness and critically placed black and
white photography adds to the brassiere design
theme. The menu changes with the seasons plus
there are dishes of the day.

Cail Bruich
◉◉◉ MODERN SCOTTISH ♨NOTABLE WINE LIST
0141 334 6265 | 752 Great Western Road, G12 8QX
www.cailbruich.co.uk
It isn't always necessary to head out into the
Highlands in search of country cuisine. Here in
Glasgow's swinging West End, the Charalambous
brothers bring it to the city doorstep, in a
modern bistro setting where hanging baskets
flank the door, and rows of tables at crimson
banquettes form a long, informal space. The
vegetarian dishes alone are inspired, offering
spelt with Jerusalem artichoke, lettuce and
Brinkburn goats' cheese, for mains. Elsewhere,
stimulating combinations distinguish the
seasonally-changing menus, perhaps Loch Fyne
scallop with smoked eel, sour cabbage and apple,
and then lamb with sprouting broccoli, anchovies
and black olives, or stone bass with langoustine,
clementine and pumpkin. For the seven-course
taster, there are fish or meat alternatives at two
stages, and caramelised whey with sea
buckthorn, apple and fennel pollen makes for a
thoroughly modern finale. Speciality beers and a
tempting list of imaginative cocktails
supplement the commendable wine list.

Chef Chris Charalambous **Seats** 48 **Closed** 25-26
December, 1 January, 1 week January **Notes** No children
under 8 years

Chez Mal Brasserie
◉ MODERN FRENCH
0141 572 1001 | Malmaison Glasgow, 278 West George
Street, G2 4LL
www.malmaison.com
The Glasgow Mal has made its home in a
deconsecrated Greek Orthodox church. A mix of
traditional and modern French brasserie cooking
is the draw, with select breeds and cuts of
thoroughbred beef the backbone. Soufflé du jour
is worth a look at for dessert.

The Gannet
◉◉◉ MODERN SCOTTISH
0141 204 2081 | 1155 Argyle Street, G3 8TB
www.thegannetgla.com
Named after the seafaring bird with the robust
appetite, The Gannet was created by a group of
friends on a research trip to the Outer Hebrides.
A showcase of Scotland's small artisan
producers, foragers and farmers, this industrial-
meets-rustic restaurant - all exposed brick,
stone walls and stripped wood - offers daily
changing four- and six-course menus. A typical
meal might include West Coast crab teamed with
squash and horseradish, which could lead on to
Hereford beef, shallot, egg yolk and nut and seed
granola. Things come to a close with a dark
chocolate delice, white chocolate mousse and
hazelnut.

Chef Peter McKenna, Ivan Stein **Seats** 45, Private
dining 14 **Closed** 25-26 December, 1-2 January
Notes Children welcome

The Hanoi Bike Shop

◎ VIETNAMESE

0141 334 7165 | 8 Ruthven Lane, G12 9BG

www.hanoibikeshop.co.uk

Sister restaurant to the Ubiquitous Chip and Stravaigin, this colourful West End venture is set across two buzzing floors. The canteen-style vibe suits the authentic street food menu of dazzling Vietnamese flavours. The menu gives the Vietnamese names of dishes followed by an English translation.

Mother India

◎ INDIAN

0141 221 1663 | 28 Westminster Terrace, Sauchiehall Street, G3 7RU

www.motherindia.co.uk

This landmark restaurant, launched in 1990, continues to draw the crowds with its inventive, flavour-packed Indian food. Spread over three floors, Mother India avoids cliché in its decor. The menu takes a step away from curry-house standards to deliver broadly appealing dishes.

Number Sixteen

◎◎ MODERN INTERNATIONAL

0141 339 2544 | 16 Byres Road, G11 5JY

www.number16.co.uk

This dinky neighbourhood restaurant has a strong local following. It's an elbow-to-elbow sort of place with a pocket-sized downstairs area, and a mini-mezzanine above, all decorated with colourful artwork, and kept ticking over by casually dressed, on-the-ball staff. The chefs in the open-to-view kitchen aren't scared to experiment with a vibrant barrage of flavours, without losing sight of the seasons.

One Devonshire Gardens by Hotel du Vin

◎◎ MODERN FRENCH ❸ NOTABLE WINE LIST

0141 339 2001 | 1 Devonshire Gardens, G12 0UX

www.hotelduvin.com

This supremely elegant Victorian terrace in the heart of Glasgow – with a long-standing foodie reputation to maintain – is the jewel in the crown of the Hotel du Vin group. The restaurant is an elegant setting for lunch and dinner where chef Gary Townsend has put his own contemporary European stamp on the kitchen's output bringing fresh, seasonal and locally sourced produce to the fore.

Opium

⊛ CHINESE, ORIENTAL FUSION
0141 332 6668 | 191 Hope Street, G2 2UL
www.opiumrestaurant.co.uk

A pin-sharp, contemporary-styled Asian-fusion restaurant in the heart of Glasgow. Big picture windows allow light to flood into a slick space where communal tables share the space with conventional seating. Kwan Yu Lee has honed an on-trend mix of classical and modern Asian fusion dishes.

Ox and Finch

⊛⊛ MODERN BRITISH
0141 339 8627 | 920 Sauchiehall Street, G3 7TF
www.oxandfinch.com
Tapas-size portions are the deal at this buzzing venue. Bare brick walls, roughly painted wooden floors, banquette and booth seating and unbuttoned service create a casual, laid-back atmosphere. The menu is divided into such headings as 'snacks' and 'raw, cured and cold'.

Shish Mahal

⊛ INDIAN, PAKISTANI
0141 339 8256 | 60-68 Park Road, G4 9JF
www.shishmahal.co.uk

Opened in the 1960s by the charismatic 'Mr Ali', Shish Mahal is a Glaswegian institution which has moved with the times. There's a smart modern feel to the restaurant, while the menu takes in old favourites as well as exploring plenty of intriguing new ideas.

Stravaigin

⊛ MODERN INTERNATIONAL, SCOTTISH
0141 334 2665 | 28 Gibson Street, Kelvinbridge, G12 8NX
www.stravaigin.co.uk

In a busy West End street, this popular all-day bar/restaurant abides by its maxim "Think global, eat local". So, expect the unexpected, such as Peterhead monkfish cheek with red lentil dhal; sticky pork belly with rice noodles; and bay leaf and cardamom custard tart, as well as others from India, Korea, Mexico and elsewhere.

GLASGOW continued

Ubiquitous Chip Restaurant

◎◎ SCOTTISH ▲ NOTABLE WINE LIST

0141 334 5007 | 12 Ashton Lane, G12 8SJ

www.ubiquitouschip.co.uk

Affectionately known by Glaswegians as The Chip, its long-held inspiration owes much to Scottish regional dishes. At least one – venison haggis – has been served here since opening day in 1971, but regardless of time served, there's Eyemouth crab, Barra scallops, Ayrshire chicken breast or Aberdeen Angus beef.

UNALOME by Graeme Cheevers NEW

◎◎◎ MODERN BRITISH

0141 501 0553 | 36 Kelvingrove Street, Glasgow, G3 7RZ

www.unalomebygc.com

After working for Martin Wishart in Loch Lomond, Graeme Cheevers has returned to his home city of Glasgow to open his first solo restaurant. A light-filled corner site on Sauchiehall Street, it's a classy dining room with brass and muted greens, a polished parquet floor and minimalist table setup. The kitchen is completely open, allowing diners to watch the focused chefs conjure tip-top Scottish produce into modern British dishes underpinned by classic technique. Veal sweetbreads, asparagus, pickled walnut and preserved lemon might lead on to a precisely cooked fillet of bass with caramelised onion and vin jaune sauce.

Chef Graeme Cheevers

■ HIGHLAND

DORNOCH   MAP 23, NH78

Grant MacNicol at the Castle NEW

◎ MODERN SCOTTISH

01862 810216 | Castle Street, IV25 3SD

www.dornochcastlehotel.com

Grant MacNicol's restaurant at Dornoch Castle is located though a low arched doorway and into a more modern extension where you'll find bistro style, wooden tables and muted colours for the decor. The windows along one side overlook the garden. Expect good seasonal cuisine with prime cuts more prevalent in the summer. There's also an impressive whisky bar serving from some 500 bottles.

Links House at Royal Dornoch

◎◎ CLASSIC SCOTTISH

01862 810279 | Links House, Golf Road, IV25 3LW

www.linkshousedornoch.com

Links House is single-mindedly devoted to the pursuit of golf and pictures of fairways and bunkers adorn the dining room, where a peat-burning fireplace is a feature. The head chef brings his classical French training to the Orangery restaurant here.

FORT AUGUSTUS   MAP 23, NH30

The Inch

◎◎ TRADITIONAL SCOTTISH

01456 450900 | Inchnacardoch Bay, PH32 4BL

www.inchhotel.com

The Inch occupies an old hunting lodge above Inchnacardoch Bay and the hotel's restaurant boasts one of the best views over the iconic Loch Ness. The food has a strong sense of place, with Scottish produce dominating the impressive menu.

Station Road NEW

◎◎ MODERN SCOTTISH

01456 459250 | Loch Ness Side, PH32 4DU

www.thelovat.com

Station Road is on the edge of Loch Ness, near the Caledonian Canal, so the surroundings are impressive to say the least. The kitchen here seeks to reflect these surroundings and does an outstanding job. Locally sourced seafood and other produce feature alongside foraged ingredients on an imaginative menu.

FORT WILLIAM
MAP 22, NN17

Michel Roux Jr at Inverlochy Castle
◉◉◉ MODERN FRENCH ⓘ NOTABLE WINE LIST
01397 702177 | Torlundy, PH33 6SN
www.inverlochycastlehotel.com
The Roux dynasty have picked a top-flight venue at Aberlochy, the very epitome of a grand baronial castle set in a verdant valley at the foot of Ben Nevis. Views are spectacular, and there's a real sense of history and opulence in the richly decorated public spaces, with all the high ceilings, antiques and crystal chandeliers you could wish for. The restaurant is intimate and extremely formal in approach – gentlemen will need their jackets – and complex dishes include wild rabbit terrine with game tea jelly, heritage carrots and pumpernickel, followed by duck breast and leg croquettes with balsamic beetroot and buckwheat.

Chef Tom Swaby **Seats** 40, Private dining 20 **Open** All Year **Parking** 20 **Notes** No children under 8 years

GLENFINNAN
MAP 22, NM98

The Prince's House
◉◉ MODERN BRITISH
01397 722246 | PH37 4LT
www.glenfinnan.co.uk
Kieron and Ina Kelly's white-fronted house has charm in bucket loads. The dining room is hung with a fine art collection and the small conservatory has ravishing views over the glen. Kieron Kelly's cooking steps up to the regional plate in four-course set menus.

GRANTOWN-ON-SPEY
MAP 23, NJ02

Garden Restaurant
◉ MODERN SCOTTISH
01479 872526 | Grant Arms Hotel, 25–27 The Square, PH26 3HF
www.grantarmshotel.com
When you've sharpened your appetite with a day's wildlife watching and outdoor activities in the magnificent Cairngorms, the restaurant of this handsome Victorian hotel makes a fitting spot for a seasonal menu of impeccable local produce. The cooking is hearty, traditional and straightforward with no frills or frippery.

INVERGARRY
MAP 22, NH30

Glengarry Castle Hotel
◉ SCOTTISH, INTERNATIONAL
01809 501254 | PH35 4HW
www.glengarry.net
The Glengarry, overlooking Loch Oich, is a slice of Victorian Scottish baronial, built in the 1860s. Spotless white linen and quality glassware glow beneath the chandelier in the opulent dining room, where lightly modernised, traditional fare is the order of the day.

INVERNESS
MAP 23, NH64

Bunchrew House Hotel
◉◉ MODERN BRITISH
01463 234917 | Bunchrew, IV3 8TA
www.bunchrewhousehotel.com
Bunchrew House is a magnificent 17th-century mansion, complete with turrets and a pink façade, on the water's edge of the Beauly Firth. There's a notable larder of ingredients and the quality comes to the fore in the modern British cuisine. A very enjoyable experience.

Contrast Brasserie
◉ PAN-ASIAN 𝑉
01463 223777 | Glenmoriston Town House Hotel, 20 Ness Bank, IV2 4SF
www.glenmoristontownhouse.com
As Glenmoriston Town House Hotel's main restaurant, Contrast has a rather romantic air, thanks to low lighting and an evening pianist. Unsurprisingly, Scottish produce makes appearances, as in spiced North Uist scallops, and West Coast sea trout. Overall, though, the cooking is modern and international, so dishes of pan-seared Gressingham duck breast, and mugi miso monkfish also star.

INVERNESS continued

Rocpool

◎◎ MODERN EUROPEAN
01463 717274 | 1 Ness Walk, IV3 5NE
www.rocpoolrestaurant.com

On the banks of the River Ness, in the heart of town, Rocpool has a sharp contemporary design featuring lots of wood and natural tones. The team are young, friendly and smartly dressed, and the place has a real brasserie feel. The kitchen style is modern Scottish with an Italian influence, and it's always busy, so be sure to book.

Rocpool Reserve Restaurant

◎◎ FRENCH, SCOTTISH
01463 240089 | 14 Culduthel Road, IV2 4AG
rocpool.com
Rocpool Reserve is a contemporary restaurant close to the castle. A vein of French classicism runs through the cooking, while the impeccable Scottish credentials of the produce is trumpeted too.

KINGUSSIE MAP 23, NH70

The Cross

◎◎◎ MODERN SCOTTISH *V* ♦NOTABLE WINE LIST
01540 661166 | Tweed Mill Brae, Ardbroilach Road, PH21 1LB
www.thecross.co.uk
Set in a converted 19th-century tweed mill in four acres of riverside grounds inside the Cairngorms National Park, The Cross is a country restaurant with rooms, great for relaxing and top-notch dining. Cooking is modern and ingredients-led, and has made locally reared meats something of a speciality - witness loin of local venison with creamed cabbage, braised oxtail, pickled beets and celeriac in a red wine jus. If you're feeling fishy, try wild sea bass with roast root vegetables, butternut squash purée, and a cep dumpling in truffle jus. A six-course taster picks out highlights, while the three-course lunch deal is great value.

Chef David Skiggs **Seats** 26 **Closed** Christmas and January (excluding New Year) **Parking** 20
Notes Children welcome

LOCHALINE MAP 20, NM64

The Whitehouse Restaurant

◎◎ MODERN SCOTTISH
01967 421777 | PA80 5XT
www.thewhitehouserestaurant.co.uk
A five-minute uphill walk from the CalMac ferry on the remote Morvern shores, this intimate little restaurant overlooks the Sound of Mull from a light-flooded, nautical-themed dining room. The kitchen cooks whatever its suppliers have provided on the day – this splendid local bounty appears in dishes that maintain integrity through simplicity.

NAIRN
MAP 23, NH85

Hickory Restaurant
◉ TRADITIONAL, INTERNATIONAL V
01667 452301 | Golf View Hotel & Spa, Seabank Road, IV12 4HD
www.crerarhotels.com/golf-view-hotel-spa
In case you get the impression there's only golf to look at, this hotel's seaside location looks out over the Moray Firth and dining at Hickory offers great views. The elegant conservatory restaurant features menus of locally-landed seafood and meat from local pedigree herds.

SPEAN BRIDGE
MAP 22, NN28

Russell's at Smiddy House
◉◉ MODERN SCOTTISH
01397 712335 | Roy Bridge Road, PH34 4EU
www.smiddyhouse.com
The AA has long recognised the well-presented Scottish cuisine served in this intimate, candlelit restaurant, once the village blacksmith's. Scottish produce is key. Menu highlights include Wester Ross salmon, Arisaig prawns, scallops from the Isle of Mull, Perthshire wood pigeon, Highland game, lamb and beef, pine nut-crusted monkfish and, of course, Scottish cheeses.

STRONTIAN
MAP 22, NM86

Kilcamb Lodge Hotel
◉◉◉ MODERN SCOTTISH, SEAFOOD ⚑NOTABLE WINE LIST
01967 402257 | PH36 4HY
See pages 400–401

TAIN
MAP 23, NH78

Dining Room
◉◉ FRENCH, SCOTTISH
01862 871671 | Glenmorangie House, Cadboll, By Fearn, IV20 1XP
www.theglenmorangiehouse.com
Glenmorangie House is an intimate country bolthole and a pilgrimage spot for fans of its eponymous single malt whisky. The cooking here is on song, its modern approach teaming up prime local ingredients with a resourceful range of ideas and techniques. And yes, the odd shot of that malt may well find its way into the dishes.

THURSO
MAP 23, ND16

Forss House Hotel
◉◉ MODERN SCOTTISH
01847 861201 | Forss, KW14 7XY
www.forsshousehotel.co.uk
You can't get much further away from urban bustle in the mainland British Isles than the northern Highlands, where this Georgian country-house hotel luxuriates in tranquillity below a waterfall on the River Forss, amid acres of woodland. Plenty of pedigree Highland produce is on parade.

TORRIDON
MAP 22, NG95

The Torridon 1887 Restaurant
◉◉◉ MODERN SCOTTISH V ⚑NOTABLE WINE LIST
01445 791242 | Torridon, by Achnasheen, IV22 2EY
www.thetorridon.com/eat-drink/1887-restaurant
Innovative British cooking is the hallmark at The Torridon 1887 Restaurant, part of the Victorian Earl of Lovelace's turreted former shooting lodge. The drive to it requires a little determination, but its remoteness, wildness and scenery are worth it. This is a region where the surrounding land, lochs and the sea play a major role in the kitchen, with vegetables and herbs coming from the two-acre kitchen garden, meats and game from the estate, and shellfish and fish from Loch Torridon and beyond. The menu offers two choices per course, one of which might be Scrabster turbot with courgette and cider sauce.

Chef Paul Green Seats 36, Private dining 16 Closed 2 January for 5 weeks Parking 18 Notes No children under 10 years

Continued on page 402

Kilcamb Lodge Hotel

◎◎◎ **MODERN SCOTTISH, SEAFOOD** 🍷 NOTABLE WINE LIST
01967 402257 | PH36 4HY
www.kilcamblodge.co.uk

Refined, balanced cuisine in an equally refined setting

Standing on the shore of Loch Sunart in 22 acres of sumptuous grounds, Kilcamb offers unruffled tranquillity and seclusion, the journey alone providing a delightful taste of the wild Ardnamurchan Peninsula in the Scottish Highlands. With just 12 rooms, the Georgian house delivers old-school, country-house comforts with plenty of tartan and plush, cosy furniture but avoids being twee with just the right amount of contemporary touches. This style carries on all the way through to the elegant dining room, with its floral curtains, fresh flowers at each table and candles in the evening, but nothing is too fussy – the linen is crisp and the cutlery and glassware sparkle. The views of the loch from here paint an unforgettable backdrop to classically influenced cuisine that comes with a modern interpretation and some international influences. The dishes are served by the friendly staff

ensuring a comfortable and quality experience. Head chef Gary Phillips provisions the larder from local crofts, estates and fishing boats, one of which, The Kirsty Ann, lands a mixed catch and provides great ingredients that are showcased in noteworthy seafood dishes, such as in the starter of smoked mackerel cannelloni with apple and wasabi sorbet, and seaweed mayonnaise – a bold combination of well-ballanced ingredients that are handled carefully; the salty, creaminess of the mayonnaise and the heat of the sorbet work delightfully together. The assiette of salted cod and potato soufflé, salmon, scallops and sea bass is a great interpretation of the classic Portuguese bacalhau - it's prepared with care and attention to detail, producing a

well thought out and fresh dish. The vanilla pannacotta dessert with basil biscuit and strawberry sorbet draws together the themes from the menu: a light and well-balanced dish with crisp buttery biscuits and shavings of white chocolate that add a little touch of indulgence.

Chef Gary Phillips
Seats 40, Private dining 14
Closed 1 January to 1 February
Parking 28
Notes Children welcome

"Standing on the shore of Loch Sunart in 22 acres of sumptuous grounds, Kilcamb offers unruffled tranquillity and seclusion..."

WICK

MAP 23, ND35

Mackay's Hotel

⊚ MODERN SCOTTISH

01955 602323 | Union Street, KW1 5ED

www.mackayshotel.co.uk

Mackay's is home to the No. 1 Bistro, a contemporary restaurant with a relaxed vibe. The kitchen makes good use of quality local ingredients, and there's a modernity to the output. There's a buzzy bar for real ales, cocktails and a terrific range of whiskies.

■ SOUTH LANARKSHIRE

BLANTYRE

MAP 20, NS65

Crossbasket Castle

⊚⊚⊚ CLASSICAL FRENCH

01698 829461 | Crossbasket Estate, Stoneymeadow Road, G72 9UE

www.crossbasketcastle.com

Not far from Glasgow, Crossbasket was conjured out of a much older castle in the 17th century, complete with crenellated façade and spiral turret staircases. An elegant dining room of pale yellow wallpaper, a winter fire and linened tables under an ornate gold-leafed plasterwork ceiling, offering superb views over the gardens, is a refined backdrop for a Roux operation, in which the classical French dishes are finished with some innovative touches. Jerusalem artichoke velouté comes with chestnut cream and artichoke crisps, while torchon of duck liver and braised pig's head is accompanied by Sauternes jelly and truffled brioche. At main course there might be roast fillet of Orkney beef, short rib and cheek with heritage carrots and bone marrow jus, or fillet of wild Scottish halibut with crisp confit chicken thigh. Desserts range from Yorkshire rhubarb with sour cream vacherin to carrot cake with praline cream, blood orange and carrot sorbet.

Chef Michel Roux Jnr, Aaron Sobey Seats 30, Private dining 250 Open All Year Parking 120 Notes Children welcome

■ EAST LOTHIAN

ABERLADY

MAP 21, NT47

Ducks Inn

⊚⊚ MODERN BRITISH

01875 870682 | Main Street, EH32 0RE

www.ducks.co.uk

Located in the heart of a small village, Ducks Inn covers all the bases with its bar-bistro, restaurant and smart accommodation. The good-looking dining area is matched by the attractiveness of what arrives on the plate. The kitchen turns out appealing flavour combinations.

GULLANE

MAP 21, NT48

Greywalls and Chez Roux

⊚⊚ MODERN FRENCH COUNTRY

01620 842144 | Muirfield, EH31 2EG

www.greywalls.co.uk

Golfers enjoy views of Muirfield's 9th and 18th holes from this elegant, Lutyens-designed country house hotel. Spread through four rooms, Chez Roux restaurant impresses and delights with Isle of Mull scallops and chicory; roast veal with sweetbreads; roast Loch Fyne salmon with fennel ravioli; and classic lemon tart with raspberry sorbet originally created by the late Albert Roux.

The Stables at The Bonnie Badger

⊚⊚ MODERN SCOTTISH *V*

01620 621111 | Main Street, EH31 2AB

bonniebadger.com

Nestled between Gullane's golf courses and beaches, The Bonnie Badger's The Stables restaurant has become a coveted destination among guests and locals in the area. It has built a reputation for boasting a stylish Highlands-meet-Scandi interior and some seriously good food driven by the 'From Nature to Plate' philosophy of its founders. Soaring rafters and original sandstone walls create the setting for a roster of updated comfort-food classics.

■ MORAY

FORRES   *MAP 23, NJ05*

Franklin's Restaurant @ Cluny Bank

◉ TRADITIONAL EUROPEAN

01309 674304 | 69 St Leonards Road, IV36 1DW

clunybankhotel.co.uk

A substantial Victorian mansion in lush gardens, Cluny Bank has traditionally styled decor and a small, smart restaurant called Franklin's. There is a lot of period charm to the restaurant and a definite air of sophistication, while the menu name-checks the local Moray suppliers.

■ PERTH & KINROSS

AUCHTERARDER   *MAP 21, NN91*

Andrew Fairlie at Gleneagles

◉◉◉◉ FRENCH, SCOTTISH ▲ NOTABLE WINE LIST

01764 694267 | The Gleneagles Hotel, PH3 1NF

www.andrewfairlie.co.uk

Andrew Fairlie's legacy is carried forward by head chef Stephen McLaughlin, whose passion for French cuisine runs deep. What is particularly striking is the pursuit of excellence that shines through in a team that delivers finely crafted, dazzlingly creative, contemporary French cuisine. The five-star hotel and its three championship golf courses need little introduction and, after so many years at the top of the Scottish dining scene, neither does the restaurant. An independent business in the heart of the hotel, the lavish windowless dining room is a deeply cossetting space, a shimmering haven with atmospheric lighting and original artworks, watched over by a passionate team who make you feel at ease. Choose between the à la carte or eight-course dégustation menus, and be prepared for high-intensity food from a team that puts in the hard graft to max out flavours. Go for broke with wine flight options from a list that is big on Burgundy, Bordeaux and Champagne.

Chef Stephen McLaughlin **Seats** 54 **Closed** 25–26 December, 3 weeks in January **Parking** 300 **Notes** No children

The Strathearn

◉◉ FRENCH, SCOTTISH

01764 694270 | The Gleneagles Hotel, PH3 1NF

www.gleneagles.com

The Strathearn is a splendid art deco room with columns and moulded ceilings. The number of trolleys wheeled to the tables may create the impression that the restaurant is in some time warp, but the kitchen embraces the contemporary as well as the classics.

DUNKELD   *MAP 21, NO04*

Woodland Bistro NEW

◉ CLASSIC

01350 727322 | Atholl Street, PH8 0AR

www.royaldunkeld.co.uk

Woodlands Bistro is one of two dining areas within The Royal Dunkeld Hotel, or three including the beer garden. Recognising its name, the bare-tabled space is designed to remind diners of woodland trails and the environment. Claiming cooking supremacy in the town, its classic dishes include pan-seared Scottish salmon fillet, sitting comfortably alongside the likes of vegetable moussaka.

FORTINGALL   *MAP 20, NN74*

Fortingall Hotel

◉ MODERN SCOTTISH

01887 830367 | PH15 2NQ

www.fortingall.com

Fortingall, though tiny, is very much a tourist destination, and many end up at this Victorian country-house hotel. Dining takes place in two rooms, the main one done out in Arts and Crafts style, with a red carpet, open fire, paintings on the walls and tartan-effect curtains.

KINCLAVEN
MAP 21, NO13

Ballathie House Hotel
◉◉ MODERN BRITISH
01250 883268 | PH1 4QN
www.ballathiehousehotel.com

This turreted mansion overlooking the River Tay hosts a restaurant that impresses with its dedication to local ingredients. The dining room has a classical elegance. Traditional flavours combine with a moderated degree of invention to create dishes that seem entirely in keeping with the setting.

MEIKLEOUR
MAP 21, NO04

The Restaurant at the Meikleour Arms NEW
◉ MODERN BRITISH
01250 883206 | PH2 6EB
www.meikleourarms.co.uk

The Restaurant at the Meikleour Arms features a large vaulted oak ceiling, with exposed stone wall and together with the darkwood, well-appointed, tables create a good initial impression. Expect seasonal menus with a daily comprehensive specials that utilise the produce of the estate were possible; game is very prominent. There's a detailed and comprehensive wine list with some to even inspire the connoisseur.

PERTH
MAP 21, NO12

63 Tay Street Restaurant
◉◉ MODERN SCOTTISH ▲NOTABLE WINE LIST
01738 441451 | 63 Tay Street, PH2 8NN
www.63taystreet.com

Graeme Pallister's 63 Tay Street Restaurant occupies part of the ground floor of an imposing stone building. There's a red and grey modern colour scheme with tartan carpet adding a touch of luxury. 'Local, honest, simple' is the aim, although the kitchen adds a degree of complexity to the offering.

63@Parklands
◉◉ MODERN EUROPEAN
01738 622451 | Parklands Hotel, 2 St Leonards Bank, PH2 8EB
www.63atparklands.com

Overlooking South Inch Park, this spacious hotel restaurant offers a good degree of dining comfort. A strong emphasis on seasonality and local produce steers the menu, which might present pigeon espice, burnt onion, honey and truffle ricotta followed by Highland red deer saddle and shoulder casserole with fermented barley and baked neeps purée.

Deans Restaurant
◉◉ MODERN SCOTTISH
01738 643377 | 77-79 Kinnoull Street, PH1 5EZ
www.letseatperth.co.uk

In the city centre, buzzy Deans and its Rose Lounge are ever popular. Here the kitchen turns out modern Scottish and other dishes, some declaring their origin up front, such as Shetland oysters with black pudding; Thai fragrant rice with pak choi and Marsala cream sauce; and Perthshire strawberries, elderflower liquor mousse and shortbread crumble.

Murrayshall Country House Hotel & Golf Club
◉ MODERN BRITISH
01738 551171 | New Scone, PH2 7PH
www.murrayshall.co.uk

With two golf courses, Murrayshall doesn't do anything by halves. The main dining option is the Old Masters restaurant, a series of elegant spaces with views over the Perthshire landscape. The menu is rich with Scottish ingredients, while cooking techniques combine contemporary and traditional elements.

The North Port Restaurant

◉◉ SCOTTISH *V*

01738 580867 | 8 North Port, PH1 5LU

www.thenorthport.co.uk

This charming restaurant is full of Jacobean charm, with dark oak panels, a spiral staircase, wooden floors and a candle-filled fireplace. Staff are friendly, and the menus focus on fresh Scottish produce from local suppliers, with a slightly more sophisticated choice of dishes available at dinner.

The Roost Restaurant

◉ MODERN SCOTTISH

01738 812111 | Forgandenny Road, Bridge of Earn, PH2 9AZ

www.theroostrestaurant.co.uk

Resembling a farmyard building, The Roost is smart as can be inside, with crisply clad tables and a plethora of pictures and mirrors. Thoroughbred Scottish ingredients include some from the Roost's own kitchen gardens and starters of seared Rougié foie gras set the scene.

Tabla

◉ INDIAN

01738 444630 | 173 South Street, PH2 8NY

www.tablarestaurant.co.uk

At the Kumar family's central Perth eaterie the ambience has more personality than many a formula Indian restaurant, with exposed stone walls, full-drop windows and a glass panel looking into the kitchen. Indian music featuring the eponymous tabla drums plays softly. A full listing of vegetarian dishes is prominent on the menu.

PITLOCHRY
MAP 23, NN95

Fonab Castle Hotel & Spa

◉◉◉ MODERN SCOTTISH

01796 470140 | Foss Road, PH16 5ND

www.fonabcastlehotel.com

Located on the edge of Loch Faskally, Fonab Castle is home to the newly refurbished fine dining Sandemans Restaurant. The castle is late Victorian, and was built for a member of the Sandeman port-shipping family. The seven-course taster menu offers an exciting programme of cutting-edge dishes, with appetisers and a pre-dessert filling in the gaps between main items. These could include crab rillette with pickled cucumber and gazpacho, confit salmon with poached oyster, asparagus and caviar, or breast of Peking duck with confit leg with potato galette in a dashi stock. Unsurprisingly, considering the Sandeman connection, the wine list is excellent.

Chef Rikki Preston **Seats** 60, Private dining 40 **Open** All Year **Parking** 50 **Notes** Children welcome

Knockendarroch Hotel Restaurant

◉◉ MODERN SCOTTISH

01796 473473 | Higher Oakfield, PH16 5HT

www.knockendarroch.co.uk

A handsome sandstone house in a wooded setting, Knockendarroch has country-house comforts and a diminutive restaurant delivering daily-changing menus of classy modern Scottish food. It's very traditional within, with warming fires in the cooler months, ornate cornicing, chandeliers and the like, while hospitality is friendly and genuine.

RANNOCH STATION
MAP 23, NN45

Moor of Rannoch Restaurant & Rooms

◉◉ SCOTTISH

01882 633238 | PH17 2QA

www.moorofrannoch.co.uk

If you're serious about getting away from it all, this remote restaurant with rooms should do the job. Lost among a vast moorland wilderness, you might be lucky to spot wildlife wandering and flying past as you tackle a daily-changing menu of skilfully-cooked food that puts a modern twist on classical ideas.

ST FILLANS
MAP 20, NN62

Lochview Restaurant NEW

◎◎ MODERN SCOTTISH

01764 685320 | On Loch Earn, PH6 2NF

www.achrayhouse.com

The Lochview Restaurant is wisely named, enjoying a stunning 180-degree view of Loch Earn and the mountains beyond. Inside it's cosy with leather upholstery, bespoke wallpaper and recovered wooden flooring. One part of the menu offers a contemporary and adventurous tasting menu, while the other concentrates on satisfyingly traditional quality dishes like burgers, pie, salmon, and beef fillet Rossini.

Seasons View

◎ MODERN INTERNATIONAL

01764 685333 | The Four Seasons, Hotel and Little Larder, A85, Lochside, PH6 2NF

www.thefourseasonshotel.co.uk

Perched right on the edge of Loch Earn, The Four Seasons Hotel has breathtaking views over the water and the wooded hills. In the waterside restaurant, those stunning views complement the modern menu which is built on spectacular Scottish ingredients.

■ SCOTTISH BORDERS

EDDLESTON
MAP 21, NT24

1536 Restaurant NEW

◎ MODERN SCOTTISH

01721 730395 | Old Manse Road, EH45 8QW

www.baronycastle.com

Part of the elegant and historic Barony Castle Hotel, 1536 Restaurant looks out onto the lovely gardens. It was the first place in the area to serve steak on a hot lava rock, so the diner can decide how well done they want it. If steak is the opposite of what you're after, there's a very decent vegan menu.

JEDBURGH
MAP 21, NT62

The Capon Tree Town House NEW

◎ FRENCH

01835 869596 | 61-63 High Street, TD8 6DQ

www.thecapontree.com

The Capon Tree Town House restaurant with rooms is located in the heart of historic border town of Jedburgh. The husband and wife team give a hands-on feel to the whole operation. There is a small bar with an ever-growing collection of gins and a real passion for recommendations. The restaurant is compact and the dining experience is quite formal – expect visually impacting French cuisine involving local produce, some foraged from the surrounding areas. There's a great wine list for such a wee place and lots of good pairings with food.

KELSO
MAP 21, NT73

The Cobbles Freehouse & Dining

◎ MODERN BRITISH

01573 223548 | 7 Bowmont Street, TD5 7JH

www.thecobbleskelso.co.uk

Tucked just off the town's main square, this old inn has successfully negotiated the pub/restaurant dynamic. There are bar snacks such as wraps and burgers on offer, but in the dapper restaurant you'll find Scottish-inspired dishes that really impress. Steaks are sourced from Scottish herds.

Ednam House Hotel

◎ MODERN EUROPEAN

01573 224168 | Bridge Street, TD5 7HT

www.ednamhouse.com

Located just off the town square and enjoying idyllic views of the Tweed, this lovely Georgian hotel is full of character. The triple-aspect restaurant looks over the gardens and across the river to Floors Castle. Main courses could be roast loin of venison with pomme purée, red cabbage, baby beetroot and bitter chocolate sauce.

PEEBLES

Sutherland's Restaurant *NEW*
◉◉ MODERN BRITISH
01721 725750 | Edinburgh Road, EH45 8PL
www.cringletie.com

Cringletie House is a stunning pink stone mansion, complete with conical turrets, and dates from the 1860s. The bright and airy Sutherlands Restaurant, with its stunning painted ceiling and impressive fireplace, is a welcoming setting for unpretentious seasonal dining, with a seven-course tasting menu available on Sunday evenings. Dishes make good use of produce from the hotel's walled garden where possible.

WALKERBURN

Windlestraw
◉◉◉ MODERN SCOTTISH, BRITISH
01896 870636 | Galashiels Road, EH43 6AA
www.windlestraw.co.uk

Located only 40 minutes from Edinburgh, in the rolling hills of the Scottish Border country, Windlestraw is a beautiful Edwardian Arts and Crafts villa set in two acres of grounds and lovingly restored by its present owners. Service is both personal and attentive in the oak panelled restaurant where contemporary Scottish menus deliver the likes of ham hock terrine pointed up with cauliflower, piccalilli and prosecco-poached sultanas, followed by venison loin with roasted and puréed celeriac, preserved blackcurrants and chard. To finish, a refined take on the classic Scottish cranachan accompanied by a silky smooth whisky ice cream hits a high note.

Chef Stu Waterston **Seats** 20, Private dining 20 **Closed** mid December to mid February **Parking** 10 **Notes** No children under 11 years

■ STIRLING

CALLANDER

Roman Camp Country House Hotel
◉◉◉ MODERN FRENCH
01877 330003 | FK17 8BG
www.romancamphotel.co.uk

Dating back to the 17th century, this stately old house with its pale pink walls is wonderfully located in the Loch Lomond and the Trossachs National Park. A hotel since the 1930s, it has 20 acres of gardens and a truly beautiful interior, with fine period details, from the secret chapel to the panelled library, and an antique grand piano and more than 40 malt whiskies in the bar. The two dining rooms are sumptuous and splendid, with attentive, well-trained staff, and the food is focused and contemporary. The short carte and set-price menus are focussed on the seasons, so caramelised sweetbreads might appear with Toulouse sausage, sweet and sour apricots and roasted garlic purée, before a main course of perfectly-timed hazelnut-crusted halibut with potato dumplings and crab and lemongrass mousse. A milk chocolate and salted caramel delice is a beautiful dish, with a deliciously refreshing blood orange sorbet.

Chef Ian McNaught **Seats** 120, Private dining 36 **Open** All Year **Parking** 80 **Notes** Children welcome

DUNBLANE

Cromlix and Chez Roux

◉◉◉ MODERN SCOTTISH ⬛ NOTABLE WINE LIST

01786 822125 | Kinbuck, FK15 9JT

www.cromlix.com

Built for one Captain Arthur Drummond in the 1870s, when it was known with becoming modesty as Cromlix Cottage, then promptly rebuilt the same decade when it burned down, the turreted manor house is now owned by local boy Sir Andy Murray. Public rooms are the height of country-house elegance, the dining room a glassed-in conservatory that looks over the sumptuous grounds. Named in honour of the late and much-garlanded Albert Roux, Darin Campbell's kitchen aims high, blending elements of French gastronomic classicism with vivacious cooking in the modern global style. Orkney hand-dived scallops come with a salad of Cromlix garden rainbow chard and edamame beans, making a fine beginning, followed perhaps with mallard from the Braco Estate. Spiced French pumpkin soufflé with chocolate orange ice cream is an unusual dessert with great depth of flavour. The French-leaning wine list offers an impressive selection of half bottles and wines by the glass.

Chef Darin Campbell **Seats** 60, Private dining 50
Open All Year **Parking** 30 **Notes** Children welcome

STIRLING

Scholars Restaurant

◉ BRITISH, EUROPEAN

01786 272727 | Spittal Street, FK8 1DU

www.stirlinghighlandhotel.co.uk

A grand Victorian property just down the hill from Stirling's historic castle, The Stirling Highland Hotel was built in the 1850s as a school. The eating takes place in three dining rooms of generous Victorian proportions. The menu takes a modern approach to familiar ideas.

SCOTTISH ISLANDS

■ ISLE OF MULL

CRAIGNURE
MAP 20, NM73

Oran Na Mara *NEW*
◉ BRASSERIE, GRILL
01680 812544 | PA65 6BB
www.crerarhotels.com/isle-of-mull-hotel-spa
With an amazing location on the Isle of Mull, Oran Na Mara offers modern brasserie cooking in a stylish setting. The team are very friendly and smiley in their tweedy uniforms, but still maintain a professional attitude. Local seafood is the highlight, but there are also plenty of great steaks and burgers from the grill.

FIONNPHORT
MAP 20, NM32

Ninth Wave Restaurant
◉ MODERN PACIFIC RIM, SEAFOOD *V*
01681 700757 | PA66 6BL
www.ninthwaverestaurant.co.uk
On the southern tip of Mull where ferries leave for Iona, John and Carla Lamont's pocket-sized restaurant is about as remote as they come. The dinner-only affair seats just 18 lucky diners, who can expect skilfully cooked menus full of inventive ideas.

TOBERMORY
MAP 22, NM55

Highland Cottage
◉◉ MODERN, CLASSIC
01688 302030 | 24 Breadalbane Street, PA75 6PD
www.highlandcottage.co.uk
Enjoying a stunning elevated location overlooking Tobermory harbour, this salmon-hued hotel close to the fishing pier is a jewel. The interiors are a delight and the place is cleverly laid out to lead you from the bar and conservatory into the suavely furnished dining room. It does a fine job of showcasing Mull produce.

■ ISLE OF SKYE

COLBOST
MAP 22, NG24

The Three Chimneys & The House Over-By
◉◉◉ SCOTTISH, NORDIC INFLUENCE ▲NOTABLE WINE LIST
01470 511258 | IV55 8ZT
www.threechimneys.co.uk
This remote whitewashed cottage restaurant is easily one of the UK's wildest restaurant locations, particularly in winter.
A warren of small rooms with low ceilings, the restaurant's polished dark wood floors and tables are offset by exposed stone walls and black slate place mats. The food from Welshman Scott Davies is firmly rooted in seafood from nearby waters and Loch Dunvegan provides a bountiful supply of langoustine. A meal could begin with dressed scallop, Jerusalem artichoke, apple and herbs or a simple plate of local oysters. Next, devilled pigeon pie with Nordic mustard and gherkin might lead on to a main course of Black Isle beef, parsley and onions. Round things off with Crowdie cheesecake, rhubarb, yogurt, gorse and lemon.

Chef Scott Davies **Seats** 40 **Closed** 16 December to 16 January **Parking** 12 **Notes** No children under 5 years at lunch and 8 years at dinner

EDINBANE
MAP 22, NG35

Edinbane Lodge *NEW*
◉◉◉ MODERN SCOTTISH *V*
01470 582217 | Edinbane, IV51 9PW
www.edinbanelodge.co.uk
The elegant dining room at the luxuriously renovated 16th-century Edinbane Lodge has an impressive stone fireplace and portraits of past owners, while the seasonal tasting menus showcase the very best produce the island has to offer. A starter of the freshest, plumpest langoustine, served on nicely braised carrot, gets things off to a great start. Next up, a simply presented dish of deliciously fresh Shetland-landed cod with Drumfearn chanterelles. Coishletter venison loin is accompanied by smoked beetroot and excellent pommes dauphine. A beautifully simple dessert of pineapple weed ice cream with lemon verbena is followed by Isle of Skye sea salt caramel parfait with sorrel.

Chef Calum Montgomery **Seats** 40 **Open** All Year **Parking** 16 **Notes** Children welcome

ISLEORNSAY
MAP 22, NG71

Duisdale House Hotel
◉◉ MODERN SCOTTISH
01471 833202 | Sleat, IV43 8QW
www.duisdale.com
Set on a remote coast, Duisdale House Hotel is a converted Victorian hunting lodge with amazing views. The restaurant has a subdued yet elegant style, leaving the views and the food to speak for themselves. Meals hit the mark, delivering a great balance of flavours. Expect modern cooking based on seasonal, regional ingredients.

Toravaig House Hotel
◉◉ MODERN SCOTTISH
01471 820200 | Knock Bay, Sleat, IV44 8RE
www.toravaig.com
Toravaig House Hotel is a small boutique property that enjoys enviable views over Knock Castle and the Sound of Sleat, while the interior is classy and stylish. The Iona restaurant is a smart candlelit space, offering up modern Scottish cuisine, in keeping with the majestic surroundings. Most of the produce comes from the island, including venison, lamb and seafood.

PORTREE
MAP 22, NG44

Dulse & Brose
◉◉ MODERN
01478 612846 | Bosville Hotel, 9–11 Bosville Terrace, IV51 9DG
www.bosvillehotel.co.uk
Dulse & Brose takes its name from a type of seaweed and an oatmeal dish, symbolising the use of Scottish ingredients at this trendy boutique hotel and restaurant. There is a casual atmosphere here, with views of the Skye scenery, wooden tables and banquette seating, plus clever cookery the order of the day.

STEIN
MAP 22, NG25

Loch Bay Restaurant
◉◉◉ SEAFOOD, TRADITIONAL SCOTTISH, FRENCH
01470 592235 | Macleods Terrace, IV55 8GA
www.lochbay-restaurant.co.uk
Enjoying a magical setting in a row of 18th-century fishermen's cottages right by the loch shore, Loch Bay is a diminutive institution around these parts. Seating only 16 diners, its unpretentious decor of warm colours and gilt-framed mirrors convey a homely charm that belies the seriously accomplished food on offer. Chef Michael Smith's finely-honed skills, attention to detail and commitment to top-class Scottish ingredients deliver dishes of deceptive simplicity and integrity, showcased in the 'Skye Fruits de Mer' – a set menu of local shellfish and fish. The happy alliance of contemporary Scottish verve and classical French foundations shine from the nibble of crisp oatmeal oyster mignonette and first course of bay prawn and shrimp bisque with crab and mull cheddar toastie through to a dessert of strawberry and iced whisky mac tart.

Chef Michael Smith **Seats** 16 **Closed** January to February, 1st week August and reduced winter hours **Parking** 6 **Notes** No children under 12 years old.

WALES

■ ISLE OF ANGLESEY

BEAUMARIS
MAP 14, SH67

Bishopsgate House Hotel
◉ TRADITIONAL WELSH

01248 810302 | 54 Castle Street, LL58 8BB
www.bishopsgatehotel.co.uk
The mint-green façade of Bishopsgate House stands out on its Georgian terrace overlooking Beaumaris Green and Snowdonia across the Menai waterfront, while the intimate, low-ceilinged restaurant is full of old-world charm. Straightforward menus might finish with pecan tart and honeycomb ice cream.

GAERWEN
MAP 14, SH47

Gaerwen Arms NEW
◉◉ MODERN BRITISH

01248 421083 | Chapel Street, LL60 6DW
gaerwen-arms.co.uk

Well executed modern British dishes with well balanced flavours are the hallmarks at this friendly pub, just across the Menai Bridge from mainland Wales. The restaurant is modern in design with tartan-style carpeting and upholstered seating, and French-polished tables. When the weather demands it, expect a blazing fire in the main bar. Three miles away is famous 58-letter Llanfair PG sign.

MENAI BRIDGE
MAP 14, SH57

Sosban & The Old Butcher's Restaurant
◉◉◉◉ MODERN

01248 208131 | Trinity House, 1 High Street, LL59 5EE
www.sosbanandtheoldbutchers.com
Dining at Sosban is a hot ticket, and definitely not your everyday restaurant experience. There is only room for 16 at any one time and it only happens three evenings and one lunch a week. But once you're inside you don't have to do much but give yourself over to the prodigiously talented Stephen Stevens, who will serve up his no-choice menu at a fixed time. Allow four hours from start to finish. The one-time butcher's shop on the high street has a rustic simplicity reflecting its former life. The procession of dishes displays amazing creativity, compelling visuals, and mightily impressive flavours. For example, reindeer moss is a stellar opening mouthful, rich with mushroom and fermented egg yolk. Duck with beetroot, anise, yogurt and mustard leaf is superb. Rhubarb and custard gets a reappraisal when a crisp rhubarb sphere is filled with duck egg custard and hits of rhubarb from poached and freeze-dried fruit. Complex, creative cuisine at its best and well worth the wait.

Chef Stephen Stevens **Seats** 12 **Closed** Christmas, New Year, January **Notes** No children

NEWBOROUGH
MAP 14, SH46

Marram Grass
◉◉ MODERN BRITISH

01248 440077 | White Lodge, LL61 6RS
www.themarramgrass.com
There's no escaping it, this restaurant is actually a shed on a campsite. But make no mistake, it's a pretty smart shed; it even has a slate-topped bar. Anglesey's island status provides the ingredients – crab risotto with roast celeriac, local apple, garlic and sea truffle, for example.

■ BRIDGEND

BRIDGEND
MAP 9, SS97

Leicesters Restaurant
◉◉ MODERN CLASSIC

01656 657644 | The Great House, 8 High Street, Laleston, CF32 0HP
www.great-house-laleston.co.uk
The 15th-century Great House, a Grade II listed building, is home to this restaurant that aims to provide an exquisite dining experience in welcoming and relaxed surroundings. Reflecting excellent Welsh cooking, expect bold, inventive food that's underpinned by a sense of quality and local sourcing.

■ CARDIFF

CARDIFF

MAP 9, ST17

Bully's
◎◎ FRENCH
029 2022 1905 | 5 Romilly Crescent, CF11 9NP
www.bullysrestaurant.co.uk
Bully's restaurant fills virtually every inch of its walls with a quirky pot pourri of pictures, mirrors and other retro paraphernalia. The kitchen may well rely on Welsh providers for its materials but wears its Gallic culinary allegiance on its sleeve in menus grounded in the French repertoire, spiced with the odd foray into global ideas.

Park House Restaurant
◎◎ MODERN FRENCH ⚱ⁿᵒᵗᵃᵇˡᵉ ʷⁱⁿᵉ ˡⁱˢᵗ
029 2022 4343 | 20 Park Place, CF10 3DQ
www.parkhouserestaurant.co.uk
Housed in a Gothic architectural extravagance, the splendid panelled restaurant overlooks the gardens of the National Museum of Wales. Do try the chocolate platter involving a rich pavé and 'pulled' chocolate with a peppermint macaroon and spearmint sorbet.

■ CARMARTHENSHIRE

LLANSTEFFAN

MAP 8, SN31

Mansion House Llansteffan
◎◎ MODERN BRITISH
01267 241515 | Pantyrathro, SA33 5AJ
www.mansionhousellansteffan.co.uk
Mansion House Llansteffan is a compact yet perfectly formed Georgian building which has kept its architectural character and blended this seamlessly with a contemporary finish. Named after the Welsh word for 'estuary', Moryd Restaurant overlooks the gardens and the Towy Estuary beyond. Menus offer straightforward and well-rendered modern brasserie food.

See advertisement below

NANTGAREDIG

Y Polyn

◎◎ CLASSIC EUROPEAN ⬤ NOTABLE WINE LIST

01267 290000 | SA32 7LH

www.ypolyn.co.uk

This hospitable country pub is certainly more about dining than propping up the bar with a pint. Its owners win praise for hauling in the finest produce they can lay their hands on – salt marsh lamb and Welsh beef, for example – and transforming it into satisfyingly rustic lip-smacking dishes. The home-baked breads are fab too.

■ CEREDIGION

EGLWYS FACH

Ynyshir Restaurant & Rooms

◎◎◎◎◎ MODERN BRITISH ⬤ NOTABLE WINE LIST

01654 781209 | EGLWYS FACH, SY20 8TA

www.ynyshir.co.uk

On the south bank of the River Dovey, deep within a 2,000-acre RSPB reserve, this country manor is one of the Principality's most treasured restaurants. Once owned by Queen Victoria, the house and its lush green gardens are framed by the imposing Cambrian Mountains, which separate two National Parks, Snowdonia to the north and Brecon Beacons to the south. With chef-patron Gareth Ward at the helm, Ynyshir has been on the foodie trail for some time. At the heart of the operation, as you would expect, are the dining room and a no-shouting-zone kitchen opening off it. While cooking is clearly the kitchen team's priority, they also do their fair share of pickling, salting, fermenting, plus preserving fruits, leaves and berries. Neither lunch nor dinner is a hurried affair – with so many courses, how could they be? – so expect at least a four-hour sitting. Each of the six small tables is served by the chefs, who happily explain the genesis of the dishes, or what Gareth calls Alternative British Snap. Using only brief descriptions, the menus signpost what's to come. With dinner lasting four hours, it's a good idea to book an overnight room too.

Chef Gareth Ward Seats 18, Private dining 4 Closed 2 weeks in summer, 2 weeks over Christmas and New Year, one week April, one week October Parking 20 Notes Children welcome

TREGARON

Y Talbot

◎◎ MODERN BRITISH

01974 298208 | The Square, SY25 6JL

www.ytalbot.com

Drovers of old began their long treks to the markets of the Midlands and London from Tregaron, no doubt first fortifying themselves in this part 17th-century inn. Through the pillared front doorway there's a bar one side and a restaurant on the other, with bilingual, wide-choice menus on offer.

■ CONWY

ABERGELE

Brasserie 1786

◎◎ MODERN BRITISH

01745 832014 | The Kinmel, St George's Road, LL22 9AS

www.thekinmel.co.uk

After a day in the Kinmel's spa, the hotel's bright, contemporary Brasserie 1786 is the place to head for some plain-speaking, seasonal food. Despite the chic, minimalist looks, the place has been in the hands of the same family since, well, the clue's in the name.

BETWS-Y-COED

Craig-y-Dderwen Riverside Hotel

◎ TRADITIONAL, INTERNATIONAL

01690 710293 | LL24 0AS

www.snowdoniahotel.com

Built in the 1890s for an industrialist, the partly timbered house became a favourite bolt-hole for Sir Edward Elgar. A hotel since the 20s, it offers the full country-house package, complete with views of a riverside teeming with wildlife (do look out for the otters).

Llugwy River Restaurant@Royal Oak Hotel
🍴 MODERN BRITISH, WELSH
01690 710219 | Holyhead Road, LL24 0AY
royaloakhotel.net
Cappuccino-coloured walls with yellow sconces and ceiling chandeliers characterise the restaurant at this Victorian coaching inn. The kitchen supports local suppliers and the menu buzzes with interest. Game shows up in season, perhaps wild mallard with root vegetable gâteau, sticky red cabbage and damson jus.

COLWYN BAY   MAP 14, SH87

Bryn Williams at Porth Eirias
🍴🍴 BRITISH, SEAFOOD
01492 577525 | The Promenade, LL29 8HH
www.portheirias.com

Floor-to-ceiling windows offer sweeping views of Colwyn Bay, and exposed steelwork, pendant lights and industrial-chic create the feeling of a hip, big-city eatery. Bryn Williams made his name alongside celebrated chefs and has been chef-patron of Odette's in London's Primrose Hill since 2008, so you can expect sharp, modern British bistro ideas.

CONWY   MAP 14, SH77

Castle Hotel Conwy
🍴🍴 MODERN BRITISH
01492 582800 | High Street, LL32 8DB
www.castlewales.co.uk
With its courtyard garden and stylish decor, Dawsons Restaurant & Bar offers modern British menus that deliver brasserie-style dishes and classic comfort options. Start with pan-seared king scallops, celeriac purèe, black pudding and chorizo jam and follow it with fillet of sea bass, sweet potato fondant, buttered tenderstem broccoli and tomato pickle.

Signatures Restaurant
🍴🍴 MODERN BRITISH
01492 583513 | Aberconwy Resort & Spa, Aberconwy Park, LL32 8GA
www.darwinescapes.co.uk/parks/aberconwy-resort-spa/signatures-restaurant
The seaside holiday park location is a little left-field, but Signatures is well worth tracking down for its inspired modern cooking. An open kitchen adds to the buzz, and menus are full of modern accents, so prepare yourself for the likes of home-made black pudding and smoked bacon and leek rösti enriched with a runny egg, and mustard dressing. There's plenty of craft and attention to detail throughout.

DEGANWY   MAP 14, SH77

Quay Hotel & Spa
🍴 MODERN EUROPEAN
01492 564100 | Deganwy Quay, LL31 9DJ
www.quayhotel.co.uk
Beautifully located on the Conwy estuary, with views across the marina to the castle, this is a stylish, modern boutique hotel. The smart Grill Room offers a relatively informal setting for straightforward European cooking. Locally-landed fish and seafood feature on the menu.

LLANDUDNO
MAP 14, SH78

Bodysgallen Hall and Spa
⊛⊛⊛ MODERN, TRADITIONAL *V* ⅟ NOTABLE WINE LIST
01492 584466 | The Royal Welsh Way, LL30 1RS
www.bodysgallen.com

A couple of miles south of Llandudno, Bodysgallen is a supremely elegant, stone-built Stuart mansion in 200 acres of parkland. In the immediate environs of the house, a box-hedged parterre laid out in the 17th century is redolent of herbs to this day. Inside, the sober oak panelling is softened by garden views through mullioned windows framed by gathered drapes, and by sympathetic, personable service. Balancing traditional and modern British modes has become an essential skill of today's aspirant chefs, and Abdula El Shershaby possesses it in abundance, garnishing barbecued ox tongue to start with deconstructed piccalilli and a cauliflower cheese fritter. A main of slow-cooked saddle of Welsh lamb is accompanied by glazed Bodysgallen root vegetables and tenderstem broccoli, and you might draw things to a conclusion with a soft and yielding cereal milk pannacotta with apricot sorbet and Mirabelle plum compôte. Excellent coffee and petits fours finish things off nicely.

Chef Abdulla El Shershaby **Seats** 60, Private dining 40 **Closed** 24–26 December **Parking** 40 **Notes** No children under 6 years

Dunoon Hotel
⊛⊛ MODERN BRITISH *V*
01492 860787 | Gloddaeth Street, LL30 2DW
www.dunoonhotel.co.uk

The restaurant here is full of old-world charm, with oak-panelled walls, brass fittings and chandeliers, flowers and linen napery on the tables and a cooking style that's more likely to reassure than to startle, the kitchen quite rightly keeping its customers happy.

Imperial Hotel
⊛⊛ MODERN, TRADITIONAL BRITISH
01492 877466 | The Promenade, Vaughan Street, LL30 1AP
www.theimperial.co.uk

The wedding-cake stucco façade of the Imperial is a landmark on Llandudno's seafront. On a balmy day, alfresco dining on the terrace with a splendid backdrop of the bay is on the cards. The kitchen turns out menus of classically-inflected modern cooking featuring a sound showing of fine Welsh produce.

Samphire *NEW*
⊛ CLASSIC BRITISH
01492 878101 | 6 Penrhyn Crescent, LL30 1BA
www.caemorhotel.co.uk

The Samphire Brasserie & Bar, to quote its full name, is on the ground floor of the seafront Cae Mor Hotel, overlooking the wide sweep of Llandudno Bay. You'd be right to expect fish and seafood to feature prominently on the menu with, for instance, seared scallops, and herb-crusted halibut. Grills and rack of Welsh lamb also feature.

St George's Hotel
⊛ MODERN, TRADITIONAL, WELSH
01492 877544 | The Promenade, LL30 2LG
www.stgeorgeswales.co.uk

Llandudno's prom is the place to be for splendid sunsets and sweeping views across the bay, and St George's Hotel sits centre stage. The place is a timeless slice of Victorian wedding-cake grandeur, with an irresistible terrace and floor-to-ceiling windows in the restaurant.

■ GWYNEDD

ABERSOCH
MAP 14, SH32

The Dining Room
⊛ WELSH BISTRO
01758 740709 | 4 High Street, LL53 7DY
www.thediningroomabersoch.co.uk

In pole position among the buzzy bars and hip surfie shops of trendy Abersoch's main drag, this low-key bistro with a tea-shop frontage and mismatched chairs and tables is building a loyal fan base for its warm hospitality and confidently executed food.

Porth Tocyn Hotel
◉◉ MODERN BRITISH ⚑NOTABLE WINE LIST
01758 713303 | Bwlchtocyn, LL53 7BU
www.porthtocynhotel.co.uk
The Fletcher-Brewer family converted a terrace of lead miners' cottages into the comfortable, relaxed and unstuffy place we see today. Inside are antique-filled lounges and a smart restaurant, with spectacular views over Cardigan Bay to Snowdonia. Louise's repertoire combines traditional values and more modern sensibilities.

Pale Hall Hotel & Restaurant
◉◉◉ BRITISH, EUROPEAN ⚑NOTABLE WINE LIST
01678 530285 | Llandderfel, LL23 7PS
www.palehall.co.uk
In the lush Dee Valley, with all Snowdonia laid out before it, Palé Hall (note the accent – there is nothing pale about Palé) is a plutocratic Victorian industrialist's idea of a bijou residence, built to the dimensions of a medieval castle. Its interiors are beautifully decorated in pastel tones and light wood panelling, with a bolder amber hue in the dining room, where still-lifes of fruit crowd the walls. Gareth Stevenson's menus are informed by the grandeur of the surroundings, but with today's ingenuity of approach adding interest throughout. As well as two tasting menus, there's the Classics Menu, with things like scallops with pea purée and fillet of Welsh Black beef. The six-course tasting menu might feature grilled mackerel with Jersey Royals, Denbighshire wood pigeon with blueberries and Savoy cabbage, and desserts of rhubarb compôte with custard and a sorrel granita, and wild strawberry mousse with yuzu, and yogurt sorbet. It's worth considering the wine flights too.

Chef Gareth Stevenson **Seats** 40, Private dining 40 **Open** All Year **Parking** 40 **Notes** Children welcome

The Gunroom Restaurant
◉ MODERN BRITISH HYBRID TASTER MENU V
01286 830214 | Plas Dinas Country House, Bontnewydd, LL54 7YF
www.plasdinas.co.uk/dining
Set in Plas Dinas, the small country house that was once the home of Lord Snowdon, the Gunroom Restaurant still displays a number of Armstrong-Jones family portraits and memorabilia. The space is intimate to say the least, with covers for only 20 at any one time. The menu changes monthly, and revolves around seasonal Welsh produce.

See advertisement on page 420

Ty Castell
◉◉ WELSH TAPAS
01286 674937 | 18 Stryd Fawr, LL55 1RN
www.tycastell.cymru
Close to Caernarfon Castle and occupying a notable 18th-century building, this contemporary restaurant looks far beyond Wales for its culinary inspiration. The interesting tapas-style menu has a global influence, from dishes like cured salmon, pink grapefruit, white radish and ponzu dressing to the teriyaki beef, braised onion and sautéed mushrooms.

Bron Eifion Country House Hotel
◉ MODERN BRITISH, WELSH
01766 522385 | LL52 0SA
www.broneifion.co.uk
Built in 1883, the creeper-clad house has the dual charm of ravishing gardens and stone's-throw proximity to Criccieth's beach. A majestic staircase, oak panelling and comfortable country-house furniture give the right impression, though the Garden Room restaurant offers a more contemporary experience.

Continued on page 421

DOLGELLAU
MAP 14, SH71

Bwyty Mawddach Restaurant
◉ EUROPEAN
01341 421752 | Pen-y-Garnedd, Llanelltyd, LL40 2TA
www.mawddach.com
As barn conversions go, this one is rather impressive. Ifan Dunn turned the old granite building on the family farm into a snazzy modern restaurant with views over the Mawddach Estuary and the slopes of Cader Idris through its glass wall.

Penmaenuchaf Hall Hotel
◉◉ MODERN BRITISH ⚑NOTABLE WINE LIST
01341 422129 | Penmaenpool, LL40 1YB
www.penhall.co.uk
The greystone Victorian hall gives spectacular views to Cader Idris and the Mawddach Estuary. Within, oak floors, panels, artwork and fresh flowers give a real sense of age and quality. The menu pays homage to indigenous produce, and there's no lack of contemporary, creative flair.

LLANBERIS
MAP 14, SH56

Padarn Brasserie
◉ MODERN BRITISH
01286 870253 | The Royal Victoria Hotel Snowdonia, LL55 4TY
www.theroyalvictoria.co.uk
Set within Snowdonia National Park, this Victorian hotel occupies a magnificent spot overlooking the village of Llanberis. Popular with walkers and tourists as much as locals, the modern British menu keeps things simple. Chicken liver parfait and onion marmalade might precede pan-fried sea bream, ratatouille, chorizo, chilli, coriander pesto and straw potatoes.

PORTMEIRION
MAP 14, SH53

The Hotel Portmeirion
◉◉ MODERN WELSH
01766 770000 | Minffordd, LL48 6ET
www.portmeirion-village.com
The fantasy Italianate village, created by Sir Clough Williams-Ellis, was conceived around the ruin of what is now the hotel. When the whole place began to materialise in 1926, the hotel became its focal point. Today, expect the fresh, lively, modern Welsh cooking to enhance the whole experience.

■ MONMOUTHSHIRE

ABERGAVENNY
MAP 9, SO21

Angel Hotel
◉ BRITISH, INTERNATIONAL
01873 857121 | 15 Cross Street, NP7 5EN
www.angelabergavenny.com
This hotel in the heart of the town was a posting inn in the first half of the 19th century, and its Georgian façade and spacious interiors are in fine fettle today. The brasserie-style menu is offered in both the Foxhunter Bar and the Oak Room restaurant.

The Hardwick
◉◉ MODERN BRITISH
01873 854220 | Old Raglan Road, NP7 9AA
www.thehardwick.co.uk
Hard at work in a revamped old inn just outside Abergavenny is Stephen Terry, a chef with a wealth of experience at the sharp end of the restaurant biz. Food is unpretentious, mood-enhancing stuff. Set lunches and Sunday lunch are a cut above the norm.

Restaurant 1861
◉◉ MODERN BRITISH, EUROPEAN
01873 821297 | Cross Ash, NP7 8PB
www.18-61.co.uk
Built as a pub in 1861, this place much, much later became Simon and Kate King's attractive, slightly isolated restaurant. A starter of ethically produced foie gras or dill-cured mackerel might be followed by a fricassée, either rose veal or woodland mushrooms; or fillet of hake or sea trout. Kate's dad grows most of the vegetables.

The Walnut Tree Inn
◉◉◉ TRADITIONAL BRITISH ⚑NOTABLE WINE LIST
See pages 422–423

See advertisement on 424

ROCKFIELD
MAP 9, SO41

The Stonemill & Steppes Farm Cottages
◉◉ MODERN BRITISH
01600 716273 | NP25 5SW
www.thestonemill.co.uk
A beautifully converted barn in a 16th-century mill complex provides an impressive setting for accomplished cooking. It's a riot of beams and vaulted ceilings, with chunky rustic tables around an ancient stone cider press. The kitchen uses regional produce to deliver simply presented, modern dishes.

Continued on page 425

ABERGAVENNY

The Walnut Tree Inn

◎◎◎ **TRADITIONAL BRITISH** 🍷 NOTABLE WINE LIST
01873 852797 | Llanddewi Skirrid, NP7 8AW
www.thewalnuttreeinn.com

Contemporary flavours in beautiful Welsh countryside

Firmly established on the gastronomic map since the 1960s, The Walnut Tree Inn, with its neatly-clipped topiary and white-painted exterior, is the perfect place to relax and unwind. Set amid rolling fields a couple of miles east of the charming market town of Abergavenny, it's a beautiful location, close to the border with England, and certainly rewards further exploration – it's surrounded by the mountains of the Brecon Beacons National Park, and only forty-five minutes from Cardiff. The Walnut Tree has been home to Shaun Hill since 2008, and he continues to cook food he himself likes to eat, which sounds so sensible it's hard to imagine a time when it was almost revolutionary to take such a comfortable, eclectic approach, unrestrained by anything except the ingredients. Hill's strong classical background and five decades of experience at the top of the culinary tree give a

> "Hill's strong classical background and five decades of experience at the top of the culinary tree give a reassuring foundation for contemporary interpretations of flavour and texture..."

reassuring foundation for contemporary interpretations of flavour and texture which may appear simple but are conceived with extreme thoughtfulness and attention to detail. The dining area is welcomingly informal and unpretentious with bare tables and striking modern art. Daily-changing menus reflect season and availability, and there's an excellent value set lunch, which might see you tucking into pork rillettes with pickles and toast before main course hake with shrimp and dill. The

a la carte offers more complex choices, so dinner might begin with squab pigeon and petit pois a la Française, or red mullet with tomato, chilli and ginger, before a main of cod with haricot beans, chorizo, mussels and anchovy dressing, or Middle White pork with glazed cheek and pressed belly. There could be gingerloaf with butterscotch and clotted cream to finish, or perhaps refreshing cherry soup with almond ice cream. The wine list leans towards smaller winemakers, and, like the food, demonstrates the tastes and interests of Shaun and his team.

Chef Shaun Hill Seats 70, Private dining 26
Closed 1 week at Christmas Parking 30
Notes Children welcome

See advertisement on 424

THE WALNUT TREE

The famous Michelin-starred restaurant located two miles east of Abergavenny offers dishes based on Shaun Hill's personal taste paire with sound cooking techniques and truly exceptional ingredients. Open Tuesday to Saturday.

01873 852797
Llanddewi Skirrid, Abergavenny, NP7 8AW
www.thewalnuttreeinn.com

USK
MAP 9, SO30

Newbridge on Usk
🌀🌀 TRADITIONAL BRITISH
01633 451000 | Tredunnock, NP15 1LY
www.celtic-manor.com
On a bend in the Usk, with river views, this restaurant with rooms is surrounded by well-tended gardens. The property dates back 200 years, so you can expect the usual beams and fireplaces, while the two-level restaurant has a rustic charm.

The Raglan Arms
🌀 MODERN BRITISH
01291 690800 | Llandenny, NP15 1DL
www.raglanarms.co.uk
This unassuming property looking more like a private house is home to bistro-style cooking and a friendly atmosphere. Log burners and scrubbed tables bring home the inn-like feel, and a decked terrace allows diners to sit and enjoy the rural location.

WHITEBROOK
MAP 4, SO50

The Whitebrook
🌀🌀🌀🌀 MODERN BRITISH, FRENCH 🍷 NOTABLE WINE LIST
01600 860254 | NP25 4TX
www.thewhitebrook.co.uk
The lush Wye Valley that surrounds this whitewashed former drovers' inn is also the source of a good deal of the menu, such is chef-patron Chris Harrod's passion for the food on his doorstep. This restaurant with rooms seems to fit organically into its environment and is an unpretentious and relaxing setting for dynamic cooking. There is real vitality to each course - an excellent plate of Cornish brill might be accompanied by sweet and creamy crown prince pumpkin, plump mussels, rainbow chard and garlic chives. Sweet courses like the palate-cleansing blackberry and chamomile with blackcurrant sage are thoughtfully conceived, while 'Tea & Cake' is a *Great British Menu*-winning dish and a stunning end to the meal, every mouthful a different journey. The vegetarian menu is equally creative and compelling, and the wine list includes bottles from organic and biodynamic growers.

Chef Chris Harrod **Seats** 26 **Closed** 2 weeks in January **Parking** 20 **Notes** No children under 12 years at dinner

◼ NEWPORT

NEWPORT
MAP 9, ST38

Gem 42
🌀🌀 MODERN BRITISH
01633 287591 | 42 Bridge Street, NP20 4NY
www.gem42.co.uk

The unassuming building is easy to miss, but once inside you're hardly likely to forget the exuberant Botticelli-style ceilings and crisply dressed tables with Murano glass ornaments. The food is a cut above the average trattoria too - the kitchen works a gleeful fusion of classical foundations and contemporary molecular techniques to deliver an entertaining medley of textures and flavours.

Rafters
🌀 WELSH
01633 413000 | The Celtic Manor Resort, Coldra Woods, NP18 1HQ
www.celtic-manor.com
There are views over the Ryder Cup course from Rafters, a classy grill restaurant within the Twenty Ten Clubhouse at the Celtic Manor Resort. Welsh ingredients take centre stage and there are locally reared, 21-day-aged steaks as the star attraction.

NEWPORT continued

Steak on Six

◎◎ MODERN BRITISH

01633 413000 | The Celtic Manor Resort, Coldra Woods, NP18 1HQ

www.celtic-manor.com/dining/restaurants/steak-on-six

The 'Six' in question is the sixth floor of the upmarket, golf-centric Celtic Manor Resort, where this stylish, contemporary steakhouse looks out over Coldra Woods. When the culinary proposition is this straightforward, the quality of the raw materials is key, and the pedigree meat here proudly flies the flag for prime British protein expertly executed.

■ PEMBROKESHIRE

HAVERFORDWEST   MAP 8, SM91

Slebech Park Estate

◎◎ MODERN, CLASSIC

01437 752000 | SA62 4AX

www.slebech.co.uk

The castellated, 18th-century Slebech manor house stands in 700 acres of parkland, part-bordered by the Eastern Cleddau River. Overlooking this so-called 'hidden waterway', the naturally lit modern restaurant is a big draw for its Little Haven picked crab and laverbread; roast halibut; 28-day, dry-aged Welsh beef fillet; and butternut squash and sweet potato pithivier.

See advertisement opposite

NARBERTH   MAP 8, SN11

The Fernery

◎◎◎ MODERN BRITISH ⚜NOTABLE WINE LIST

01834 860915 | Grove, Molleston, SA67 8BX

www.thegrove-narberth.co.uk

The Fernery is part of the 17th-century Grove of Narberth, a manor house converted into a boutique hotel. It's set in 26 acres including four acres of pretty gardens, part of which is the kitchen garden. The interior is an elegant blend of traditional comforts and contemporary touches, while the Fernery itself is an intimate and understated setting for dynamic,

contemporary food. Choose from a five or eight-course tasting menu, all courses with matching wine recommendations. Possible dishes include oyster with cucumber and jalapeño; lamb with baba ghanoush, goats' curd and cumin, or sea bass with squid and a Thai broth.

Chef Douglas Balish **Seats** 34, Private dining 25 **Open** All Year **Parking** 42 **Notes** No children under 12 years

PORTHGAIN   MAP 8, SM83

The Shed

◎ FISH, TRADITIONAL BRITISH, MEDITERRANEAN

01348 831518 | SA62 5BN

www.theshedporthgain.co.uk

Seafood is king at this simple beach hut-style 'fish and chip bistro' right on the quayside in this dinky fishing village. The place sells its own-caught and local sustainable fresh fish and seafood from a counter during the warmer months, and sitting outdoors with a glass of wine, you couldn't ask for a more delightfully unaffected venue.

ST DAVIDS   MAP 8, SM72

Blas Restaurant

◎◎ MODERN BRITISH

01437 725555 | Twr Y Felin Hotel, Caerfai Road, SA62 6QT

www.twryfelinhotel.com

Lovers of street art, and of modern British cooking, will enjoy Blas. Meaning 'taste' in Welsh, Blas is Twr y Felin Hotel's restaurant, occupying a converted windmill down a narrow lane close to the sea. Expect a wide choice of fish and seafood, while locally farmed beef, lamb and duck, and foraged samphire and monk's beard often feature.

Continued on page 428

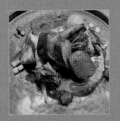

SAUNDERSFOOT
MAP 8, SN10

Coast Restaurant
◎◎ MODERN BRITISH, SEAFOOD *V*
01834 810800 | Coppet Hall Beach, SA69 9AJ
coastsaundersfoot.co.uk

On the shoreline of Coppet Hall Beach, this contemporary restaurant provides diners with unrivalled bay views. Modern furnishings with handcrafted tables are enhanced by beautiful mirrors which ensure every table has a sea view. The menu reflects the coastal location and is inspired by local wild, seasonal and sustainable ingredients, from the land and sea.

St Brides Spa Hotel
◎ MODERN BRITISH
01834 812304 | St Brides Hill, SA69 9NH
www.stbridesspahotel.com
In a marvelous location overlooking Carmarthen Bay, St Brides Spa Hotel has two main dining options, the open-plan Cliff Restaurant and the more informal Gallery, all with excellent sea views. The kitchen's approach is modern British, with a heavy focus on seafood, including fresh lobster straight from the tank.

See advertisement opposite

SOLVA
MAP 8, SM82

Crug Glâs Country House
◎◎ MODERN BRITISH
01348 831302 | Abereiddy, SA62 6XX
www.crug-glas.co.uk
Owners Janet and Perkin Evans have renovated 12th-century Crug Glâs using local materials to achieve smart modernity without trampling on the house's history. At the end of the day, kick off the walking boots and settle into the formal Georgian dining room for country-house cooking.

TENBY
MAP 8, SN10

Penally Abbey Hotel
◎◎ MODERN/CLASSIC *V*
01834 843033 | Penally Abbey Hotel, Penally, SA70 7PY
www.penally-abbey.com
Overlooking Carmarthen Bay, with the 12th-century ruins of the original chapel still be seen in the grounds, the fully restored 18th-century Penally Abbey has soothingly elegant interiors, where the pale colour scheme and delightful period details lend an air of quiet luxury. In the candlelit restaurant you can look forward to relaxed fine dining, with intensely flavoured, well-constructed dishes.

The Salt Cellar
◎◎ MODERN BRITISH
01834 844005 | Atlantic Hotel, The Esplanade, SA70 7DU
www.thesaltcellartenby.co.uk
Occupying an enviable spot in a Victorian seafront hotel, The Salt Cellar is run by an independent team with a passion for prime Pembrokeshire produce. The setting is appropriately modern and the kitchen doesn't try to reinvent the culinary wheel.

Trefloyne Manor

◉ CLASSIC BRITISH

01834 842165 | Trefloyne Lane, Penally, SA70 7RG

www.trefloyne.com

This elegant manor house provides a relaxed country club setting in the heart of bustling Tenby. Accessed through a cosy bar area, the restaurant occupies a large glass-fronted orangery. The menu is supplemented with blackboard specials and a fish board, with classic British dishes.

WOLF'S CASTLE   MAP 8, SM92

Wolfscastle Country Hotel

◉◉ MODERN, TRADITIONAL

01437 741225 | SA62 5LZ

wolfscastle.com

It's said that Welsh rebel leader Owain Glyndwr may be buried in the field alongside this old stone country hotel. Here, the principal restaurant offers unclothed tables and a menu of modern classics. Save room for chocolate fondant, served with salted caramel ice cream and orange jelly.

POWYS

BRECON
MAP 9, SO02

Peterstone Court
MODERN BRITISH, EUROPEAN
01874 665387 | Llanhamlach, LD3 7YB
www.peterstone-court.com
Georgian proportions and its position in the Brecon Beacons make Peterstone Court an ideal base for exploring the landscape. There's a contemporary feel and the classy finish includes a swish bar and a spa. Best of all, there's nifty modern food in the Conservatory Restaurant.

Three Horseshoes Inn
BRITISH
01874665672 | Groesffordd, LD3 7SN
threehorseshoesgroesffordd.com

Just what you need to fuel a day in the great outdoors, this cosy pub is justifiably popular with hikers and bikers. The interior looks up to snuff with its original slate floors, heritage paint palette and modern sheen, while the food is buttressed by local suppliers - the lamb, for example, comes from the neighbouring farm.

HAY-ON-WYE
MAP 9, SO24

Old Black Lion Inn
MODERN BRITISH
01497 820841 | 26 Lion Street, HR3 5AD
www.oldblacklion.co.uk
Dating from the 17th century, the whitewashed inn has bags of character, with beams, low ceilings and stone fireplaces. You can eat in the bar or in the dining room. The kitchen proudly sources all their meats from organic farms in the foothills of Hay Bluff.

LLANFYLLIN
MAP 15, SJ11

Seeds
MODERN BRITISH
01691 648604 | 5-6 Penybryn Cottages, High Street, SY22 5AP
www.farmhouseinwales.com/seeds-restaurant-in-llanfyllin
When you don't require your food to push culinary boundaries or feature froths and gels, head towards Seeds, a little bistro with just 20 seats, run by an amiable husband-and-wife team. Mellow jazz floats around the artworks and curios decorating the low-beamed, slate-floored dining room as chef-patron Mark Seager turns out simple, tasty classic bistro dishes at the stoves of a bijou kitchen.

LLANWDDYN
MAP 15, SJ01

Lake Vyrnwy Hotel & Spa
MODERN BRITISH
01691 870692 | Lake Vyrnwy, SY10 0LY
www.lakevyrnwy.com
Looking down the length of Lake Vyrnwy, while dining on good food, some grown on the hotel estate itself, is a treat indeed. You might begin with goats' cheese, caramelised onion and crystallised walnut tart, then follow with lamb loin, confit belly and dauphinoise potatoes, finishing with banana, peanut butter, salted caramel and milk chocolate ice cream.

Llangoed Hall

⊛⊛⊛ MODERN BRITISH ⧉ NOTABLE WINE LIST

01874 754525 | LD3 0YP

www.llangoedhall.co.uk

An extensive kitchen garden and a smokehouse in the 17-acre grounds of this handsome Edwardian mansion in the Wye Valley attest to the culinary focus at Llangoed. Originally Jacobean, Clough Williams-Ellis (of Portmeirion fame) rebuilt the place in the early 20th century, so expect luxurious lounges full of original features, fine furniture, and original artworks by Whistler and Augustus John. Sam Bowser and his team put organic pickings from the garden into various tersely-worded menus (including vegan/gluten-free versions) of polished modern British cooking. What arrives is savvy, sophisticated and complex stuff, including fashionably foraged and fermented ingredients – perhaps langoustine with coffee bisque and foie gras, or beef tartare with oyster, brioche and egg yolk, then a main course matching suckling pork with kimchi, shiitake and bok choi. Presentation is delightful, and there's no lack of invention among desserts either; a dish starring rhubarb, passionfruit and ginger, for example, or mango with mascarpone and ravioli.

Chef Sam Bowser **Seats** 40, Private dining 80 **Open** All Year **Parking** 150 **Notes** Children welcome

The Nags Head Inn

⊛ MODERN BRITISH *V*

01686 640600 | Garthmyl, SY15 6RS

www.nagsheadgarthmyl.co.uk

The Grade II listed coaching inn on the A483 stands only a few yards from the Severn and the Montgomery Canal, a pleasant spot for an intelligently renovated country pub. The dining area is an expansive space opening on to a patio.

■ RHONDDA CYNON TAF

La Luna

⊛ MODERN INTERNATIONAL

01443 239600 | 79-81 Talbot Road, Talbot Green, CF72 8AE

www.la-lunarestaurant.com

The family-run La Luna has an easy-going atmosphere and a contemporary finish, which fits the kitchen's sunny Med-style, brasserie-inspired output. There's an early evening menu, too, and some fair-weather outside tables.

Llechwen Hall Hotel

⊛ MODERN WELSH

01443 742050 | Llanfabon, CF37 4HP

www.llechwen.co.uk

The low-ceilinged, heavily beamed restaurant at this mid-sized manor house has plenty of atmosphere with its whitewashed walls, tiled floor and bare wood tables. The restaurant has been extended with a garden room-style glazed extension to the original room. The uniformed staff serve up well-considered seasonally changing menus.

■ SWANSEA

The Plough & Harrow

⊛ MODERN EUROPEAN

01792 234459 | 88 Oldway, Murton, SA3 3DJ

www.ploughandharrowmurton.co.uk

In a lovely village not far from Swansea, The Plough & Harrow is an unassuming gastro pub with smart modern interiors; panelled walls and furniture painted in blues, creams and greys, a wood-burner, stacked logs and some bare stone walls. The menu features plenty of Welsh beef, lamb, cheese and even laverbread.

Beach House Restaurant at Oxwich Beach

⊛⊛⊛ MODERN WELSH ⧉ NOTABLE WINE LIST

See pages 432–433

OXWICH   MAP 8, SS48

Beach House Restaurant at Oxwich Beach

◉◉◉ **MODERN WELSH** ⚑ NOTABLE WINE LIST
01792 390965 | SA3 1LS
www.beachhouseoxwich.co.uk

Welsh ingredients and sea views inspire precise cooking

With its stone walls rising from the sands of Oxwich Bay on the Gower Peninsula, the views from the Beach House are hard to beat. The repurposed coalhouse, which once provided coal to the main house on the Penrice Estate overlooking the bay, is now a bright and breezy contemporary venue. It's decorated in beachcomber-chic tones of blue, with stylish, copper light fittings, exposed rafters and full-length windows opening onto the bay. The tables are large with wooden tops, to create the illusion of driftwood, and are laid with high-quality tableware. Outside, there's a decked seating area with glass and wood fencing to help protect you from the elements. Proud Welshman and head chef Hywel Griffith opened the Beach House in 2016. His menu is concise, written in Welsh and English, and the modern bistro cooking is built on pedigree Welsh produce. Dishes delight with a gleeful fusion of local and

global flavours, starting with a pairing of scallops and pork belly with hazelnut, pak choi and XO broth. Lobster landed that morning from the boats you can see in Oxwich Bay provides inspiration for a variety of dishes, such as lobster cannelloni, braised vegetables, and Lyonnaise potatoes. Hywell's take on these potatoes is more of a slice from a potato cake with lemon and thyme within the layers; it has a great flavour that doesn't overpower the cannelloni. Fish fans might also enjoy turbot with summer vegetables, pearl barley and hen in the wood mushrooms. Finally, top-class pastrywork distinguishes a richly eggy, vanilla and nutmeg-scented custard tart offset by the

"Dishes delight with a gleeful fusion of local and global flavours..."

sharp kiss of poached rhubarb and blood orange ice cream. Even though the small sourdough loaf is only a part of the meal, it is very well-baked bread - the crust is spot on with the middle offering good depth of flavour.

Chef Hywel Griffith
Seats 46
Closed 2nd and 3rd week January
Notes Children welcome

SWANSEA
MAP 9, SS69

Hanson at the Chelsea Restaurant
◉ MODERN WELSH, FRENCH
01792 464068 | 17 St Mary Street, SA1 3LH
www.hansonatthechelsea.co.uk
Andrew Hanson's unassuming-looking restaurant resembles a classic modern bistro inside with clothed tables pressed in cheek by jowl, blackboard menus and small framed pictures against a delicate yellow colour scheme. The cooking is an appealing mix of local produce and French influences, with the emphasis on fish and seafood, but not forgetting fine Welsh lamb.

◼ TORFAEN

CWMBRAN
MAP 9, ST29

The Parkway Hotel & Spa
◉◉ MODERN EUROPEAN
01633 871199 | Cwmbran Drive, NP44 3UW
www.parkwayhotelandspa.com
Over seven acres of gardens surround the Parkway Hotel, making for a relaxing ambience, and Ravellos Restaurant is at the heart of it all. There's a strong emphasis on excellent Welsh produce, and the modern menus reveal sensibly balanced and confident dishes. There's also the option to try out the famous Parkway Carvery.
See advertisement opposite

PONTYPOOL
MAP 9, SO20

The Lion
◉ CLASSIC WELSH *V*
01495 792516 | 41 Broad Street, Blaenavon, NP4 9NH
www.thelionhotelblaenavon.co.uk
At the heart of UNESCO World Heritage-recognised Blaenavon, The Lion has been revamped with a clean-lined modern look. Its relaxed dining room blends bare tables with neutral grey hues and light fittings that reference the bygone mining days. The food fits the bill, deploying excellent local ingredients in hearty, crowd-pleasing dishes.

◼ VALE OF GLAMORGAN

COWBRIDGE
MAP 9, SS97

Hare & Hounds
◉◉ BRITISH, WELSH
01446 774892 | Maendy Road, Aberthin, CF71 7LG
www.hareandhoundsaberthin.com
If you're looking for elevated country classics where local sourcing is key then look no further than the innovative and interesting food at the Hare & Hounds. This unassuming stone pub sits quietly on the main road in this peaceful Welsh village. Inside, a large inglenook fireplace, open kitchen and relaxed yet attentive service completes the picture.

HENSOL
MAP 9, ST07

Llanerch Vineyard
◉◉ MODERN WELSH
01443 222716 | CF72 8GG
www.llanerch-vineyard.co.uk
Around 22 acres of south-facing slopes of the Ely Valley have been planted with vines since 1986, and you can raise a glass to the industrious owners while dining in their restaurant or bistro, both of which offer the same menu. To wash it down – what else? ... Welsh wine of course.

LLANCARFAN
MAP 9, ST07

The Fox & Hounds
◉ MODERN CLASSIC BRITISH
01446 781287 | CF62 3AD
www.fandhllancarfan.co.uk
Next to a stream in the heart of the pretty village of Llancarfan, The Fox & Hounds occupies a peaceful location next to the 15th-century St Cadoc's Church, but it's only 15 minutes from the M4. The restaurant offers pub classics.

◼ WREXHAM

LLANARMON DYFFRYN CEIRIOG
MAP 15, SJ13

The Hand at Llanarmon
◉◉ CLASSIC BRITISH
01691 600666 | Ceiriog Valley, LL20 7LD
www.thehandhotel.co.uk
All the usual suspects – beams, open fires, etc – are in this whitewashed country inn; the stuffed fox, however, is decidedly more unusual. The classic and modern pub food menu changes frequently, but old favourites, like slow-braised Welsh lamb shoulder, refuse to budge. Grilled Ceiriog trout is also one to try.

The Parkway Hotel and Spa

Cwmbran Drive
Cwmbran
NP44 3UW

Tel: 01633 871199

parkwayhotelandspa.com

Food...Just the way you like it

Located at the heart of the hotel, Ravellos is popular with both hotel residents
and guests who live in the surrounding area.

Our two AA Rosettes reflect the passion that our Kitchen Brigade puts into their food.
An outstanding à la carte menu that reflects the use of fresh, local produce.

We pride ourselves on the best Sunday lunch for miles, using only the best cuts of local meats.

For opening hours, please visit our website.

NORTHERN IRELAND

Galgorm

◉◉◉ MODERN IRISH 𝑉 ⚑ NOTABLE WINE LIST

028 2588 1001 | 136 Fenaghy Road, Galgorm, BT42 1EA

www.galgorm.com

Beautiful setting for technically skilled contemporary dining

Set in more than 160 acres of beautiful parkland, but handily just half an hour from Belfast, Galgorm is quite the luxurious country resort, with friendly, welcoming staff and a stunning setting. The sumptuous spa is state-of-the-art, and there are all the wedding and conference facilities you could ever dream of, plus various dining options including a relaxed Italian venue and a brasserie and grill housed in the former stables.

For something a bit more adventurous, look to the River Room Restaurant, with its dramatic floor-to-ceiling windows overlooking a stretch of the River Maine that's atmospherically floodlit at night. Those windows mean the views are available to everyone, just like the dishes on chef Chris Rees's seasonally evolving five-course tasting menus - a veggie version is also available - which showcases his impressive skills, as well as making

exemplary use of the splendid local produce, some from the hotel's own kitchen garden. The style is clean and contemporary, with excellent technical skills a reassuring basis for exploring newer ideas. Flavours are clear and carefully considered and dishes are precisely constructed with all the attention to detail one expects at this level. Get things off to a good start with the excellent home-made bread, served with good Irish butter before beginning with burrata, cured Irish ham, tomato dressing and local peas. Next up, foie gras with cherries, baked celeriac, almonds, sherry, before a halibut and scallop dish with carrot, lemongrass and courgette flower. Main course 35-day aged beef comes with lardo, mushroom and black truffle before rounding things off

> "The style is clean and contemporary, with excellent technical skills a reassuring basis for exploring newer ideas."

nicely with a dessert of caramelised pineapple with coconut, mango sorbet and dark rum. And you can have three, five, seven or even nine excellent Irish artisan cheeses, should you be so inclined.

Chef Israel Robb (executive chef), Chris Rees (head chef)
Seats 50, Private dining 50
Open All Year
Parking 200
Notes No children under 12 years

See advertisement on page 441

■ COUNTY ANTRIM

BALLYMENA
MAP 1, D5

Galgorm
◉◉◉ MODERN IRISH *V* ⬝ NOTABLE WINE LIST
See pages 438–439

See advertisement opposite

BUSHMILLS
MAP 1, D1

Bushmills Inn Hotel
◉ MODERN, TRADITIONAL
028 2073 3000 | 9 Dunluce Road, BT57 8QG
www.bushmillsinn.com
For centuries a coaching inn at the heart of this world-famous whiskey village, this is now an upmarket boutique hotel. The peat fires may remain from the days when guests arrived by horse but modern-day visitors are more likely to arrive via helipad.

NEWTOWNABBEY
MAP 1, D5

Sleepy Hollow
◉ MODERN IRISH
028 9083 8672 | 15 Kiln Road, BT36 4SU
www.sleepyhollowrestaurant.com
It would take a jaded palate not to be thrilled by the hearty modern Irish cooking in this rustic restaurant. Locally-sourced artisan produce is at the heart of things, with meat and game supplied by neighbouring farms and estates, butchered in-house, and handled without fuss.

■ BELFAST

BELFAST
MAP 1, D5

Deanes at Queens
◉◉ MODERN IRISH
028 9038 2111 | 1 College Gardens, BT9 6BQ
www.michaeldeane.co.uk

This modern, light-filled restaurant with its large picture windows is just across the road from Queens University and the area is busy, vibrant and buzzing with activity. Here you'll find excellent, reliable modern Irish cooking, with a menu that never disappoints and offers great value. A very good wine list is on offer too.

Deanes EIPIC
◉◉◉ MODERN EUROPEAN ⬝ NOTABLE WINE LIST
028 9033 1134 | 36–40 Howard Street, BT1 6PF
www.deaneseipic.com
First time visitors to Deanes may be slightly disoriented as the calm EIPIC dining room is accessed via the bustling meat and fish restaurants that form part of this popular three-in-one operation. A sleek monochrome decor and linen-clad tables add an elegant touch to the restaurant where service is confident and knowledgable. The modern cooking is assertive, with high quality ingredients driving the menus. Scallop, peas, broad beans, bisque and sea herbs might be followed by lamb, garlic, hispi cabbage, soy, honey and miso. A tartlet of strawberry with meadowsweet ice cream makes for a stunning finale.

Chef Michael Deane, Alex Greene **Seats** 30 **Closed** 1 week mid April, 2 weeks in early July, 25–26 December, 2 weeks early January **Notes** Children welcome

Continued on page 442

GALGORM
SPA & GOLF RESORT

A Culinary Destination

122 Guestrooms

Unique Spa Village

4 Restaurants

4 Bars

Galgorm Spa & Golf Resort
Co. Antrim, Northern Ireland
BT42 1EA

028 2588 1001
reservations@galgorm.com
galgorm.com

AA Rosette Award for Culinary Excellence

BELFAST continued

Fitzwilliam Hotel Belfast

◉ MODERN

028 9044 2080 | 1–3 Victoria Street, BT2 7BQ
www.fitzwilliamhotelbelfast.com

Next door to the newly restored Grand Opera House, the swish Fitzwilliam Hotel makes a fine city-centre base. Decked out in warm, contemporary colours and local artwork, the elegant restaurant features both sharing tables for groups, and more intimate booths. As for the food, expect steak, venison, salmon, duck, hake, pizzas and paninis, with a pre-theatre menu for opera-goers.

James St

◉ MODERN, CLASSIC

028 9560 0700 | 21 James Street South, BT2 7GA
www.jamesstandco.com

Since closing the fine dining side of things and combining with its sister restaurant, James St offers the best of both worlds. Favourites like fruits de mer and chargrilled steaks are served alongside modern Irish dishes. Start with baked scallop, sweetcorn and chorizo, then spatchcock chicken, parmesan, tomato and watercress.

The Merchant Hotel

◉◉ MODERN CLASSIC 🍷 NOTABLE WINE LIST

028 9023 4888 | 16 Skipper Street, Cathedral Quarter, BT1 2DZ
www.themerchanthotel.com

The former headquarters of Ulster Bank is a grand building and these days the beneficiaries are those who rock up for lunch or dinner. The kitchen delivers a classical-meets-modern repertoire where tip-top regional produce, such as lobster and scallops, is treated with respect.

OX

◉◉◉ MODERN IRISH

028 9031 4121 | 1 Oxford Street, BT1 3LA
www.oxbelfast.com

Right by the famous 'Rings' statue on the Lagan waterfront, OX is a pared-down space with board floors, teal colour scheme and a mezzanine level with extra tables. Friendly staff are ready with explanations of the tasting menus, which deal in first-class regional produce prepared with innovative flair. Lunch might open with spelt risotto adorned with girolles, shaved summer truffle and persillade, before delicately Indian-spiced halibut appears with bergamot-scented fennel and romanesco. Pedigree meats such as Chateaubriand and bone marrow with salsify and wild garlic are the stars of the evening show, perhaps following cured sea trout with pickled mussels in buttermilk. Intriguing, refreshingly light desserts encompass blood orange on caramelised pastry with mascarpone, or blackberry sorbet and lemon verbena on a sablé biscuit and custard. The attention to detail in extras like the onion galette topped with tomato, olive and shiso, or the hand-churned Cuinneog butter with the sourdough, inspires confidence.

Chef Stephen Toman **Seats** 40 **Closed** Christmas, 1 week April, 2 weeks July **Notes** Children welcome

Seahorse Restaurant

◉ MODERN

028 9023 1066 | Hastings Grand Central Hotel, Bedford Street, BT2 7FF
www.grandcentralhotelbelfast.com

The hotel's main dining room is built to impress with its high ceilings, soaring walls of glass and sleek art deco-inspired lines. Caramel leather banquettes, plush fabrics and marble-topped tables add further to the allure, while the modern cooking scores a hit for its local ingredients handled with finesse, style and imagination.

Shu

◉◉ MODERN IRISH

028 9038 1655 | 253–255 Lisburn Road, BT9 7EN
www.shu-restaurant.com

Situated in a Victorian terrace, Shu is an airy, good-looking space with an open-to-view kitchen, a lively buzz, and service taken care of by a smartly turned-out team. The cooking has its heart in French classics but global influences – particularly Japanese flavours – all make themselves felt in creative dishes.

■ COUNTY DOWN

NEWTOWNARDS   MAP 1, D5
Balloo House
◉ MODERN BRITISH
028 9754 1210 | 1 Comber Road, Killinchy, BT23 6PA
www.balloohouse.com

Balloo House's original historical features remain, while the additions of darkwood panelling and peacock-blue and tan leather booth seating help create an intimate atmosphere. Dishes like roast Kilmore pigeon with apple and celeriac remoulade set the menu style.

■ COUNTY FERMANAGH

ENNISKILLEN   MAP 1, C5
Lough Erne Resort
◉◉◉ MODERN, TRADITIONAL
028 6632 3230 | Belleek Road, BT93 7ED
www.lougherneresort.com
Piling on the style with Thai spa treatments, up-to-the-minute golf facilities and restorative views of the Fermanagh Lakelands, Lough Erne is one of the joys of north-west Ireland. Among the dining options, the pick is The Catalina restaurant, named after the seaplanes that were once stationed on the lough. There are views over the 18th hole, but for those with their minds on dining, the charming service approach lends a mood of relaxed civility. Noel McMeel maintains his highly burnished style of locally supplied, traditionally rooted cooking, opening perhaps with a salad of Kilkeel crab, with a Ballycastle scallop, shaved pickled fennel and fresh orange salad with blood orange gel. 'Sperrin Venison' is the signature dish here – dry aged venison loin with crispy shoulder and pickled shallots, quince

and apple butter, braised leek and celeriac. Incomparable technique makes a white chocolate parfait with violet meringue, raspberry gel and croquant tuile, a real delight.

Chef Noel McMeel **Seats** 72, Private dining 30 **Open** All Year **Parking** 200 **Notes** Children welcome

Manor House Country Hotel
◉ IRISH, EUROPEAN
028 6862 2200 | Killadeas, BT94 1NY
www.manorhousecountryhotel.com
The colonel who rebuilt this old manor in the 1860s brought craftsmen over from Italy to spruce up the interior. The fine-dining action takes place in the Belleek Restaurant, housed in a conservatory extension that gets the very best of the view of the lough.

■ COUNTY LONDONDERRY DERRY

LONDONDERRY DERRY   MAP 1, C5
Browns Bonds Hill
◉ MODERN IRISH
028 7134 5180 | 1 Bonds Hill, Waterside, BT47 6DW
www.brownsrestaurant.com
Situated on the edge of the city centre by Lough Foyle, Browns has built a local following for over 10 years. Get in the mood with some bubbly in the champagne lounge, then head for one of the white linen-swathed tables in the sleek, contemporary dining room. The kitchen turns out an appealing roll call of modern Irish ideas, with fish and seafood strong suits.

MAGHERA   MAP 1, C5
Ardtara Country House
◉◉ MODERN IRISH *V*
028 7964 4490 | 8 Gorteade Road, BT46 5SA
www.ardtara.com
Built in the 19th century by a linen magnate, Ardtara is a country-house hotel in glorious grounds. It's an engaging spot for afternoon tea, and the restaurant, with its real fireplaces and oak panels, is a smart setting for the bright, contemporary cooking on offer.

REPUBLIC OF IRELAND

■ COUNTY CARLOW

LEIGHLINBRIDGE *MAP 1, C3*

Lord Bagenal Inn
MODERN IRISH
059 9774000 | Main Street
www.lordbagenal.com
In 1979, the original roadside restaurant was almost killed off by the advent of a new motorway, but the enterprising owners built a hotel on the site. It's distinctly contemporary these days, with its Signature Restaurant and bar revamped to create an open-plan space.

■ COUNTY CAVAN

CAVAN *MAP 1, C4*

The Cedar Rooms
CLASSIC IRISH
049 4377700 | Farnham Estate
www.farnhamestate.ie
Whether you're here for the golf, spa pampering or simply recharging the batteries on Farnham Estate's 1,300 acres, The Cedar Rooms restaurant is the place to end the day in an atmospheric setting of exposed stone walls and sleek modern decor. The kitchen's passion for prime local ingredients underpins the unfussy cooking.

Opus One
MODERN IRISH
049 4360600 | Cavan Crystal Hotel, Dublin Road
www.cavancrystalhotel.com
Sharing the same site as its factory, Ireland's second oldest crystal manufacturer also has a smart contemporary hotel, a leisure club and the clean-lined Opus One restaurant. It's a relaxed spot and food chimes in tune with the setting: confident, modern and uncomplicated.

■ COUNTY CLARE

BALLYVAUGHAN *MAP 1, B3*

The Dining Room at Gregans Castle
MODERN IRISH, EUROPEAN
065 7077005 | Gregans Castle
www.gregans.ie
It may not be an actual castle, but the 18th-century manor house is undeniably a luxurious hideaway filled with antiques and period Georgian elegance that is unlikely to disappoint. The location is a dream, set in the photogenic south-western wilderness that is The Burren, with sweeping views towards Galway Bay. The restaurant is a romantic and traditional room where picture windows open on to the views, candlelight flickers in the evening and the family-run hospitality is warm and welcoming. Head chef Robbie McCauley's menus are packed with modern ideas, where flavour, seasonality and ingredients from the local landscape point the way. Dishes are picture perfect, from starters of heritage beetroot with St Tola goats' curd, sorrel and apple, to mains like Kilshanny lamb with wild garlic, violet artichoke and white asparagus, or free-range suckling pig with broad beans, fennel and preserved lemon. For dessert, there could be forced rhubarb with Ivoire white chocolate and crème fraîche.

Chef Robbie McCauley **Seats** 50, Private dining 30 **Closed** December to mid February **Parking** 20 **Notes** No minimum child age

ENNIS *MAP 1, B3*

Legends Restaurant
MODERN INTERNATIONAL
065 6823300 | Temple Gate Hotel, The Square
www.templegatehotel.com
Set in a former convent, the fine dining restaurant of the Temple Gate Hotel is an impressive space with its soaring hammerbeam roof and striking contemporary decor. There's a capable hand in the kitchen, and daily specials mean that seasonal produce is well represented.

LAHINCH
MAP 1, B3

VL Restaurant
◎◎ MODERN FRENCH, IRISH
065 7081111 | Vaughan Lodge Hotel, Ennistymon Road
www.vaughanlodge.ie

Overlooking beautiful Liscannor Bay, this modern townhouse hotel is located right next to the world-famous Lahinch Golf Course. Vaughan Lodge's stunning coastal position means the kitchen is blessed with a bountiful supply of excellent fish and seafood including daily landings of langoustine, lobster and scallops.

LISDOONVARNA
MAP 1, B3

Sheedy's Restaurant
◎◎ CLASSIC IRISH
065 7074026 | Sheedy's Hotel
www.sheedys.com

This small-scale country-house hotel exudes the sort of family-run, unpretentious tradition that keeps fans returning. John Sheedy has long-established local supply lines, and the kitchen garden provides fresh herbs and vegetables to supplement local organic meat and fish landed at nearby Doolin.

NEWMARKET-ON-FERGUS
MAP 1, B3

The Earl of Thomand
◎◎ TRADITIONAL IRISH, EUROPEAN
061 368144 | Dromoland Castle
www.dromoland.ie

As well as a golf course and spa, you'll find turrets and ramparts at this fabulous country-house hotel. Formal dining takes place in The Earl of Thomond restaurant, a spectacular room filled with antiques, oak-panelled period character and a resident harpist.

SHANNON
MAP 1, B3

The Old Lodge Gastro Pub
◎ MODERN IRISH
061 364047 | Shannon Springs Hotel, Ballycasey, V14 A336
www.shannonspringshotel.com

Five minutes from Shannon International Airport, the Old Lodge Gastro Pub is part of the Shannon Springs Hotel. Its three bars offer a variety of menus listing their "uniquely Irish-style food", typically slow-braised rump of local lamb, confit Silverhill duck leg and pan-fried hake. Even Irish and American tapas get to feature.

See advertisement on page 448

■ COUNTY CORK

BALLINGEARY
MAP 1, B2

Gougane Barra Hotel
◎ CLASSIC, TRADITIONAL
026 47069 | Gougane Barra
www.gouganebarrahotel.com

The Cronin family has owned property in hauntingly beautiful Gougane Barra since Victorian times, when its potential as an idyllic retreat was first fully realised. Views over the lake towards the mountains of Cork look especially magnificent from the ample windows of the dining room.

BALLYLICKEY
MAP 1, B2

Seaview House Hotel
◎◎ TRADITIONAL IRISH
027 50073
www.seaviewhousehotel.com

The grand white-painted Seaview has the promised vista over Bantry Bay, glimpsed through the trees in the pretty gardens, while the restaurant comprises three rooms including a conservatory. There's much local produce on the menu and everything is handled with care.

BALTIMORE
MAP 1, B1

Rolfs Country House
◎ FRENCH, EUROPEAN
028 20289
www.rolfscountryhouse.com

Set in beautiful sub-tropical gardens overlooking Baltimore Harbour to Roaringwater Bay and Carbery's 100 islands, it is hardly surprising that the Haffner family have put down roots here since 1979. The kitchen uses produce that is locally grown, reared and caught, organic whenever possible.

CASTLETOWNBERE
MAP 1, A2

The Coastal Restaurant
◎ MODERN, SEAFOOD
027 71446 | The Beara Coast Hotel, Cametringane
www.bearacoast.com

The Beara Coast Hotel's principal dining space, this restaurant has a very loyal local custom. Given its location at one of Ireland's main fishing ports, seafood is a feature, simply cooked and paired, for example, with crusts and risottos. Expect polished timber tables, banquette seating and comfy tartan upholstered dining chairs. All bakery is done in-house.

CORK
MAP 1, B2

Bellini's Restaurant
◉◉ MODERN INTERNATIONAL
021 4365555 | Maryborough Hotel & Spa,
Maryborough Hill, Douglas
www.maryborough.com
There's a whiff of glamour at this Georgian country-house hotel, with later additions tacked on, surrounded by 14 acres of well-maintained gardens and woodland. The bar and restaurant, Bellini's, provide a modern glossy sheen. Fresh, locally-sourced produce is the kitchen's stock in trade for their up-to-date menus.

Greenes
◉◉ MODERN
021 4500011 | Hotel Isaacs, 48 MacCurtain Street
www.hotelisaacscork.com
Set in a Georgian former warehouse and given the boutique hotel treatment, Greenes is a bright and airy spot that overlooks a terrace with a red granite waterfall feature. The kitchen goes for home ingredients, serving well-conceived, modern dishes cooked with pin-sharp accuracy, and with a fondness for deploying fashionable pickling and fermenting treatments.

Panorama Bistro & Terrace
◉ MODERN *V*
021 4530050 | The Montenotte Hotel,
Middle Glanmire Road, Montenotte
www.themontenottehotel.com
Splendid views over the River Lee and the cityscape beyond are guaranteed whatever the weather thanks to the glass wall and covered cantilevered terrace of this smart boutique hotel's restaurant. A cracking grill-style menu peppered with local artisan flavours and supported by kitchen garden produce offers plenty to please all comers.

Perrotts Garden Bistro
◉◉ MODERN IRISH, MEDITERRANEAN
021 4845900 | Hayfield Manor, Perrott Avenue,
College Road, T12 HT97
www.hayfieldmanor.ie
Early 19th-century iron baron Richard Perrott lived here in what is today's Hayfield Manor, where the bistro occupies the contemporary conservatory. Glass-topped metal or timber tables, sofas and wine cabinets create a relaxing environment for international-style dining; eat alfresco, if you prefer. Lunch and dinner menus change frequently.

DURRUS
MAP 1, A2

Blairscove House & Restaurant
◉◉ MODERN EUROPEAN
027 61127 | P75 FE44
www.blairscove.ie
Blairscove brims with charm, on a promontory overlooking peaceful Dunmanus Bay. The main house is Georgian, and the accommodation and restaurant occupy a pretty development facing a pond, in what were the piggery, stables and barn. The dining room is full of character.

GOLEEN
MAP 1, A1

The Heron's Cove
◉ CLASSIC IRISH, SEAFOOD
028 35225 | The Harbour, P81 FT51
www.heronscove.com
This delightful restaurant sits in an idyllic spot on Goleen harbour near to Mizen Head, where the lonely Fastnet Rock lighthouse beams out across the Atlantic. This is an exceptionally easy-going, friendly place, where you can enjoy sublime sea views from the balcony.

KINSALE
MAP 1, B2

The Fish Market *NEW*
◉ IRISH, SEAFOOD
021 477 2209 | Blue Haven Hotel, 3–4 Pearse Street
www.bluehavenkinsale.com
The Blue Haven Hotel is a smart, boutique hotel, and the Fish Market is right next door in what was, indeed, the town's original fish market. It has a nautical feel, with unusual, curved ceilings, polished tables and chunky leather chairs. There's a bright outdoor space for dining outside when the weather's suitable. The all-day menu has an emphasis on seafood as you might expect – no fancy techniques just good, well timed cookery.

The White House
◉ MODERN IRISH
021 4772125 | Pearse Street, The Glen
www.whitehouse-kinsale.com
The White House occupies a prime site in the centre of a town that holds a Gourmet Festival every autumn, so there's plenty to live up to in the gastronomic stakes. The kitchen team triumphs with a resourceful repertoire of modern Irish dishes.

MALLOW
MAP 1, B2
Springfort Hall Country House Hotel
⊚ MODERN, IRISH

022 21278

www.springfort-hall.com

This is an immaculately-preserved Georgian country house where the enthusiastic kitchen team don't cut corners – meat and fish is smoked in-house and everything is made from scratch. In the palatial Lime Tree Restaurant, a crystal chandelier hangs above pristine white linen-clothed tables.

ROSSCARBERY
MAP 1, B2
Kingfisher Bistro
⊚ SEAFOOD

023 8848722 | The Celtic Ross Hotel

www.celticrosshotel.com

Part of the wonderfully-situated Celtic Ross Hotel, a contemporary building right on the waterfront, with fabulous views, the Kingfisher Bistro is ideally placed to take advantage of the great local produce available in the region. Signature dishes include 'the finest seafood chowder in West Cork', so definitely worth trying.

SHANAGARRY
MAP 1, C2
Ballymaloe House
⊚⊚ IRISH, EUROPEAN

021 4652531

www.ballymaloe.com

The Allens were ahead of the curve 50 years ago when they opened a restaurant in their farmhouse. Now there's a cookery school and hotel too, and the idea of fresh produce brought to the table in double-quick time seems the happy norm.

SKIBBEREEN
MAP 1, B1
Kennedy Restaurant
⊚ CLASSIC, TRADITIONAL

028 21277 | West Cork Hotel, Ilen Street

www.westcorkhotel.com

This riverside hotel's restaurant offers a carvery at lunchtime with a dessert buffet, while in the evening the à la carte focuses on locally sourced ingredients to ensure a sense of place. It all takes place in a modest yet stylish room with a buzzy atmosphere.

The Restaurant at Liss Ard
⊚⊚ CLASSIC, MODERN

028 40000 | Castletownsend Road, Russagh, P81 NP44

www.lissardestate.com

The Liss Ard Estate offers 163 acres of secluded grounds in which to work up an appetite for some taste-packed food served in the vaulted restaurant. It's all made using the area's finest produce, as well as goodies from their own kitchen garden. Based on sound classical ideas, dishes are given a modern country-house tweak here and there.

■ COUNTY DONEGAL

BALLYLIFFIN
MAP 1, C6
Jacks Restaurant
⊚ MODERN EUROPEAN

074 9378146 | Ballyliffin Lodge & Spa, Shore Road

www.ballyliffinlodge.com

Brown leather seats and banquettes, bare tables and dark wood floors – backed by a pubby bar and an unbuttoned menu are a hit with the guests at Ballyliffin Lodge. There's a clear penchant for oriental accents in starters such as Thai salmon fishcakes, but there's a strong showing of regional flavours too.

DONEGAL
MAP 1, B5
Cedars Restaurant *NEW*
⊚⊚ IRISH

074 972 5100 | Lough Eske

www.lougheskecastlehotel.com

Part of the beautiful Lough Eske Castle complex, Cedars Restaurant is quite the spot to enjoy good food with floor-to-ceiling windows that offer delightful views of the castle gardens and woodland. Modern design influences combine with timeless glamour in an elegant dining space, showcasing dishes that are fine but not pretentious.

Lakeside Restaurant
⊚⊚ EUROPEAN, SEAFOOD

074 9722208 | Harvey's Point Hotel, Lough Eske

www.harveyspoint.com

At a glorious location on the shores of Lough Eske, the Lakeside Restaurant is the heart and soul of this luxurious hotel complex. The open kitchen uses top-notch seasonal produce from local and regional artisan producers in imaginative, contemporary dishes like pan-fried stone bass, pink prawn, artichoke and tonka bean beurre blanc.

DUNGLOE
MAP 1, B5
The Waterfront Bistro
◉ MODERN IRISH
074 9522444 | Waterfront Hotel Dungloe, Mill Road
www.waterfronthoteldungloe.ie
This bright, busy and buzzy all-day bistro has views of the tide ebbing and flowing into Dungloe Bay. Polished timber tables with comfy leather upholstery provide customers with comfortable seating while they await a daily special from the semi-open kitchen. Primarily a grill, but lots of seafood too.

LETTERKENNY
MAP 1, C5
Port Bar & Grill
◉ MODERN IRISH
074 9194444 | Radisson Blu Hotel Letterkenny, Paddy Harte Road
www.radissonhotels.com/en-us/hotels/radisson-blu-letterkenny/restaurant-bar
A modern hotel of glass and steel, this outpost of the Radisson Blu group features the Port Bar & Grill when you can enjoy pub-style food in a casual and relaxed dining environment. Plasma-screen TVs mean you won't miss the latest sports action.

MOVILLE
MAP 1, C6
The Edge
◉◉ MODERN, INTERNATIONAL
074 9385555 | Redcastle Hotel, Golf & Spa Resort, Inishowen Peninsula
www.redcastlehotel.com
The Redcastle Estate can trace its lineage all the way back to a 16th-century proprietor called Cathal O'Doherty. At one point, it was owned by a Pennsylvania farming family, but today it makes a superbly located northwestern seafront hotel in the modern boutique style.

■ DUBLIN

DUBLIN
MAP 1, D4
Balfes at The Westbury
◉ CONTEMPORARY IRISH
01 6463353 | Grafton Street
www.balfes.ie
With its own street entrance, and pavement tables, Balfes is an affable place with white walls, dark leather seats and a long bar-counter down one end. Kick off in the morning with an omelette or blueberry pancakes or come for lunch of roast sea trout.

Cliff Townhouse
◉◉ SEAFOOD
01 6383939 | 22 St Stephens Green
clifftownhouse.ie
Dubliners love this intimate seafood-focused restaurant, whether it's for lunch after shopping in classy Grafton Street, or for a pre-theatre dinner in the Oyster & Champagne Bar. Afternoon tea features Yawl Bay crabs and Irish smoked salmon open sandwiches. Thoughtful sourcing of ingredients is, naturally, behind everything.

Earth & Vine
◉ TRADITIONAL IRISH
01 6406300 | Castleknock Hotel, Porterstown Road, Castleknock
www.castleknockhotel.com
Just 15 minutes from Dublin, Castleknock has plenty of pizazz. The pick of its eating and drinking choices is the elegantly finished Earth and Vine Restaurant. There are floor-to-ceiling windows with swagged curtains, richly-coloured walls and large artworks. Steak is the mainstay of the kitchen's output.

Fahrenheit Restaurant
◉◉ MODERN IRISH
01 8332321 | Clontarf Castle Hotel, Castle Avenue, Clontarf
www.clontarfcastle.ie
Fahrenheit is the destination restaurant of Dublin's Clontarf Castle Hotel, a beguiling mix of the ancient (12th-century roots) and a modern boutique, and it's a dramatic showcase for some striking modern Irish cooking. Try beetroot-cured wild salmon with smoked salmon mousse, beetroot gel and horseradish.

The Garden Room NEW
◉◉ MODERN EUROPEAN
01 6030600 | The Merrion Hotel, 21 Upper Merrion Street
www.merrionhotel.com/dine/the-garden-room
Part of the elegant Merrion Hotel, located in the birthplace and former home of the 1st Duke of Wellington, The Garden Room is a light and airy space where global flavours drive the modern menu. Start with kataifi prawns and mango salsa before a main course of beef cheek tortellini with brown butter, carrot purée and Cipollini onions.

DUBLIN continued

The Italian Kitchen

◎ ITALIAN

018711255 | Clayton Hotel Dublin Airport,
Stockhole Lane, Swords
www.theitaliankitchen.ie
The Italian Kitchen is a smart, contemporary
addition to the dining options at the Clayton
Hotel Dublin Airport. They have gone to great
lengths to create an authentic Italian experience
by importing ingredients directly from the
mother country, together with an interesting
wine selection. There is always a good selection
of seasonal fish on offer, with high quality meats
also a feature.

The Iveagh Bar

◎ IRISH, EUROPEAN

01 6772324 | Ashling Hotel, Dublin, Parkgate Street
www.ashlinghotel.ie
The Ashling is a large, modern and glitzy hotel
near Phoenix Park and Dublin Zoo, where the
restaurant occupies a spacious, softly lit room
with plushly upholstered, comfortable dining
chairs. The kitchen takes a modern tack with its
combinations of flavours.

Marker Brasserie

◎◎ MODERN INTERNATIONAL

01 6875100 | The Marker, Grand Canal Square
www.themarkerhoteldublin.com
Set in a cool, contemporary canalside hotel in
the rejuvenated Docklands zone, this sleek
brasserie is making quite a splash on the local
dining scene, and celebrates the pick of Irish
produce in its ambitious modernist food. Global
accents abound.

McLoughlins Restaurant

◎ TRADITIONAL EUROPEAN

01 8433118 | Roganstown Hotel and Country Club,
Naul Road, Swords
www.roganstown.com
Golf, spa and conference facilities all feature at
this large resort, but for dinner you'll be wanting
the impressive, wood-panelled McLoughlins
Restaurant. There's plenty of room between the
well-dressed tables, and the kitchen seeks out
first-class ingredients and delivers an ambitious,
contemporary menu.

No. 10 Fleet Street Restaurant

◎ MODERN, SEAFOOD

01 6437000 | The Morgan Hotel, 10-12 Fleet Street
www.themorgan.com
Occupying the lion's share of the ground floor of
the über-stylish Morgan Hotel, this buzzy
restaurant and bar sports a sleek big-city
aesthetic with its mirrored walls, caramel leather
banquettes and pale wood floors. This is a
kitchen that focuses on local ingredients,
particularly fish and seafood, and knows how to
create big-hearted, feel-good flavours.

The Purple Sage Restaurant

◎ MODERN FUSION

01 2001800 | Talbot Hotel Stillorgan, Stillorgan Road
www.talbothotelstillorgan.com
A hotel with wedding packages among its
attractions, the Talbot Hotel Stillorgan is also
home to The Purple Sage Restaurant, with its
breezy air and contemporary finish. The menu
has a gently conceived, modern fusion tack. For
dessert, expect bread-and-butter pudding made
with croissants.

Restaurant Patrick Guilbaud

◎◎◎◎ MODERN FRENCH ♦NOTABLE WINE LIST

01 6764192 | The Merrion Hotel,
21 Upper Merrion Street
www.restaurantpatrickguilbaud.ie
Patrick Guilbaud is a name that has been the
touchstone of fine dining in Ireland since first
opening its doors back in 1981. Remarkably, the
Paris-born patron has kept the same chef,
Guillaume Lebrun (now executive chef), running
the kitchen since opening its doors all those
decades ago, and the same manager, Stéphane
Robin for nearly as long. This remarkable level of
consistency has provided a steadfast platform
for head chef Kieran Glennon to build upon. The
dining room, with its barrel-vaulted ceiling, is a
soothing contemporary space, with warm tones
and striking artworks from Irish artists on the
walls, the room watched over by a professional
and knowledgeable service team. Outstanding
produce sourced with passion and care from the
local area underpins the kitchen's output. Brimful
of luxuries, the cooking shows genuine ambition
and creativity. The wine list is a tour de force;
the cellar contains some 30,000 bottles in total,
so it is worth making use of the passionate and
knowledgeable sommelier to guide the way.

Chef Guillaume Lebrun, Kieran Glennon **Seats** 80,
Private dining 30 **Closed** 25-31 December, 1st week in
January **Notes** Children welcome

The Saddle Room

@@ CLASSIC, TRADITIONAL

01 6634500 | The Shelbourne Dublin, Autograph Collection, 27 St Stephen's Green

www.theshelbourne.com

This grand modern hotel is in a prime location on St Stephen's Green, and offers a range of eating and drinking options culminating in the tip-top Saddle Room. Here a menu of modern brasserie dishes specialises in seafood (including generously loaded platters).

Seasons Restaurant

@@ CONTEMPORARY IRISH

01 6654000 | Intercontinental Dublin

www.intercontinentaldublin.ie

Set in the des-res area of Ballsbridge, the Intercontinental Dublin's posh Seasons Restaurant proves a comfy fit for the upmarket neighbourhood. It's an elegant high-ceilinged room with picture windows looking into the courtyard garden. The kitchen deals in classic ideas executed with precision and made with as much local produce as can be hauled in.

Talavera

@ ITALIAN

01 2186000 | Radisson Blu St Helens Hotel, Stillorgan Road

www.radissonblu.ie/sthelenshotel-dublin

This grand old house dates from the mid-17th century but has all the expected mod cons. The Talavera restaurant serves up smart Italian food – especially from Lombardy – in a series of rooms with either traditional country-house decor or more contemporary chic.

Tom's Table

@ IRISH

01 4593650 | Red Cow Moran Hotel, Red Cow Complex, Naas Road

www.redcowmoranhotel.com

The modern Red Cow Moran Hotel is amply equipped with drinking and dining opportunities, the top choice being Tom's Table, an expansive space done out in contemporary city-slicker style. Lit by soaring floor-to-ceiling windows, its toffee-brown banquettes and clean-lined brasserie-style looks make a suitable setting for uncomplicated, modern cooking.

Wilde

@@ MODERN IRISH ♪ NOTABLE WINE LIST

01 6463311 | The Westbury, Grafton Street

www.wilde.ie

This prestigious city-centre hotel has a fine-dining restaurant dedicated to Oscar Wilde. The kitchen showcases the cream of Ireland's produce. Puddings are a strong suit especially when they include an authentic rendition of classic crema Catalana, or vanilla pannacotta with poached rhubarb.

■ COUNTY DUBLIN

PORTMARNOCK   MAP 1, D4

The Seaview

@@ MODERN IRISH

01 846 0611 | Portmarnock Hotel and Golf Links

www.portmarnock.com

Portmarnock Hotel and Golf Links stands on the estate that was once home to the Jameson Irish Whiskey family and a bar named after the dynasty is a fitting venue for a pint or a dram before a meal at the stylish Seaview restaurant. The coastal location means there are close links between the kitchen and local fishermen and seafood is handled with respect. Local meat is also well represented.

SAGGART   MAP 1, D3

Woodlock Brasserie

@ MODERN

01 4010500 | Citywest Hotel

www.citywesthotel.com/hotel/woodlock-brasserie

Ireland's largest hotel not only boasts 240 acres of parkland with its own golf course, but also this relaxed modern brasserie. Spread over a series of connecting spaces, you can take in the action on the fairways through large windows while the kitchen delivers a please-all roster of straightforward grilled meats and seafood.

■ COUNTY GALWAY

BARNA
MAP 1, B3

The Pins Gastro Bar
❀ INTERNATIONAL, MODERN IRISH 𝑉
091 597000 | The Twelve, Barna Village, H91Y3KA
www.thetwelvehotel.ie
Part of the boutique-style The Twelve, The Pins is an unusual amalgam of bar, bakery, bistro and pizzeria, the latter being authentic Neapolitan-style thin and crispy pizzas made in a Vesuvian stone oven. There's also a modern gastro-pub menu of championing regional suppliers.

West Restaurant
❀❀ MODERN IRISH 𝑉 ⚡ NOTABLE WINE LIST
091 597000 | The Twelve, Coast Road, H91Y3KA
www.westrestaurant.ie
A boutique hotel with bags of swagger, The Twelve is in a coastal area a short distance from the town centre. There's a lot going on: a cool bar, a bakery, and a pizza place, but the main action takes place in the upstairs restaurant.

CASHEL
MAP 1, A4

Cashel House Hotel
❀❀ FRENCH, IRISH
095 31001 |
cashelhouse.ie
Standing at the head of Cashel Bay, Cashel House is a gracious 19th-century country pile that has belonged to the McEvilly family since 1968. The restaurant offers French-accented classics, served in either an airy conservatory extension, or a polished traditional setting amid antiques and artworks.

GALWAY
MAP 1, B3

The Ardilaun Hotel
❀ MODERN IRISH
091 521433 | Taylor's Hill
www.theardilaunhotel.ie
Formerly Glenarde House, The Ardilaun was built in 1840 for the Persse family, Galway landowners of some grandeur. It was launched as a modern hotel in 1962, and the Bistro is its venue for dynamic modern Irish cooking that is ambitious in its endeavours.

Dillisk on the Docks
❀ MODERN, TRADITIONAL
091 894800 | The Harbour Hotel, New Dock Road
www.harbour.ie/en/dillisk-on-the-docks-galway
The main restaurant of the waterfront Harbour Hotel sports a sharp contemporary brasserie-style look. It's a buzzy spot with royal blue seats, banquettes and high-level tables providing a variety of settings to suit the mood. Food-wise, the kitchen takes an uncomplicated, please-all approach.

Marinas Grill
❀ MODERN IRISH, SEAFOOD
091 538300 | The Galmont Hotel & Spa,
Lough Atalia Road
www.thegalmont.com
Part of The Galmont Hotel & Spa on the banks of Lough Atalia, Marinas Grill overlooks Galway Bay which supplies much of the seafood on the menu. The kitchen lets the raw materials do the talking and the stylish modern dishes are unpretentious and produce-driven.

Park House Restaurant
❀ MODERN IRISH, INTERNATIONAL
091 564924 | Park House Hotel & Restaurant, Forster Street, Eyre Square
www.parkhousehotel.ie
Standing just off Eyre Square and built of striking pink granite, Park House has offered high standards of food and accommodation for over 35 years. Park Restaurant, where paintings of old Galway help keep the past alive, bustles at lunchtime and mellows in the evening.

Pullman Restaurant
❀❀ MODERN FRENCH
091 519600 | Glenlo Abbey Hotel, Kentfield, Bushypark
www.glenloabbeyhotel.ie
As if this grandiose country house built in the early Georgian era didn't have architectural diversion enough, its dining room has been fashioned from a pair of Orient Express railway carriages. It's a splendid design concept, and makes an elegant setting.

Restaurant gigi's at the g Hotel & Spa
◎◎ MODERN IRISH
091 865200 | Wellpark, Dublin Road
www.theghotel.ie
Looking a little like a modern office building, the g is a fashionista's magnet, with an eye-popping dining room in pulsating violet and many another hue. Artful presentations of dishes are the norm, but the food itself is more intuitive than you might expect.

Screebe House
◎◎ IRISH, SEAFOOD
091 574110 | Rosmuc
www.screebe.com
This house was a hunting and fishing lodge in the 19th century and is situated right on the edge of Camus Bay – it cannot get any closer to the Atlantic. Dinner is a particular highlight; the daily-changing, seven-course set menu is driven by the season and the market.

ORANMORE *MAP 1, B3*
Basilico Restaurant
◎ ITALIAN
091 788367 | The Coach House Hotel, Main Street
www.basilicorestaurant.ie
Now over 10 years old, Basilico brings an authentic slice of Italy to the heart of Oranmore, just 20 minutes from Galway. A contemporary restaurant decorated with artwork by owner Fabiano Mulas, there is a genuine buzz at each sitting. Crowd-pleasing pizzas are made in a partly-open kitchen.

RECESS *MAP 1, A4*
Lough Inagh Lodge Hotel
◎◎ IRISH, FRENCH
095 34706 | Inagh Valley
www.loughinaghlodgehotel.ie
This boutique hotel, in a lovely spot on the lough shore, has an oak-panelled bar, a library with a log fire, and a restaurant where silver and glassware reflect candlelight and an oval window gives wonderful views. Chatty and attentive staff are happy to help you choose.

The Owenmore Restaurant
◎◎ MODERN IRISH *V*
095 31006 | Ballynahinch Castle Hotel, Recess, Connemara, H91F4A7
www.ballynahinch-castle.com
Set in 700 acres of woodland, rivers and walks in the heart of Connemara, Ballynahinch is one of Ireland's most celebrated castle hotels. The work of many great Irish painters hangs on the walls of the elegant Owenmore Restaurant, which overlooks a salmon river. Its position is reflected in the kitchen's commitment to local provenance.

■ COUNTY KERRY

KENMARE *MAP 1, A2*
The Dining Room
◎◎ CLASSIC IRISH ♣ NOTABLE WINE LIST
064 6641200 | Park Hotel Kenmare
www.parkkenmare.com
Set against a backdrop of the Cork and Kerry Mountains, with stunning views over Kenmare Bay, this landmark Victorian hotel dates from 1897. Top-notch ingredients sourced from the surrounding area dominate the menu. A carefully chosen and comprehensive wine list offers some notable bottles.

The Falls Restaurant
◎◎ MODERN EUROPEAN, FRENCH
064 6641600 | Sheen Falls Lodge
www.sheenfallslodge.ie
The cascading, floodlit Sheen Falls make for a memorable backdrop to a meal at this former fishing lodge. The refined Falls Restaurant offers classical French dishes served by informed staff. An opener of pan-fried foie gras, pistachio, fig and port might precede fillet of halibut, mussels, cauliflower and leek.

KILLARNEY

MAP 1, A2

The Castlelough Restaurant

◉◉ MODERN IRISH

064 6631035 | The Lake Hotel, On the Shore,
Muckross Road
www.lakehotelkillarney.com

Part of the beautiful 19th-century Lake Hotel, the Castlelough Restaurant is an impressive space, with high ceilings, large mirrors, chandeliers, and amazing views of the breathtaking scenery of lake and mountain that surrounds it. The kitchen delivers hearty meals prepared and presented with expertise and care. Local lamb, beef and chicken feature heavily.

Danu at The Brehon

◉◉ MODERN EUROPEAN

064 6630700 | The Brehon Killarney, Muckross Road
www.thebrehon.com

Brehon was the name for the ancient body of law that governed Ireland. It gave its subjects an obligation of hospitality, so is a logical name for a hotel. The kitchen fast-forwards us to the present day with contemporary Irish cooking of impressive depth.

Herbert Restaurant

◉◉ CLASSIC, TRADITIONAL

064 6631895 | Cahernane House Hotel, Muckross Road
www.cahernane.com

Guests can take a meal in the original dining room of this 19th-century manor house while enjoying views across parkland which dips down to the lake. Interesting desserts on the menu might include choux pastry with blackberry curd, wild berry crème fraîche.

The Lake Room

◉◉ MODERN

064 6631766 | Aghadoe Heights Hotel & Spa,
Lakes of Killarney
www.aghadoeheights.com/dining/the-lake-room

In a perfect setting on the shore of the lake, amidst some of Kerry's most beautiful landscapes, the restaurant is part of the impossibly luxurious Aghadoe Heights Hotel. You can expect a fine wine list, a cosmopolitan atmosphere and stunning views – the sunsets are amazing. On the menu, you'll find precisely constructed dishes.

KILLORGLIN

MAP 1, A2

Carrig House Country House & Restaurant

◉◉ MODERN IRISH, EUROPEAN

066 9769100 | Caragh Lake
www.carrighouse.com

Carrig is a lovingly restored Victorian country manor in acres of colourful woodland gardens with views across Caragh Lake to the Kerry Mountains. Inside, the dining room is the image of 19th-century chic, with William Morris wallpapers, swagged curtains, polished floorboards, and formally laid tables.

■ COUNTY KILDARE

MAYNOOTH

MAP 1, D4

The Linden Tree Restaurant NEW

ROSETTES SUSPENDED CLASSIC BRITISH

01 5052000 | Carton House
www.cartonhouse.com

The Rosette award for this establishment has been suspended due to a change of chef and reassessment will take place in due course.

Carton House Hotel is an astonishingly grand and impressive stately home, a huge Palladian building with incredible interiors, acres of grounds and formal gardens. The split-level Linden Tree Restaurant makes the most of these, with fine garden views and offers classic contemporary dining in the country house style.

Open All year

STRAFFAN
MAP 1, C/D4

The Barton Restaurant
◉◉ TRADITIONAL FRENCH
01 6017200 | The K Club, W23 YX53
www.kclub.ie

Once home to the Barton wine family, this luxurious hotel has the look of a French château and there are dining options aplenty, not least of which is The Barton Restaurant, with its impressive views of the Liffey. The cooking is built around classic technique.

■ COUNTY KILKENNY

KILKENNY
MAP 1, C3

The Yew Restaurant
◉◉ MODERN IRISH, EUROPEAN
056 7760088 | Lyrath Estate, Paulstown Road
www.lyrath.com

The hotel and spa occupies an imposing 17th-century property set in 170 acres of parkland that includes lakes and ornamental gardens. The Yew Restaurant, a large room overlooking the rose garden, is the gem among the dining options. The kitchen works around a modern Irish and European repertoire.

THOMASTOWN
MAP 1, C3

The Hound
◉◉ IRISH
056 7773000 | Hunters Yard at Mount Juliet, Mount Juliet Estate
www.mountjuliet.ie/the-hound

Sweeping views of the Jack Nicklaus-designed golf course are just one attraction at this easygoing eatery in the Hunters Yard hotel on the Mount Juliet Estate. Factor in a welcoming, family-friendly ambience and a kitchen that deals in crowd-pleasing dishes built on prime Irish produce, and you're onto a winner.

The Lady Helen Restaurant
◉◉◉◉ MODERN
056 7773000 | The Manor House at Mount Juliet Estate
www.mountjuliet.ie/lady-helen

The Mount Juliet is a fine example of the Georgian country house and estate, offering spa treatments and golf in addition to inspirational fine dining in The Lady Helen Restaurant. Named

after previous owner Lady Helen McCalmont, it's a coolly elegant, high-ceilinged room with intricate plasterwork and magnificent windows overlooking the grounds. Attention to detail is second to none and produce from the estate often features in chef John Kelly's modern Irish cooking. Dinner might begin with a single, silky raviolo, stuffed with black truffle-studded potato and accompanied by a fine parmesan cream, followed by breast of Anjou squab pigeon, served on York cabbage, topped with hen of the woods and toasted hazelnuts, and finished with a rich, glossy veal jus, alongside a bowl of the braised leg and thigh meat. Caramelised banana ice cream is a deceptively simple dessert, served with tonka bean cremeux and brightly coloured, astringent calamansi gel.

Chef John Kelly Seats 50, Private dining 30
Notes Children welcome

■ COUNTY LAOIS

BALLYFIN
MAP 1, C3

Ballyfin Demesne
◉◉ EUROPEAN ▮NOTABLE WINE LIST
057 8755866
www.ballyfin.com

In possibly Ireland's most opulent Regency house, the high-ceilinged dining room gazes out towards a temple where a water feature cascades. A walled garden supplies plenty of produce, as do the resident bees, and lucky humans are regaled with French-inspired contemporary cooking of considerable dazzle.

■ COUNTY LEITRIM

MOHILL
MAP 1, C4

Sandstone Restaurant NEW
◉ MODERN IRISH, BRITISH
071 9632700 | Lough Rynn
www.loughrynn.ie

Lough Rynn Castle Estate Hotel dates from the 19th century and is a grand and impressive location for the Sandstone Restaurant, with its exposed stone walls and classic country house look, with snowy white tablecloths and high-backed chairs. Kick things off with scallops and Parma ham, followed, perhaps by Thornhill duck from County Cavan. Great bread too.

■ COUNTY LIMERICK

ADARE
MAP 1, B3

The Oak Room
◎◎ MODERN IRISH
061 605200 | Adare Manor
www.adaremanor.com/dining/the-oak-room
It's hard not to be impressed when you take a seat in the elegant oak-panelled space that was once the dining room of the Earls of Dunraven. Everything here dazzles, from the opulent decor to the crisp linen, gleaming silver and sparkling glassware. The kitchen rises to the occasion, delivering intricate dishes of refined, contemporary Irish cooking.

LIMERICK
MAP 1, B3

The East Room Restaurant *NEW*
◎◎ MODERN IRISH
061 202 186 | Plassey House, University of Limerick
www.Eastroom.ie
The East Room Restaurant is an elegant dining space in the Italianate villa Plassey House in the centre of the University of Limerick campus. Some ingredients come from the rooftop gardens ensuring the availability of fresh, seasonal ingredients. There are impressive and well-compiled menus with clear flavours always to the fore.

The River Restaurant
◎ CONTEMPORARY IRISH
061 421800 | Limerick Strand Hotel, Ennis Street
www.strandlimerick.ie
A new-build riverside hotel with all mod cons, including a bright, airy dining room. Sourcing from within the county supplies a menu of populist brasserie dishes, with an Irish contemporary gloss on international ideas. Good breads come with intensely anchovied tapenade.

■ COUNTY LOUTH

CARLINGFORD
MAP 1, D4

Ghan House
◎◎ MODERN IRISH
042 9373682
www.ghanhouse.com

Set on the shores of Carlingford Lough, just before it reaches the sea, Ghan House is a Georgian townhouse with a walled garden and a large pond. The restaurant has a high ceiling, gilded plasterwork and a baby grand piano. Cuisine has a French base, but offers plenty of interesting combinations. Good use is made of seafood from the lough.

DROGHEDA
MAP 1, D4

Scholars Townhouse Hotel
◎◎ MODERN IRISH
041 9835410 | King Street,
www.scholarshotel.com
Built as a Christian Brothers monastery in 1867, ceiling frescoes of the Battle of the Boyne in the interlinked dining rooms furnish a historical note that's a contrast to the modern Irish cooking. Praline soufflé with pumpkin ice cream is an interesting way to finish.

■ COUNTY MAYO

BALLINA
MAP 1, B4

Belleek Castle
◉◉ MODERN IRISH
096 22400 | Belleek
www.belleekcastle.com
The multi-award-winning Library Restaurant's three menus – Early Evening, Market five-course tasting, and the eight-course Gourmet (all with vegetarian options) – reflect a change of culinary focus from international to modern Irish. For example, West Coast seafood includes Donegal fresh crab and in-house, hot-smoked gravad lax, while mountain lamb comes from Achill Island to the southwest.

The Kitchen Restauant
◉◉ TRADITIONAL
096 74472 | Mount Falcon Estate, Foxford Road
www.mountfalcon.com
The restaurant at this grand baronial-style hotel on the River Moy is the Kitchen Restaurant, which occupies the original kitchen and pantry area, looking good with its linen-clad tables and food-related prints on the walls. There's a definite French classicism to the kitchen's output.

CONG
MAP 1, B4

The George V Dining Room
◉◉ TRADITIONAL EUROPEAN, INTERNATIONAL ▲NOTABLE WINE LIST
094 9546003 | Ashford Castle,
www.ashfordcastle.com
Once home to the Guinness family, Ashford Castle dates from the 13th century and sits grandly on the shores of Lough Corrib, amid 350 acres of parkland. The dining room was built to host a reception for the Prince of Wales in 1906.

Wilde's at The Lodge
◉◉ CONTEMPORARY IRISH
094 9545400 | The Lodge at Ashford Castle, Ashford Estate
www.thelodgeac.com/dining-and-drinks
Wilde's restaurant is named after Sir William Wilde, a local surgeon who founded the first eye and ear hospital in Dublin, and, from its first-floor setting in the original Victorian building, offers fabulous views over Lough Corrib. The kitchen impresses with an ambitious, contemporary range of dishes.

MULRANNY
MAP 1, A4

The Nephin Restaurant
◉◉ MODERN INTERNATIONAL, CLASSIC
098 36000 | Mulranny Park Hotel,
www.mulrannyparkhotel.ie
Once the station hotel for Mulranny, opened in the 1890s, this is now a sumptuous country-house with sweeping views over the Atlantic. A duo of Keem Bay smoked salmon and barbecued fresh salmon with honey-mustard aïoli, pickled cucumber and red onion dressing might start proceedings.

WESTPORT
MAP 1, B4

Islands Restaurant
◉ MODERN IRISH, BRITISH, EUROPEAN
098 25122 | Hotel Westport Leisure, Spa & Conference, Newport Road
www.hotelwestport.ie
Heavenly scenery frames this expansive family-run hotel and spa set in seven acres of mature woodland. Miles of walking and cycling on the Great Western Greenway close by are more reasons to bring a keen appetite with you to the restaurant here.

La Fougère Restaurant
◉◉ MODERN IRISH
098 28600 | Knockranny House Hotel
www.knockrannyhousehotel.ie
This tranquil spa hotel makes the most of its Mayo situation, with stunning views every which way. Inside comes with all the accoutrements of an upscale hotel, including a full-dress dining room, La Fougère, which eschews modern minimalism in favour of immaculate linen, glassware and table settings.

■ COUNTY MEATH

DUNBOYNE
MAP 1, D4

The Ivy Restaurant
◉◉ MODERN EUROPEAN
01 8013500 | Dunboyne Castle Hotel & Spa
www.dunboynecastlehotel.com
Part of the Dunboyne Castle complex, The Ivy is a relaxing space with muted colours and views of the Castle grounds. The menu focuses on the best ingredients from the finest local suppliers, and is the product of a passionate and committed kitchen team. Dishes are hearty and imaginatively presented, and all the beef is Irish.

ENFIELD
MAP 1, C4
Fire & Salt
◉ MODERN IRISH

046 9540000 | The Johnstown Estate

www.thejohnstownestate.com

The main restaurant at the sporty Johnstown Estate, is this bright and airy steakhouse offering a variety of seating options. Although grass-fed, Irish-bred beef steaks cooked over charcoal on the grill are the main draw here, there are plenty of other options on the à la carte including local seafood.

KILMESSAN
MAP 1, C4
The Signal Restaurant
◉ MODERN IRISH *V*

046 9025239 | The Station House Hotel, C15 N40D

www.stationhousehotel.ie

In the heart of the stunning Boyne Valley Drive in County Meath, The Station House Hotel is set in its own attractive gardens and surrounded by beautiful countryside. Its rural location is reflected in the accomplished food served in the charming and elegant Signal Restaurant.

NAVAN
MAP 1, C4
Eden Restaurant
◉◉ MODERN EUROPEAN

046 9030900 | Bellinter House

www.bellinterhouse.com

A country-house hotel that is popular on the wedding scene, its interior combining period charm with 21st-century boutique glamour. Down in the vaulted basement there's a slick contemporary finish to the space and a menu to match. The kitchen's output is focused on regional produce.

SLANE
MAP 1, D4
Conyngham Arms Hotel
◉ TRADITIONAL, INTERNATIONAL

041 9884444 | Main Street

www.conynghamarms.ie

This 18th-century coaching inn is home to a smart brasserie-style restaurant offering straightforward food from breakfast through to dinner. There's a decent amount of Irish produce on the menu, including goods from the owners' bakery and coffee shop in the village.

Tankardstown – Brabazon Restaurant
◉◉ CLASSIC INTERNATIONAL
041 9824621
www.tankardstown.ie
In the restaurant situated in the one-time cow shed, expect a smart rustic finish with exposed stonework, a central fireplace and pretty terrace. The kitchen calls on the walled organic garden for supplies, and a smoker brings a potent aroma to proceedings.

TRIM   *MAP 1, C4*

Rococo Restaurant
◉ IRISH, INTERNATIONAL
046 9482100 | Knightsbrook Hotel, Spa & Golf Resort, Iffernock, Dublin Road
www.knightsbrook.com
Part of the Knightsbrook Hotel, Spa & Golf Resort, there is a pronounced Irish accent to the international food served in the restaurant. Typical main courses include pork belly with root vegetable purée, tenderstem broccoli, cherry apple and cider jus. If the warm apple crumble doesn't tempt, there's always the board of Irish cheeses.

■ COUNTY MONAGHAN

GLASLOUGH   *MAP 1, C5*

Snaffles Restaurant
◉◉ TRADITIONAL IRISH, INTERNATIONAL *V*
047 88100 | The Lodge, Castle Leslie Estate, H18 FY04
www.castleleslie.com
Part of the thousand-acre Castle Leslie Estate, Snaffles is a bright, apex-ceilinged, open-plan space sitting up on a balcony overlooking a courtyard bar and lounge below. Many of the signature dishes are re-inventions of recipes from the Castle Leslie Estate Cook Book, a collection of family recipes that go back centuries. Extensive gin menu.

See advertisement opposite

■ COUNTY ROSCOMMON

ROSCOMMON   *MAP 1, B4*

The Douglas Hyde Restaurant
◉◉ MODERN EUROPEAN
071 9618000 | Kilronan Castle Estate & Spa, Ballyfarnon
www.kilronancastle.ie
Named after Douglas Hyde, the first President of Ireland (1938-45) who was born about 20 miles away, this charming restaurant is part of the magnificent Kilronan Castle Estate. There are three different dining areas, all are elegant and intimate, and all serving modern Irish dishes with a nod to the traditions of country house cuisine.

See advertisement on page 462

■ COUNTY SLIGO

SLIGO   *MAP 1, B5*

Classiebawn Restaurant
◉ MODERN IRISH
071 9140008 | Radisson Blu Hotel & Spa Sligo, Rosses Point Road, Ballincar
www.radissonblu.ie/sligo
A classy modern hotel designed with plenty of vivid colour, notably reds and purples in the Classiebawn dining room. Here, the bill of fare is contemporary Irish cooking of notable technical ambition. Why not try a deconstructed egg for your starter?

Hazelwood Restaurant
◉ MODERN IRISH
071 9190400 | Sligo Park Hotel & Leisure Club, Pearse Road
www.sligopark.com
Covering all the bases, Sligo Park's full-on leisure facilities and surrounding verdant countryside means there's plenty of opportunity to build up an appetite. The dining option is the Hazelwood Restaurant, which has a warm contemporary finish. The kitchen stays true to Irish produce.

■ COUNTY TIPPERARY

CLONMEL   *MAP 1, C3*
Hotel Minella
◉ TRADITIONAL
052 6122388
www.hotelminella.com
The hotel's garden runs down to the banks of the River Suir and the Comeragh Mountains loom in the background – it's a charming spot. The restaurant is in the original Georgian house, so has plenty of character and a traditional, period feel. An all-day menu is available.

■ COUNTY WATERFORD

ARDMORE   *MAP 1, C2*
The House Restaurant
ROSETTES SUSPENDED MODERN IRISH ⚑ NOTABLE WINE LIST
See page 464

WATERFORD   *MAP 1, C2*
Bianconi Restaurant
◉ TRADITIONAL IRISH
051 305555 | Granville Hotel, The Quay
www.granvillehotel.ie
Occupying pole position on Waterford's river quay, the Georgian Granville Hotel's genteel and elegant Bianconi Restaurant makes the most of those views over the River Suir and the marina from linen-clad tables beneath a coffered ceiling. The kitchen displays a feel for what's right on the plate.

The Munster Room Restaurant
◉◉ IRISH, INTERNATIONAL
051 878203 | Waterford Castle Hotel and Golf Club, The Island
www.waterfordcastleresort.com
With its dark oak panelling, intricate plasterwork ceiling and ancestral portraits, The Munster Room is exactly what you'd expect from the dining room of a luxe hotel set on its own private 300-acre island. It's a jacket-and-tie affair with a pianist adding to the ambience.

The Roseville Rooms
◉◉ MODERN IRISH, FRENCH
051 382000 | Faithlegg House Hotel & Golf Resort, Faithlegg
www.faithlegg.com
The original mansion was built in the 1780s and is immaculately restored, while the high-ceilinged restaurant overlooks the garden from what was a pair of drawing rooms. The cooking is based on native produce and a range of neat ideas really makes an impact.

■ COUNTY WEXFORD

GOREY   *MAP 1, D3*
Clonganny House
◉◉ CONTEMPORARY IRISH, FRENCH
053 9482111 | Ballygarrett
www.clonganny.com
A handsome creeper-covered Georgian house at the end of a tree-lined drive, Cloganny has a refined, traditional interior. The highly experienced French chef-patron cooks with confidence and delivers a classically-inspired repertoire via a bilingual carte. Kick off with drinks and canapés in the drawing room.

The Conservatory Restaurant
◉◉ CLASSIC
053 9421124 | Marlfield House Hotel, Courtown Road
www.marlfieldhouse.com
This opulent Regency home is now a smart and luxurious hotel whose dining room consists of several handsomely decorated spaces, leading into an impressive conservatory. Murals and mirrors are interspersed with huge windows opening onto the immaculate garden. The hotel's own kitchen garden delivers first-rate seasonal produce.

Greenroom Restaurant
◉◉ MODERN IRISH, MEDITERRANEAN
053 9424000 | Seafield Hotel & Spa Resort, Ballymoney
www.seafieldhotel.com
We've Italian designers to thank for the super-cool interior at this luxe spa hotel on the cliffs. The high-end finish extends to the restaurant, where a huge bronze female centaur keeps watch, lighting and music are soft, and the decor is cool black.

ARDMORE   MAP 1, C2

The House Restaurant

ROSETTES SUSPENDED **MODERN IRISH** 🍷 NOTABLE WINE LIST
024 87800 | Cliff House Hotel
cliffhousehotel.ie

The Rosette award for this establishment has been suspended due to a change of chef and reassessment will take place in due course. It may be simply named, but The House Restaurant at The Cliff House Hotel is far from simple. Stunningly positioned, the restaurant, with floor-to-ceiling windows, and its terrace overlook Ardmore Bay and the West Waterford coast. Seating is upholstered in locally sourced tweeds and the crystal glassware, not too surprisingly, is from nearby Waterford city. In support of local fishermen and farmers, the new executive chef, Ian Doyle, is continuing to present the long-celebrated, regularly changing eight-course tasting menus, with a wine pairing curated by a sommelier accompanying each dish. Making the most of the oceanside location, there's a natural emphasis on seafood, such as a starter of carrot, seaweed paste and crispy barley, and later courses of langoustine with pear, sorrel and cucumber and gin sauce, and Ardmore lobster with carrot and oyster sauce, while from the local Comeragh mountains comes duck with spring onion.

Seats 64, Private dining 20 Closed 23–26 December Parking 30 Notes Children welcome

GOREY continued

The Rowan Tree
◉ IRISH, INTERNATIONAL
053 9480500 | Ashdown Park Hotel, Station Road
www.ashdownparkhotel.com
This modern hotel on a grand scale, within walking distance of Gorey, has 22 acres of grounds to explore before a trip to its Rowan Tree Restaurant. Here, tables are dressed up in crisp white linen, and the kitchen turns out pleasingly straightforward dishes.

ROSSLARE   *MAP 1, D2*
Beaches Restaurant at Kelly's Resort Hotel
◉◉ TRADITIONAL EUROPEAN
053 9132114
www.kellys.ie
Beaches Restaurant sits on the golden sands in Rosslare, and is set up to capitalise on the views. The space is bathed in light through good-sized windows, and has restful pastel hues, white linen on the tables, and a mini gallery of original artworks on the walls. The kitchen lets the quality of local produce do the talking in simple contemporary dishes.

La Marine Bistro
◉ IRISH, FRENCH
053 9132114 | Kelly's Resort Hotel & Spa
www.kellys.ie
The more casual stand-alone restaurant of Kelly's Resort Hotel is an easy-going venue with an open kitchen. The shipshape bistro theme suits the beachside setting, as does its menu. Top-class fish and seafood come a short way from Kilmore Quay.

WEXFORD   *MAP 1, D2*
Aldridge Lodge Restaurant and Guest Accommodation
◉◉ MODERN IRISH *V*
051 389116 | Duncannon
www.aldridgelodge.com
With its fashionably pared-back looks – wood floors, bare tables and black high-backed seats – chef-patron Billy Whitty's restaurant with rooms achieves a stylish informality. It has also become something of a hot spot on the local foodie scene thanks to its sharply-executed dishes on the daily-changing menus.

Reeds Restaurant at Ferrycarrig Hotel
◉◉ MODERN IRISH
053 9120999 | Ferrycarrig
www.ferrycarrighotel.ie

Overlooking the beautiful Slaney River as it meanders towards Wexford town and the sea, the contemporary Reeds Restaurant menu proudly declares that dishes are largely sourced from the Emerald Isle. Examples are West Coast oyster fritters, Kilmore monkfish, roast rump of Slaney Valley lamb and prime grilled Irish rib-eye steak.

■ COUNTY WICKLOW

BLESSINGTON   *MAP 1, D3*
Lime Tree Restaurant
◉ MODERN IRISH
045 867600 | Tulfarris Hotel & Golf Resort
www.tulfarrishotel.com
Part of the Tulfarris Hotel & Golf Resort, the first-floor restaurant offers panoramic views towards the Blessington Lakes. The cooking uses intelligent combinations of quality ingredients, whether it's delicious pork belly from Tipperary or fresh fish off the boats in Howth.

DELGANY   *MAP 1, D3*
The Woodlands Restaurant
◉◉ MODERN IRISH, EUROPEAN
01 2873399 | Glenview Hotel, Glen o' the Downs
www.glenviewhotel.com/dining
The Woodlands Restaurant at this hotel is on the first floor to maximise the view over the Glen o' the Downs, with arched windows looking down the valley. Inside, all is soothing pastels and sparkling glassware. The style is what is loosely termed modern Irish.

ENNISKERRY
MAP 1, D3

The Sika Restaurant
◉◉ MODERN EUROPEAN
01 2748888 | Powerscourt Hotel, Powerscourt Estate
www.powerscourthotel.com
With a sweeping Palladian mansion at its heart, the Powerscourt resort has two golf courses, a luxurious spa and an Irish pub, but the main event food-wise is the glamorous Sika Restaurant. There are glorious mountain views from its third-floor dining room.

MACREDDIN
MAP 1, D3

The Strawberry Tree
◉◉ MODERN IRISH, ORGANIC
0402 36444 | BrookLodge & Macreddin Village, Y14 A362
www.brooklodge.com
Set in a beautiful ivy-clad building, The Strawberry Tree is busy and atmospheric. Walls and even part of the ceiling are lined with mirrors. The same owners been here for over 30 years, but show no sign of resting on their laurels. The menu is proudly organic and focuses on the best produce this part of Ireland has to offer.

See advertisement below

NEWTOWNMOUNTKENNEDY
MAP 1, D3

Garden Rooms
◉ MODERN
01 2870877 | Druids Glen Hotel & Golf Resort
www.druidsglenresort.com
The Garden Rooms is the second dining option at the wonderful Druids Glen Resort. It's a bright and airy space, overlooking the renowned 13th green. The wide-ranging menu is sure to please the most discerning diner and there are a number of vegan options on offer in collaboration with a nearby specialist vegan restaurant. The dishes are quite light, with an emphasis on salads and dressings rather than heavy sauces.

Hugo's Restaurant
◉◉ MODERN EUROPEAN
01 2870800 | Druids Glen Hotel & Golf Resort
www.druidsglenresort.com
Druids Glen boasts the full package of spa, golf and leisure facilities with the Wicklow Hills thrown in as a backdrop. Stylishly decorated in muted hues, with a feature fire set in a huge granite hearth, the main dining room here is Hugo's Restaurant.

GIBRALTAR

■ GIBRALTAR

GIBRALTAR

Nunos

◎◎ ITALIAN, MEDITERRANEAN

00 350 200 76501 | Caleta Hotel, Sir Herbert Miles
Road, GX11 1AA

www.caletahotel.com

Nunos restaurant at the Caleta has a fine-dining
air and a stand-alone restaurant vibe, thanks to
slick London-style service and Italian cooking.
An open-to-view kitchen offers all the theatre of
chefs on show. The menu is typically extensive,
the colourful, modern-European approach
intelligently uncomplicated.

The Rock

◎ MODERN MEDITERRANEAN

00 350 200 73000 | Europa Road, GX11 1AA

www.rockhotelgibraltar.com

Since it opened in 1932, this iconic hotel has
attracted notable guests, including Winston
Churchill, and John Lennon and Yoko Ono who
stayed here when they married in Gibraltar. The
restaurant's wisteria-clad terrace is a draw in
itself, while the modern Mediterranean food is
classy and interesting.

Sunborn Yacht Hotel

◎◎ MEDITERRANEAN

00 350 2001 6000 | Ocean Village, GX11 1AA

www.sunbornyacht.com/gibraltar

Located on a luxurious floating hotel moored in
Gibraltar's Ocean Village Marina, this is a rooftop
restaurant that offers a contemporary dining
experience with views out to sea or overlooking
Gibraltar itself. A wrap-around deck offers
pleasant alfresco dining.

COUNTY MAPS

England

1 Bedfordshire
2 Berkshire
3 Bristol
4 Buckinghamshire
5 Cambridgeshire
6 Greater Manchester
7 Herefordshire
8 Hertfordshire
9 Leicestershire
10 Northamptonshire
11 Nottinghamshire
12 Rutland
13 Staffordshire
14 Warwickshire
15 West Midlands
16 Worcestershire

Scotland

17 City of Glasgow
18 Clackmannanshire
19 East Ayrshire
20 East Dunbartonshire
21 East Renfrewshire
22 Perth & Kinross
23 Renfrewshire
24 South Lanarkshire
25 West Dunbartonshire

Wales

26 Blaenau Gwent
27 Bridgend
28 Caerphilly
29 Denbighshire
30 Flintshire
31 Merthyr Tydfil
32 Monmouthshire
33 Neath Port Talbot
34 Newport
35 Rhondda Cynon Ta
36 Torfaen
37 Vale of Glamorgan
38 Wrexham

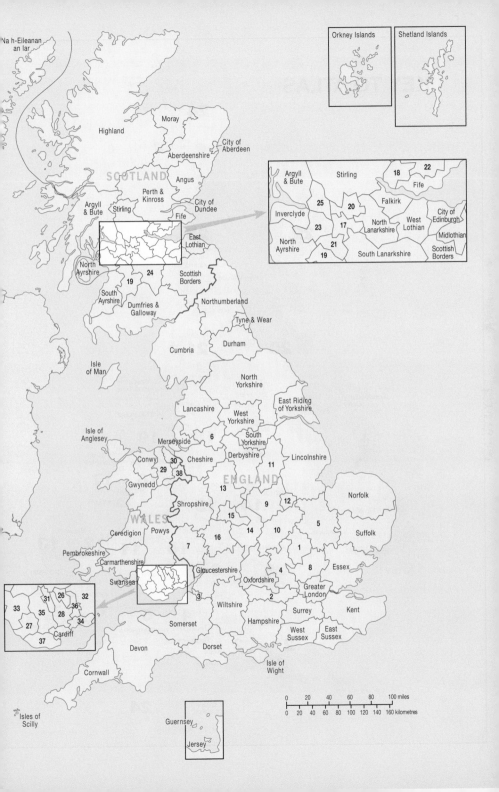

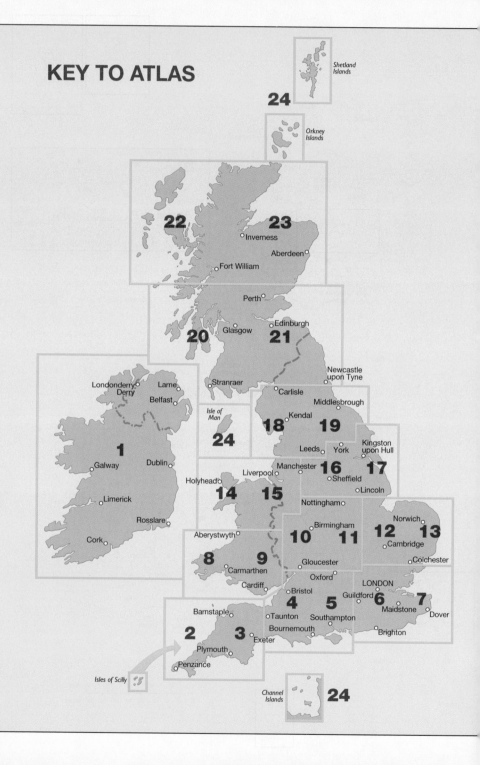

KEY TO ATLAS

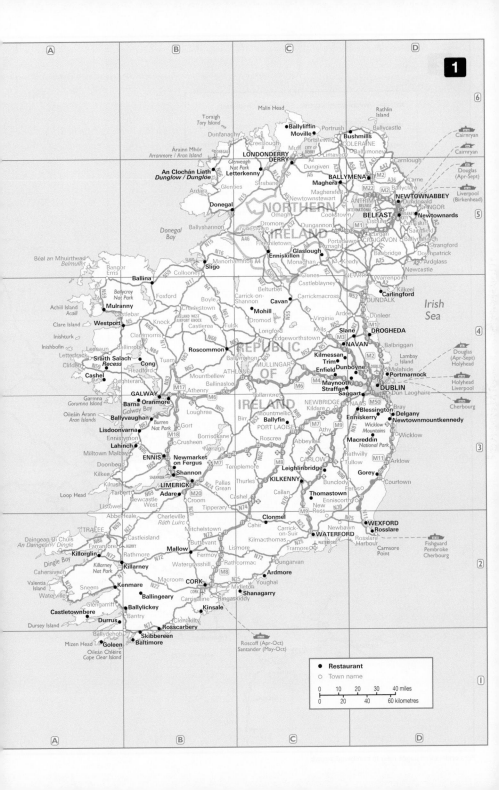

Legend:

Motorway/toll motorway	**M4**
Motorway junction full/restricted	
Primary route single/dual carriageway	A3
Service area/rest area	◈ ◈ ◈
Other A road single/dual carriageway	A1123
B road	B2070
Unclassified road	
Vehicle ferry (all year, seasonal)	
Restaurant	● St Ives
Town/Village name	○ Hayle
Fast vehicle ferry or catamaran	
National boundary	
English county name & boundary	ESSEX
Welsh county name & boundary	CONWY
Scottish county name & boundary	MORAY
National Park	

Lundy

Hartland Point

Hartl

Morwenstow

Kilkhamp

Bude

Bude Bay

Widemouth Bay

Crackington Haven

Week St Mary

Boscastle

Tintagel

Delabole

Camelford

Port Gaverne

Port Isaac

St Teath

Polzeath

Rock

St Tudy

BODMIN MOOR

Bolventor

Harlyn

Padstow

Blisland

Porthcothan

Little Petherick

Wadebridge

C O R N W A L L

St Cle

Bodmin

Dobwalls

Mawgan Porth

St Mawgan

St Columb Major

Lanivet

St Keyne

Newquay

Roche

Bugle

Lostwithiel

West Pentire

St Blazey

Pelyn

Perranporth

Summercourt

St Austell

Porthallow

A3

St Agnes

Zelah

Ladock

St Stephen

Fowey

Polpe

Polruan

Porthtowan

Grampound

Pentewan

Portreath

St Ives Bay

Porthreath

St Day

Carnon Downs

Truro

Tregony

Mevagissey

Gwithian

Redruth

Gorran Haven

St Ives

Zennor

Camborne

Lelant

Hayle

St Just-in-Roseland

Veryan

Portloe

Penryn

Portscatho

St Just

A3071

Marazion

Falmouth

St Mawes

Penzance

Perranuthnoe

Newlyn

Praa Sands

Constantine

Mawnan Smith

LAND'S END

Sennen

St Buryan

Mousehole

Helston

Gweek

Manaccan

Porthcurno

Treen

Mount's Bay

Porthleven

St Keverne

Coverack

Mullion

Cadgwith

Lizard

Lizard Point

Isles of Scilly inset:

Lower Town

Old Grimsby

St Martin's

Bryher

New Grimsby

Higher Town

Tresco

ISLES OF SCILLY

St Mary's

Hugh Town

Old Town (St Mary's)

Isles of Scilly (St Mary's)

Middle Town

St Agnes

SV

SW

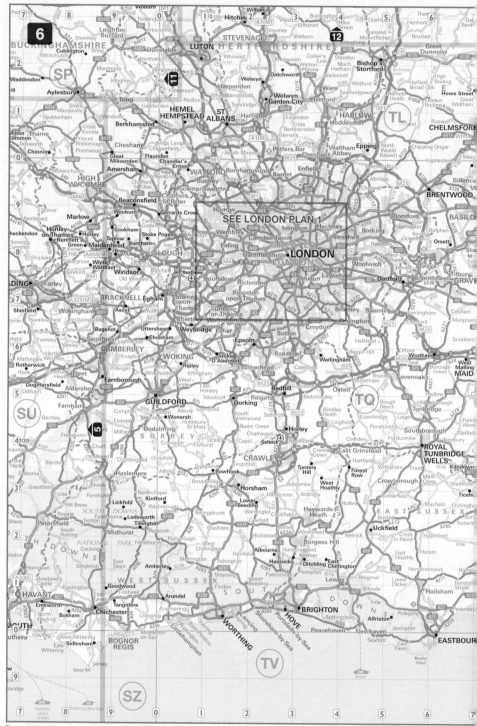

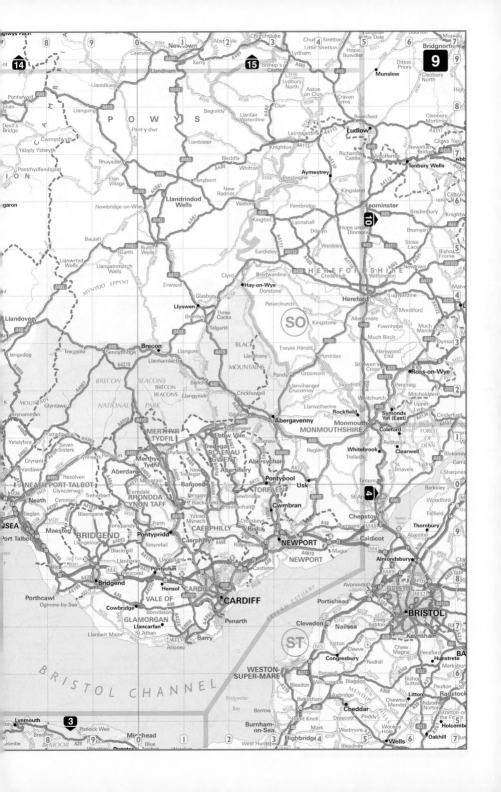

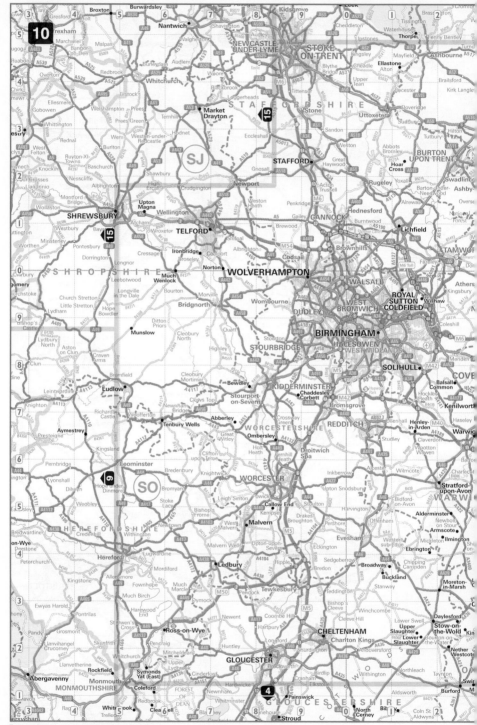

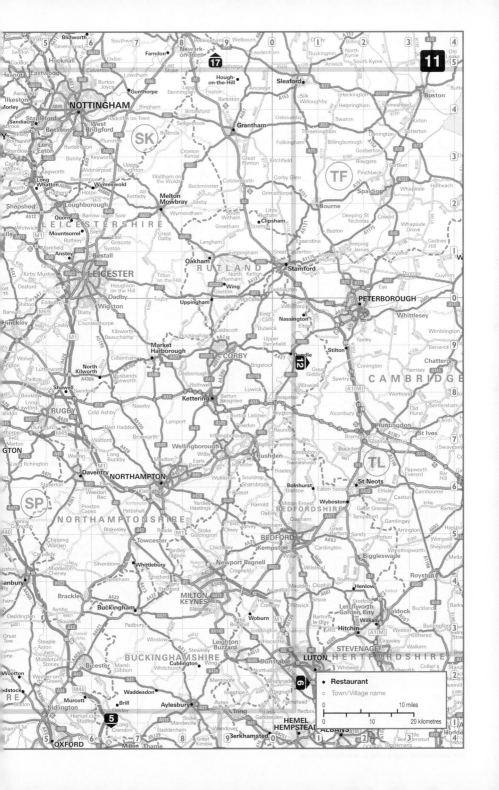

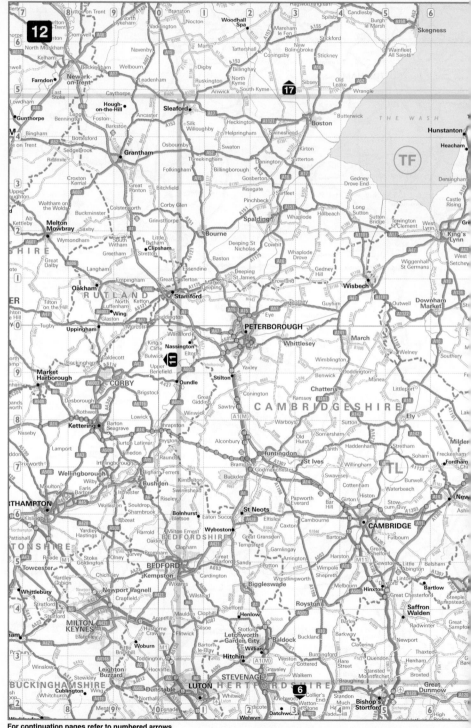

14

For continuation pages refer to numbered arrows

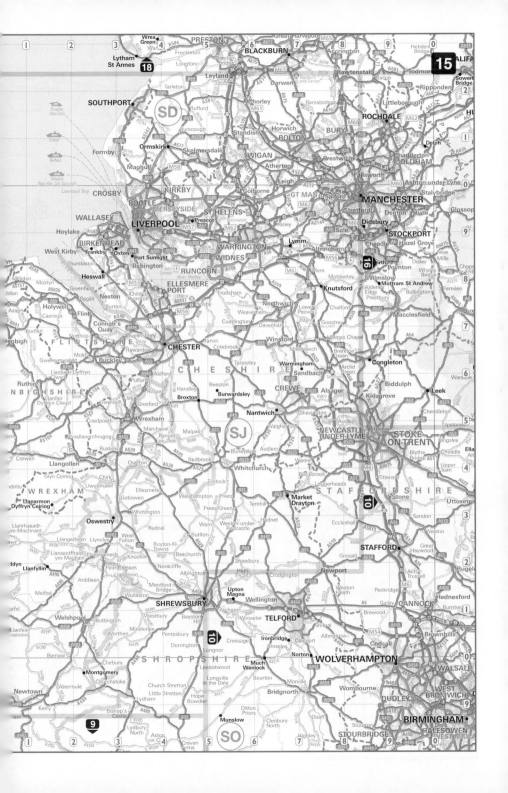

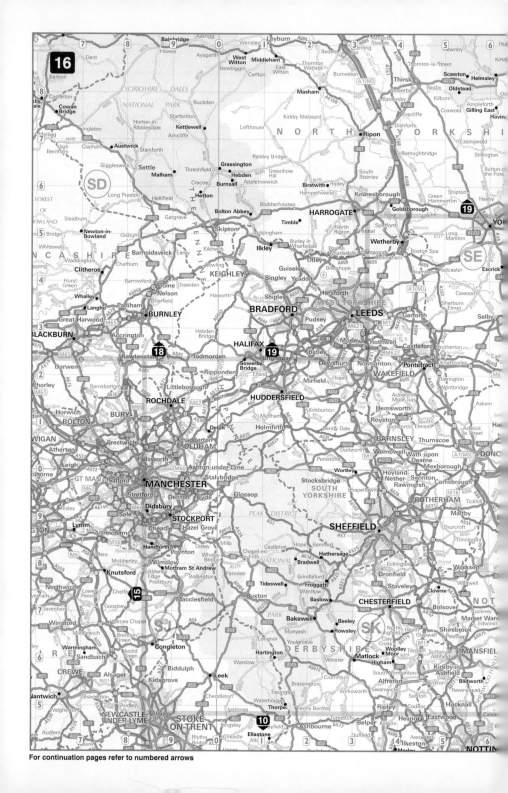

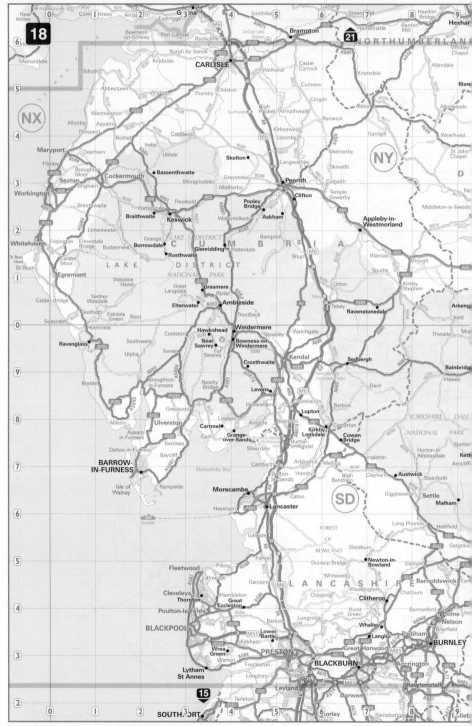

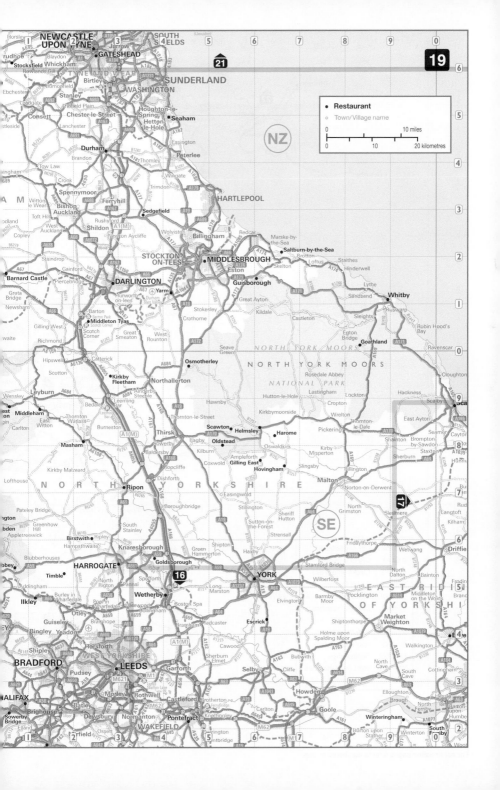

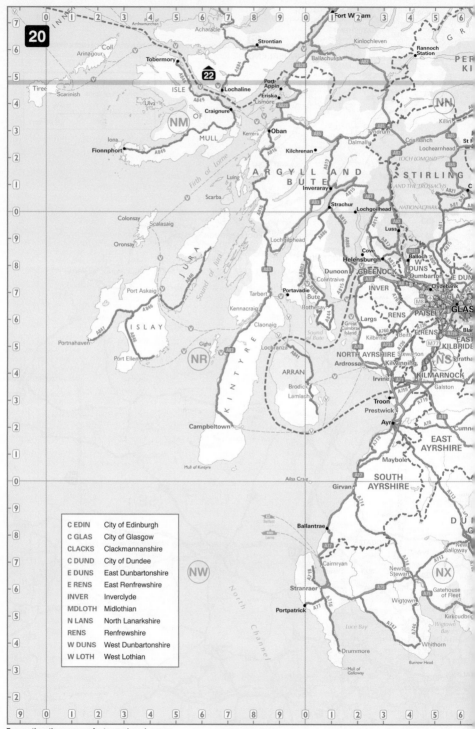

C EDIN	City of Edinburgh
C GLAS	City of Glasgow
CLACKS	Clackmannanshire
C DUND	City of Dundee
E DUNS	East Dunbartonshire
E RENS	East Renfrewshire
INVER	Inverclyde
MDLOTH	Midlothian
N LANS	North Lanarkshire
RENS	Renfrewshire
W DUNS	West Dunbartonshire
W LOTH	West Lothian

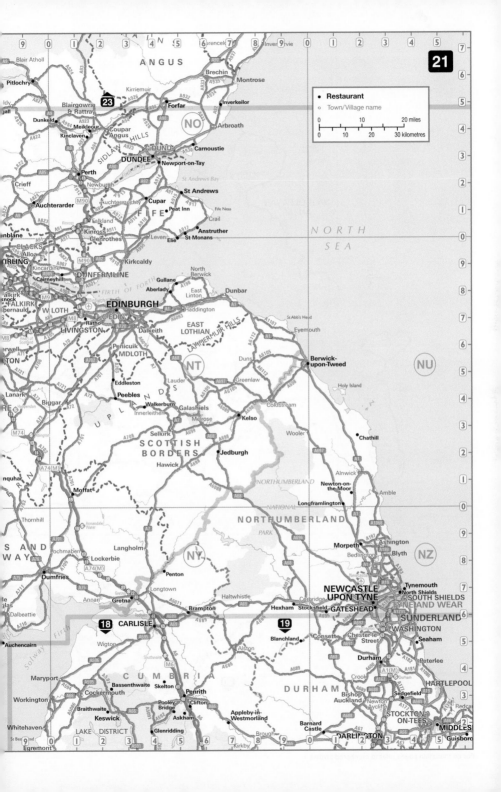

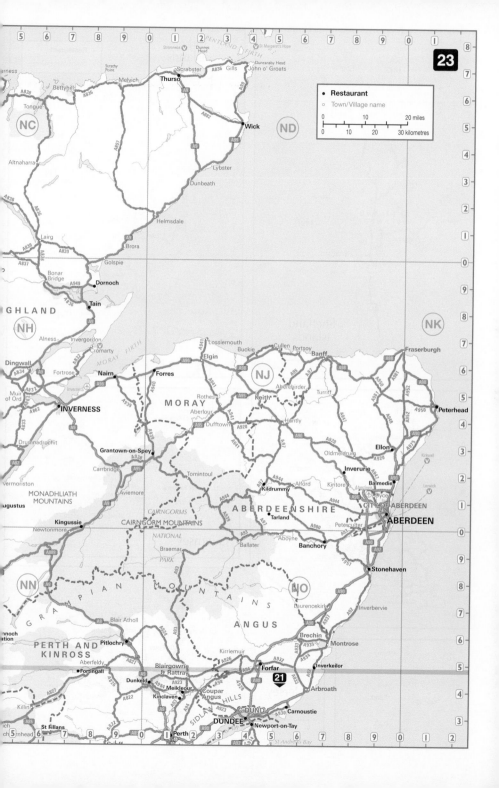

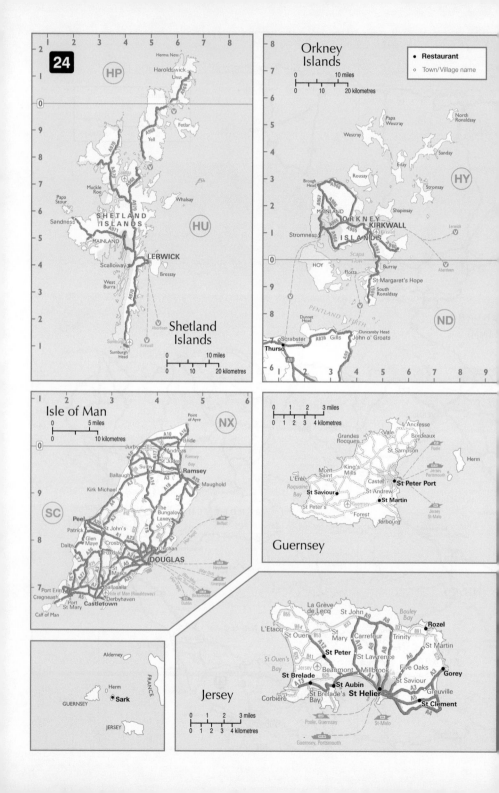

Index

Discover a rated place to stay

Find AA-inspected hotels, B&Bs, campsites and so much more at RatedTrips.co

AA Rated Trips